W9-BSD-347

TEACHER'S EDITION

Essentials of Mathematics

CONSUMER / CAREER SKILLS APPLICATIONS

William J. Gerardi   Wilmer L. Jones   Thomas R. Foster

Harcourt Brace Jovanovich, Publishers

Orlando   New York   Chicago   San Diego   Atlanta   Dallas

We do not include a Teacher's Edition automatically with each shipment of a classroom set of textbooks. We prefer to send a Teacher's Edition only when it is requested by the teacher or administrator concerned or by one of our representatives. A Teacher's Edition can easily be mislaid when it arrives as part of a shipment delivered to a school stockroom and since it contains answer materials, we want to be sure that it is sent directly to the person who will use it or to someone concerned with the use or selection of textbooks.

If your class assignment changes and you no longer are using or examining this Teacher's Edition, you may wish to pass it on to a teacher who has use for it.

A "Teacher's Resource Book" is available for "Essentials of Mathematics: Consumer and Career Skills and Applications." For information, please call your sales representative.

CONTENTS

Printed in the United States of America

ISBN 0-15-353611-X

INTRODUCTION

Overview

This textbook is aimed primarily at students who are in a second year of general mathematics. Since the major portion of the textbook is concerned with consumer applications, it can also be used as a consumer mathematics textbook. Further, some school systems will consider this textbook as a viable alternative for use with students in their first year of general mathematics.

The flexibility of the program is evidenced by its five-unit structure (see the Table of Contents). The six chapters that comprise Unit I review the essential skills that are required for the consumer applications that appear in Units II-V. Two optional Appendices are also included: *Appendix A: Introduction to Algebra* and *Appendix B: Introduction to Computers*.

Unit I

Each skill lesson in Chapters 1-5 contains a separate set of "Applications" exercises. These problems are, for the most part, one-step word problems that most students should be able to handle. Each lesson in *Chapter 6: Statistics* does not contain a separate set of Applications exercises, as applications are an integral part of most lessons in the chapter. Both the arithmetic skills and the applications in Unit I represent the types of items that are required on most competency tests. Thus, a second objective for Unit I is to help prepare students for competency tests. Each of Chapters 1-6 also contains optional *Career* lessons and optional *Calculator* exercises.

Units II-V

The twelve chapters in Units II-V deal with consumer applications. These units have been structured so that they can be taught in any sequence that the teacher desires. This flexibility is an added feature of the program that the authors feel is essential for this type of course of study.

Problem Solving

Various problem-solving techniques are taught in Chapters 7-18. The "hidden-question" technique for solving word problems that require more than one step has proven to be particularly helpful to students.

Since many of the students enrolled in this course of study have reading difficulties, the structure of the *Exercises* should also prove to be very helpful. The *Exercises* for most lessons in Chapters 7-18 are of two types: (a) those that apply the content and problem-solving technique to non-verbal problems and then to (b) word problems.

Chapters 7-18 also contain lessons on *Rounding and Estimation* and optional *Career* lessons. Many of these *Career* lessons illustrate the use of a calculator in the given career.

Description

Pages M-2 through M-10 describe the structure of the program both verbally and pictorially.

The Chapter Opener

Each chapter opens with a **Review of Related Skills.** These exercises review prior-taught skills that will be used in the chapter. The exercises are referenced to those pages in the text where the skill was presented.

Skills Lessons: Chapters 1-6

Each of the skills lessons in Chapters 1-6 follows this structure.

Procedure This outlines the steps.

Examples These illustrate the Procedure.

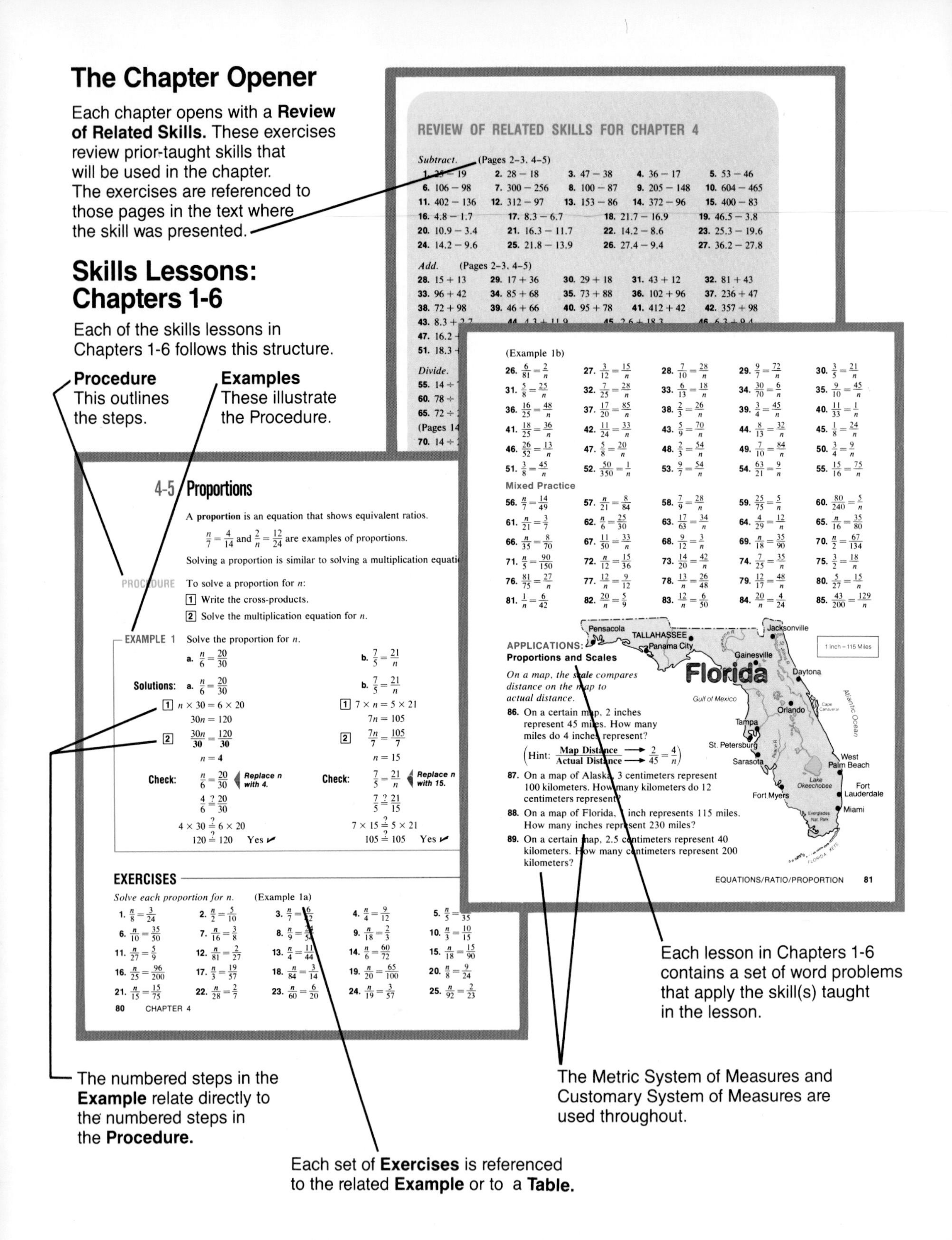

REVIEW OF RELATED SKILLS FOR CHAPTER 4

Subtract. (Pages 2-3, 4-5)

1. 35 − 19 2. 28 − 18 3. 47 − 38 4. 36 − 17 5. 53 − 46
6. 106 − 98 7. 300 − 256 8. 100 − 87 9. 205 − 148 10. 604 − 465
11. 402 − 136 12. 312 − 97 13. 153 − 86 14. 372 − 96 15. 400 − 83
16. 4.8 − 1.7 17. 8.3 − 6.7 18. 21.7 − 16.9 19. 46.5 − 3.8
20. 10.9 − 3.4 21. 16.3 − 11.7 22. 14.2 − 8.6 23. 25.3 − 19.6
24. 14.2 − 9.6 25. 21.8 − 13.9 26. 27.4 − 9.4 27. 36.2 − 27.8

Add. (Pages 2-3, 4-5)

28. 15 + 13 29. 17 + 36 30. 29 + 18 31. 43 + 12 32. 81 + 43
33. 96 + 42 34. 85 + 68 35. 73 + 88 36. 102 + 96 37. 236 + 47
38. 72 + 98 39. 46 + 66 40. 95 + 78 41. 412 + 42 42. 357 + 98
43. 8.3 + 2.7
47. 16.2
51. 18.3

Divide.

55. 14 ÷
60. 78 ÷
65. 72 ÷
(Pages 14
70. 14 ÷

4-5 Proportions

A **proportion** is an equation that shows equivalent ratios.

$\frac{n}{7} = \frac{4}{14}$ and $\frac{2}{n} = \frac{12}{24}$ are examples of proportions.

Solving a proportion is similar to solving a multiplication equati

PROCEDURE To solve a proportion for n:

1. Write the cross-products.
2. Solve the multiplication equation for n.

EXAMPLE 1 Solve the proportion for n.

a. $\frac{n}{6} = \frac{20}{30}$ **b.** $\frac{7}{5} = \frac{21}{n}$

Solutions: **a.** $\frac{n}{6} = \frac{20}{30}$

1. $n \times 30 = 6 \times 20$

$30n = 120$

2. $\frac{30n}{30} = \frac{120}{30}$

$n = 4$

Check: $\frac{n}{6} = \frac{20}{30}$ *Replace n with 4.*

$\frac{4}{6} \stackrel{?}{=} \frac{20}{30}$

$4 \times 30 \stackrel{?}{=} 6 \times 20$

$120 \stackrel{?}{=} 120$ Yes ✓

b. $\frac{7}{5} = \frac{21}{n}$

1. $7 \times n = 5 \times 21$

$7n = 105$

2. $\frac{7n}{7} = \frac{105}{7}$

$n = 15$

Check: $\frac{7}{5} = \frac{21}{n}$ *Replace n with 15.*

$\frac{7}{5} \stackrel{?}{=} \frac{21}{15}$

$7 \times 15 \stackrel{?}{=} 5 \times 21$

$105 \stackrel{?}{=} 105$ Yes ✓

EXERCISES

Solve each proportion for n. (Example 1a)

1. $\frac{n}{8} = \frac{3}{24}$ 2. $\frac{n}{2} = \frac{5}{10}$ 3. $\frac{n}{7} = \frac{6}{[illegible]}$ 4. $\frac{n}{4} = \frac{9}{12}$ 5. $\frac{n}{5} = \frac{[illegible]}{35}$
6. $\frac{n}{10} = \frac{35}{50}$ 7. $\frac{n}{16} = \frac{3}{8}$ 8. $\frac{n}{9} = \frac{24}{54}$ 9. $\frac{n}{18} = \frac{2}{3}$ 10. $\frac{n}{3} = \frac{10}{15}$
11. $\frac{n}{27} = \frac{5}{9}$ 12. $\frac{n}{81} = \frac{2}{27}$ 13. $\frac{n}{4} = \frac{11}{44}$ 14. $\frac{n}{6} = \frac{60}{72}$ 15. $\frac{n}{18} = \frac{15}{90}$
16. $\frac{n}{25} = \frac{96}{200}$ 17. $\frac{n}{3} = \frac{19}{57}$ 18. $\frac{n}{84} = \frac{3}{14}$ 19. $\frac{n}{20} = \frac{65}{100}$ 20. $\frac{n}{8} = \frac{9}{24}$
21. $\frac{n}{15} = \frac{15}{75}$ 22. $\frac{n}{28} = \frac{2}{7}$ 23. $\frac{n}{60} = \frac{6}{20}$ 24. $\frac{n}{19} = \frac{3}{57}$ 25. $\frac{n}{92} = \frac{2}{23}$

80 CHAPTER 4

(Example 1b)

26. $\frac{6}{81} = \frac{2}{n}$ 27. $\frac{3}{12} = \frac{15}{n}$ 28. $\frac{7}{10} = \frac{28}{n}$ 29. $\frac{9}{7} = \frac{72}{n}$ 30. $\frac{3}{5} = \frac{21}{n}$
31. $\frac{5}{8} = \frac{25}{n}$ 32. $\frac{7}{25} = \frac{28}{n}$ 33. $\frac{6}{13} = \frac{18}{n}$ 34. $\frac{30}{70} = \frac{6}{n}$ 35. $\frac{9}{10} = \frac{45}{n}$
36. $\frac{16}{25} = \frac{48}{n}$ 37. $\frac{17}{20} = \frac{85}{n}$ 38. $\frac{2}{3} = \frac{26}{n}$ 39. $\frac{3}{4} = \frac{45}{n}$ 40. $\frac{11}{33} = \frac{1}{n}$
41. $\frac{18}{25} = \frac{36}{n}$ 42. $\frac{11}{24} = \frac{33}{n}$ 43. $\frac{5}{9} = \frac{70}{n}$ 44. $\frac{8}{13} = \frac{32}{n}$ 45. $\frac{1}{8} = \frac{24}{n}$
46. $\frac{26}{52} = \frac{13}{n}$ 47. $\frac{5}{8} = \frac{20}{n}$ 48. $\frac{2}{3} = \frac{54}{n}$ 49. $\frac{7}{10} = \frac{84}{n}$ 50. $\frac{3}{4} = \frac{9}{n}$
51. $\frac{3}{8} = \frac{45}{n}$ 52. $\frac{50}{350} = \frac{1}{n}$ 53. $\frac{9}{7} = \frac{54}{n}$ 54. $\frac{63}{21} = \frac{9}{n}$ 55. $\frac{15}{16} = \frac{75}{n}$

Mixed Practice

56. $\frac{n}{7} = \frac{14}{49}$ 57. $\frac{n}{21} = \frac{8}{84}$ 58. $\frac{7}{9} = \frac{28}{n}$ 59. $\frac{25}{75} = \frac{5}{n}$ 60. $\frac{80}{240} = \frac{5}{n}$
61. $\frac{n}{21} = \frac{3}{7}$ 62. $\frac{n}{6} = \frac{25}{30}$ 63. $\frac{17}{63} = \frac{34}{n}$ 64. $\frac{4}{29} = \frac{12}{n}$ 65. $\frac{n}{16} = \frac{35}{80}$
66. $\frac{n}{35} = \frac{8}{70}$ 67. $\frac{11}{50} = \frac{33}{n}$ 68. $\frac{9}{12} = \frac{3}{n}$ 69. $\frac{n}{18} = \frac{35}{90}$ 70. $\frac{n}{2} = \frac{67}{134}$
71. $\frac{n}{5} = \frac{90}{150}$ 72. $\frac{n}{12} = \frac{15}{36}$ 73. $\frac{14}{20} = \frac{42}{n}$ 74. $\frac{7}{25} = \frac{35}{n}$ 75. $\frac{3}{2} = \frac{18}{n}$
76. $\frac{81}{75} = \frac{27}{n}$ 77. $\frac{12}{n} = \frac{9}{12}$ 78. $\frac{13}{n} = \frac{26}{48}$ 79. $\frac{12}{17} = \frac{48}{n}$ 80. $\frac{5}{27} = \frac{15}{n}$
81. $\frac{1}{n} = \frac{6}{42}$ 82. $\frac{20}{n} = \frac{5}{9}$ 83. $\frac{12}{n} = \frac{6}{50}$ 84. $\frac{20}{n} = \frac{4}{24}$ 85. $\frac{43}{200} = \frac{129}{n}$

APPLICATIONS: **Proportions and Scales**

On a map, the scale compares distance on the map to actual distance.

86. On a certain map, 2 inches represent 45 miles. How many miles do 4 inches represent?

(Hint: $\frac{\text{Map Distance}}{\text{Actual Distance}} \rightarrow \frac{2}{45} = \frac{4}{n}$)

87. On a map of Alaska, 3 centimeters represent 100 kilometers. How many kilometers do 12 centimeters represent?

88. On a map of Florida, 1 inch represents 115 miles. How many inches represent 230 miles?

89. On a certain map, 2.5 centimeters represent 40 kilometers. How many centimeters represent 200 kilometers?

EQUATIONS/RATIO/PROPORTION 81

Each lesson in Chapters 1-6 contains a set of word problems that apply the skill(s) taught in the lesson.

The numbered steps in the **Example** relate directly to the numbered steps in the **Procedure.**

The Metric System of Measures and Customary System of Measures are used throughout.

Each set of **Exercises** is referenced to the related **Example** or to a **Table.**

Consumer Skills and Applications Lessons: Chapters 7-18

Each lesson in Chapters 7-18 follows this structure.

Real-life consumer situation
Each lesson in Chapters 7-18 opens with a real-life setting.

In addition to the **Review of Related Skills** page that opens each chapter, each lesson in Chapters 7-18 contains a set of **Review of Related Skills** exercises that review prior-taught skills that are used in the lesson.

The reference is to the page where the skill was taught.

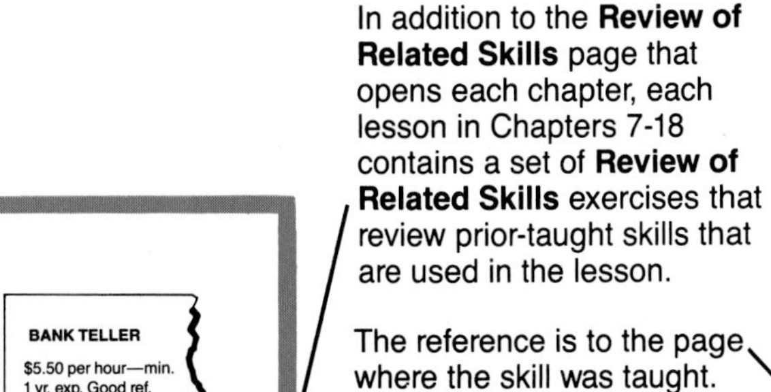

7-1 Hourly Wages

Tom Benedict is looking for a job as a bank teller. He notices the advertisement at the right in a newspaper.

BANK TELLER
$5.50 per hour—min.
1 yr. exp. Good ref.
Call 799-0104

EXAMPLE 1 Tom applies for and gets the job. What will be his weekly income for a 40-hour week?

Solution: **Amount per Hour × Number of Hours = Amount Earned**
$\$5.50 \times 40 = \$220$ Tom's weekly income will be **$220.**

Alice Brown also applied for a job that was advertised in a newspaper. She asked about the overtime guarantee. Working **overtime** means that she will receive $1\frac{1}{2}$, or 1.5 times the regular hourly pay when she works more than 35 hours in a week. This is also called **time and a half.**

TRAINEE-MECHANIC
$5 per hr.—35 hrs. Time and a half for overtime. Gd benefits. Equal Oppty Employer. Contact Mr.

To find Alice's total weekly income, first answer the **hidden questions:**

What is the weekly pay for 35 hours of work?

What is the overtime pay?

Then you can find her total weekly income.

EXAMPLE 2 Alice worked 48 hours one week. Find her total income for that week.

Solutions:
1. Find the pay for 35 hours.
$\$5.00 \times 35 = \$175.00$
2. Find the overtime pay per hour.
$\$5.00 \times 1.5 = \$7.50$ ◀ *Regular Pay Per Hour × 1.5 = Overtime Pay Per Hour*
3. Find the overtime pay for 13 hours. ◀ *48 − 35 = 13*
$\$7.50 \times 13 = \$97.50$
4. Find the total income.
$\$175.00 + 97.50 = \$272.50$ ◀ *Regular Pay + Overtime Pay = Total Income*

Alice's total income that week was **$272.50.**

138 CHAPTER 7

Examples
These show how to apply prior-taught skills to a consumer application.

REVIEW OF RELATED SKILLS

Multiply. (Pages 8–9, 56–57)

1. $3.25 × 30	2. $4.60 × 40	3. $5.80 × 38	4. $6.15 × 35
5. $5.00 × $38\frac{1}{2}$	6. $8.00 × $30\frac{1}{2}$	7. $8.50 × $3\frac{1}{2}$	8. $12.00 × $6\frac{1}{2}$
9. $14.50 × 1.5	10. $7.00 × 1.5	11. $8.20 × 1.5	12. $6.70 × 1.5
13. $6.00 × $1\frac{1}{2}$	14. $4.00 × $1\frac{1}{2}$	15. $12.00 × $1\frac{1}{2}$	16. $8.00 × $1\frac{1}{2}$

EXERCISES

For Exercises 1–6, find the weekly income. (Example 1)

	Hourly Wage	Hours Worked	Weekly Income
1.	$4.00	40	?
2.	$5.00	38	?
3.	$5.25	40	?
4.	$3.75	25	?

5. An auto mechanic earns $8.50 per hour and works 35 hours per week. Find the weekly income.
6. A machinist earns $10 per hour and works 40 hours per week. Find the weekly income.

For Exercises 7–10, find the total income. Time and a half is paid for all hours worked over 40. (Example 2)

	Hourly Wage	Hours Worked	Total Income
7.	$7.00	42	?
8.	$5.50	44	?
9.	$5.00	$44\frac{1}{2}$	?
10.	$8.40	42	?

Use the information from the advertisements at the right to answer Exercises 11–14.

DRIVER
with own late model 4-door car or station wagon. $5 per hour. 35 hr. per wk. Time and a half for overtime. Will train. 622-0500

GUARD
$4/hr. 40 hr. week. Good benefits. Overtime guaranteed (at time and a half). No exp. required. Call for interview between 9:00 and

11. Jane Youngblood applied for the job of driver. Find her pay for a 35-hour work week.
12. One week Jane worked 43 hours. Find her total income for the week.
13. Toby Felch was just hired for the guard's position. Find his pay for a regular work week.
14. The first week Toby worked 42 hours. Find his total income for the first week.

INCOME 139

In most of the lessons, the **Exercises** are of two types. Those that apply the consumer skill to
1. Non-verbal problems.
2. Word problems.

Career Skills and Applications Lessons: Chapters 1-18

These lessons are one-page or two-page lessons. The career areas focus on those that are realistic career goals for students who are not mathematically talented.

Where appropriate, the career lessons show how the calculator is used in the given career.

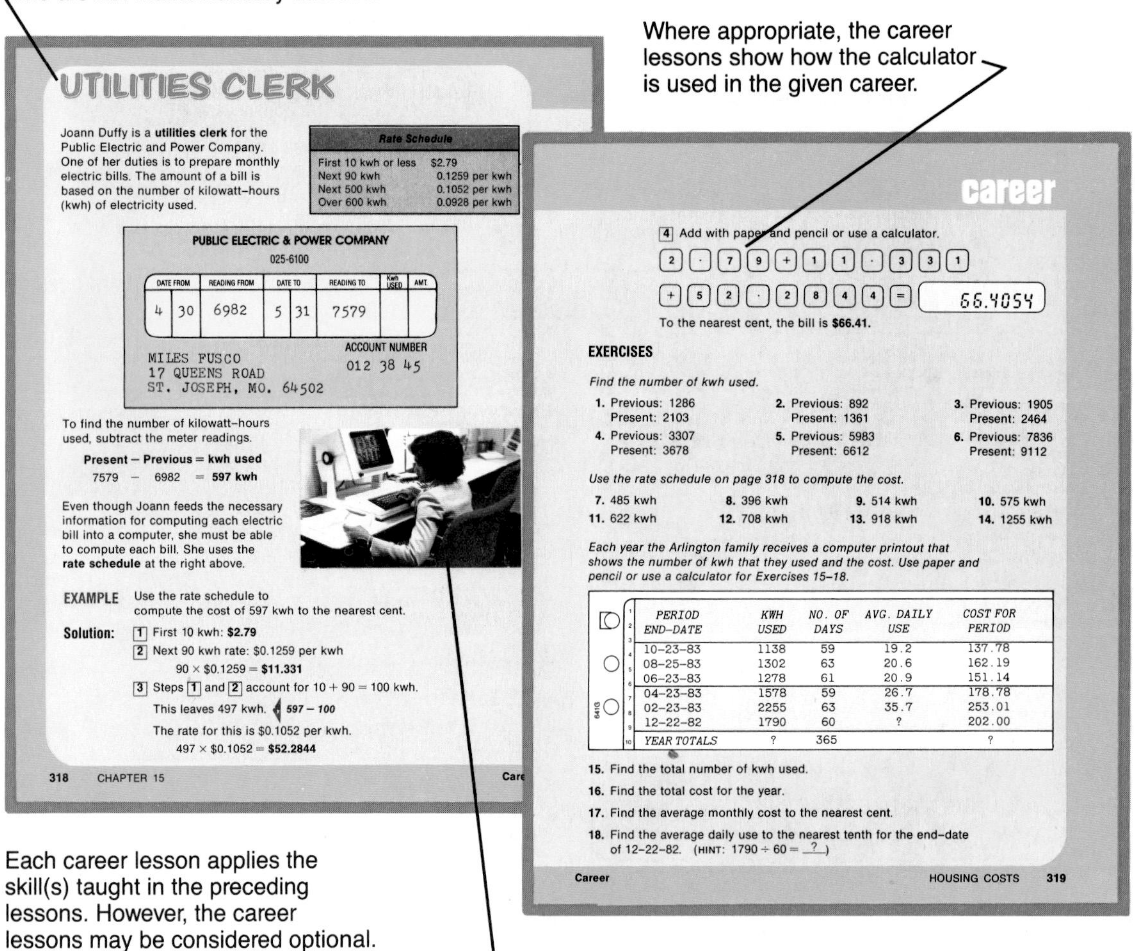

UTILITIES CLERK

Joann Duffy is a **utilities clerk** for the Public Electric and Power Company. One of her duties is to prepare monthly electric bills. The amount of a bill is based on the number of kilowatt-hours (kwh) of electricity used.

Rate Schedule	
First 10 kwh or less	$2.79
Next 90 kwh	0.1259 per kwh
Next 500 kwh	0.1052 per kwh
Over 600 kwh	0.0928 per kwh

PUBLIC ELECTRIC & POWER COMPANY
025-6100

DATE FROM		READING FROM	DATE TO		READING TO	Kwh USED	AMT.
4	30	6982	5	31	7579		

MILES FUSCO
17 QUEENS ROAD
ST. JOSEPH, MO. 64502

ACCOUNT NUMBER
012 38 45

To find the number of kilowatt-hours used, subtract the meter readings.

Present − Previous = kwh used
7579 − 6982 = **597 kwh**

Even though Joann feeds the necessary information for computing each electric bill into a computer, she must be able to compute each bill. She uses the **rate schedule** at the right above.

EXAMPLE Use the rate schedule to compute the cost of 597 kwh to the nearest cent.

Solution:
1. First 10 kwh: **$2.79**
2. Next 90 kwh rate: $0.1259 per kwh
   90 × $0.1259 = **$11.331**
3. Steps 1 and 2 account for 10 + 90 = 100 kwh.
   This leaves 497 kwh. ◀ *597 − 100*
   The rate for this is $0.1052 per kwh.
   497 × $0.1052 = **$52.2844**

318 CHAPTER 15

career

4. Add with paper and pencil or use a calculator.

2 . 7 9 + 1 1 . 3 3 1 + 5 2 . 2 8 4 4 = 66.4054

To the nearest cent, the bill is **$66.41**.

EXERCISES

Find the number of kwh used.

1. Previous: 1286 Present: 2103
2. Previous: 892 Present: 1361
3. Previous: 1905 Present: 2464
4. Previous: 3307 Present: 3678
5. Previous: 5983 Present: 6612
6. Previous: 7836 Present: 9112

Use the rate schedule on page 318 to compute the cost.

7. 485 kwh
8. 396 kwh
9. 514 kwh
10. 575 kwh
11. 622 kwh
12. 708 kwh
13. 918 kwh
14. 1255 kwh

Each year the Arlington family receives a computer printout that shows the number of kwh that they used and the cost. Use paper and pencil or use a calculator for Exercises 15–18.

PERIOD END-DATE	KWH USED	NO. OF DAYS	AVG. DAILY USE	COST FOR PERIOD
10-23-83	1138	59	19.2	137.78
08-25-83	1302	63	20.6	162.19
06-23-83	1278	61	20.9	151.14
04-23-83	1578	59	26.7	178.78
02-23-83	2255	63	35.7	253.01
12-22-82	1790	60	?	202.00
YEAR TOTALS	?	365		?

15. Find the total number of kwh used.
16. Find the total cost for the year.
17. Find the average monthly cost to the nearest cent.
18. Find the average daily use to the nearest tenth for the end-date of 12-22-82. (HINT: 1790 ÷ 60 = ?)

Career HOUSING COSTS 319

Each career lesson applies the skill(s) taught in the preceding lessons. However, the career lessons may be considered optional.

Where appropriate, the use of computers in the career is included.

Rounding and Estimation

Each of Chapters 7-18 ends with a **Rounding and Estimation** section.

Note the two types of **Skills** exercises.

The **Applications** portion applies the skills of rounding and estimation to the types of consumer topics that were presented in the chapter.

Consumers use rounding and estimation to solve problems related to buying a car.

EXERCISES

Skills

Choose the best estimate. Choose a, b, or c.

		a.	b.	c.
1.	7421 + 188	7420 + 180	7420 + 190	7430 + 1
2.	8397 + 118	8400 + 100	8300 + 100	8400 + 2
3.	111.05 × 48	110 × 50	110 × 40	120 × 50
4.	$5\frac{1}{2}\%$ × 8025	$\frac{1}{20}$ × 8000	$\frac{1}{20}$ × 9000	$\frac{1}{10}$ × 900
5.	$4\frac{3}{4}\%$ of 8995	$\frac{1}{10}$ × 9000	$\frac{1}{20}$ × 9000	$\frac{1}{8}$ × 9000
6.	601.16 − 399.88	600 − 400	700 − 400	600 − 30
7.	221.07 + 32.97	210 + 30	220 + 30	230 + 40

Choose the best estimate. Choose a, b, c, or d.

		a.	b.	c.	d.
8.	8603 + 221	8700	8600	8900	8
9.	9489 + 112	9600	9500	9700	9
10.	132.04 × 48	6000	6500	7000	7
11.	$9\frac{1}{2}\%$ of 9012	1000	1100	900	8
12.	$10\frac{1}{2}\%$ of 7975	800	700	1000	9
13.	729.30 − 411.25	300	400	200	500
14.	302.70 + 29.95	320	330	340	350

Applications

15. The base price of an Onyx is $7500. The total cost of the options is $904.20 and the destination charge is $196.75. Estimate the sticker price.
    a. $7500 + $1000 + $200
    b. $7500 + $900 + $200
    c. $7500 + $800 + $100
    d. $8000 + $1000 + $200

16. June can purchase a certain car by making 48 monthly payments of $151.20. Estimate the total of the monthly payments.
    a. $160 × 40
    b. $150 × 40
    c. $150 × 50
    d. $160 × 50

17. Patrick pays a premium of $698 for his liability insurance. Sue, who is the same age as Patrick, pays $361. Estimate the difference in their premiums.
    a. $690 − $360 b. $700 − $360
    c. $700 − $350 d. $690 − $340

18. In a certain automobile insurance policy, the premium for liability insurance without driver training is $404.25. The premium with driver training is $342.16. Estimate the difference.
    a. $400 − $340 b. $400 − $350
    c. $400 − $330 d. $450 − $350

19. The base price of a certain car is $8341. The total cost of options is $862.40 and the destination charge is $178.95. Estimate the sticker price.
    a. $9400 b. $9500
    c. $9300 d. $9600

20. Larry can purchase a certain car by making 48 monthly payments of $133.16. Estimate the total of the monthly payments.
    a. $6000 b. $7000 c. $6500 d. $7500

21. On a certain automobile insurance policy, the premium for liability insurance without driver training is $397.85. The premium with it is $328.98. Estimate the difference.
    a. $70 b. $60 c. $80 d. $90

22. The collision insurance premium for a certain car is $181.25. The comprehensive insurance premium is $28.98. Estimate the total premium.
    a. $200 b. $210 c. $220 d. $230

PURCHASER'S ADDRESS 2179
RESIDENCE PHONE 212 - 363
PLEASE ENTER MY ORDER FOR ONE
BODY TYPE STATION WAGON
350 ENGINE
AUTOMATIC TRANSMISSI
POWER STEERING
POWER BRAKES
ROOF RACK
SALESMAN HAROLD FORBES
NEW YORK 11554
DELIVERY DATE 11/17/8
MODEL
IDENT No. D09494 209
AIR CONDITIONING
SPORTS MIRROR

The **Calculator** exercises may be considered optional.

Each applies the use of a calculator to skills presented in the respective chapter.

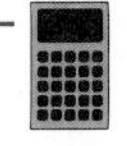

ESTIMATION AND THE CALCULATOR

You can use the rules for rounding and estimation and the calculator to solve problems.

EXAMPLE: 25.2 ÷ 4.8 = ?

Solution: Use paper and pencil to estimate the answer: 25 ÷ 5 = **5**

Use the calculator to find the exact answer.

2 5 . 2 ÷ 4 . 8 = 5.25

Since the estimate is 5, 5.25 is a reasonable answer.

EXERCISES

First estimate each answer. Then use a calculator to find the exact answer.

Problem	Estimated Answer	Exact Answer
1. 29 + 141 + 38 + 73	?	?
2. 14.17 + 129.7 + 18.1	?	?
3. 5418 − 1799	?	?
4. 74.9 − 19.07	?	?
5. 209 × 61	?	?
6. 38.1 × 20.8	?	?
7. 3498.6 ÷ 51	?	?
8. 90.09 ÷ 9.1	?	?

Review and Testing

The **Review of Related Skills** that open each chapter and the **Review of Related Skills** for each lesson in Chapters 7-18 provide an excellent method for continual review.

NOTE: The answers to all of the exercises in the **Review of Related Skills** are provided in the back of the student textbook.

For all other exercises, the answers to the odd-numbered exercises are provided in the back of the student textbook.

REVIEW OF RELATED SKILLS FOR CHAPTER 7

Multiply. (Pages 8–9, 56–57)

1. $7.35 × 25 **2.** $6.30 × 20 **3.** $5.50 × 28 **4.** $4.20 × 48
5. $16.30 × 1.5 **6.** $12.40 × 1.5 **7.** $7.50 × 1.5 **8.** $11.00 × 1.5
9. $3.00 × 12$\frac{1}{2}$ **10.** $7.50 × 7$\frac{1}{2}$ **11.** $13.00 × 6$\frac{1}{2}$ **12.** $14.00 × 10$\frac{1}{2}$
13. $6.00 × 1$\frac{1}{2}$ **14.** $8.00 × 1$\frac{1}{2}$ **15.** $10.20 × 1$\frac{1}{2}$ **16.** $7.60 × 1$\frac{1}{2}$
17. $17,500 × 0.0705 **18.** $18,980 × 0.0935 **19.** $16,480 × 0.099
20. $21,590 × 0.093 **21.** $23,450 × 0.067 **22.** $38,500 × 0.0705

Write a decimal for each per cent. (Pages 90–91)

23. 6% **24.** 8% **25.** 10% **26.** 12% **27.** 7$\frac{1}{2}$% **28.** 3$\frac{1}{2}$%
29. 3.5% **30.** 9.1% **31.** 47.8% **32.** 2.30% **33.** 4.01% **34.** 12.33%
35. 7.04% **36.** 1.9% **37.** 21.8% **38.** 11.2% **39.** 6.74% **40.** 18.43%

Write a fraction for each per cent. (Pages 90–91)

41. 50% **42.** 75% **43.** 10% **44.** 66$\frac{2}{3}$% **45.** 12$\frac{1}{2}$% **46.** 80%
47. 15% **48.** 25% **49.** 30% **50.** 55% **51.** 70% **52.** 48%
53. $\frac{1}{2}$% **54.** $\frac{1}{4}$% **55.** 37$\frac{1}{2}$% **56.** 33$\frac{1}{3}$% **57.** 62$\frac{1}{2}$% **58.** 14$\frac{2}{7}$%

Find each answer. (Pages 94–95)

59. 8% ... 5% of $10,500 **61.** 14% of $5700
62. 12% ... Steve's total ... **64.** 8% of $6800

REVIEW OF RELATED SKILLS

Write a decimal for each per cent. (Pages 90–91)

1. 5% **2.** 7% **3.** 14% **4.** 20% **5.** 4$\frac{1}{2}$% **6.** 10$\frac{1}{2}$%

Write a fraction for each per cent. (Pages 90–91)

7. 10% **8.** 25% **9.** 5% **10.** 15% **11.** 33$\frac{1}{3}$% **12.** 12$\frac{1}{2}$%

Find each answer. (Pages 94–95)

13. 3% of $1500 **14.** 6% of $12,500 **15.** 10% of $3600 **16.** 3$\frac{1}{2}$% of $400

142 CHAPTER 7

Each **Chapter Review** consists of
1. Vocabulary review
2. Skills review
3. Applications review
Note the help reference.

Chapter Review

Part 1: VOCABULARY

For Exercises 1–6, choose from the box at the right the word(s) that completes each statement.

taxes
gross pay
graduated
overtime pay
net pay
deductions
commission
social security

1. Pay for working extra hours is called __?__. (Pages 138–139)
2. A per cent of sales that a salesperson earns is called __?__. (Pages 142–143)
3. When the commission rate changes as the amount of sales increases, the commission is __?__. (Pages 142–143)
4. The total amount a person earns at a job is __?__. (Pages 144–145)
5. After taxes and voluntary deductions are subtracted from a person's gross pay, the remaining amount is the __?__. (Pages 144–145).
6. Federal Insurance Contributions Act (F.I.C.A.) taxes are also called __?__ taxes. (Pages 146–147)

Part 2: SKILLS

Multiply. (Pages 8–9, 56–57)

7. $6.25 × 21 **8.** $5.40 × 38 **9.** $7.00 × 3$\frac{1}{2}$ **10.** $12.80 × 7
11. $15,500 × 0.075 **12.** $19,960 × 0.0525 **13.** $17,480 × 0.0615

Write a decimal for each per cent. (Pages 90–91)

14. 3% **15.** 5% **16.** 11.43% **17.** 7.5% **18.** 3$\frac{1}{2}$% **19.** 16

Write a fraction for each per cent. (Pages 90–91)

20. 25% **21.** 33$\frac{1}{3}$% **22.** 20% **23.** 50% **24.** 75% **25.** 10%

Find each answer. (Pages 94–95)

26. 7% of $1800 **27.** 5% of $2500 **28.** 3$\frac{1}{2}$% of $7000 **29.** 10% of $83

Add or subtract. (Pages 4–5)

30. 3.75 + 12.50 + 18.65 **31.** 6.83 + 12.95 + 3.15 **32.** 30.51 + 17.30 + 9.
33. 219.48 − 117.19 **34.** 750.00 − 219.83 **35.** 385.00 − 119.75

152 CHAPTER 7 Chapter Revi

Part 3: APPLICATIONS

For Exercises 36–39, find the total income. (Pages 138–139)

	Hourly Wage	Hours Worked	Total Income
36.	$6.00	28	?
37.	$4.00	40	?

	Hourly Wage	Hours Worked	Total Income
38.	$3.25	20	?
39.	$4.20	35	?

40. Donna is an electrician. She earns $10.50 per hour for a 40-hour work week, with time and a half for overtime. Find her income for a 45-hour week. (Pages 138–139)

41. Bill is a travel agent. He is paid $5.50 per hour for a 35-hour work week. What is his income for a 40-hour week if he is paid time and a half for overtime? (Pages 138–139)

42. Megan sells appliances, and is paid an 8% commission on all sales. What is her commission on $4200 in sales? (Pages 142–143)

43. Hector earns a weekly salary of $150 plus a 20% commission on sales. Find his total income on sales of $2500. (Pages 142–143)

For Exercises 44–47, use the statement of earnings below. (Pages 144–145)

DEPT.	EMPLOYEE	CHECK #	WEEK ENDING	GROSS PAY	NET PAY	
12	Tynan, B.	11352	5/03/--	205.20	?	
TAX DEDUCTIONS				PERSONAL DEDUCTIONS		
FIT	FICA	STATE	LOCAL	MEDICAL	UNION DUES	OTHERS
19.10	13.75	8.10	1.21	3.24	4.00	3.15

44. What is the gross pay? **45.** Find the total tax deductions.
46. Find the total personal deductions. **47.** Find the net pay.

For Exercises 48–51 find the F.I.C.A. tax. Refer to the table on page 146. (Pages 146–147)

	Year	Income	F.I.C.A.
48.	1985	$17,395	?
49.	1982	$21,550	?

	Year	Income	F.I.C.A.
50.	1983	$27,050	?
51.	1984	$19,398	?

52. Roger earns $5.25 per hour. He works 38$\frac{1}{2}$ hours per week. Estimate his weekly gross pay. (Pages 150–151)
a. $240 **b.** $150
c. $180 **d.** $200

53. Leona receives a 9$\frac{3}{4}$% commission on all sales. Last week, her total sales were $21,250. Estimate the commission. (Pages 150–151)
a. $2000 **b.** $200
c. $20,000 **d.** $4000

Chapter Review INCOME 153

Review and Testing

Each **Chapter Test** parallels the content of the formal **Chapter Test** included in the **Teacher's Resource Book.**

In Chapters 7-18, a page of **Additional Practice** follows the **Chapter Test.** It provides further practice for students who did not perform well on the formal **Chapter Test.**

Chapter Test

Perform the indicated operation.

1. $6.95 × 35
2. $3.75 × 42
3. $9600 × 0.0
4. 41.5 + 9.40 + 6.45
5. 7.04 + 12.38 + 9.16
6. 341.12 − 89.08
7. 259.63 − 104.19

Write a decimal for each per cent.

8. 8%
9. $22\frac{1}{2}$%

Write a fraction for each per cent.

10. 80%
11. $37\frac{1}{2}$%

Find each answer.

12. 12% of $2045
13. 5% of $9820
14. 20% of $26

15. Josh is paid $6.20 per hour for a 35-hour week with time and a half for overtime. How much is he paid for working 40 hours one week?

16. Jane works at a skating rink and earns $3.50 per hour. Find her pa for a 25-hour week.

17. A broker receives a 2.2% commission on stock sales, in addition to a weekly salary of $250. Find the total income on weekly sales of $8300.

18. Juan is a sales representative, and receives a commission of 11% on total sales. Find the commission on sales of $19,700.

19. Sue Ellen earned $38,900 in 1982. The social security tax that year was 6.70%. The maximum amount taxed was $32,700. Find her total F.I.C.A. tax.

20. Mark's deductions are: federal tax-$97.50; social security tax-$28.60; medical insurance-$2.70. Estimate the total deductions.
 a. $130 b. $180
 c. $200 d. $100

154 CHAPTER 7 Chapter T

Additional Practice

Skills

Perform the indicated operations. (Pages 4-5, 8-9)

1. $5.83 × 31
2. $7.05 × 39
3. $9.15 × 42
4. $3.90 × 28
5. 15.05 + 10.00 + 14.75
6. 4.92 + 10.69 + 16.49
7. 25.61 + 10.57 + 38.05
8. 187.55 − 119.04
9. 208.64 − 75.38
10. 504.14 − 256.77

Find each answer. (Pages 94-95)

11. 14% of $780
12. 8% of $1025
13. 12% of $1563
14. 24% of $3828

Applications

15. Jack King works as a clerk and earns $3.50 per hour. He works 28 hours each week. Find his weekly income. (Pages 138-139)

16. Paula Vance works as a toll collector for $4.30 per hour. How much does she earn for a 35-hour work week? (Pages 138-139)

For Exercises 17-20, find the total income. Time and a half is paid for overtime work. (Pages 138-139)

	Hourly Wage	Regular Hours	Hours Worked	Total Income
17.	$3.80	35	42	?
18.	$5.50	40	43	?
19.	$6.95	40	46	?
20.	$7.50	30	35	?

21. Luis Lazar receives a 9% commission on his sales. Estimate his commission on sales of $5030. (Pages 150-151)
 a. $50 b. $1000 c. $500 d. $100

22. Sue Santelli earned $425 last week. The deductions were: federal tax-$93.50; social security tax-$28.48; state tax-$31.98. Find her net pay that week. (Pages 144-145)

23. Use the statement of earnings below to find the net pay. (Pages 144-145)

DEPT.	EMPLOYEE	CHECK #	WEEK ENDING	GROSS PAY	NET PAY
M	Boylan, T.	347528	11/2/--	342.25	?

TAX DEDUCTIONS				PERSONAL DEDUCTIONS		
FIT	FICA	STATE	LOCAL	MEDICAL	UNION DUES	OTHERS
60.40	22.91	6.88	---	4.50	----	12.00

24. Bill Gomez earned $25,400 in 1982. The F.I.C.A. tax rate that year was 6.70% on a maximum of $32,700. Find the amount of tax. (Pages 146-147)

25. Kim Li earned $45,300 in 1982. The F.I.C.A. tax rate was 6.70%. The maximum amount taxed was $32,700. Find the F.I.C.A. tax. (Pages 146-147)

Additional Practice INCOME 155

A **Cumulative Review** appears after Chapters 3, 6, 9, 12, 15 and 18. The multiple-choice format will help to prepare students for standardized exams and competency tests.

A **Sample Competency Test** appears after Chapter 6. It parallels the one included in the **Teacher's Resource Book,** which also contains a **Consumer Competency Test.**

Cumulative Review: Chapters 13–15

Choose the correct answer. Choose a, b, c, or d.

1. Add: 3.01 + 2.97 + 0.46
 a. 6.53 b. 10.58
 c. 6.44 d. 10.67

2. Subtract. Round the answer to the nearest whole number.
 21 − 5.5
 a. 3.4 b. 15.5 c. 34 d. 16

3. Multiply: $2208 × $\frac{3}{4}$
 a. $1656 b. $552
 c. $736 d. $428

4. Divide. Round the answer to the nearest tenth.

9. A 12-ounce can of tomato paste costs 53¢. Find the unit price.
 a. 4.4¢ b. 22¢
 c. 5.2¢ d. 23¢

10. Jim bought three no-name items 59¢, 87¢, and 51¢. Elisa bought three similar brand-name items f 72¢, 95¢, and 68¢. How much di Jim save on the total purchase?
 a. $1.14 b. $0.38
 c. $0.60 d. $0.76

11. Susan bought a jar of instant coff marked $2.19 at a store giving double coupon savings. She used

Sample Competency Test: Chapters 1–6

Choose the correct answer. Choose a, b, c, or d.

1. Subtract: 4607 − 3929
 a. 768 b. 688
 c. 678 d. 768

4. Divide: 39)15.405
 a. 0.39 R 24 b. 395.0
 c. 0.395 d. 39.5

Appendix A: Introduction to Algebra

This optional chapter is provided primarily for those students who intend to elect a course in algebra one.

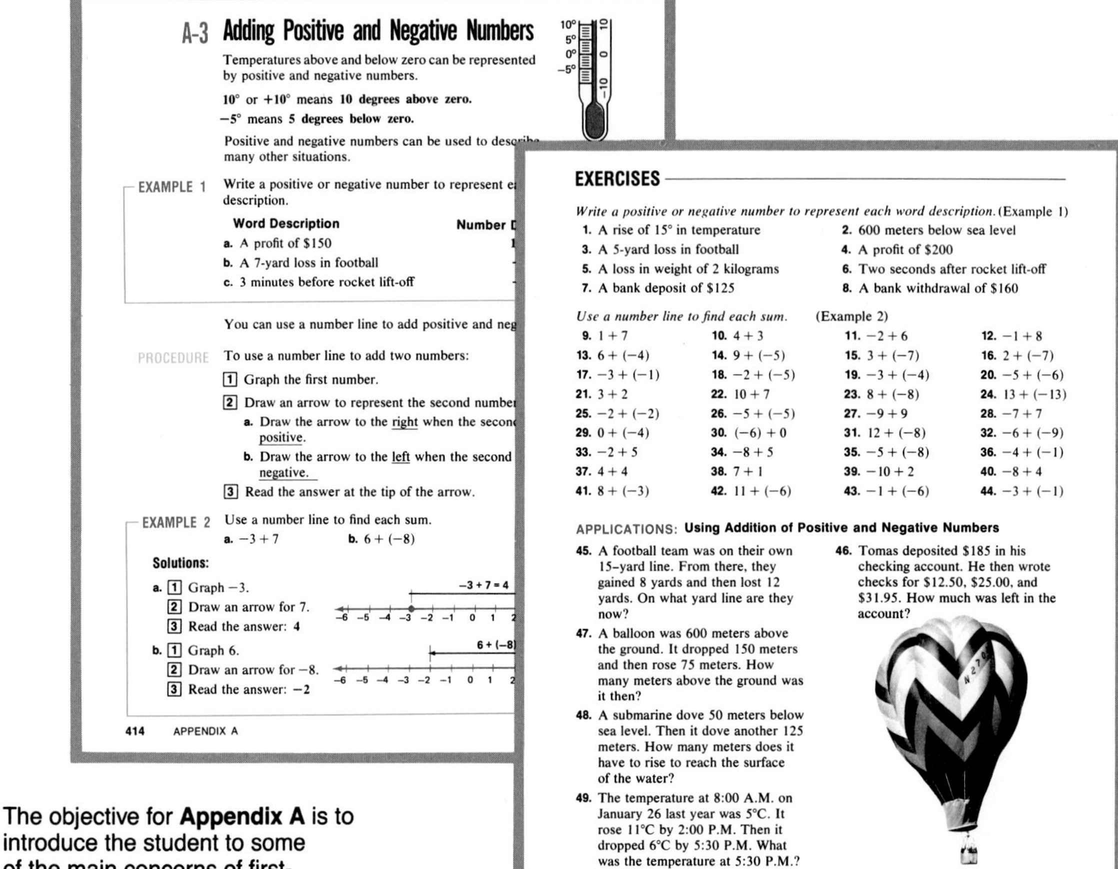

A-3 Adding Positive and Negative Numbers

Temperatures above and below zero can be represented by positive and negative numbers.

10° or +10° means 10 degrees above zero.
−5° means 5 degrees below zero.

Positive and negative numbers can be used to describe many other situations.

EXAMPLE 1 Write a positive or negative number to represent e[ach] description.

Word Description	Number [D...]
a. A profit of $150	1
b. A 7-yard loss in football	
c. 3 minutes before rocket lift-off	

You can use a number line to add positive and neg[ative]

PROCEDURE To use a number line to add two numbers:

1 Graph the first number.
2 Draw an arrow to represent the second numbe[r]
   a. Draw the arrow to the right when the secon[d] positive.
   b. Draw the arrow to the left when the second negative.
3 Read the answer at the tip of the arrow.

EXAMPLE 2 Use a number line to find each sum.
a. $-3 + 7$ b. $6 + (-8)$

Solutions:

a. 1 Graph −3.
2 Draw an arrow for 7.
3 Read the answer: 4

b. 1 Graph 6.
2 Draw an arrow for −8.
3 Read the answer: −2

414 APPENDIX A

EXERCISES

Write a positive or negative number to represent each word description. (Example 1)

1. A rise of 15° in temperature
2. 600 meters below sea level
3. A 5-yard loss in football
4. A profit of $200
5. A loss in weight of 2 kilograms
6. Two seconds after rocket lift-off
7. A bank deposit of $125
8. A bank withdrawal of $160

Use a number line to find each sum. (Example 2)

9. $1 + 7$	10. $4 + 3$	11. $-2 + 6$	12. $-1 + 8$
13. $6 + (-4)$	14. $9 + (-5)$	15. $3 + (-7)$	16. $2 + (-7)$
17. $-3 + (-1)$	18. $-2 + (-5)$	19. $-3 + (-4)$	20. $-5 + (-6)$
21. $3 + 2$	22. $10 + 7$	23. $8 + (-8)$	24. $13 + (-13)$
25. $-2 + (-2)$	26. $-5 + (-5)$	27. $-9 + 9$	28. $-7 + 7$
29. $0 + (-4)$	30. $(-6) + 0$	31. $12 + (-8)$	32. $-6 + (-9)$
33. $-2 + 5$	34. $-8 + 5$	35. $-5 + (-8)$	36. $-4 + (-1)$
37. $4 + 4$	38. $7 + 1$	39. $-10 + 2$	40. $-8 + 4$
41. $8 + (-3)$	42. $11 + (-6)$	43. $-1 + (-6)$	44. $-3 + (-1)$

APPLICATIONS: **Using Addition of Positive and Negative Numbers**

45. A football team was on their own 15-yard line. From there, they gained 8 yards and then lost 12 yards. On what yard line are they now?
46. Tomas deposited $185 in his checking account. He then wrote checks for $12.50, $25.00, and $31.95. How much was left in the account?
47. A balloon was 600 meters above the ground. It dropped 150 meters and then rose 75 meters. How many meters above the ground was it then?
48. A submarine dove 50 meters below sea level. Then it dove another 125 meters. How many meters does it have to rise to reach the surface of the water?
49. The temperature at 8:00 A.M. on January 26 last year was 5°C. It rose 11°C by 2:00 P.M. Then it dropped 6°C by 5:30 P.M. What was the temperature at 5:30 P.M.?

INTRODUCTION TO ALGEBRA 415

The objective for **Appendix A** is to introduce the student to some of the main concerns of first-year algebra, particularly the operations with positive and negative numbers and graphing on the coordinate plane. Thus, the topics are not treated in a formal manner.

The answers to the odd-numbered exercises are provided in the back of the student textbook.

Appendix B: Introduction to Computers

Access to a computer is not essential for the study of **Appendix B.**

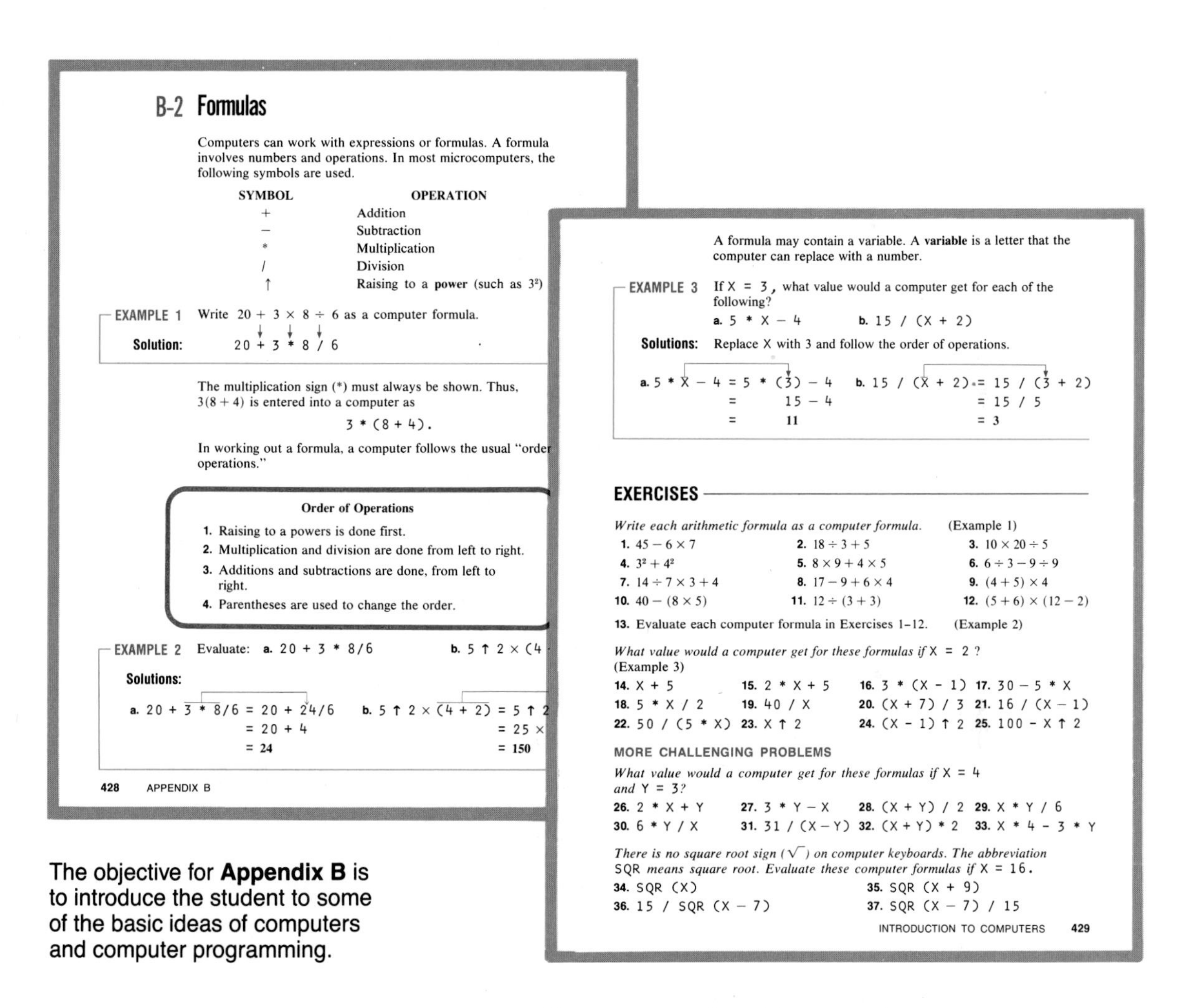

B-2 Formulas

Computers can work with expressions or formulas. A formula involves numbers and operations. In most microcomputers, the following symbols are used.

SYMBOL	OPERATION
+	Addition
−	Subtraction
*	Multiplication
/	Division
↑	Raising to a **power** (such as 3^2)

EXAMPLE 1 Write $20 + 3 \times 8 \div 6$ as a computer formula.

Solution: 20 + 3 * 8 / 6

The multiplication sign (*) must always be shown. Thus, $3(8 + 4)$ is entered into a computer as

3 * (8 + 4).

In working out a formula, a computer follows the usual "order operations."

Order of Operations

1. Raising to a powers is done first.
2. Multiplication and division are done from left to right.
3. Additions and subtractions are done, from left to right.
4. Parentheses are used to change the order.

EXAMPLE 2 Evaluate: **a.** 20 + 3 * 8/6 **b.** 5 ↑ 2 × (4

Solutions:

a. 20 + 3 * 8/6 = 20 + 24/6
= 20 + 4
= 24

b. 5 ↑ 2 × (4 + 2) = 5 ↑ 2
= 25 ×
= 150

A formula may contain a variable. A **variable** is a letter that the computer can replace with a number.

EXAMPLE 3 If X = 3, what value would a computer get for each of the following?

a. 5 * X − 4 **b.** 15 / (X + 2)

Solutions: Replace X with 3 and follow the order of operations.

a. 5 * X − 4 = 5 * (3) − 4
= 15 − 4
= 11

b. 15 / (X + 2) = 15 / (3 + 2)
= 15 / 5
= 3

EXERCISES

Write each arithmetic formula as a computer formula. (Example 1)

1. $45 - 6 \times 7$
2. $18 \div 3 + 5$
3. $10 \times 20 \div 5$
4. $3^2 + 4^2$
5. $8 \times 9 + 4 \times 5$
6. $6 \div 3 - 9 \div 9$
7. $14 \div 7 \times 3 + 4$
8. $17 - 9 + 6 \times 4$
9. $(4 + 5) \times 4$
10. $40 - (8 \times 5)$
11. $12 \div (3 + 3)$
12. $(5 + 6) \times (12 - 2)$
13. Evaluate each computer formula in Exercises 1–12. (Example 2)

What value would a computer get for these formulas if X = 2 ? (Example 3)

14. X + 5
15. 2 * X + 5
16. 3 * (X - 1)
17. 30 − 5 * X
18. 5 * X / 2
19. 40 / X
20. (X + 7) / 3
21. 16 / (X − 1)
22. 50 / (5 * X)
23. X ↑ 2
24. (X - 1) ↑ 2
25. 100 - X ↑ 2

MORE CHALLENGING PROBLEMS

What value would a computer get for these formulas if X = 4 *and* Y = 3?

26. 2 * X + Y
27. 3 * Y − X
28. (X + Y) / 2
29. X * Y / 6
30. 6 * Y / X
31. 31 / (X − Y)
32. (X + Y) * 2
33. X * 4 - 3 * Y

There is no square root sign (√‾) *on computer keyboards. The abbreviation* SQR *means square root. Evaluate these computer formulas if* X = 16.

34. SQR (X)
35. SQR (X + 9)
36. 15 / SQR (X − 7)
37. SQR (X − 7) / 15

The objective for **Appendix B** is to introduce the student to some of the basic ideas of computers and computer programming.

The answers to the odd-numbered exercises are provided in the back of the student textbook.

Teacher's Resource Book

This paperback consists of perforated and pre-holed copying masters. You are given permission to reproduce these pages.

It consists of a:

1. Test Booklet
2. Workbook Section
3. Answer section

The Test Booklet

There are two forms of each chapter test. Plus
6 Cumulative tests
1 Sample competency test
1 Consumer competency test

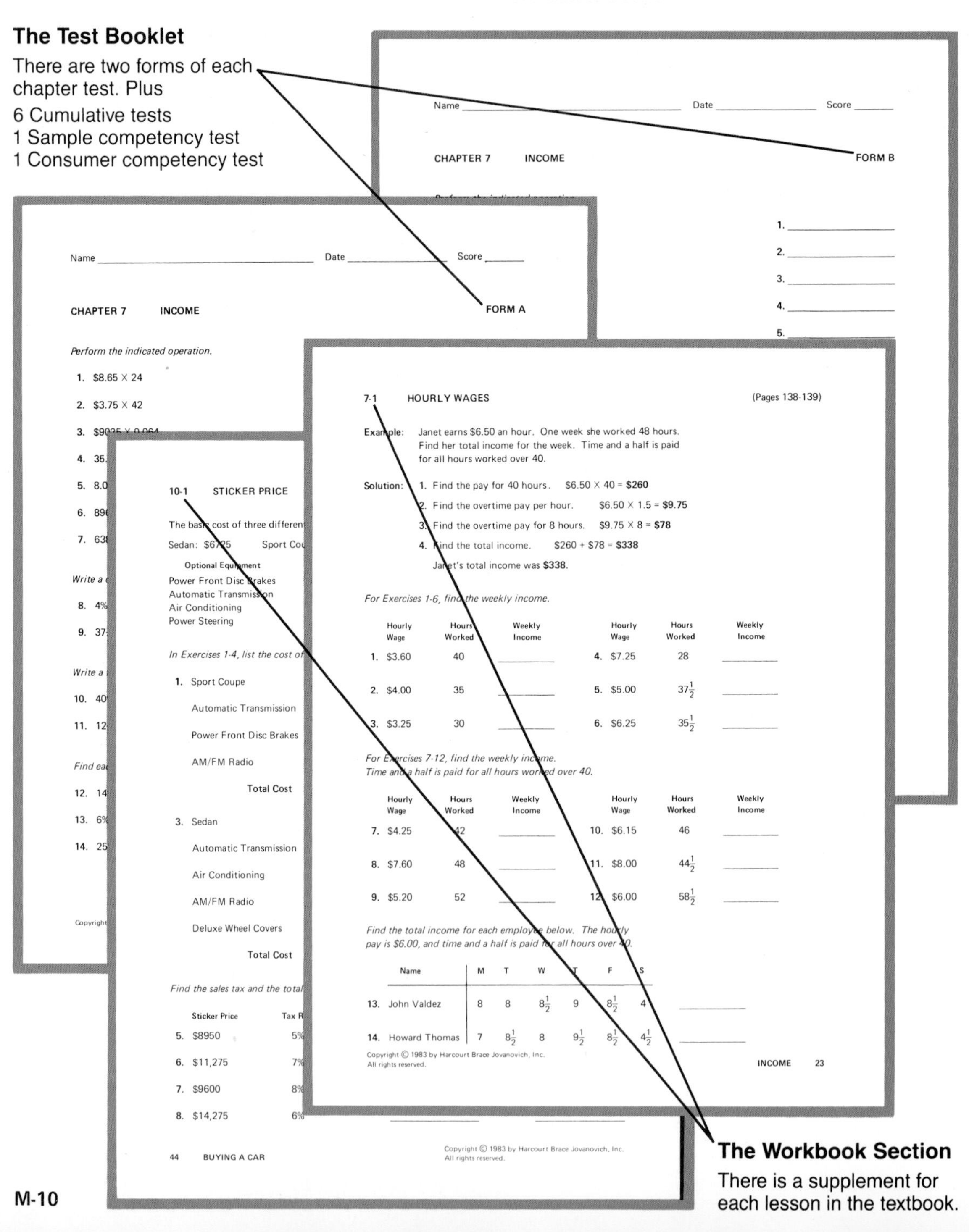

Name ______ Date ______ Score ______

CHAPTER 7 INCOME FORM B

1. ______
2. ______
3. ______
4. ______
5. ______

Name ______ Date ______ Score ______

CHAPTER 7 INCOME FORM A

Perform the indicated operation.

1. $8.65 X 24
2. $3.75 X 42

10-1 STICKER PRICE

Optional Equipment
Power Front Disc Brakes
Automatic Transmission
Air Conditioning
Power Steering

1. Sport Coupe
Automatic Transmission
Power Front Disc Brakes
AM/FM Radio
Total Cost

3. Sedan
Automatic Transmission
Air Conditioning
AM/FM Radio
Deluxe Wheel Covers
Total Cost

	Sticker Price
5.	$8950
6.	$11,275
7.	$9600
8.	$14,275

44 BUYING A CAR

7-1 HOURLY WAGES (Pages 138-139)

Example: Janet earns $6.50 an hour. One week she worked 48 hours. Find her total income for the week. Time and a half is paid for all hours worked over 40.

Solution:
1. Find the pay for 40 hours. $6.50 X 40 = **$260**
2. Find the overtime pay per hour. $6.50 X 1.5 = **$9.75**
3. Find the overtime pay for 8 hours. $9.75 X 8 = **$78**
4. Find the total income. $260 + $78 = **$338**

Janet's total income was **$338**.

For Exercises 1-6, find the weekly income.

	Hourly Wage	Hours Worked	Weekly Income		Hourly Wage	Hours Worked	Weekly Income
1.	$3.60	40	______	4.	$7.25	28	______
2.	$4.00	35	______	5.	$5.00	$37\frac{1}{2}$	______
3.	$3.25	30	______	6.	$6.25	$35\frac{1}{2}$	______

For Exercises 7-12, find the weekly income. Time and a half is paid for all hours worked over 40.

	Hourly Wage	Hours Worked	Weekly Income		Hourly Wage	Hours Worked	Weekly Income
7.	$4.25	42	______	10.	$6.15	46	______
8.	$7.60	48	______	11.	$8.00	$44\frac{1}{2}$	______
9.	$5.20	52	______	12.	$6.00	$58\frac{1}{2}$	______

Find the total income for each employee below. The hourly pay is $6.00, and time and a half is paid for all hours over 40.

	Name	M	T	W	T	F	S	
13.	John Valdez	8	8	$8\frac{1}{2}$	9	$8\frac{1}{2}$	4	______
14.	Howard Thomas	7	$8\frac{1}{2}$	8	$9\frac{1}{2}$	$8\frac{1}{2}$	$4\frac{1}{2}$	______

INCOME 23

The Workbook Section

There is a supplement for each lesson in the textbook.

TEACHER'S RESOURCE BOOK

In addition to receiving a copy of the Teacher's Edition, upon request, each teacher will also receive a copy of the *Teacher's Resource Book*, upon request. This paperback publication consists of copying masters that are perforated and pre-holed. This title has the following components.

Tests

The *Test Booklet* portion contains two forms of each chapter test. Teachers may wish to use one form as a pretest and the other form as a posttest. The aspect of pretesting may be particularly helpful for Chapters 1-6, the skills chapters. There are cumulative reviews that cover Chapters 1-3, 4-6, 7-9, 10-12, 13-15, and 16-18. There is also a *Sample Competency Test* that covers the content in Chapters 1-6 and a *Consumer Competency Test* that covers the content in Chapters 7-18.

Workbook

The *Workbook* portion contains additional practice for each lesson in the student textbook. The *Workbook* pages for Chapters 7-18 also contain examples. The reference to the related pages in the student textbook is clearly indicated.

Answers

The answers for the tests and the workbook exercises are included in the back of the *Teacher's Resource Book*.

NOTE: The *Test Booklet* portion is also available as a separate 96-page, self-cover publication with perforated pages.

The *Workbook* portion is also available as a separate 112-page paperback publication with perforated pages. In addition, there is an annotated Teacher's Edition of the *Workbook*.

LESSON PLAN GUIDE

Pages M-14 through M-42 consist of a *Lesson Plan Guide* for each chapter. Each consists of the following components.

Overview

1. An Overview of the chapter

Objectives

2. A listing of the objectives in two categories

   a. Chapters 1-6: *Arithmetic Skills and Applications*
      Chapters 7-18: *Consumer Skills and Applications*

   b. Chapters 1-18: *Career Skills and Applications*

Suggested Timetable

3. The *Suggested Timetable* on page M-13 is the third component. The three levels illustrated in the *Suggested Timetable* are defined by the authors as follows.

   Level 1: This represents a minimal course with a primary emphasis on arithmetic skills and a secondary emphasis on word problems related to consumer applications.

   Level 2: This represents a course with a balance between arithmetic skills and word problems related to consumer applications.

   Level 3: This represents an enriched course with a primary emphasis on word problems related to consumer applications.

Annotated Pages

4. The *Overview* for each chapter presents a picture of the chapter and, where appropriate, offers general teaching suggestions. However, specific teaching suggestions are not included in the *Lesson Plan Guide.* The authors believe that specific teaching suggestions and other commentary for the teacher are more meaningful if they appear as annotations on the student page. You will note that each annotation is inserted in an appropriate position on the student page. Thus, the annotated pages represent the fourth component of the *Lesson Plan Guide.*

SUGGESTED TIMETABLE

Overview

The following *Suggested Timetable* is structured to accommodate three levels of ability. The total number of days for each chapter includes three days per chapter for review and testing for Level One, two or three days for Level Two, and one or two days for Level Three. The *Suggested Timetable* for Levels One and Two does not include any days for the optional Career lessons. However, their use is included for Level Three. These provisions notwithstanding, the *Suggested Timetable* should be considered as a guideline only. This is especially the case because of the flexible structure of Units II-V, as these units can be taught in any sequence that the teacher desires.

	Level One		Level Two		Level Three	
Chapter	**Sections**	**Days**	**Sections**	**Days**	**Sections**	**Days**
1	All	14	All	11	Selected	6
2	All	11	All	9	All	6
3	All	12	All	10	Selected	7
4	All	10	All	8	All	6
5	All	12	All	10	All	8
6	All	12	All	10	All	8
7	All	10	All	9	All	9
8	All	12	All	10	All	10
9	Omit 9-3, 9-6	10	Omit 9-3	11	All	11
10	All	12	All	10	All	10
11	All	10	All	9	All	9
12	All	8	All	7	All	7
13	All	10	All	9	All	9
14	All	12	All	11	All	10
15	Omit	0	All	11	All	10
16	Omit	0	All	12	All	11
17	Omit	0	Omit	0	All	12
18	Omit	0	Omit	0	All	9
Cumulative Reviews		15		13		12
Total Days		**170**		**170**		**170**

CHAPTER 1 WHOLE NUMBERS AND DECIMALS

Overview

We suggest that some or all of page x be reviewed before proceeding with the chapter.

The four operations with whole numbers and decimals are presented in Chapter 1. In addition to the large number of numerical problems in the Exercises, each section also contains a set of word problems. These word problems apply the skill(s) taught in the section to real-life situations. The Mid-Chapter Review on page 10 reviews the content presented in the first four sections, including the applications. It may be appropriate to administer a mid-chapter quiz at this point in the chapter.

Objectives: Arithmetic Skills and Applications

Section 1-1
Pages 2-3

To add whole numbers when the addition involves carrying (Example 1)
To subtract whole numbers when the subtraction involves renaming, including renaming with zeros (Example 2)
To apply the skills of adding and subtracting whole numbers to solving word problems that involve population

Section 1-2
Pages 4-5

To add decimals (Example 1)
To subtract decimals, including the annexing of zeros (Example 2)
To apply the skills of adding and subtracting decimals to word problems that involve rainfall

Section 1-3
Pages 6-7

To multiply a whole number by a two- or three-digit multiplier (Example 1)
To multiply whole numbers when there are zeros in one or both factors (Example 2)
To apply the skill of multiplying whole numbers to word problems that involve calories

Section 1-4
Pages 8-9

To multiply decimals (Example 1)
To multiply decimals that involve inserting zeros in the product (Example 2)
To apply the skill of multiplying decimals to word problems that involve food costs

Calculator: Checking Page 10	*To use a calculator to check the answers to addition, subtraction, and multiplication problems that involve whole numbers and decimals*
Section 1-5 Pages 12-13	*To round whole numbers to the nearest ten, to the nearest hundred, and to the nearest thousand (Example 1)* *To divide a whole number by a nonzero, one-, two-, or three-digit whole number (Example 2)* *To apply the skill of dividing whole numbers to word problems that involve customary measures (Exercises 60-63)*
Section 1-6 Pages 14-15	*To divide a decimal by a nonzero whole number (Example 1)* *To divide a decimal by a decimal (Example 2)* *To apply the skill of dividing decimals to word problems that involve the fuel economy of a car (Exercises 61-64)*
Section 1-7 Pages 16-17	*To round decimals to the nearest tenth, to the nearest hundredth, and to the nearest thousandth (Example 1)* *To divide by a decimal, rounding the quotient to a specified decimal place (Example 2)* *To apply the skills of dividing by a decimal and rounding the quotient to word problems that involve batting averages*
Section 1-8 Pages 18-19	*To estimate the answers to problems that involve addition, subtraction, multiplication, and division of whole numbers and decimals (Example)* *To apply the skills of estimating answers to problems that involve whole numbers and decimals to the various types of word problems presented in the chapter*
Calculator: Estimation Page 19	*To be able to determine the reasonableness of an answer found on a calculator by applying the skill of estimation*

Objectives: Career Skills and Applications

Stock Clerk Page 11	*To apply addition skills and the techniques of using a code and a formula to solving problems that involve selling price*
Bus Driver Pages 20-21	*To use a letter-number pair to locate cities on a map*

CHAPTER 2 APPLYING METRIC MEASURES

Overview

We suggest that some or all of page 26 be reviewed before proceeding with the chapter.
The metric units of length, mass, capacity, and temperature are presented in Chapter 2. Geometric ideas related to perimeter, area, and volume (rectangular prism) are also treated.

Objectives: Arithmetic Skills and Applications

Section 2-1
Pages 28-29

To determine suitable metric units of length (Table)
To determine equivalent metric units of length (Example)
To apply the skill of determining equivalent metric units of length to word problems that involve measurement

Section 2-2
Pages 30-31

To find the perimeter of polygons (Example 1)
To use the formulas $P = 2(\ell + w)$ and $P = 4 \times s$ to find the perimeter of a rectangle and a square, respectively (Example 2)
To apply the technique of drawing a rectangle or square to solving word problems that involve perimeter

Section 2-3
Pages 32-33

To determine suitable metric units of mass (Table 1)
To determine equivalent metric units of mass (Example)
To apply computational skills to word problems that involve metric units of mass

Section 2-4
Pages 34-35

To determine suitable metric units of capacity (Table)
To determine equivalent metric units of capacity (Example)
To apply the skill of determining equivalent units of capacity to word problems that involve common measuring utensils

Section 2-5
Pages 36-37

To find the area of a rectangle (Example 1)
To find the volume of a rectangular prism (Example 2)
To apply the skills of finding area and volume to word problems that involve rectangles and rectangular prisms

Section 2-6
Page 38

To determine suitable temperatures on the Celsius scale (Table)
To apply the skill of determining suitable Celsius temperatures to word problems

Objective: Career Skills and Applications

Electrician
Page 39

To apply multiplication skills and the technique of using a formula to solving problems that involve the number of watts needed in wiring a given area

CHAPTER 3 FRACTIONS

Overview

We suggest that some or all of page 44 be reviewed before proceeding with the chapter.

Although the United States is moving toward the metric system, the customary system of measures will be with us for some time to come. Consequently, the applications (word problems) that appear in the Exercises for Section 3-2 through Section 3-7 deal with various units in the customary system. You may need to refer to the *Table of Measurements* on page 436 when your class is working with these word problems.

You will note that the lessons on addition and subtraction of fractions present the problems in both horizontal form and vertical form. It is important that students be familiar with the horizontal form, as various competency tests present fractions in this way.

The *Mid-Chapter Review* on page 54 reviews the content presented in the first four sections, including the applications. It may be appropriate to administer a mid-chapter quiz at this point in the chapter.

A *Cumulative Review* covering Chapters 1-3 appears on pages 68-69. Note that it is structured in a multiple choice format, which is similar to that of many competency tests. The *Test Booklet* portion of the *Teacher's Resource Book* also contains a *Cumulative Review* for Chapters 1-3 should you decide to administer a formal test.

Objectives: Arithmetic Skills and Applications

Section 3-1
Pages 46-47

To write a mixed number for a fraction greater than 1 (Example 1)
To write a fraction in lowest terms (Example 2)
To apply the skill of writing a mixed number for a fraction to word problems that involve cost comparisons

Section 3-2
Pages 48-49

To add or subtract like fractions (Example 1)
To write like fractions for unlike fractions (Example 2)
To apply the skills of adding and subtracting like fractions to solving word problems that involve customary measures

Section 3-3
Pages 50-51

To add unlike fractions (Example 1)
To add mixed numbers (Example 2)
To apply the skills of adding unlike fractions and mixed numbers to solving problems that involve customary measures

Section 3-4
Pages 52-53

To subtract unlike fractions (Example 1)
To subtract mixed numbers when borrowing is involved (Example 2)
To apply the skills of subtracting fractions and mixed numbers to word problems that involve customary measures

Section 3-5
Pages 56-57

To multiply fractions (Example 1)
To multiply mixed numbers (Example 2)
To apply the skills of multiplying fractions and mixed numbers to word problems that involve recipes

Section 3-6
Pages 58-59

To divide with fractions (Example 1)
To divide with mixed numbers (Example 2)
To apply the skills of dividing with fractions and mixed numbers to word problems that involve customary measures

Section 3-7
Pages 60-61

To round fractions to the nearest whole number (Example)
To estimate the answers to problems that involve addition, subtraction, multiplication, and division of fractions
To apply the skill of estimating answers to problems that involve fractions to the various types of word problems presented in the chapter

Calculator: Fractions
Page 61

To use a calculator for computing the decimal equivalent of the answer to a problem that involves multiplying and dividing with fractions

Objectives: Career Skills and Applications

Travel Agent
Page 55

To apply addition and subtraction skills and the technique of reading a table to solving word problems that involve airline distances

Air Conditioning Technician
Pages 62-63

To apply multiplication and division skills and the techniques of using a formula to solving word problems that involve the cooling capacity of air conditioners

CHAPTER 4 EQUATIONS/RATIO/PROPORTION

Overview

We suggest that some or all of page 70 be reviewed before proceeding with the chapter.

The content in Sections 4-1, 4-2, and 4-3 will provide the student with the techniques for solving equations that are needed in Chapter 5. These sections also provide the student with the opportunity to review operations with whole numbers and decimals through the vehicle of solving equations. The work in Sections 4-4 and 4-5 on ratio and proportion not only will prepare the student for the chapters that follow, but it also provides a review of the concept of fractions.

Objectives: Arithmetic Skills and Applications

Section 4-1
Pages 72-73

To solve addition equations (Example 1)
To solve subtraction equations (Example 2)
To apply the skill of solving addition equations to word problems that involve markup

Section 4-2
Pages 74-75

To solve multiplication equations (Example 1)
To solve division equations (Example 2)
To apply the skill of solving multiplication equations to solving word problems that involve the distance/rate/time formula

Section 4-3
Pages 76-77

To solve equations by using subtraction and division (Example 1)
To solve equations by using addition and multiplication (Example 2)
To apply the skill of solving equations to problems that involve Fahrenheit and Celsius temperatures

Section 4-4
Pages 78-79

To write a ratio as a fraction in lowest terms (Table)
To determine whether two ratios are equivalent (Example)
To apply the skill of writing a ratio as a fraction in lowest terms to solving word problems

Section 4-5
Pages 80-81

To solve a proportion for n (Example)
To apply the skill of solving proportions to word problems that involve the scale on a map

Objective: Career Skills and Applications

Nurse
Pages 82-83

To apply the skills of solving proportions and rounding decimals to problems that involve the measurement of prescribed doses of medicine

CHAPTER 5 PER CENT

Overview

We suggest that some or all of page 88 be reviewed before proceeding with the chapter.

This chapter treats the three cases of per cent. Each case is taught by the same method: writing an equation and solving the equation by using the techniques presented in Chapter 4. This is an important chapter, as per cent plays a big part in the study of many of the consumer topics taught in Chapters 7-18. Including a set of word problems in the Exercises for each section will help to prepare the student for the word problems in Chapters 7-18 that deal with per cent, particularly the first case of per cent.

Many students have difficulty with per cent problems. Thus, if your students require more practice, additional exercises for each section can be found in the *Workbook* section of the *Teacher's Resource Book*.

Objectives: Arithmetic Skills and Applications

Section 5-1
Pages 90-91

To write a decimal for a per cent (Example 1)
To write a fraction for a per cent (Example 2)
To apply the skills of writing a decimal or a fraction for a per cent to word problems that involve U.S. production data

Section 5-2
Pages 92-93

To write a per cent for a decimal (Example 1)
To write a per cent for a fraction (Example 2)
To apply the skills of writing a per cent for a decimal or a fraction to word problems that involve sale price

Section 5-3
Pages 94-95

To find a per cent of a number by writing a decimal for a per cent (Example 1a)
To find a per cent of a number by writing a fraction for a per cent (Example 1b)
To apply the skill of finding a per cent of a number to solving word problems that involve blood types

Section 5-4
Pages 96-97

To find what per cent one number is of another (Example)
To apply the skill of finding what per cent one number is of another to solving word problems that involve sports

Section 5-5
Pages 100-101

To find a number when a per cent of it is known by writing a decimal for the per cent (Example 1)
To find a number when a per cent of it is known by writing a fraction for the per cent (Example 2)
To apply the skill of finding a number when a per cent of it is known to solving word problems that involve population data

Calculator: Per Cent
Page 103

To use a calculator to find the per cent of a number

Section 5-6
Pages 102-103

To estimate a per cent of a number by rounding the number (Example 1)
To estimate a per cent of a number by rounding the per cent (Example 2)
To apply the skill of estimating answers to per cent problems of the various types of word problems presented in the chapter

Objective: Career Skills and Applications

Photographer
Pages 98-99

To apply the skills of solving a proportion and of writing a ratio as a per cent together with the technique of using a formula to solving word problems that involve reducing and enlarging photographs and finding scale factors

CHAPTER 6 STATISTICS

Overview

We suggest that some or all of page 108 be reviewed before proceeding with the chapter.

Reading and constructing bar graphs, line graphs, and circle graphs are important consumer-related topics. Presenting these topics through real-world applications will help to give these skills, reading and constructing graphs, greater meaning. Before presenting circle graphs, angles are reviewed on page 114.

The application included with the work on mean, median, and mode (Sections 6-5 and 6-6) will help to motivate these topics.

Objectives: Arithmetic Skills and Applications

Section 6-1
Pages 110-111

To read a bar graph (Example)
To apply the skills of reading data from a table to constructing a bar graph for representing data

Section 6-2
Pages 112-113

To read a line graph (Example)
To apply the skill of reading data from a table to constructing a line graph for representing data

Section 6-3
Page 114

To use a protractor to measure angles (Example)
To determine whether an angle is acute, right, or obtuse (Definition)

Section 6-4
Pages 116-117

To draw a circle graph (Page 116)
To apply the skill of reading a circle graph to word problems that involve the composition of the human body

Section 6-5
Pages 118-119

To find the mean or average of a list of measures (Example 1)
To find the mode of a list of measures (Example 2)

Section 6-6
Pages 120-121

To find the median for an odd number of measures (Example 1)
To find the median for an even number of measures (Example 2)

Objective: Career Skills and Applications

Store Manager
Pages 122-123

To apply the skills of finding the mean, mode, and median to solving word problems that involve the statistical basis for business decisions related to managing a department store

CHAPTER 7 INCOME

Overview

We suggest that some or all of page 136 be reviewed before proceeding with the chapter.

Finding a job and earning money are certainly key issues which will help to motivate the study of this chapter. Each section contains a set of *Review of Related Skills* exercises that you may wish to use as a "warm up" before teaching each section.

The *Exercises* for each section (lesson) contain two types (or levels) of applications, non-verbal and word problems. (Refer to the *Workbook* section of the *Teacher's Resource Book* should you desire additional exercises for each section.) The following objectives apply to both types.

Objectives: Consumer Skills and Applications

Section 7-1
Pages 138-139

To apply the technique of using a formula to solving one-step problems that involve earnings (Example 1)

To apply the technique of the "hidden question" to solving multi-step problems that involve earnings (Example 2)

Section 7-2
Pages 142-143

To apply the technique of using a formula to solving one-step problems that involve commission (Example 1)

To apply the technique of the "hidden question" to solving two-step problems that involve commission (Example 2)

Section 7-3
Pages 144-145

To solve two-step problems that involve gross pay, deductions, and net pay

Section 7-4
Pages 146-147

To apply the skill of reading a table to solving one-step problems that involve social security tax

Rounding and Estimation
Pages 150-151

To apply the skills of rounding and estimation to computational problems (Exercises 1-18)

To apply the skills of rounding and estimation to word problems that involve earnings (Exercises 19-26)

Objectives: Career Skills and Applications

Truck Driver
Pages 140-141

To apply multiplication skills and the skill of reading a mileage chart to solving multi-step problems that involve earnings

Personnel Worker
Pages 148-149

To apply addition, subtraction, and multiplication skills and the skill of reading a table to solving multi-step problems that involve social security benefits

CHAPTER 8 INCOME TAX

Overview

We suggest that some or all of page 156 be reviewed before proceeding with the chapter.

This chapter presents information related to Federal income tax, adjusted gross income, and Federal income tax deductions. Wage and Tax Statements as related to income tax returns, taxable income, and state and city income taxes are also discussed. Note that the Exercises for Section 8-3 help the student to complete an income tax return (Form 1040A).

With the exception of Section 8-3, the Exercises for each section contain two types of applications, non-verbal and word problems. Thus, even those student who require remediation with reading skills will have the opportunity to meet with some success. (Refer to the *Workbook* section of the *Teacher's Resource Book* should you desire additional exercises for each section.) The following objectives apply to both types.

Objectives: Consumer Skills and Applications

Section 8-1
Pages 158-159

To apply the skill of reading a table to solving two-step problems that involve Federal income tax (Example 1)

To apply the skill of reading a table to solving multi-step problems that involve gross income and Federal income tax (Example 2)

Section 8-2
Pages 160-161

To solve one-step problems that involve adjusted gross income (Example 1)

To apply the skill of reading a table to solving one-step problems that involve Federal income tax deductions (Example 2)

Section 8-3
Pages 163-165

To identify the information on a Wage and Tax Statement (W-2 form) needed to complete an income tax return (Example 1)

To complete an income tax return (Example 2)

Section 8-4
Pages 166-167

To apply the technique of using a formula to solving multi-step problems that involve taxable income (Example 1)

To apply the skill of reading a table to solving problems that involve Federal income tax (Example 2)

Section 8-5
Pages 170-171

To apply the skill of reading a table to solving multi-step problems that involve state and city income taxes

Rounding and Estimation
Pages 172-173

To apply the skills of rounding and estimation to computational problems (Exercises 1-15)

To apply the skills of rounding and estimation to solving word problems that involve income tax (Exercises 16-23)

Objectives: Career Skills and Applications

Sales Clerk
Page 162

To apply addition and multiplication skills, the skill of reading a table, and the technique of the "hidden question" to solving multi-step problems that involve sales tax

Payroll Clerk
Pages 168-169

To apply addition, multiplication, and rounding skills and the skill of reading a table to solving multi-step problems that involve weekly gross pay

CHAPTER 9 BANKING

Overview

We suggest that some or all of page 178 be reviewed before proceeding with the chapter.

The topics of interest and compound interest are presented in this chapter. Students are also shown how to complete a check stub and a check register, how to write a check, and how to reconcile a bank statement.

The use of actual forms in many of the Exercises relate the content of this chapter to real-life situations. The *Workbook* section of the *Teacher's Resource Book* contains the forms covered in this chapter. Thus, the student has the opportunity to actually complete the types of forms related to banking. (Refer to the *Workbook* section of the *Teacher's Resource Book* should you desire additional exercises for each section.) The following objectives apply to both types of problems.

A *Cumulative Review* that covers the content in Chapters 7-9 appears on pages 204-205. The *Test Booklet* portion of the *Teacher's Resource Book* contains a *Cumulative Review* for these chapters as well.

Objectives: Consumer Skills and Applications

Section 9-1
Pages 180-181

To solve multi-step problems that involve completing deposit slips for a checking account (Example 1)
To solve multi-step problems that involve completing deposit slips for a savings account (Example 2)

Section 9-2
Pages 182-183

To apply the technique of using a formula to solve one-step problems that involve simple interest (Example 1)
To solve multi-step problems that involve compound interest (Table)

Section 9-3
Pages 184-185

To solve multi-step problems that involve compound interest by using a compound interest table (Example)

Section 9-4
Pages 188-190

To solve multi-step problems that involve completing check stubs for a checking account (Example 1)
To solve multi-step problems that involve completing check registers for a checking account (Example 2)

Section 9-5 Pages 191-192	*To apply place-value and the skill of writing a decimal in words to writing the amount of a check* *To solve problems that involve writing checks*
Section 9-6 Pages 193-195	*To solve multi-step problems that involve reconciling a check register balance with a bank statement balance (Example)*
Rounding and Estimation Pages 198-199	*To apply the skills of rounding and estimation to computational problems (Exercise 1-14)* *To apply the skills of rounding and estimation to word problems that involve banking (Exercises 15-22)*

Objectives: Career Skills and Applications

Loan Officer Pages 186-187	*To apply the skills of multiplication and raising to a power and the technique of using a formula to solving multi-step problems that involve compound interest*
Cashier Pages 196-197	*To apply the skills of addition, subtraction, and multiplication to solving multi-step problems that involve making change*

CHAPTER 10 BUYING A CAR

Overview

We suggest that some or all of page 206 be reviewed before proceeding with the chapter.

The first three lessons of this chapter deal with buying and financing a car. The last two sections deal with liability, collision, and comprehensive car insurance.

With the exception of Section 10-3, the Exercises for each section contain two types (or levels) of applications, non-verbal and word problems. (Refer to the *Workbook* section of the *Teacher's Resource Book* should you desire additional exercises for each section.) The following objectives apply to both types of problems.

Objectives: Consumer Skills and Applications

Section 10-1
Pages 208-209

To solve one-step problems that involve sticker price (Example 1)
To apply the skill of rounding and the technique of the "hidden question" to solving two-step problems that involve the total cost of a new car (Example 2)

Section 10-2
Pages 210-211

To solve multi-step problems that involve the dealer's cost of a new car

Section 10-3
Pages 212-213

To apply the techniques of the "hidden question" and of using a formula to solving two-step problems that involve down payments and monthly payments (Example 1)
To apply the techniques of the "hidden question" and of using a formula to solving two-step problems that involve finance charges (Example 2)

Section 10-4
Pages 216-217

To apply the skill of reading a table to solving one-step problems that involve liability insurance

Section 10-5
Pages 218-219

To solve one-step problems that involve collision insurance (Example 1)
To apply the skill of reading a table to solving one-step problems that involve collision/comprehensive insurance (Example 2)

Rounding and Estimation
Pages 222-223

To apply the skills of rounding and estimation to computational problems (Exercises 1-14)
To apply the skills of rounding and estimation to word problems that involve buying a car (Exercises 15-22)

Objectives: Career Skills and Applications

Used Car Dealer
Pages 214-215

To apply the skills of addition and subtraction, per cent skills, and the skill of reading a table to solving problems that involve buying used cars

Radiator Technician
Pages 220-221

To apply the skill of reading a table to solving two-step problems that involve the amount of coolant needed for car radiators

CHAPTER 11 OWNING A CAR

Overview

We suggest that some or all of page 228 be reviewed before proceeding with the chapter.

The content of this chapter deals with the costs of owning and operating a car. Topics treated include maintenance costs, depreciation, gasoline costs, and yearly driving costs. Note that both metric and customary units of measure are used throughout the chapter.

The high price of new cars have caused consumers to attempt to get more years out of their cars. Thus, maintenance costs (Section 11-1) are of issue. Gasoline costs (Section 11-3) have forced consumers to purchase energy-efficient automobiles. The "bottom-line" cost, cost per mile, treated in Section 11-4 should prove to be most enlightening to your students.

As is the case with most sections in the textbook, the Exercises in the first three sections contain two types of applications, non-verbal and word problems. (Refer to the *Workbook* portion of the *Teacher's Resource Book* should you desire additional exercises for each section.) The following objectives pertain to both types.

Objectives: Consumer Skills and Applications

Section 11-1
Pages 230-231

To solve multi-step problems that involve automobile repair cost (Example 1)

To apply the skill of reading a table and the technique of using a formula to solving one-step problems that involve maintenance costs per mile (Example 2)

Section 11-2
Pages 232-233

To apply the skill of reading a table to solving two-step problems that involve depreciation (Example 1)

To solve two-step problems that involve depreciation per kilometer and depreciation per mile (Example 2)

Section 11-3
Pages 236-237

To apply the technique of using a formula to solving multi-step problems that involve fuel economy (Example 1)

To apply the technique of using a formula to solving one-step problems that involve fuel costs per kilometers and fuel costs per mile (Example 2)

Section 11-4 Pages 238-239	*To solve multi-step problems that involve yearly driving costs per mile*
Rounding and Estimation Pages 242-243	*To apply the skills of rounding and estimation to computational problems (Exercises 1-14)* *To apply the skills of rounding and estimation to word problems that involve owning a car (Exercises 15-23)*

Objectives: Career Skills and Applications

Automobile Mechanic Pages 234-235	*To apply the skills of multiplication and raising to a power, and the technique of using a formula to solving problems that involve engine displacement (measurement of volume)*
Police Officer Pages 240-241	*To apply multiplication skills and the technique of using a formula to solving one-step problems that involve reaction distance (Example 1)* *To apply multiplication and division skills, the skill of reading a table, and the technique of using a formula to solving one-step problems that involve braking distance (Example 2)*

CHAPTER 12 OTHER WAYS TO TRAVEL

Overview

We suggest that some or all of page 248 be reviewed before proceeding with the chapter.

Because the costs of renting a car (Section 12-1), commuting to work (Section 12-2), and traveling by bus, train, and plane change from time-to-time, it would be well to have your students bring newspaper advertisements to class in order to keep these costs up to date.

Objectives: Consumer Skills and Applications

Section 12-1
Pages 250-251

To solve multi-step problems that involve the costs of renting a car

Section 12-2
Pages 254-255

To solve multi-step problems that involve the costs of commuting to work (Example 1)
To solve multi-step problems that involve the costs of commuting to work using more than one method of transportation (Example 2)

Section 12-3
Pages 256-257

To apply the skill of reading a table to solving multi-step problems that involve travel costs

Rounding and Estimation
Pages 260-261

To apply the skills of rounding and estimation to computational problems (Exercises 1-14)
To apply the skills of rounding and estimation to word problems that involve commuting and travel costs (Exercises 15-22)

Objectives: Career Skills and Applications

Car Leasing Agent
Pages 252-253

To apply addition and multiplication skills and the skill of reading an advertisement to solving multi-step problems that involve car leasing costs

Flight Attendant
Pages 258-259

To apply addition and subtraction skills and the skill of reading a chart to multi-step problems that involve time zones

CHAPTER 13 FOOD COSTS

Overview

We suggest that some or all of page 268 be reviewed before proceeding with the chapter.
Although high school students are not, in general, overly concerned with food costs, the primary objective of the chapter, saving money, is a major concern of all consumers.

Objectives: Consumer Skills and Applications

Section 13-1
Pages 270-271

To apply the techniques of using a formula to solving multi-step problems that involve unit price

Section 13-2
Pages 272-273

To solve multi-step problems that involve computing savings on food costs

Section 13-3
Pages 276-277

To solve multi-step problems that involve double-coupon savings on food costs

Section 13-4
Pages 278-279

To apply the skill of reading a table and the technique of using a formula to solving multi-step problems that involve computing the amount of food needed for a given number of servings (Example 1)
To apply the skill of reading a table and the technique of using a formula to solving multi-step problems that involve cost per serving (Example 2)

Rounding and Estimation
Pages 282-283

To apply the skills of rounding and estimation to computational problems (Exercises 1-14)
To apply the skills of rounding and estimation to word problems that involve food costs (Exercises 15-25)

Objectives: Career Skills and Applications

Accounting Clerk
Pages 274-275

To apply addition skills and the skill of reading a code to solving multi-step problems that involve monthly operating expenses for a business

Waiter/ Waitress
Pages 280-281

To apply addition and multiplication skills and the technique of the "hidden question" to solving multi-step problems that involve the tax on a restaurant bill (Example 1)
To apply multiplication, per cent, and rounding skills to solving problems that involve the amount of a tip for a restaurant bill (Example 2)

CHAPTER 14 HOUSING

Overview

We suggest that some or all of page 288 be reviewed before proceeding with the chapter.

Chapter 14 presents information related to renting costs, down payments on a house, and monthly mortgage payments. Topics related to owning a home, such as homeowner's insurance and property taxes, are also treated.

This chapter employs many of the problem-solving techniques used in the previous chapters, particularly the "hidden question" approach (Sections 14-3 and 14-5) for solving two-step problems and using tables (Sections 14-3 and 14-4).

Because the Exercises for each section contain two types of applications, non-verbal and word problems, students who exhibit shortcomings with their reading skills will have an opportunity to meet with some success. (Refer to the *Workbook* section in the *Teacher's Resource Book* should you desire additional exercises.) The following objectives apply to both types of applications.

Objectives: Consumer Skills and Applications

Section 14-1
Pages 290-291

To solve two-step problems that involve renting costs

Section 14-2
Pages 292-293

To solve one-step problems that involve down payments and the amount of a mortgage

To solve two-step problems that involve the total of monthly payments and the total interest charged on mortgage loans

Section 14-3
Pages 296-297

To apply the skill of reading a table and the technique of the "hidden question" to solving multi-step problems that involve monthly mortgage payments

Section 14-4
Pages 299-301

To apply the skill of reading a table to solving one-step problems that involve homeowner's insurance coverage (Example 1)

To apply the skill of reading a table to solving two-step problems that involve monthly premiums for homeowner's insurance (Example 2)

Section 14-5 Pages 304-305	*To solve one-step problems that involve assessed value (Example 1)* *To apply the technique of the "hidden question" to solving problems that involve property taxes (Example 2)*
Rounding and Estimation Pages 306-307	*To apply the skills of rounding and estimation to computational problems (Exercises 1-14)* *To apply the skills of rounding and estimation to word problems that involve housing (Exercises 15-23)*

Objectives: Career Skills and Applications

Surveyor Pages 294-295	*To apply addition and multiplication skills together with the skills of squaring numbers and of reading a square root table to solving problems that involve the Rule of Pythagoras*
Property Manager Page 298	*To apply multiplication skills and the technique of using a formula to solving problems that involve yearly operating costs for a mall or shopping center*
Real Estate Agent Pages 302-303	*To apply per cent and rounding skills to solving multi-step problems that involve commission and selling price*

CHAPTER 15 HOUSING COSTS

Overview	We suggest that all or some of page 312 be reviewed before proceeding with the chapter. The two major concerns for this chapter are energy costs and conservation (Sections 15-1 through Section 15-3) and applying estimation (Sections 15-4 and 15-5).

Objectives: Consumer Skills and Applications

Section 15-1 Pages 314-315	*To solve two-step problems that involve savings on home heating costs (Example 1)* *To apply the skill of reading a table to solving problems that involve savings on home cooling costs (Example 2)*
Section 15-2 Pages 316-317	*To apply the skill of reading a table to solving one-step problems that involve costs for operating appliances*
Section 15-3 Pages 320-321	*To apply the skill of reading an electric meter to computing the number of kilowatt-hours of electricity used (Example 1)* *To apply the skill of reading a gas meter to computing the number of cubic feet of gas used (Example 2)*
Section 15-4 Pages 322-323	*To apply estimation skills, the skill of reading a table, and the technique of the "hidden question" to solving multi-step problems that involve wallpapering*
Section 15-5 Pages 326-327	*To apply estimation skills and the technique of the "hidden question" to solving multi-step problems that involve painting a room*
Rounding and Estimation Pages 328-329	*To apply the skills of rounding and estimation to computational problems (Exercises 1-14)* *To apply the skills of rounding and estimation to word problems related to housing costs (Exercises 15-23)*

Objectives: Career Skills and Applications

Utilities Clerk Pages 318-319	*To apply the skill of reading a utilities rate schedule to solving multi-step problems that involve computing cost of electricity*
Drafting Technician Pages 324-325	*To apply the skills of writing and solving proportions to problems that involve scale drawings*

CHAPTER 16 BUYING GOODS

Overview

We suggest that some or all of page 336 be reviewed before proceeding with the chapter.

A good understanding of per cent is central to the topics covered in this chapter -- discount, interest, sales tax, credit cards, and installment loans. Section 16-2: *Buying by Mail* is, of course, concerned with the cost of ordering from a catalog.

Objectives: Consumer Skills and Applications

Section 16-1
Pages 338-339
To apply the techniques of the "hidden question" to solving two-step problems that involve discount (Examples 1 and 2)

Section 16-2
Pages 340-342
To apply the skill of reading a table to solving two-step problems that involve shipping charges (Example 1)
To complete a catalog order form (Example 2)

Section 16-3
Pages 344-345
To apply the technique of using a formula to solving multi-step problems that involve credit card statements

Section 16-4
Pages 346-347
To apply the skill of reading a table to solving multi-step problems that involve minimum payments on credit card balances

Section 16-5
Pages 350-351
To apply the technique of using a formula to solving multi-step problems that involve installment loans

Rounding and Estimation
Pages 352-353
To apply the skills of rounding and estimation to computational problems (Exercises 1-14)
To apply the skills of rounding and estimation to word problems related to buying goods (Exercises 15-22)

Objectives: Career Skills and Applications

Postal Clerk
Page 343
To apply addition and subtraction skills and the skill of reading a table to solving multi-step problems that involve postage costs

Credit Manager
Pages 348-349
To apply multiplication skills and the technique of using a formula to solving problems that involve promissory notes (Example 1)
To apply multiplication and subtraction skills and the technique of using a formula to solving multi-step problems that involve discount loans (Example 2)

CHAPTER 17 INVESTING MONEY

Overview

We suggest that some or all of page 358 be reviewed before proceeding with the chapter.

This chapter has a two-part structure. The first part of the chapter consists of two sections on term, straight-life, limited payment life, and endowment insurance. The three sections that make up the second part cover certificates of deposit, buying and selling stocks, dividends, and annual yield. It is hoped that there will be time to at least cover the first two sections, as insurance is a part of every consumer's life.

The Exercises for each section consist of two types of applications, nonverbal and word problems. (Refer to the *Workbook* portion of the *Teacher's Resource Book* should you desire additional exercises.) The following objectives pertain to both types of applications.

Objectives: Consumer Skills and Applications

Section 17-1
Pages 360-362

To apply the skill of reading a table and the technique of using a formula to solving multi-step problems that involve term life insurance (Example 1)

To apply the skill of reading a table to solving multi-step problems that involve straight-life insurance (Example 2)

Section 17-2
Pages 363-365

To apply the skill of reading a table to solving multi-step problems that involve limited-payment life insurance (Example 1)

To solve multi-step problems that involve endowment insurance (Example 2)

Section 17-3
Pages 368-369

To apply the skill of reading a table to multi-step problems that involve certificates of deposit

Section 17-4
Pages 370-372

To apply the technique of using a formula to solving two-step problems that involve buying shares of stock (Example 1)

To apply the technique of using a formula to solving multi-step problems that involve selling shares of stock (Example 2)

Section 17-5 Pages 374-375	*To solve two-step problems that involve yearly dividends (Example 1)* *To apply the technique of using a formula and rounding skills to solving two-step problems that involve annual yield (Example 2)*
Section 17-6 Page 376-377	*To solve one-step problems that involve bond prices (Example 1)* *To apply the technique of using a formula and rounding skills to solving two-step problems that involve current yield (Example 2)*
Rounding and Estimation Pages 380-381	*To apply the skills of rounding and estimation to computational problems (Exercises 1-14)* *To apply the skills of rounding and estimation to word problems that involve investing money (Exercises 15-23)*

Objectives: Career Skills and Applications

Insurance Clerk Pages 366-367	*To apply addition and estimation skills and the skill of reading a table to solving multi-step problems that involve life expectancy (Example 1)* *To apply the skills of multiplication and division and the technique of using a formula to solving multi-step problems that involve mortality tables (Example 2)*
Securities Teller Page 373	*To apply multiplication and subtraction skills to solving multi-step problems that involve series EE bonds*
Investment Counselors Pages 378-379	*To apply division skills, the skill of reading a table, and the technique of using a formula to solving problems that involve mutual funds (Example 1)* *To apply addition, multiplication, and division skills, and the technique of using a formula to solving multi-step problems that involve an IRA account (Example 2)*

CHAPTER 18 BUDGETING MONEY

Overview

We suggest that all or some of page 386 be reviewed before proceeding with the chapter.

Section 18-3: *Health Insurance* is included in this chapter because too often medical expenses are not included in a family budget. Medical costs have increased considerably over the years and because of this, it should be part of each family's budget.

Objectives: Consumer Skills and Applications

Section 18-1 Pages 388-389	*To apply rounding skills and the technique of using a formula to solving problems that involve preparing a budget*
Section 18-2 Pages 390-391	*To apply the skill of reading a circle graph to solving one-step problems that involve average spending (Example 1)* *To apply the skills of estimation and of reading a circle graph to two-step problems that involve average spending (Example 2)*
Section 18-3 Pages 394-395	*To solve multi-step problems that involve health insurance*
Section 18-4 Pages 396-397	*To solve two-step problems that involve adjusting a budget*
Rounding and Estimation Pages 400-401	*To apply the skills of rounding and estimation to computational problems (Exercises 1-14)* *To apply the skills of rounding and estimation to word problems that involve budgets (Exercises 15-21)*

Objectives: Career Skills and Applications

Statistical Clerk Page 393	*To apply per cent skills and the skill of reading a circle graph to solving problems that involve statistical data*
Financial Counselor Pages 398-399	*To apply addition, subtraction, multiplication, and division skills and the technique of using a formula to solving problems that involve variable expenses in a budget*

APPENDIX A INTRODUCTION TO ALGEBRA

Overview *Appendix A* is included for those students who would like to elect algebra one as their next course in mathematics.

Objectives: Algebraic Skills and Applications

Section A-1
Page 410

To square a number (Example 1)
To find the square root of a number (Example 2)

Section A-2
Pages 411-413

To apply the skill of reading a table to squaring a number (Example 1)
To apply the skill of reading a table to finding the square root of a number (Example 2)
To apply the skills of multiplication, of reading a table, and of finding the square root of a number to word problems that involve speed and skidding distance

Section A-3
Pages 414-415

To use positive and negative numbers to represent word descriptions (Example 1)
To use a number line to add positive and negative numbers (Example 2)
To apply addition skills to word problems that involve positive and negative numbers

Section A-4
Pages 416-417

To use a number line to subtract positive and negative numbers
To apply subtraction skills to word problems that involve wind chill temperatures

Section A-5
Pages 418-419

To multiply two numbers having unlike signs (Example 1)
To multiply two numbers having like signs (Example 2)
To apply multiplication skills to word problems that involve sports, earnings, and temperature

Calculator: Checking
Page 419

To use a calculator to check the answers to multiplication problems that involve positive and negative numbers

Section A-6
Page 420

To divide positive and negative numbers

Section A-7
Pages 421-422

To graph points in the coordinate plane (Example 1)
To graph equations (Example 2)

APPENDIX B INTRODUCTION TO COMPUTERS

Overview

Access to a computer is *not* essential for the study of *Appendix B*. The objective for *Appendix B* is to introduce the student to some of the basic ideas of computers and computer programming. A basic knowledge of computers, especially microcomputers, is increasing in its importance for every individual. As microcomputers become more accessible to the average person, the pressures to include computer literacy as an integral part of every student's education will increase. It is the authors' hope that time will be available during the school year to study *Appendix B*.

Objectives: Computer Skills and Applications

Section B-1
Pages 426-427

To identify the components of a computer system

Section B-2
Pages 428-429

To write a computer formula for an arithmetic expression (Example 1)
To use "order of operations" to simplify a computer formula (Example 2)
To evaluate computer formulas that contain a variable (Example 3)

Section B-3
Pages 430-431

To use a computer program to determine a value stored in computer memory (Example 1)
To use a computer program to determine the result of a PRINT command (Example 2)
To use a computer program with an INPUT command to determine a value stored in computer memory (Example 3)

Section B-4
Pages 432-434

To write a BASIC program for solving problems that involve making change (Example 1)
To write a BASIC program for solving problems that involve batting averages (Example 2)
To write a BASIC program for solving problems that involve perimeter (Example 3)
To apply the skill of writing programs in BASIC to solving word problems that involve sports, fuel economy, earnings, and measurement

ANSWERS: FORM A TESTS

Chapter 1 1. 4385 2. 68.841 3. 617 4. 14.467 5. 32.25 6. 5.63 7. 0.0648 8. 80 9. 15 r 1 10. 2914 11. 0.067 12. 40 13. 22.36 14. 28 15. 76.5 16. 57.271 17. a 18. b 19. a 20. c 21. 462,200 22. 3.93 in 23. 16 24. c 25. 21

Chapter 2 1. a 2. c 3. b 4. c 5. b 6. 7000 7. 0.42 8. 6000 9. 0.0175 10. 4600 11. 2.572 12. 88 cm 13. 76 m 14. 63 cm^2 15. 9.45 cm^2 16. 120 cm^3 17. 320 m^3 18. 60 19. 2400 kg 20. 225 m^2

Chapter 3 1. $\frac{9}{4}$ 2. $\frac{22}{5}$ 3. 12 4. 24 5. $\frac{3}{4}$ 6. $1\frac{5}{8}$ 7. $\frac{1}{4}$ 8. $\frac{2}{15}$ 9. $10\frac{1}{6}$ 10. $6\frac{31}{40}$ 11. $2\frac{1}{6}$ 12. $3\frac{13}{15}$ 13. $\frac{5}{21}$ 14. $\frac{1}{4}$ 15. $2\frac{1}{2}$ 16. 6 17. $1\frac{7}{8}$ 18. $2\frac{1}{6}$ 19. $2\frac{3}{4}$ 20. $\frac{3}{22}$ 21. $10\frac{1}{8}$ mi 22. 22 teaspoons 23. 32 24. c 25. $6\frac{7}{8}$ in

Chapter 4 1. 14 2. 22 3. 5 4. 1.8 5. 9.6 6. 3 7. 2 8. 17 9. $\frac{7}{10}$ 10. $\frac{7}{3}$ 11. $\frac{4}{5}$ 12. $\frac{1}{4}$ 13. Yes 14. No 15. No 16. Yes 17. 5 18. 17 19. 24 20. 30 21. 7 sec 22. 62.5 23. 16 24. $34.35 25. 20°C

Chapter 5 1. 78% 2. 5.5% 3. 80% 4. $87\frac{1}{2}$% 5. 150% 6. 6 7. 416 8. 40% 9. 20% 10. 30 11. 60% 12. 48 13. 125 14. c 15. a 16. b 17. 960 18. 80% 19. $7000 20. b

Chapter 6 1. Baltimore 2. 50,000 3. Chicago 4. July 5. February 6. 6 in 7. Sept. 8.

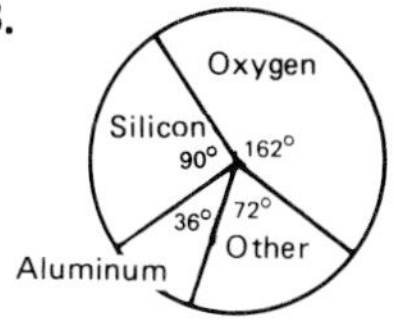

Oxygen
Silicon
90°
162°
36°
72°
Other
Aluminum

9. 5 in 10. $16.00 11. Mysteries 12. 1000

Chapter 7 1. $207.60 2. $157.50 3. $577.60 4. 51.29 5. 34.94 6. 268.66 7. 392.87 8. 0.04 9. $0.37\frac{1}{2}$ 10. $\frac{2}{5}$ 11. $\frac{1}{8}$ 12. $437.50 13. $556.80 14. $1195.00 15. $270.00 16. $112.50 17. $332.50 18. $1917 19. $1775.50 20. c

Chapter 8 1. $331.20 2. $229.68 3. $480.00 4. $672.10 5. $6894.00 6. $10,644.40 7. $17,988.00 8. $4625.00 9. $528.76 10. 0.08 11. 0.15 12. 0.27 13. 0.045 14. 0.072 15. 0.059 16. 60 17. 17.4 18. 16 19. 5.13 20. $18.60 21. $16.80 22. $22,325.00 23. $1715.00 24. c 25. $366

Chapter 9 1. 547.24 2. 212.04 3. 156.00 4. $19.12 5. 0.25 6. $0.04\frac{1}{2}$ 7. 69.07 8. 27.33 9. Total: $208.10; Net Deposit: $158.10 10. Total: $278.72; Balance Forward: $241.47 11. Signature 12. ABC Auto 13. Auto repair 14. $50.75 15. May 2, 1984 16. $24.00 17. $60.00 18. $337.50 19. d 20. $1688.25

Chapter 10 1. $10,245 2. $9648.63 3. $543.83 4. $528.00 5. $24.79 6. $727.62 7. $4560 8. $6192 9. $534.60 10. $1072.50 11. 120 12. 504 13. 5379.4 14. 9360 15. $8994 16. $8100 17. $6925 18. $2295 19. c 20. $275.80

Chapter 11 1. 86 2. $106.53 3. $204.95 4. 0.08 5. 0.01 6. 0.15 7. 0.21 8. 0.17 9. 0.52 10. 252,000 11. 3230 12. 1378 13. $0.04 14. 0.07 15. 0.20 16. b 17. $2688 18. 22.9 mpg 19. 10.7 km per liter 20. $3070

Chapter 12 1. \$280.00 2. \$300.30 3. \$145.60 4. \$760.80 5. \$2880.00 6. \$2940.00 7. \$64.00 8. \$67.20 9. \$430.38 10. \$804.51 11. \$1.20 12. \$1.10 13. \$1.35 14. \$193.00 15. \$638.50 16. \$392.00 17. \$772.50 18. c 19. \$110.30 20. \$1470

Chapter 13 1. \$13.39 2. \$11.35 3. \$10.14 4. \$1.84 5. \$2.57 6. \$5.38 7. \$1.52 8. \$3.80 9. \$6.48 10. \$11.00 11. \$3.52 12. \$2.28 13. \$2.84 14. \$2.36 15. \$0.037 16. 50-oz jar 17. \$0.59 18. \$0.29 19. \$0.70 20. \$0.38 21. \$3.93 22. a 23. 4 24. 6 25. 33¢

Chapter 14 1. \$1293.00 2. \$1782 3. \$573.75 4. \$144,000 5. 0.14 6. 0.70 7. 0.14 8. 0.38 9. 0.85 10. \$45,000 11. \$55,800 12. \$64,000 13. \$51.25 14. \$23.58 15. \$62.50 16. Yes 17. \$195,272 18. \$768.60 19. c 20. \$2587.25

Chapter 15 1. 14 2. 28 3. 26 4. 190 5. 1045 6. 430 7. 12.5 8. 15.8 9. 15.3 10. 14.7 11. 9000 12. 0.6 13. \$39 14. \$109.90 15. \$1.08 16. \$2 17. 53.95 18. 84.64 19. 8 20. 13 21. \$216 22. c 23. 1245 24. 12 25. 11

Chapter 16 1. \$48 2. \$32.50 3. \$4.90 4. \$60.19 5. \$40.13 6. \$73.20 7. \$14.85 8. \$13.10 9. \$297 10. \$565 11. \$410.30 12. \$338.40 13. \$205.30 14. \$332.90 15. \$10.50 16. \$14.40 17. \$1.77 18. c 19. \$434.44 20. \$324.80

Chapter 17 1. \$8 2. \$7 3. 0.166 4. 0.083 5. \$220.92 6. \$34,726.50 7. \$37,668.00 8. \$12,379.20 9. \$8367.33 10. \$6286.17 11. \$3400 12. \$3721 13. \$4193.03 14. \$5942.88 15. $0.66\frac{2}{3}$ 16. 0.4 17. 0.7 18. 0.3 19. 0.6 20. $0.37\frac{1}{2}$ 21. \$330 22. \$45,220 23. \$10,833 24. \$11,930.15 25. d

Chapter 18 1. \$22.64 2. \$39.53 3. \$42 4. \$69 5. \$22 6. \$128 7. \$20 8. \$64 9. \$360 10. \$310 11. \$195 12. 25% 13. 60% 14. $33\frac{1}{3}\%$ 15. $37\frac{1}{2}\%$ 16. 10% 17. $83\frac{1}{3}\%$ 18. \$840 19. \$1080 20. \$2935 21. \$84 22. \$110 23. greater 24. \$520 25. c

ANSWERS: FORM B TESTS

Chapter 1 1. 4828 2. 37.623 3. 435 4. 24.188 5. 21.08 6. 11.27 7. 0.0581 8. 90 9. 16.098 10. 2158 11. 0.058 12. 60 13. 21.83 14. 73 15. 38.7 16. 55.474 17. c 18. a 19. c 20. b 21. 821,710 22. 5.06 in 23. 12 24. b 25. 7

Chapter 2 1. a 2. c 3. c 4. b 5. a 6. 5000 7. 0.38 8. 8000 9. 0.0275 10. 9500 11. 1.265 12. 500 cm 13. 140 cm 14. 63 m^2 15. 4 km^2 16. 140 m^3 17. 108 cm^3 18. 16 19. 1350 kg 20. 56,000 cm^2

Chapter 3 1. $\frac{7}{3}$ 2. $\frac{11}{4}$ 3. 12 4. 12 5. $\frac{5}{7}$ 6. $1\frac{1}{4}$ 7. $\frac{3}{4}$ 8. $\frac{7}{15}$ 9. $6\frac{1}{12}$ 10. $8\frac{9}{40}$ 11. $4\frac{2}{15}$ 12. $1\frac{7}{12}$ 13. $\frac{3}{20}$ 14. $\frac{7}{24}$ 15. $2\frac{1}{3}$ 16. 12 17. $2\frac{1}{4}$ 18. $\frac{11}{16}$ 19. $2\frac{1}{10}$ 20. $\frac{4}{27}$ 21. $13\frac{1}{8}$ 22. 57 lb 23. 90 24. b 25. $8\frac{5}{8}$ in

Chapter 4 1. 14 2. 21 3. 7 4. 2.5 5. 5.1 6. 4 7. 6 8. 7 9. $\frac{4}{5}$ 10. $\frac{8}{3}$ 11. $\frac{4}{5}$ 12. $\frac{2}{3}$ 13. No 14. Yes 15. No 16. Yes 17. 3 18. 17 19. 24 20. 54 21. 15 sec 22. 135 23. 15 24. \$34.50 25. 5°C

Chapter 5 1. 65% 2. 7.2% 3. 75% 4. $83\frac{1}{3}\%$ 5. $233\frac{1}{3}\%$ 6. 20 7. 240 8. $66\frac{2}{3}\%$ 9. 60% 10. 20 11. $37\frac{1}{2}\%$ 12. 25 13. 18 14. a 15. c 16. b 17. 9000 18. 30% 19. \$12,000 20. c

Chapter 6 1. U.S. 2. 30,000 3. France 4. July 5. January 6. 10°C 7. May
8.

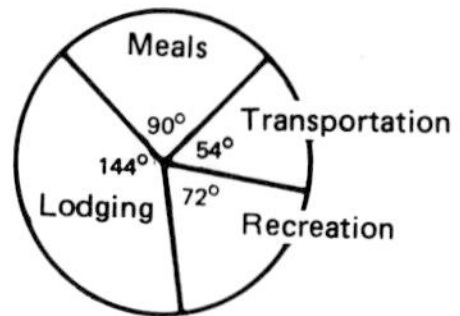

9. 7 in 10. $11 11. K. Ings 12. 45,250

Chapter 7 1. $196.25 2. $204.00 3. $586.92 4. 45.28 5. 31.06 6. 636.23 7. 260.64
8. 0.06 9. $0.17\frac{1}{2}$ 10. $\frac{7}{10}$ 11. $\frac{5}{8}$ 12. $609.75 13. $512.50 14. $961.00 15. $270.40
16. $86.40 17. $462.50 18. $3850 19. $2190.90 20. a

Chapter 8 1. $338.00 2. $352.80 3. $427.50 4. $643.50 5. $9403.00 6. $9375.15
7. $18,658.00 8. $5396.00 9. $436.54 10. 0.07 11. 0.13 12. 0.32 13. 0.074
14. 0.068 15. 0.043 16. 36 17. 32.8 18. 11.2 19. 6.035 20. $15.00 21. $29.10
22. $25,242.00 23. $1448.00 24. a 25. $448

Chapter 9 1. 915.48 2. 354.23 3. 180.00 4. $14.75 5. 0.62 6. $0.03\frac{1}{2}$ 7. 72.11
8. 24.91 9. Total: $111.90; Net Deposit: $71.90 10. Total: $140.38; Balance Forward: $111.88
11. Fifteen and $\frac{50}{100}$ 12. A. C. Cleaners 13. cleaning clothes 14. $15.50 15. Feb. 3, 1983
16. $8.00 17. $225 18. $260 19. d 20. $1910.52

Chapter 10 1. $9183 2. $8690.63 3. $684 4. $278 5. $50.93 6. $455.57 7. $3610
8. $11,664 9. $892.52 10. $1560.00 11. 168 12. 255 13. 5907.5 14. 8250
15. $5941 16. $9360 17. $6861 18. $1770 19. a 20. $375.60

Chapter 11 1. 107 2. $130.58 3. $196.57 4. 0.02 5. 0.09 6. 0.17 7. 0.43 8. 0.16
9. 0.62 10. 144,000 11. 2856 12. 2437.5 13. $0.04 14. 0.10 15. 0.28 16. b
17. $3515 18. 22.6 mpg 19. 9.9 km per liter 20. $2545

Chapter 12 1. $196.00 2. $659.20 3. $259.20 4. $540.00 5. $3420.00 6. $3750.00
7. $72.00 8. $59.50 9. $327.97 10. $809.03 11. 95¢ 12. $1.30 13. $1.40
14. $273.00 15. $379.30 16. $502.80 17. $1372.75 18. b 19. $88.60 20. $1039.50

Chapter 13 1. $12.50 2. $15.29 3. $10.80 4. $1.92 5. $3.52 6. $3.16 7. $3.32
8. $1.84 9. $4.50 10. $6.48 11. $3.89 12. $2.18 13. $4.28 14. $2.35 15. $0.066
16. 32-oz jar 17. $0.29 18. $0.29 19. $0.28 20. $0.51 21. $3.84 22. c 23. 5
24. 4 25. $1.39

Chapter 14 1. $1473 2. $593 3. $630.72 4. $156,000 5. 0.60 6. 0.18 7. 0.25
8. 0.45 9. 0.81 10. $43,000 11. $25,500 12. $65,000 13. $50.17 14. $23.75
15. $61.67 16. Yes 17. $140,452 18. $632.00 19. b 20. $2650.50

Chapter 15 1. 23 2. 37 3. 5 4. 370 5. 2032 6. 430 7. 13.5 8. 17.5 9. 16.2
10. 16.1 11. 7500 12. 0.54 13. $59.50 14. $107.10 15. 72¢ 16. $1.62 17. 51
18. 51.84 19. 11 20. 14 21. $225 22. b 23. 2129 24. 12 25. 14

Chapter 16 1. $56 2. $63 3. $5.28 4. $51.08 5. $20.43 6. $18.80 7. $14.40
8. $13.24 9. $204 10. $1434 11. $346.60 12. $1429.50 13. $194.44 14. $325.17
15. $5.60 16. $36.00 17. $1.83 18. b 19. $423.08 20. $212

Chapter 17 1. $5 2. $3 3. 0.088 4. 0.080 5. $300 6. $14,720.40 7. $21,735
8. $12,068.80 9. $6827.44 10. $6295.76 11. $2800 12. $972 13. $4402.52
14. $8300.27 15. 0.25 16. 0.6 17. 0.1 18. $0.66\frac{2}{3}$ 19. 0.4 20. $0.12\frac{1}{2}$ 21. $152.40

22. $25,368 23. $5309 24. $4930.25 25. b

Chapter 18 1. $23.49 2. $42.05 3. $16 4. $73 5. $83 6. $30 7. $24 8. $85 9. $280 10. $405 11. $187.50 12. 20% 13. 80% 14. $66\frac{2}{3}$% 15. $62\frac{1}{2}$% 16. 75% 17. 70% 18. $650 19. $1080 20. $3655 21. $286 22. $51.82 23. less 24. $397.50 25. a

ANSWERS: CUMULATIVE REVIEWS

Chapters 1-3 1. b 2. a 3. d 4. a 5. d 6. c 7. b 8. a 9. c 10. c 11. d 12. b 13. d 14. b 15. c 16. b 17. d 18. b 19. c 20. b 21. d 22. b 23. d 24. c 25. d

Chapters 4-6 1. c 2. a 3. b 4. b 5. d 6. c 7. b 8. c 9. d 10. a 11. d 12. d 13. b 14. a 15. a 16. b 17. c 18. c 19. c 20. c 21. b 22. d 23. c 24. d 25. a

Chapters 7-9 1. d 2. a 3. b 4. b 5. c 6. d 7. c 8. a 9. b 10. a 11. b 12. d 13. c 14. a 15. c 16. b 17. d 18. d 19. a 20. c 21. b 22. a 23. c 24. d 25. b

Chapters 10-12 1. b 2. c 3. a 4. b 5. d 6. a 7. c 8. d 9. a 10. b 11. a 12. b 13. c 14. d 15. c 16. c 17. d 18. a 19. c 20. b

Chapters 13-15 1. c 2. a 3. a 4. b 5. d 6. b 7. c 8. c 9. c 10. a 11. d 12. c 13. d 14. c 15. a 16. c 17. d 18. b 19. c 20.

Chapters 16-18 1. c 2. a 3. b 4. d 5. a 6. c 7. c 8. a 9. d 10. c 11. a 12. b 13. c 14. c 15. d 16. a 17. d 18. a 19. b 20. d

ANSWERS: SAMPLE COMPETENCY TESTS

Chapters 1-6 1. b 2. d 3. c 4. c 5. c 6. a 7. d 8. a 9. d 10. b 11. a 12. b 13. b 14. a 15. c 16. b 17. c 18. a 19. d 20. d 21. a 22. b 23. a 24. c 25. d 26. d 27. b 28. d 29. a 30. c 31. a 32. d 33. b 34. a 35. b 36. a 37. c 38. a 39. b 40. c

Chapters 7-18 1. b 2. a 3. d 4. a 5. b 6. c 7. c 8. d 9. b 10. b 11. d 12. b 13. a 14. a 15. b 16. d 17. d 18. c 19. d 20. c 21. d 22. b 23. c 24. a 25. d 26. c 27. d 28. a 29. b 30. b 31. d 32. a 33. c 34. a 35. b 36. d 37. b 38. c 39. d 40. c

5
E 6
F 7
G 8
H 9
I 0
J 1

Essentials of Mathematics

CONSUMER / CAREER SKILLS APPLICATIONS

William J. Gerardi   Wilmer L. Jones   Thomas R. Foster

Orlando New York Chicago San Diego Atlanta Dallas

ABOUT THE AUTHORS

WILLIAM J. GERARDI
Mathematics Teacher
Boys' Latin School
Baltimore, Maryland
Formerly Principal
Baltimore Polytechnic Institute

WILMER L. JONES
Coordinator of Mathematics
Baltimore City Public Schools
Baltimore, Maryland

THOMAS R. FOSTER
Deputy Superintendent
Educational Support Services
Baltimore City Public Schools
Baltimore, Maryland

EDITORIAL ADVISORS

The contributions of Brother Neal Golden, S.C. who wrote Appendix B, Introduction to Computers, are gratefully acknowledged.

Printed in the United States of America

ISBN 0-15-353610-1

CONTENTS

UNIT II CONSUMER SKILLS AND APPLICATIONS: EARNING MONEY

UNIT III CONSUMER SKILLS AND APPLICATIONS: TRANSPORTATION COSTS

UNIT IV CONSUMER SKILLS AND APPLICATIONS: LIVING COSTS

UNIT V CONSUMER SKILLS AND APPLICATIONS: MANAGING MONEY

REVIEW OF RELATED SKILLS FOR CHAPTER 1

We suggest that some or all of this page be reviewed before proceeding with the chapter.

Add.

1. $9 + 4$ 13 **2.** $8 + 5$ 13 **3.** $6 + 9$ 15 **4.** $4 + 7$ 11 **5.** $3 + 8$ 11 **6.** $5 + 5$ 10 **7.** $7 + 8$ 15

8. $6 + 4 + 7$ 17 **9.** $5 + 3 + 9$ 17 **10.** $8 + 6 + 2$ 16 **11.** $6 + 7 + 5$ 18 **12.** $4 + 3 + 9$ 16 **13.** $8 + 8 + 3$ 19 **14.** $4 + 5 + 6$ 15

15. $5 + 3 + 7 + 2$ 17 **16.** $9 + 8 + 1 + 7$ 25 **17.** $2 + 10 + 6 + 1$ 19 **18.** $21 + 5 + 11 + 2$ 39 **19.** $14 + 3 + 1 + 11$ 29 **20.** $22 + 11 + 2 + 14$ 49 **21.** $13 + 4 + 12 + 20$ 49

22. $4 + 13 + 2$ 19 **23.** $2 + 3 + 23$ 28 **24.** $14 + 21 + 4$ 39 **25.** $11 + 5 + 32$ 48

Subtract.

26. $6 - 3$ 3 **27.** $8 - 5$ 3 **28.** $7 - 2$ 5 **29.** $9 - 4$ 5 **30.** $5 - 1$ 4 **31.** $8 - 7$ 1

32. $28 - 13$ 15 **33.** $37 - 12$ 25 **34.** $68 - 23$ 45 **35.** $84 - 51$ 33 **36.** $76 - 55$ 21 **37.** $49 - 37$ 12

38. $437 - 226$ 211 **39.** $635 - 214$ 421 **40.** $2798 - 1737$ 1061 **41.** $9358 - 7216$ 2142 **42.** $2198 - 1044$ 1154 **43.** $7239 - 5118$ 2121

44. $6848 - 536$ 6312 **45.** $2957 - 1843$ 1114 **46.** $8197 - 7076$ 1121 **47.** $2297 - 186$ 2111

Multiply.

48. 8×9 72 **49.** 4×5 20 **50.** 7×6 42 **51.** 3×8 24 **52.** 5×8 40 **53.** 6×9 54

54. 21×2 42 **55.** 43×5 215 **56.** 56×7 392 **57.** 42×8 336 **58.** 29×3 87 **59.** 36×5 180

60. 631×7 4417 **61.** 275×5 1375 **62.** 407×3 1221 **63.** 804×7 5628 **64.** 230×6 1380 **65.** 190×9 1710

66. 238×5 1190 **67.** 384×9 3456 **68.** 287×5 1435 **69.** 438×8 3504

Divide.

70. $28 \div 4$ 7 **71.** $90 \div 9$ 10 **72.** $56 \div 8$ 7 **73.** $63 \div 7$ 9 **74.** $54 \div 9$ 6

75. $84 \div 7$ 12 **76.** $48 \div 6$ 8 **77.** $96 \div 6$ 16 **78.** $91 \div 7$ 13 **79.** $48 \div 3$ 16

80. $105 \div 7$ 15 **81.** $144 \div 3$ 48 **82.** $128 \div 8$ 16 **83.** $135 \div 5$ 27 **84.** $102 \div 6$ 17

85. $855 \div 9$ 95 **86.** $217 \div 7$ 31 **87.** $513 \div 3$ 171 **88.** $924 \div 4$ 231 **89.** $445 \div 5$ 89

CHAPTER

1 WHOLE NUMBERS AND DECIMALS

ESSENTIAL SKILLS/APPLICATIONS

1-1 Addition and Subtraction: Whole Numbers
1-2 Addition and Subtraction: Decimals
1-3 Multiplication: Whole Numbers
1-4 Multiplication: Decimals
1-5 Division: Whole Numbers
1-6 Division: Decimals
1-7 Rounding the Quotient
1-8 Rounding and Estimation

CAREER APPLICATIONS

Stock Clerk
Bus Driver

1-1 Addition and Subtraction: Whole Numbers

See the Teacher's Manual for the objectives.

To add whole numbers, first write the numbers one under the other. Line up the "ones" on the right.

PROCEDURE To add whole numbers:

[1] Add the ones.

[2] Add the tens.

[3] Add the hundreds, and so on.

EXAMPLE 1 Add: $74 + 352 + 721 + 5$

Solution:

[1] Add the ones. Carry the "ten" to the tens column.

$4 + 2 + 1 + 5 = 12$

$$\begin{array}{r} {\scriptstyle 1} \\ 74 \\ 352 \\ 721 \\ +\ \ 5 \\ \hline 2 \end{array}$$

[2] Add the tens. Carry the "hundred" to the hundreds column.

$10 + 70 + 50 + 20 = 150$

$$\begin{array}{r} {\scriptstyle 11} \\ 74 \\ 352 \\ 721 \\ +\ \ 5 \\ \hline 52 \end{array}$$

[3] Add the hundreds.

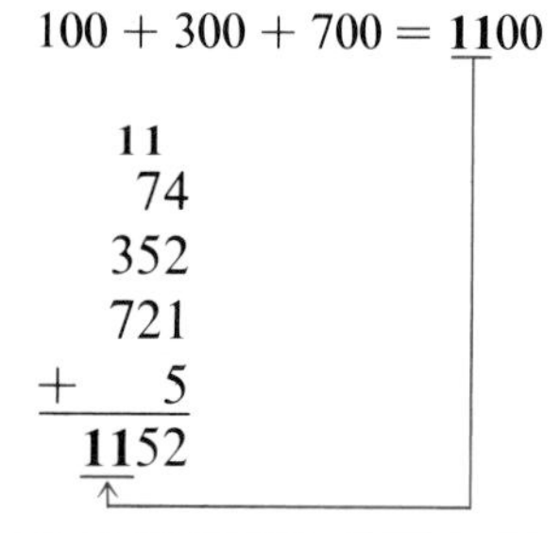

After completing Example 1, you may wish to have students do some or all of Exercises 1-19.

Sometimes you have to rename in subtraction.

PROCEDURE To subtract when renaming is necessary:

[1] Rename the tens and ones. Subtract the ones.

[2] Rename the hundreds and tens. Subtract the tens.

[3] Rename the thousands and hundreds. Subtract the hundreds, and so on.

Be careful when renaming with zeros.

EXAMPLE 2 Subtract: **a.** $902 - 775$ **b.** $5000 - 327$

Solutions:

a. $$\begin{array}{r} {\scriptstyle 8\ 9\ 12} \\ \not{9}\,\not{0}\,\not{2} \\ -7\ 7\ 5 \\ \hline 1\ 2\ 7 \end{array}$$ *902 = 8 hundreds + 9 tens + 12 ones*

b. $$\begin{array}{r} {\scriptstyle 4\ 9\ 9\ 10} \\ \not{5}\,\not{0}\,\not{0}\,\not{0} \\ -\ \ 3\ 2\ 7 \\ \hline 4\ 6\ 7\ 3 \end{array}$$ *5000 = 4 thousands + 9 hundreds + 9 tens + 10 ones*

EXERCISES

Add. (Example 1)

1. 367 + 292 + 245 = 904

2. 439 + 803 + 287 = 1529

3. 175 + 622 + 437 = 1234

4. 299 + 370 + 808 = 1477

5. 816 + 993 + 201 = 2010

6. 4317 + 2675 + 1817 + 2923 = 11,732

7. 3162 + 139 + 7144 + 284 = 10,729

8. 83 + 297 + 4415 + 67 = 4862

9. 803 + 2925 + 47 + 33 = 3808

10. 1008 + 235 + 47 + 8179 = 9469

11. 6822 + 137 + 192 + 14 = 7165

12. 1403 + 62 + 79 + 873 = 2417

13. 2934 + 182 + 19 + 11 = 3146

14. 603 + 1728 + 23 + 2921 = 5275

15. 807 + 8622 + 435 + 176 = 10,040

16. 97 + 243 + 3135 + 27 3502

17. 4325 + 188 + 11 + 225 4749

18. 193 + 27 + 481 + 22 723

19. 113 + 22 + 976 + 80 1191

Subtract. (Example 2)

20. 827 − 126 = 701

21. 2235 − 1974 = 261

22. 2081 − 1733 = 348

23. 4072 − 1614 = 2458

24. 367 − 198 = 169

25. 225 − 176 = 49

26. 600 − 286 = 314

27. 8092 − 1397 = 6695

28. 6688 − 1839 = 4849

29. 4175 − 2086 = 2089

30. 492 − 96 = 396

31. 2311 − 129 = 2182

32. 2000 − 1629 = 371

33. 8000 − 366 = 7634

34. 397 − 28 = 369

35. 863 − 39 824

36. 211 − 68 143

37. 8034 − 247 7787

38. 6315 − 88 6227

39. 4800 − 863 3937

40. 1299 − 437 862

41. 606 − 209 397

42. 137 − 108 29

APPLICATIONS: Using Addition and Subtraction of Whole Numbers

These word problems apply the skills taught in the lesson.

This table lists the populations of the ten largest cities in the world.

43. What is the total population of the two largest cities? 20,054,000

44. What is the total population of New York City, São Paulo, and London? 21,709,000

45. How many more people live in New York City than live in Cairo? 1,349,000

46. What is the difference between the population of London and the population of Seoul? 138,000

Population of the World's Ten Largest Cities

City	Population
Shanghai	10,820,000
Mexico City	9,234,000
Tokyo	8,220,000
Moscow	7,831,000
Peking	7,570,000
New York City	7,482,000
São Paulo	7,199,000
London	7,028,000
Seoul	6,890,000
Cairo	6,133,000

1-2 Addition and Subtraction: Decimals

See the Teacher's Manual for the objectives.

Adding and subtracting with decimals is similar to adding and subtracting with whole numbers.

PROCEDURE To add or subtract with decimals:

1. Line up the decimal points one under the other.
2. Annex final zeros when necessary.
3. Add or subtract.

EXAMPLE 1 Add: **a.** $12.067 + 234.06 + 9.32 + 26.7$

b. $147.034 + 36 + 9.5 + 16.1$

Solutions: Line up the decimal points.

a.
$$\begin{array}{r} 12.067 \\ 234.060 \\ 9.320 \\ +\ 26.700 \\ \hline \mathbf{282.147} \end{array}$$
Annex a zero to help line up the decimal points.

b.
$$\begin{array}{r} 147.034 \\ 36.000 \\ 9.500 \\ +\ 16.100 \\ \hline \mathbf{208.634} \end{array}$$

After completing Example 1, you may wish to have students do some or all of Exercises 1-18.

Sometimes it is necessary to annex zeros in subtraction of decimals.

EXAMPLE 2 Subtract.

a. $87.3 - 55.42$ **b.** $7 - 3.263$

Solutions: Line up the decimal points.

a.
$$\begin{array}{r} 87.30 \\ -55.42 \\ \hline \mathbf{31.88} \end{array}$$
Annex one zero.

b.
$$\begin{array}{r} 7.000 \\ -3.263 \\ \hline \mathbf{3.737} \end{array}$$
Insert the decimal point. Annex three zeros.

Check: **a.**
$$\begin{array}{r} 31.88 \\ +55.42 \\ \hline 87.30 \end{array}$$
87.30 = 87.3

b.
$$\begin{array}{r} 3.737 \\ +3.263 \\ \hline 7.000 \end{array}$$
7.000 = 7

Note that you use addition to check subtraction.

EXERCISES

Add. (Example 1)

1. 36.93, 2.07, +14.4 — 53.40

2. 235.07, 11.914, + 18.2 — 265.184

3. 67.335, 211.8, + 6.42 — 285.555

4. 61.18, 2.09, +127.375 — 190.645

5. 864.27, 43.998, + 2.407 — 910.675

6. 31.974, 2.08, 163.48, +109.335 — 306.869

7. 172.431, 6.87, 14.881, + 2.9 — 197.082

8. 83.884, 2.93, 17.623, + 4.093 — 108.530

9. 16.027, 8.1, 170.33, + 42.91 — 237.367

10. 6.03, 111.97, 6.18, + 2.937 — 127.117

11. 93.2 + 18.75 + 17.811 + 8.2 137.961

12. 93.18 + 8.231 + 11.7 + 121.81 234.921

13. 46.4 + 3.9 + 6.081 + 2.9 59.281

14. 34.75 + 13.2 + 814.76 + 2.035 864.745

15. 18.16 + 7.391 + 2.07 + 200.1 227.721

16. 6.88 + 7.9 + 48.26 + 8.003 71.043

17. 311.27 + 9.48 + 2.44 + 80.1 403.29

18. 272.01 + 18.37 + 224.1 + 4.009 518.489

Subtract. Check each answer. (Example 2)

19. 21.93 − 8.42 13.51

20. 94.84 −13.66 81.18

21. 7.291 −3.407 3.884

22. 6.315 −2.196 4.119

23. 9.08 −3.19 5.89

24. 6.277 −0.2431 6.0339

25. 4.81 −2.307 2.503

26. 16.18 − 2.113 14.067

27. 3.8 −0.91 2.89

28. 62.89 − 1.476 61.414

29. 11 − 2.613 8.387

30. 14 − 8.071 5.929

31. 39 − 4.821 34.179

32. 67 − 7.335 59.665

33. 20 − 1.27 18.73

34. 1000 − 91.25 908.75

35. 62.18 − 41.19 20.99

36. 16.219 − 12.403 3.816

37. 82.19 − 4.236 77.954

38. 6.208 − 2.35 3.858

39. 49.217 − 1.75 47.467

40. 17.06 − 2.954 14.106

APPLICATIONS: Using Addition and Subtraction of Decimals

These word problems apply the skills taught in the lesson.

41. Last month, 0.02 inch, 1.38 inches, 0.08 inch, and 0.57 inch of rain fell. What was the total rainfall? 2.05 inches

42. Find the total rainfall over a 6-month period in which 0.5 inch, 1.43 inches, 1.3 inches, 0.8 inch, 0.84 inch, and 0.31 inches of rain fell. 5.18 inches

43. The normal annual rainfall in Des Moines, Iowa is 30.85 inches. It is 42.5 inches in Boston, Massachusetts. Find the difference. 11.65 inches

44. The normal annual rainfall in Houston, Texas is 48.19 inches. It is 46 inches in Nashville, Tennessee. How much more rain falls in Houston? 2.19 inches

1-3 Multiplication: Whole Numbers

See the Teacher's Manual for the objectives.

When you multiply two numbers, the numbers are called **factors.** The answer is the **product.**

```
  23  ← Factors
× 3   ←
  69  ← Product
```

PROCEDURE To multiply whole numbers:

1. Multiply by the ones.
2. Multiply by the tens.
3. Multiply by the hundreds, and so on.
4. Add the products obtained in steps 1–3.

EXAMPLE 1 Multiply: **a.** 32 × 67 **b.** 256 × 85

Solutions:

a.
```
   32
  ×67
  224  ← 7 × 32
 1920  ← 60 × 32
 2144  ← 224 + 1920
```

b.
```
   256
  × 85
  1280  ← 5 × 256
 20480  ← 80 × 256
21,760  ← 1280 + 20,480
```

After completing Example 1, you may wish to have students do some or all of Exercises 1-28.

When multiplying, you can leave out the zeros as shown at the right. Be sure to line up the products under the corresponding multipliers.

```
   32
  ×67
  224  ← 7 × 32
 192   ← 6 × 32
 2144
```

Sometimes there are zeros in one or both factors of a multiplication problem. Remember!

Zero times any number is zero.

EXAMPLE 2 Multiply: **a.** 432 × 703 **b.** 304 × 605

Solutions:

a.
```
    432
   ×703
   1296  ← 3 × 432
   0000  ← 0 tens × 432
 302400  ← 700 × 432
303,696
```

b.
```
    304
   ×605
   1520
   0000  ← 0 tens × 304
 182400
183,920
```

Another way to do the multiplication in Example 2b is shown at the right. Use the method that is easier for you.

```
    304
   ×605
   1520
  18240
183,920
```

Replace the row of zeros with one zero.

EXERCISES

Multiply. (Example 1)

1. 46×82 3772
2. 97×83 8051
3. 213×74 15,762
4. 518×63 32,634
5. 63×29 1827
6. 652×75 48,900
7. 686×143 98,098
8. 775×214 165,850
9. 871×29 25,259
10. 844×47 39,668
11. 69×27 1863
12. 35×83 2905
13. 217×87 18,879
14. 395×84 33,180
15. 71×63 4473
16. 27×48 1296
17. 293×723 211,839
18. 173×294 50,862
19. 21×79 1659
20. 83×34 2822
21. 463×27 12,501
22. 821×65 53,365
23. 624×87 54,288
24. 129×73 9417
25. 616×243 149,688
26. 817×324 264,708
27. 16×28 448
28. 84×27 2268

(Example 2)

29. 84×30 2520
30. 801×60 48,060
31. 883×207 182,781
32. 419×807 338,133
33. 804×236 189,744
34. 509×234 119,106
35. 404×309 124,836
36. 209×503 105,127
37. 240×87 20,880
38. 208×435 90,480
39. 607×26 15,782
40. 405×34 13,770
41. 503×29 14,587
42. 709×36 25,524
43. 810×67 54,270
44. 750×42 31,500
45. 803×207 166,221
46. 901×308 277,508
47. 801×27 21,627
48. 403×43 17,329
49. 702×209 146,718
50. 608×405 246,240
51. 709×21 14,889
52. 503×63 31,689
53. 808×292 235,936
54. 903×481 434,343
55. 606×27 16,362
56. 204×43 8772

APPLICATIONS: Using Multiplication of Whole Numbers

These word problems apply the skills taught in the lesson.

57. One carrot contains 21 calories. How many calories are in 5 carrots? 105
58. One tablespoon of peanut butter contains 96 calories. Find the total number of calories in 4 tablespoons of peanut butter. 384
59. Milo eats 3 slices of whole wheat bread each day. There are 55 calories in each slice. How many calories are there in 3 slices? 165
60. Diana has two scrambled eggs for breakfast. Each egg contains 112 calories. Find the total number of calories. 224
61. Julia drinks four glasses of milk each day. Each glass contains 159 calories. What is the total number of calories? 636

The Four Basic Food Groups

1-4 Multiplication: Decimals

See the Teacher's Manual for the objectives.

When multiplying with decimals, you count the number of decimal places in the factors in order to place the decimal point correctly in the product. The **number of decimal places** means the number of digits to the right of the decimal point.

PROCEDURE To multiply with decimals:

[1] Multiply as with whole numbers.

[2] Add the number of decimal places in the factors to place the decimal point in the product.

EXAMPLE 1 Multiply: **a.** 636×0.12 **b.** 13.06×1.23

Solutions:

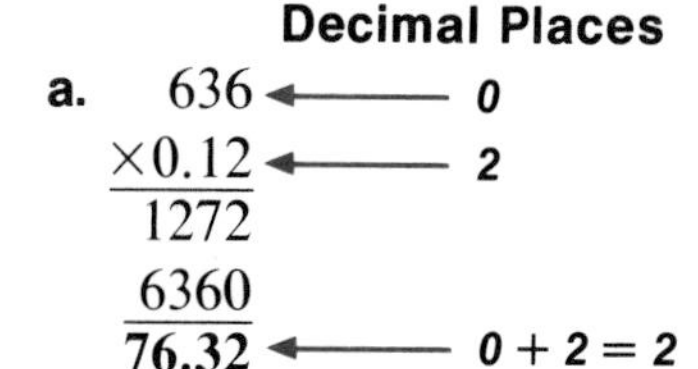

b. Decimal Places

	Decimal Places
13.06	2
× 1.23	2
3918	
26120	
130600	
16.0638	2 + 2 = 4

After completing Example 1, you may wish to have students do some or all of Exercises 1-25.

Sometimes you have to insert zeros in order to have the correct number of decimal places in a product.

EXAMPLE 2 Multiply: **a.** 2.3×0.002 **b.** 0.31×0.0024

Solutions:

a.

	Decimal Places
2.3	1
×0.002	3
0.0046	1 + 3 = 4

Insert two zeros to make 4 decimal places.

b.

	Decimal Places
0.31	2
×0.0024	4
124	
620	
0.000744	2 + 4 = 6

Insert three zeros to make 6 decimal places.

EXERCISES

Copy each product. Then insert the decimal point. (Example 1)

1. 16 × 0.8 = 128 12.8

2. 1.6 × 0.8 = 128 1.28

3. 1.6 × 8 = 128 12.8

4. 0.16 × 8 = 128 1.28

5. 1.60 × 0.8 = 1280 1.280

Multiply. (Example 1)

6. 28×0.6 16.8 **7.** 73×0.8 58.4 **8.** 62×1.7 105.4 **9.** 29×2.9 84.1 **10.** 6×0.09 0.54

11. 8×0.08 0.64 **12.** 723×0.02 14.46 **13.** 197×0.07 13.79 **14.** 4321×0.09 388.89 **15.** 8647×0.06 518.82

16. 1.83×4.87 8.9121 **17.** 12.08×4.07 49.1656 **18.** 6.97×0.73 5.0881 **19.** 7.28×0.16 1.1648 **20.** 9.04×2.5 22.600

21. 4.81×1.3 6.253 **22.** 49.7×0.66 32.802 **23.** 82.7×0.79 65.333 **24.** 12.83×29.5 378.485 **25.** 48.76×45.2 2203.952

Copy each product. Then insert the decimal point. (Example 2)

26. 0.19×0.07 = 133 0.0133 **27.** 0.019×0.07 = 133 0.00133 **28.** 0.19×0.007 = 133 0.00133 **29.** 0.019×0.007 = 133 0.000133 **30.** 0.19×0.7 = 133 0.133

Multiply. (Example 2)

31. 2.7×0.002 0.0054 **32.** 3.5×0.005 0.0175 **33.** 1.6×0.04 0.064 **34.** 1.7×0.007 0.0119 **35.** 8.1×0.0008 0.00648

36. 3.17×0.005 0.01585 **37.** 0.8×0.001 0.0008 **38.** 0.4×0.004 0.0016 **39.** 0.07×0.07 0.0049 **40.** 0.12×0.09 0.0108

41. 0.29×0.0062 0.001798 **42.** 0.3×0.0012 0.00036 **43.** 3.09×0.0067 0.020703 **44.** 0.27×0.0091 0.002457 **45.** 0.15×0.13 0.0195

46. 0.73×0.075 0.05475 **47.** 2.07×0.0066 0.013662 **48.** 98.72×0.0002 0.019744 **49.** 39.17×0.0004 0.015668 **50.** 8.43×0.0029 0.024447

These word problems apply the skills taught in the lesson.

APPLICATIONS: Using Multiplication of Decimals

51. Steak costs \$2.40 per pound. How much will 3.8 pounds of steak cost? \$9.12

52. Apples cost \$0.80 per pound. How much will 4.8 pounds of apples cost? \$3.84

53. Onions cost \$0.40 per pound. How much will 2.7 pounds of onions cost? \$1.08

54. Susan is cooking a beef roast for 8 people. She estimates that each person will eat 0.6 pound of meat. How much meat should she buy? 4.8 pounds

55. Wiley is cooking veal cutlets for 7 people. He estimates that each person will eat 0.9 pound of veal. How many pounds will he need? 6.3 pounds

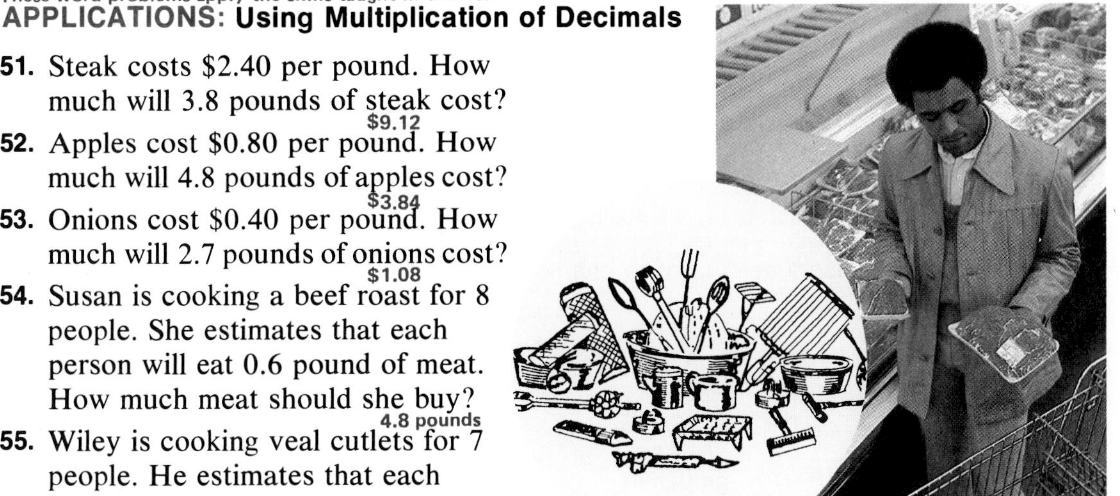

Mid–Chapter Review

This reviews all the skills presented in Sections 1-1, 1-2, 1-3, and 1-4.

Add or subtract as indicated. (Pages 2–5)

1.	**2.**	**3.**
367 197 +243 **807**	243 378 +591 **1212**	2071 243 + 67 **2381**

4. 2318 + 17 + 393 + 4084 **6812**

5. 5277 + 4139 + 27 + 663 **10,106**

6.	**7.**	**8.**
687 −251 **436**	3395 −1243 **2152**	2214 −1022 **1192**

9. 677 − 38 **639**

10. 7013 − 295 **6718**

11. 299 − 89 **210**

12. 8000 − 3016 **4984**

13.	**14.**	**15.**
16.32 2.93 113.87 + 21.08 **154.20**	74.38 227.1 86.395 + 2.81 **390.685**	3.27 101.241 63.7 +123.56 **291.771**

16. 8.307 + 29.55 + 213.86 + 9.57 **261.287**

17. 426.37 + 21.9 + 11.342 + 9.75 **469.362**

18.	**19.**	**20.**
3.975 −2.081 **1.894**	21.883 − 3.75 **18.133**	91.835 − 2.76 **89.075**

21. 102.45 − 12.8 **89.65**

22. 81 − 27.63 **53.37**

23. 48 − 2.39 **45.61**

24. 12 − 9.36 **2.64**

Multiply. (Pages 6–9)

25.	**26.**	**27.**
634 × 24 **15,216**	849 × 58 **49,242**	762 ×385 **293,370**

28. 682 × 257 **175,274**

29. 129 × 509 **65,661**

30. 608 × 43 **26,144**

31. 604 × 207 **125,028**

32.	**33.**	**34.**
35 ×0.03 **1.05**	29 ×1.7 **49.3**	0.003 ×0.027 **0.000081**

35. 9.71 × 0.0035 **0.033985**

36. 7.11 × 0.008 **0.05688**

37. Christopher ate 4 ounces of cheese yesterday. Each ounce contains 116 calories. Find the total number of calories. (Pages 6–7) **464**

38. In February, 0.1 inch, 1.23 inches, 0.89 inch, and 0.07 inch of rain fell. Find the total amount of rainfall. (Pages 4–5) **2.29 inches**

39. In 1980, the population in Boston was 3,917,400. By 1990, it is expected to be 3,986,000. Find the increase in population. (Pages 2–3) **68,600**

40. Liza is planning a dinner for 5 people. She is buying 0.7 pound of meat for each person. How much meat should she buy? (Pages 8–9) **3.5 pounds**

CHECKING ADDITION/SUBTRACTION/MULTIPLICATION

Calculator exercises are optional.

Use a calculator to check each answer. Correct any wrong answers.

1.	**2.**	**3.**	**4.**
4,334 489 62,573 98 +395,164 462,658	435.62 7481.09 327.5 28.673 + 572.864 8845.747	64,200 −49,867 14,433 **14,333**	685 −469.27 215.73

5.	**6.**
3206 × 604 1,937,424 **1,936,424**	2.07 ×0.048 0.09936

Calculator

STOCK CLERK

career

Career lessons are optional.
This lesson applies the skills of reading a code and using a formula.

As a **stock clerk,** Anita Ruiz organizes the items in a warehouse. She also marks the dealer's cost on each item with a **code.**

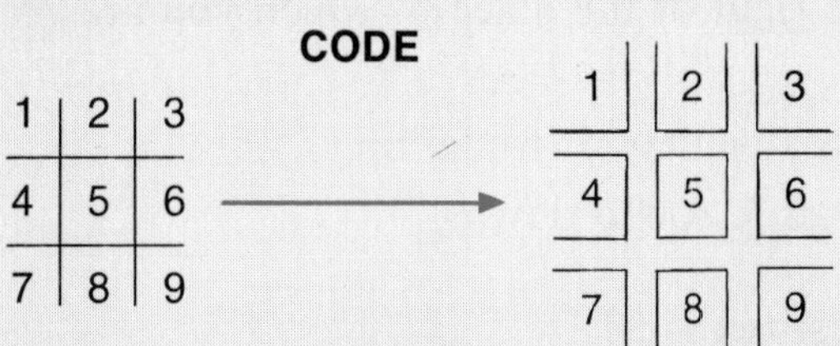

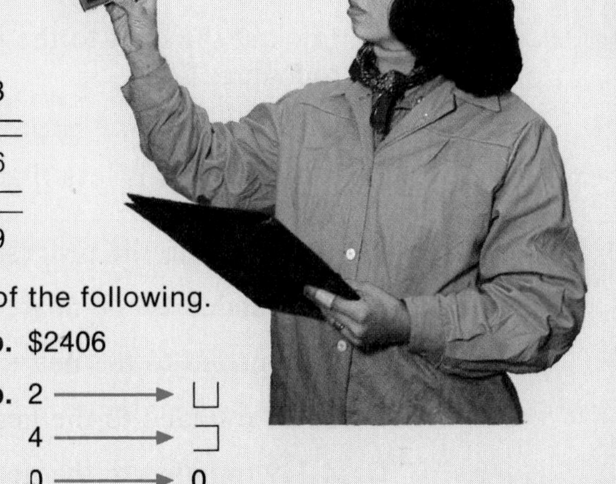

EXAMPLE 1 Write the code for each of the following.

a. \$125 **b.** \$2406

Solutions:

a. 1 ⟶ ┘
2 ⟶ ⊔
5 ⟶ □
\$125 ⟶ ┘⊔□

b. 2 ⟶ ⊔
4 ⟶ ⊐
0 ⟶ 0
6 ⟶ ⊏
\$2406 ⟶ ⊔⊐0⊏

In order to make a profit and to pay for expenses, the dealer adds an amount called the **markup** to the cost. This sum is the **selling price.**

Selling Price = Dealer's Cost + Markup

EXAMPLE 2 A computer coded ⊐□⊔0 is to be sold at markup of \$1130. Find the selling price.

Solution:

1 Find the dealer's cost. ⊐□⊔0 ⟶ **\$4520**

2 **Selling Price = Dealer's Cost + Markup**
Selling Price = \$4520 + \$1130
Selling Price = **\$5650**

EXERCISES Note that Exercises 1–6 are non-verbal.

Write the code for each of the following. (Example 1)

1. \$9201 ┌⊔0┘ **2.** \$4358 ⊐└□⊓ **3.** \$2976 ⊔┌┐⊏ **4.** \$6006 ⊏00⊏ **5.** \$7432 ┐⊐└⊔ **6.** \$9015 ┌0┘□

7. A television set coded ⊏┌┌ is to be sold at a markup of \$158. Find the selling price. (Example 2) \$857

8. A car coded ⊓┌00 is to be sold at a markup of \$3000. Find the selling price. (Example 2) \$11,900

1-5 Division: Whole Numbers

See the Teacher's Manual for the objectives.

Rounding is a useful tool in division.

PROCEDURE To round whole numbers:

1. Look at the digit to the right of the place to which you are rounding.
2. **a.** If the digit is 5 or greater than 5, round up.
   b. If the digit is less than 5, round down.

EXAMPLE 1

a. 46 rounded to the nearest **ten** is 50.

b. 322 rounded to the nearest **ten** is 320.

c. 678 rounded to the nearest **hundred** is 700.

d. 25,413 rounded to the nearest **hundred** is 25,400.

e. 14,329 rounded to the nearest **thousand** is 14,000.

f. 36,540 rounded to the nearest **thousand** is 37,000.

After completing Example 1, you may wish to have students do some or all of Exercises 1-34.

Rounding can be used to help find a trial divisor.

PROCEDURE To divide by two- or three-digit divisors:

1. Determine where to place the first digit in the quotient.
2. Round to find a trial divisor.
3. Divide.

EXAMPLE 2 Divide: 1121 ÷ 36 (The **divisor** is 36. The **dividend** is 1121.)

Solution:

1. 36)11|21 — ***11 is less than 36. Draw a new line.*** → 36)112|1 (X above the new line)

2. 36 rounded to the nearest ten is 40. ***Trial Divisor***

   Think: $40\overline{)112}$ with 2 above. Try 2 for the first digit.

3. $36\overline{)1121}$ with 2 above
   72
   40 — ***Since 40 is greater than 36, 2 is not enough. Try 3.***

   $36\overline{)1121}$ with 31 above
   108
   41 — $40\overline{)41}$ with 1 above
   36
   5

   Answer: **31 r 5**

Check: Multiply the quotient and the divisor.

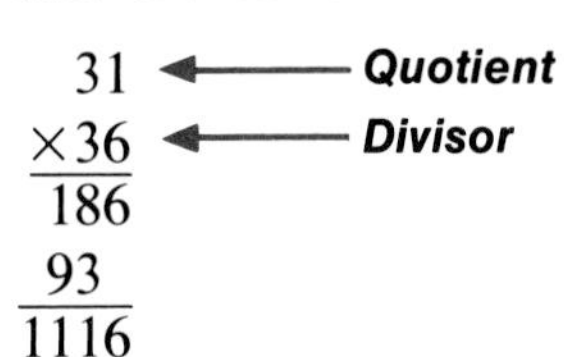

Then add the remainder. This should equal the dividend.

```
  1116
+    5  ← Remainder
  1121
```

EXERCISES

Round to the nearest ten. (Example 1)

1. 43 40 **2.** 57 60 **3.** 263 260 **4.** 872 870 **5.** 439 440 **6.** 598 600

7. 774 770 **8.** 813 810 **9.** 2613 2610 **10.** 7085 7090 **11.** 1917 1920 **12.** 9376 9380

Round to the nearest hundred. (Example 1)

13. 763 800 **14.** 871 900 **15.** 4935 4900 **16.** 2817 2800 **17.** 7449 7400 **18.** 2193 2200

19. 408 400 **20.** 579 600 **21.** 16,066 16,100 **22.** 27,029 27,000 **23.** 8109 8100 **24.** 4450 4500

Round to the nearest thousand. (Example 1)

25. 8700 9000 **26.** 4315 4000 **27.** 11,269 11,000 **28.** 18,436 18,000 **29.** 14,781 15,000

30. 29,585 30,000 **31.** 37,998 38,000 **32.** 2499 2000 **33.** 8615 9000 **34.** 6329 6000

Divide. (Example 2)

35. 5)435 87 **36.** 7)294 42 **37.** 3)228 76 **38.** 4)3604 901 **39.** 6)4218 703

40. 24)504 21 **41.** 32)416 13 **42.** 22)635 28 r 19 **43.** 43)498 11 r 25 **44.** 18)644 35 r 14

45. 13)942 72 r 6 **46.** 26)2669 102 r 17 **47.** 34)3726 109 r 20 **48.** 43)2513 58 r 19 **49.** 67)1683 25 r 8

50. 325)3900 12 **51.** 143)9295 65 **52.** 549)7447 13 r 310 **53.** 223)8451 37 r 200 **54.** 357)1393 3 r 322

55. 426)2768 6 r 212 **56.** 292)16936 58 **57.** 662)12578 19 **58.** 283)14189 50 r 39 **59.** 662)20304 30 r 444

APPLICATIONS: Using Division of Whole Numbers

These word problems apply the skills taught in the lesson.

60. A worker has 15,588 yards of cord to be wound equally on 12 spools. How many yards of cord will be on each spool? 1299 yards

61. A weaver has 56,898 yards of yarn. He wants to weave 18 rugs of equal size. How much yarn will be used for each rug? 3161 yards

62. Lila bought 6380 feet of wire. She wants to sell it in packages of 150 feet. How many packages will she have? How much will be left over? 42 packages; 80 yards left over

63. Sal sells macrame cord. He buys 5650 yards of cord to be sold in 80-yard units. How many units can he sell? How much will be left over? 70 units; 50 yards left over

1-6 Division: Decimals

See the Teacher's Manual for the objectives.

Dividing a decimal by a whole number is similar to dividing with whole numbers.

PROCEDURE To divide a decimal by a whole number (not zero):

1. Place the decimal point in the quotient directly above the decimal point in the dividend.
2. Divide as with whole numbers.

EXAMPLE 1 Divide 5.292 by 63. Check your answer.

Solution: 1 Place the decimal point in the quotient. $63\overline{)5.292}$ (decimal point placed above)

2 $63\overline{)5.292}$, quotient 0. — *Since 5 is not divisible by 63, write a 0 above the 5.*

$63\overline{)5.292}$, quotient 0.0 — *Since 52 is not divisible by 63, write a 0 above the 2.*

```
   0.084
63)5.292
   5 04
     252
     252
```

Check:

```
   0.084
 ×    63
     252
    504
   5.292
```

These should be the same. (The dividend 5.292 and the check product 5.292.)

After completing Example 1, you may wish to have students do some or all of Exercises 1-28.

When dividing by a decimal, the first step is to multiply the divisor and the dividend by the same number in order to obtain a whole-number divisor.

PROCEDURE To divide by a decimal:

1. Multiply both the divisor and dividend by 10, or by 100, or by 1000, and so on, in order to obtain a whole-number divisor.
2. Divide.

EXAMPLE 2 Divide: $0.224\overline{)5.6}$

Solution: 1 Since the divisor is 224 thousandths, multiply the divisor and the dividend by 1000.

$0.224_\wedge\overline{)5.600_\wedge}$ — *Annex two zeros.*

2

```
      25
224)5600.
    448
    1120
    1120
```

Check:

```
  0.224
 ×   25
   1120
   448
  5.600
```

EXERCISES

Divide. (Example 1)

1. $4\overline{)18.72}$ 4.68	**2.** $6\overline{)38.76}$ 6.46	**3.** $7\overline{)8.869}$ 1.267	**4.** $8\overline{)9.976}$ 1.247
5. $7\overline{)0.966}$ 0.138	**6.** $4\overline{)0.732}$ 0.183	**7.** $6\overline{)0.564}$ 0.094	**8.** $9\overline{)0.486}$ 0.054
9. $4\overline{)24.36}$ 6.09	**10.** $5\overline{)10.45}$ 2.09	**11.** $7\overline{)1.428}$ 0.204	**12.** $8\overline{)1.632}$ 0.204
13. $21\overline{)68.46}$ 3.26	**14.** $32\overline{)88.96}$ 2.78	**15.** $18\overline{)46.098}$ 2.561	**16.** $14\overline{)51.408}$ 3.672
17. $97\overline{)54.32}$ 0.56	**18.** $42\overline{)28.14}$ 0.67	**19.** $83\overline{)1.743}$ 0.021	**20.** $24\overline{)1.344}$ 0.056
21. $122\overline{)434.32}$ 3.56	**22.** $163\overline{)402.61}$ 2.47	**23.** $211\overline{)66.887}$ 0.317	**24.** $123\overline{)39.975}$ 0.325
25. $162\overline{)5.508}$ 0.034	**26.** $247\overline{)9.386}$ 0.038	**27.** $397\overline{)42.082}$ 0.106	**28.** $261\overline{)53.244}$ 0.204

(Example 2)

29. $0.7\overline{)4.34}$ 6.2	**30.** $0.4\overline{)3.88}$ 9.7	**31.** $0.5\overline{)46.5}$ 93	**32.** $0.8\overline{)52.8}$ 66
33. $0.08\overline{)1.84}$ 23	**34.** $0.09\overline{)2.16}$ 24	**35.** $0.006\overline{)3.456}$ 576	**36.** $0.004\overline{)2.744}$ 686
37. $0.04\overline{)2.6}$ 65	**38.** $0.05\overline{)3.4}$ 68	**39.** $0.008\overline{)6.28}$ 785	**40.** $0.006\overline{)5.25}$ 875
41. $1.4\overline{)3.64}$ 2.6	**42.** $2.8\overline{)4.76}$ 1.7	**43.** $4.9\overline{)5.145}$ 1.05	**44.** $2.2\overline{)6.732}$ 3.06
45. $0.48\overline{)0.576}$ 1.2	**46.** $0.36\overline{)0.864}$ 2.4	**47.** $0.29\overline{)1.102}$ 3.8	**48.** $0.51\overline{)2.448}$ 4.8
49. $0.46\overline{)39.1}$ 85	**50.** $0.74\overline{)25.9}$ 35	**51.** $4.6\overline{)115}$ 25	**52.** $3.2\overline{)144}$ 45
53. $2.17\overline{)11.935}$ 5.5	**54.** $4.01\overline{)10.025}$ 2.5	**55.** $4.56\overline{)12.312}$ 2.7	**56.** $2.43\overline{)17.253}$ 7.1
57. $1.54\overline{)92.4}$ 60	**58.** $3.19\overline{)63.8}$ 20	**59.** $0.582\overline{)75.66}$ 130	**60.** $0.199\overline{)63.68}$ 320

APPLICATIONS: Using Division of Decimals

These word problems apply the skills taught in the lesson.

61. A certain car travels 361.6 miles on a full tank of fuel. The tank holds 11.3 gallons when full. How far does it travel on one gallon? 32 miles

62. The fuel tank of a luxury car holds 24.4 gallons when full. The car travels 402.6 miles on a full tank. How many miles does it travel on one gallon? 16.5 miles

63. A sub-compact car travels 434.6 miles on a full tank of fuel. A full tank holds 10.6 gallons. How far does it travel on one gallon? 41 miles

64. The fuel tank in a certain sports car holds 15 gallons of fuel when full. The car travels 184.5 miles on a full tank. How far will it travel on one gallon? 12.3 miles

1-7 Rounding the Quotient

See the Teacher's Manual for the objectives.

Rounding decimals is similar to rounding whole numbers.

PROCEDURE To round a decimal, look at the digit to the right of the place to which you are rounding.

1. If the digit is 5 or more, round up.
2. If the digit is less than 5, round down.

EXAMPLE 1

a. 23.7453 rounded to the nearest whole number is **24.**

b. 23.7453 rounded to the nearest tenth is 23.7

c. 23.7453 rounded to the nearest hundredth is 23.75

d. 23.7453 rounded to the nearest thousandth is 23.745

After completing Example 1, you may wish to have students do some or all of Exercises 1-48.

It is sometimes useful to round a quotient to a given decimal place.

PROCEDURE To find a quotient to a given decimal place:

1. Carry the division to one additional decimal place.
2. Round the quotient to the given decimal place.

EXAMPLE 2 Divide 57.5 by 6.6. Round the quotient to the nearest tenth.

Solution: 1. Carry the division to hundredths.

```
        8.71
6.6 ) 57.500     ◀ Annex two zeros.
      528
       470
       462
         80
         66
         14
```

2. Round the quotient. 8.71 rounded to the nearest tenth is **8.7.**

EXERCISES

Round to the nearest whole number. (Example 1)

1. 29.7 30 **2.** 4.34 **3.** 25.9 26 **4.** 8.7 9 **5.** 9.9 10 **6.** 5.8 6

7. 16.82 17 **8.** 14.49 14 **9.** 11.38 11 **10.** 19.95 20 **11.** 6.27 6 **12.** 13.15 13

Round to the nearest tenth. (Example 1)

13. 31.27 31.3 **14.** 14.49 14.5 **15.** 17.84 17.8 **16.** 83.35 83.4 **17.** 76.13 76.1 **18.** 11.29 11.3

19. 62.294 62.3 **20.** 81.349 81.3 **21.** 11.409 11.4 **22.** 67.98 68.0 **23.** 124.649 124.6 **24.** 18.551 18.6

Round to the nearest hundredth. (Example 1)

25. 37.285 37.29 **26.** 43.634 43.63 **27.** 59.136 59.14 **28.** 14.188 14.19 **29.** 77.114 77.11 **30.** 264.818 264.82

31. 47.297 47.30 **32.** 11.276 11.28 **33.** 88.225 88.23 **34.** 19.349 19.35 **35.** 62.194 62.19 **36.** 18.399 18.40

Round to the nearest thousandth. (Example 1)

37. 8.2941 8.294 **38.** 7.3939 7.394 **39.** 0.29247 0.292 **40.** 1.1777 1.178 **41.** 2.6455 2.646 **42.** 2.0058 2.006

43. 1.3297 1.330 **44.** 0.4846 0.485 **45.** 2.1121 2.112 **46.** 12.3998 12.400 **47.** 1.1944 1.194 **48.** 6.6666 6.667

Divide. Round each answer to the nearest tenth. (Example 2)

49. $3.2\overline{)59.73}$ 18.7 **50.** $7.4\overline{)11.7}$ 1.6 **51.** $18.1\overline{)27.2}$ 1.5 **52.** $14.9\overline{)18.1}$ 1.2

53. $6.89\overline{)21.03}$ 3.1 **54.** $7.22\overline{)18.331}$ 2.5 **55.** $11.9\overline{)35.88}$ 3.0 **56.** $1.03\overline{)4.233}$ 4.1

57. $11.1\overline{)54.83}$ 4.9 **58.** $6.83\overline{)12.94}$ 1.9 **59.** $1.9\overline{)18.37}$ 9.7 **60.** $4.05\overline{)11}$ 2.7

61. $8.7\overline{)12.976}$ 1.5 **62.** $1.4\overline{)16.93}$ 12.1 **63.** $7.22\overline{)8.89}$ 1.2 **64.** $7.3\overline{)28.1}$ 3.8

Divide. Round each answer to the nearest hundredth. (Example 2)

65. $8.72\overline{)11.84}$ 1.36 **66.** $2.38\overline{)16.96}$ 7.13 **67.** $4.18\overline{)7.3}$ 1.75 **68.** $18.3\overline{)19.7}$ 1.08

69. $1.93\overline{)14.887}$ 7.71 **70.** $7.72\overline{)18.11}$ 2.35 **71.** $3.9\overline{)11.71}$ 3.00 **72.** $4.9\overline{)18.61}$ 3.80

73. $12.7\overline{)7.83}$ 0.62 **74.** $8.8\overline{)6.5}$ 0.74 **75.** $1.5\overline{)60.1}$ 40.07 **76.** $2.9\overline{)5.77}$ 1.99

77. $9.7\overline{)9.941}$ 1.02 **78.** $68.3\overline{)292.4}$ 4.28 **79.** $5.85\overline{)9.807}$ 1.68 **80.** $3.92\overline{)2.9}$ 0.74

These exercises apply the skills taught in the lesson.

APPLICATIONS: Using Rounding in Division

For Exercises 81–87, use:

Number of hits ÷ Number of times at bat = Batting average

Round each answer to the nearest thousandth.

	Number of Hits	*Times at Bat*	*Batting Average*
81.	19	68	0.279 ?
82.	24	73	0.329 ?
83.	32	102	0.314 ?
84.	23	116	0.198 ?
85.	36	121	0.298 ?
86.	48	133	0.361 ?
87.	54	203	0.266 ?

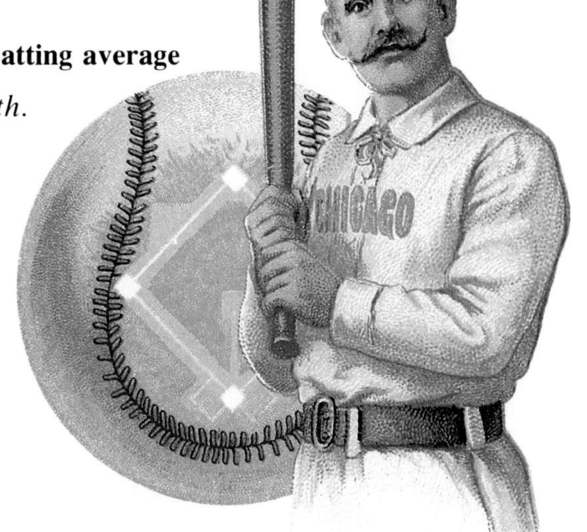

1-8 Rounding and Estimation

See the Teacher's Manual for the objectives.

You can use rounding to help you estimate answers. Recall the symbol $\approx$ means "is approximately equal to."

EXAMPLE Estimate each answer.

a. $5.89 + 3.12$ **b.** $794 - 418$ **c.** 59×71 **d.** $207.5 \div 28.4$

Solutions:

a. Round each number to the nearest whole number.

Think: $5.89 + 3.12 \approx 6 + 3$
$\approx \mathbf{9}$

b. Round each number to the nearest hundred.

Think: $794 - 418 \approx 800 - 400$
$\approx \mathbf{400}$

c. Round each number to the nearest ten.

Think: $59 \times 71 \approx 60 \times 70$
$\approx \mathbf{4200}$

d. Round each number to the nearest ten.

Think: $207.5 \div 28.4 \approx 210 \div 30$
$\approx \mathbf{7}$

EXERCISES

Choose the best estimate. Choose a, b, or c.

1. $438 + 21$ b **a.** $430 + 20$ **b.** $440 + 20$ **c.** $440 + 30$

2. $3.7 + 5.2$ a **a.** $4 + 5$ **b.** $3 + 5$ **c.** $4 + 6$

3. $961 - 329$ c **a.** $970 - 330$ **b.** $970 - 320$ **c.** $960 - 330$

4. $10.2 - 7.8$ a **a.** $10 - 8$ **b.** $11 - 8$ **c.** $10 - 7$

5. 22×49 c **a.** 30×40 **b.** 30×50 **c.** 20×50

6. 3.8×10.1 a **a.** 4×10 **b.** 4×11 **c.** 3×10

7. $321 \div 83$ b **a.** $330 \div 80$ **b.** $320 \div 80$ **c.** $330 \div 90$

8. $60.3 \div 29.8$ c **a.** $61 \div 20$ **b.** $70 \div 30$ **c.** $60 \div 30$

Choose the best estimate. Choose a, b, c, or d.

9. $39 + 572$ c **a.** 640 **b.** 620 **c.** 610 **d.** 600

10. $14.8 + 6.75$ b **a.** 25 **b.** 22 **c.** 20 **d.** 18

11. $397 - 241$ d **a.** 180 **b.** 170 **c.** 150 **d.** 160

12. $24.6 - 19.9$ a **a.** 5 **b.** 4 **c.** 8 **d.** 6

13. 42×18 b **a.** 700 **b.** 800 **c.** 900 **d.** 1000

14. 10.3×28.9 c **a.** 500 **b.** 400 **c.** 300 **d.** 200

15. $78 \div 19$ d **a.** 2 **b.** 3 **c.** 5 **d.** 4

16. $19.9 \div 1.8$ b **a.** 15 **b.** 10 **c.** 5 **d.** 20

APPLICATIONS: Using Estimation

17. At Ryan's Stationery, Peter paid \$1.98 for staples, \$2.10 for paper, and 98¢ for glue. The tax was 39¢. Estimate the total bill. c

a. \$4.00 **b.** \$4.50

c. \$5.00 **d.** \$5.50

18. The population of London is 7,028,000. The population of São Paulo is 7,199,000. Estimate the difference in population. a

a. 200,000 **b.** 100,000

c. 300,000 **d.** 400,000

19. Lobster costs \$4.10 per pound in season. Estimate the cost of 4.8 pounds. b

a. \$40 **b.** \$20

c. \$50 **d.** \$55

20. 5,980 feet of twine is wound in equal amounts onto 29 spools. Estimate the number of feet of twine on each spool. b

a. 150 **b.** 200

c. 250 **d.** 300

Calculator exercises are optional.

ESTIMATION AND THE CALCULATOR

You can use the rules for rounding and estimation and the calculator to solve problems.

EXAMPLE: $25.2 \div 4.8 = \underline{\ ?\ }$

Solution: Use paper and pencil to estimate the answer: $25 \div 5 =$ **5**

Use the calculator to find the exact answer.

[2] [5] [.] [2] [÷] [4] [.] [8] [=] 5.25

Since the estimate is 5, 5.25 is a reasonable answer.

EXERCISES Estimated answers will vary, depending on the places to which the given numbers are rounded.

First estimate each answer. Then use a calculator to find the exact answer.

Problem	Estimated Answer	Exact Answer
1. $29 + 141 + 38 + 73$	?	? 281
2. $14.17 + 129.7 + 18.1$	?	? 161.97
3. $5418 - 1799$	?	? 3619
4. $74.9 - 19.07$	?	? 55.83
5. 209×61	?	? 12,749
6. 38.1×20.8	?	? 792.48
7. $3498.6 \div 51$	?	? 68.6
8. $90.09 \div 9.1$	?	? 9.9

BUS DRIVER

Career lessons are optional.
This lesson applies the skill of using a letter-number pair to read a map.

As a long-distance **bus driver,** Clyde Ings must know how to use a map. This map is marked off in squares. Each square is identified by a letter and a number.

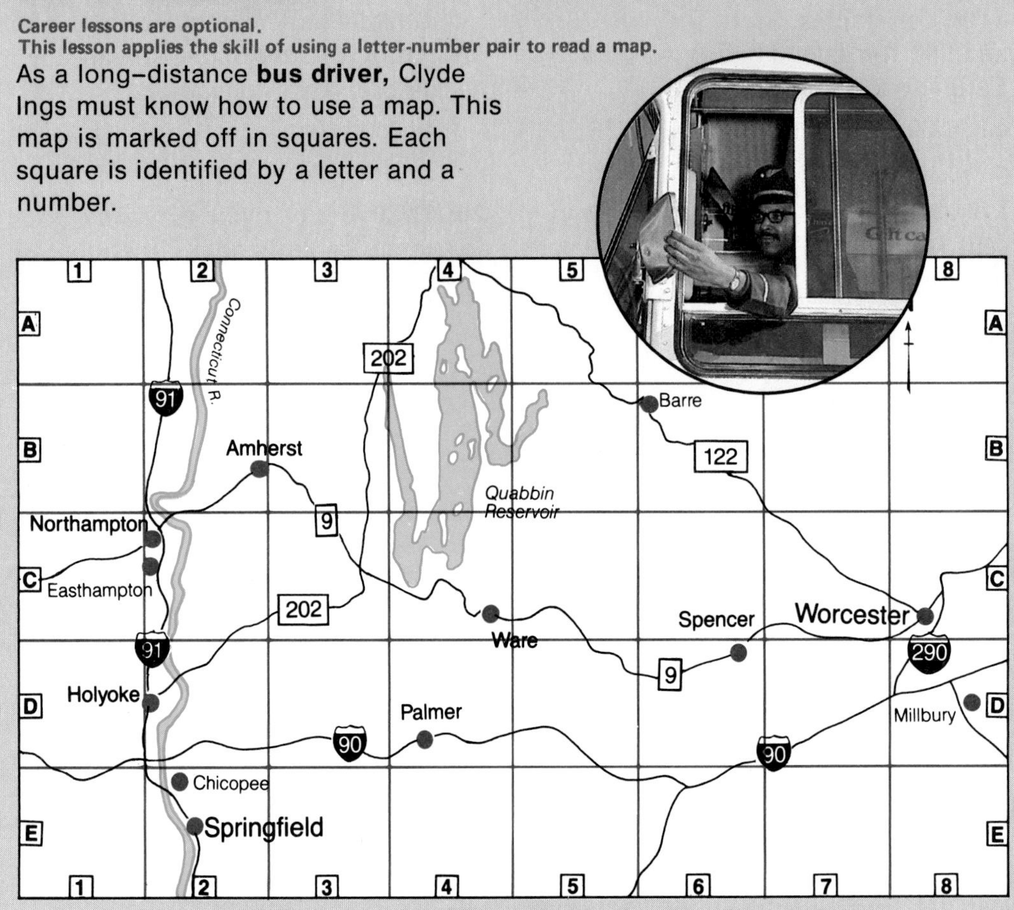

EXAMPLE 1 What cities are located in C–2?

Solution:

1 Locate the letter C on the left side.

2 Move to the right of C and stop at the square opposite the number 2.

The cities in C–2 are **Northampton** and **Easthampton.**

NOTE: You could have used the letters on the right side in Example 1.

The **letter-number** code is called a **coordinate.**

EXAMPLE 2 What is the coordinate for Worcester?

Solution:

1 The letter to the left (or right) of Worcester is C.

2 The number directly below (or above) Worcester is 8.

Thus, the coordinate for Worcester is **C–8.**

EXERCISES

For Exercises 1–10, refer to the map on page 20.
For Exercises 1–6, identify the city or cities located in each square. (Example 1)

1. D–8 Millbury **2.** B–6 Barre **3.** E–2 Chicopee, Springfield **4.** C–4 Ware **5.** D–4 Palmer **6.** D–6 Spencer

For Exercises 7–10, identify the coordinate for each city. (Example 2)

7. Holyoke D–2 **8.** Amherst B–2 **9.** Chicopee E–2 **10.** Palmer D–4

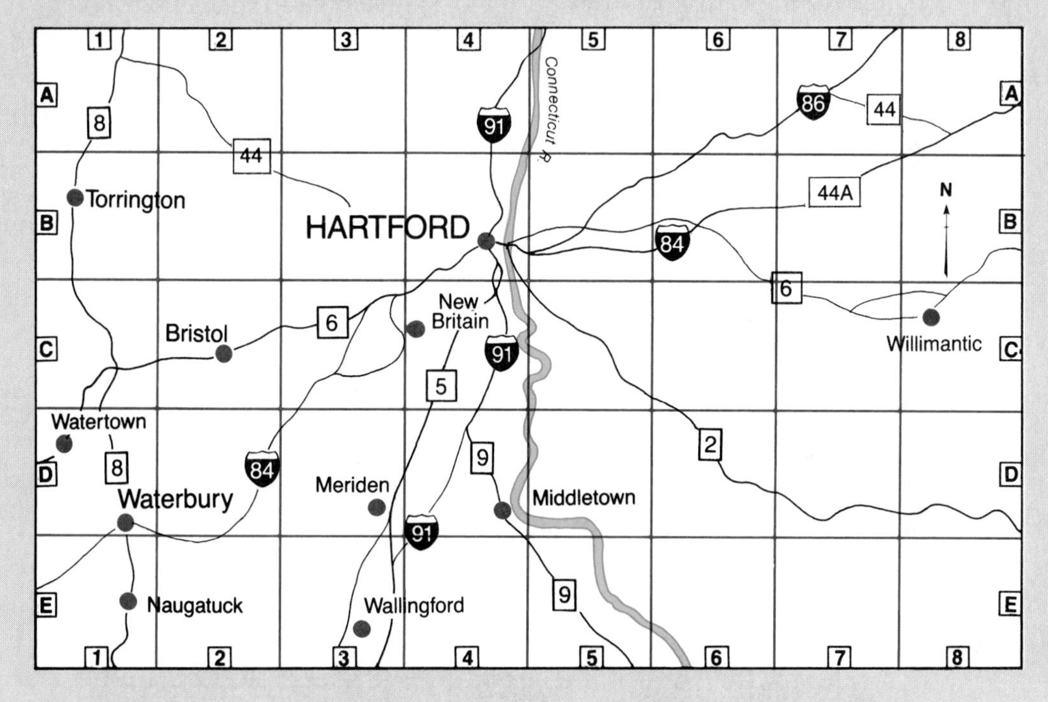

For Exercises 11–16, identify the city or cities located in each square. Refer to the map above. (Example 1)

11. E–3 Wallingford **12.** C–8 Willimantic **13.** B–4 Hartford **14.** D–1 Watertown, Waterbury **15.** D–3 Meriden **16.** B–1 Torrington

For Exercises 17–20, identify the coordinate for each city. (Example 1)

17. Middletown D–4 **18.** New Britain C–3 **19.** Watertown D–1 **20.** Bristol C–2

21. Identify the coordinates of the squares Route 6 passes through between Bristol and Hartford. C–2, C–3, C–4, B–4

22. Identify the coordinates of the squares the Connecticut River flows through on the map. A–5, A–4, B–4, C–4, C–5, D–5, D–4, E–5, E–6

Chapter Review

These exercises review the vocabulary, skills and applications presented in the chapter, as a preparation for the chapter test.

Part 1: VOCABULARY

For Exercises 1–6, choose from the box at the right the word(s) that completes each statement.

zeros
approximately equal to
factors
rounding
product
decimal points
quotient

1. When you add with decimals, you first line up the __?__. (Pages 4–5) decimal points

2. In multiplication, the numbers you multiply are called __?__. (Pages 6–7) factors

3. The answer in a multiplication problem is called the __?__. (Pages 6–7) product

4. Sometimes you have to insert __?__ in order to have the correct number of decimal places in a product. (Pages 8–9) zeros

5. The symbol $\approx$ means __?__. (Pages 18–19) approximately equal to

6. Writing $59 \approx 60$ is called __?__ to the nearest ten. (Pages 18–19) rounding

Part 2: SKILLS

Add or subtract. (Pages 2–3)

7. 36 + 42 + 59 = 137

8. 46 + 8 + 524 + 7 = 585

9. 3346 + 28 + 265 + 49 = 3688

10. 2095 + 355 + 7243 + 81 9774

11. 2886 + 43 + 8771 + 972 12,672

12. 87 + 293 + 4167 + 188 4735

13. 3939 + 17 + 243 + 118 4317

14. 871 − 240 631

15. 787 − 195 592

16. 4227 − 1355 2872

17. 4981 − 2095 2886

18. 704 − 28 676

19. 1300 − 243 1057

20. 7115 − 48 7067

21. 8140 − 837 7303

22. 549 − 126 = 423

23. 387 − 244 = 143

24. 305 − 297 = 8

25. 408 − 359 = 49

26. 5000 − 3886 = 1114

Add. (Pages 4–5)

27. 9.27 + 21.3 + 8.15 + 17.29 = 56.01

28. 1.37 + 98.28 + 46.332 + 7.1 = 153.082

29. 42.3 + 105.21 + 13.4 + 1.47 = 162.38

30. 7.25 + 11.8 + 21.93 + 4.045 45.025

31. 1.49 + 3.002 + 7.885 + 11.7 24.077

Subtract. Check each answer. (Pages 4–5)

32. 36.87 − 9.29 = 27.58

33. 8.913 − 2.47 = 6.443

34. 3.88 − 2.087 = 1.793

35. 18.88 − 0.93 = 17.95

36. 11 − 9.01 1.99

37. 4 − 1.88 2.12

38. 16.33 − 1.91 14.42

39. 8.708 − 2.42 6.288

Multiply. (Pages 6–7)

40. 42×27 1134 **41.** 87×29 2523 **42.** 362×38 13,756 **43.** 903×704 635,712 **44.** 704×609 428,736 **45.** 370×25 9250

(Pages 8–9)

46. 3.95×2.7 10.665 **47.** 86.3×0.84 72.492 **48.** 0.007×0.33 0.00231 **49.** 0.0038×0.41 0.001558 **50.** 7.29×0.4040 2.945160

Round to the nearest ten. (Pages 12–13)

51. 74 70 **52.** 87 90 **53.** 63 60 **54.** 195 200 **55.** 247 250 **56.** 842 840

Round to the nearest hundred. (Pages 12–13)

57. 735 700 **58.** 267 300 **59.** 4312 4300 **60.** 8757 8800 **61.** 9149 9100 **62.** 8074 8100

Round to the nearest thousand. (Pages 12–13)

63. 7800 8000 **64.** 7145 7000 **65.** 88,437 88,000 **66.** 39,504 40,000 **67.** 49,499 49,000

Divide. (Pages 12–13)

68. $462 \div 7$ 66 **69.** $520 \div 8$ 65 **70.** $922 \div 16$ 57 r 10 **71.** $488 \div 23$ 21 r 5

72. $43\overline{)726}$ 16 r 38 **73.** $37\overline{)1620}$ 43 r 29 **74.** $476\overline{)24{,}994}$ 52 r 242 **75.** $842\overline{)29{,}905}$ 35 r 435

(Pages 14–15)

76. $24.5 \div 7$ 3.5 **77.** $38.4 \div 6$ 6.4 **78.** $4.65 \div 5$ 0.93 **79.** $5.81 \div 7$ 0.83

80. $8\overline{)0.432}$ 0.054 **81.** $14\overline{)0.406}$ 0.029 **82.** $723\overline{)421.509}$ 0.583 **83.** $719\overline{)245.898}$ 0.342

84. $0.2\overline{)18.318}$ 91.59 **85.** $0.19\overline{)5.0692}$ 26.68 **86.** $0.318\overline{)13.674}$ 43 **87.** $0.847\overline{)82.159}$ 97

Round to the nearest whole number. (Pages 16–17)

88. 87.3 87 **89.** 9.51 10 **90.** 16.49 16 **91.** 85.91 86 **92.** 73.3 73

Divide. Round each answer to the nearest tenth. (Pages 16–17)

93. $14.62 \div 0.4$ 36.6 **94.** $22.39 \div 0.7$ 32.0 **95.** $15.78 \div 2.1$ 7.5 **96.** $28.94 \div 9.7$ 3.0

97. $7.6\overline{)39.53}$ 5.2 **98.** $18.6\overline{)77.84}$ 4.2 **99.** $2.17\overline{)13}$ 6.0 **100.** $17.53\overline{)29.1}$ 1.7

Divide. Round each answer to the nearest hundredth. (Pages 16–17)

101. $1.249 \div 0.5$ 2.50 **102.** $3.631 \div 0.8$ 4.54 **103.** $24.72 \div 3.8$ 6.51 **104.** $15.32 \div 2.2$ 6.96

105. $7.29\overline{)83.7}$ 11.48 **106.** $6.9\overline{)8.942}$ 1.30 **107.** $2.7\overline{)1.339}$ 0.50 **108.** $7.4\overline{)18.76}$ 2.54

Choose the best estimate. Choose a, b, c, or d. (Pages 18–19)

109. $82 + 571$ d **a.** 600 **b.** 670 **c.** 550 **d.** 650

110. $17.7 \div 1.9$ a **a.** 9 **b.** 8 **c.** 6 **d.** 7

111. $125 - 67$ b **a.** 50 **b.** 60 **c.** 70 **d.** 80

112. 29.8×3.1 a **a.** 90 **b.** 900 **c.** 9 **d.** 100

The word problems covered in this chapter are presented here in a mixed setting.

Part 3: APPLICATIONS

Note: each problem is referenced to the related page(s).

113. The normal annual rainfall in New Orleans, Louisiana is 56.77 inches. It is 59.8 inches in Miami, Florida. How much more does it rain in Miami? (Pages 4–5) 3.03 inches

114. In 1980, the population of Houston was 1,700,000. The population of Dallas was 914,000 the same year. What was the total population of these Texas cities? (Pages 2–3) 2,614,000

115. Find the total rainfall over a 6-month period in which 0.8 inch, 1.2 inches, 0.9 inch, 1.3 inches, 0.79 inch, and 1.23 inches of rain fell. (Pages 4–5) 6.22 inches

116. Wanda eats one bowl of oatmeal every morning for breakfast. A bowl of oatmeal contains 148 calories. How many calories is this per week? (Pages 6–7) 1036

117. A sub-compact car travels 388.8 miles on a full tank of gasoline. The tank holds 10.8 gallons. How many miles can the car travel on one gallon? (Pages 14–15) 36 miles

118. Juanita plays softball for the Speedways. In 85 times at bat she had 31 hits. Find her batting average. (Pages 16–17) 0.365

119. Chicken cutlets cost $1.29 per pound. Estimate the cost of 2.8 pounds. (Pages 18–19) b

a. $2.00 **b.** $3.90

c. $2.50 **d.** $4.50

120. How many rafters 36 inches long can be cut from a piece of lumber 216 inches long? (Pages 12–13) 6

121. A weaver has 49,970 yards of yarn. She wants to weave 19 rugs of equal size. Find the amount of yarn in each rug. (Pages 12–13) 2630 yards

122. Shelly bought 5 balls of yarn at Needleworks. Each ball cost $3.98. Estimate the total cost. (Pages 18–19) c

a. $15 **b.** $10 **c.** $20 **d.** $25

Chapter Test

The Teacher's Resource Book contains two forms of each chapter test.

Perform the indicated operations.

1.	**2.**	**3.**	**4.**	**5.**
$\begin{array}{r} 347 \\ 2063 \\ 972 \\ +\ 188 \\ \hline \end{array}$ 3570	$\begin{array}{r} 2.71 \\ 3.009 \\ 16.4 \\ +21.303 \\ \hline \end{array}$ 43.422	$\begin{array}{r} 723 \\ -219 \\ \hline \end{array}$ 504	$\begin{array}{r} 16.33 \\ -\ 2.941 \\ \hline \end{array}$ 13.389	$\begin{array}{r} 3.9 \\ \times 2.7 \\ \hline \end{array}$ 10.53

6. $11 - 2.87$ 8.13 **7.** 0.064×0.8 0.0512 **8.** $810 \div 9$ 90 **9.** $738 \div 41$ 18

10. 73×27 1971 **11.** $8\overline{)0.592}$ 0.074 **12.** $0.231\overline{)9.24}$ 40 **13.** $10.43 + 7.6 + 2.83$ 20.86

Round each number as indicated.

14. 67.5 to the nearest whole number 68

15. 88.47 to the nearest tenth 88.5

16. 49.4904 to the nearest thousandth 49.490

Choose the best estimate. Choose a, b, or c.

17. $81 + 375$ b	**a.** $80 + 370$	**b.** $80 + 380$	**c.** $90 + 380$
18. $89.8 - 31.2$ c	**a.** $80 - 30$	**b.** $90 - 40$	**c.** $90 - 30$
19. 68×31 a	**a.** 2100	**b.** 1200	**c.** 1800
20. $29.5 \div 2.7$ a	**a.** 10	**b.** 12	**c.** 8

Solve.

21. In 1980, the population of Washington, D.C. was 3,074,100. By 1990, it is expected to be 3,247,000. Find the difference. 172,900

22. In April, 0.14 inch, 1.5 inches, 0.8 inch, 1.03 inches, and 1.2 inches of rain fell. What was the total rainfall? 4.67 inches

23. Louisa is a butcher at Price Rite Market. She has 18 pounds of sirloin that she wants to cut into steaks. How many 1.5–pound steaks can she cut? 12

24. Veal costs $3.29 per pound. Estimate the cost of 4.9 pounds. b

a. $12 **b.** $15

c. $20 **d.** $24

25. An electrician needs 449.5 yards of wire to wire an apartment. Wire comes in rolls of 76 yards. How many whole rolls are needed? 6

We suggest that some or all of this page be reviewed before proceeding with the chapter.

REVIEW OF RELATED SKILLS FOR CHAPTER 2

Multiply. (Pages 6–7)

1. 46×10 460 **2.** 28×10 280 **3.** 56×100 5600 **4.** 72×1000 72,000

5. 463×10 4630 **6.** 729×100 72,900 **7.** 244×1000 244,000 **8.** 62×100 6200

9. 54×1000 54,000 **10.** 64×1000 64,000 **11.** 57×100 5700 **12.** 480×10 4800

(Pages 8–9)

13. 3.2×10 32 **14.** 4.8×100 480 **15.** 6.7×1000 6700 **16.** 0.8×10 8

17. 0.7×100 70 **18.** 0.4×1000 400 **19.** 21.2×10 212 **20.** 43.8×1000 43,800

21. 624×0.1 62.4 **22.** 382×0.1 38.2 **23.** 481×0.01 4.81 **24.** 389×0.01 3.89

25. 2546×0.001 2.546 **26.** 1381×0.001 1.381 **27.** 1462×0.001 1.462 **28.** 3648×0.01 36.48

29. 5623×0.1 562.3 **30.** 3729×0.1 372.9 **31.** 62×0.1 6.2 **32.** 75×0.1 7.5

33. 8.1×0.01 0.081 **34.** 9.7×0.01 0.097 **35.** 3.6×0.001 0.0036 **36.** 8.6×0.001 0.0086

37. 0.7×0.1 0.07 **38.** 0.6×0.01 0.006 **39.** 0.3×0.001 0.0003 **40.** 0.4×0.1 0.04

Add. (Pages 2–3, 4–5)

41. $6 + 7 + 3 + 8$ 24 **42.** $12 + 13 + 10 + 16$ 51 **43.** $21 + 42 + 24 + 38$ 125

44. $17 + 14 + 17 + 14$ 62 **45.** $29 + 18 + 29 + 18$ 94 **46.** $36 + 43 + 36 + 43$ 158

47. $4.6 + 3.9 + 7.8$ 16.3 **48.** $4.9 + 5.7 + 6.4$ 17 **49.** $8.3 + 9.2 + 7.1$ 24.6

50. $21.2 + 18.3 + 9$ 48.5 **51.** $13.8 + 16.7 + 15$ 45.5 **52.** $0.4 + 1.9 + 3$ 5.3

53. $83.6 + 47.4 + 71.2$ 202.2 **54.** $95.4 + 89.3 + 62.8$ 247.5 **55.** $46.3 + 65.9 + 83.1$ 195.3

Multiply. (Pages 6–7)

56. 14×7 98 **57.** 15×9 135 **58.** 24×36 864 **59.** 38×18 684

60. 42×16 672 **61.** 54×36 1944 **62.** 28×41 1148 **63.** 75×12 900

64. 21×13 273 **65.** 42×37 1554 **66.** 18×19 342 **67.** 35×20 700

68. $3 \times 4 \times 9$ 108 **69.** $8 \times 6 \times 7$ 336 **70.** $5 \times 3 \times 8$ 120 **71.** $6 \times 4 \times 7$ 168

72. $38 \times 23 \times 6$ 5244 **73.** $53 \times 17 \times 9$ 8109 **74.** $72 \times 16 \times 10$ 11,520 **75.** $34 \times 26 \times 18$ 15,912

(Pages 8–9)

76. 2.8×3.4 9.52 **77.** 7.9×8.1 63.99 **78.** 1.6×3.4 5.44

79. 21.3×14.8 315.24 **80.** 16.2×18.1 293.22 **81.** 25.2×36.3 914.76

82. $47.8 \times 19.2 \times 2$ 1835.52 **83.** $8.3 \times 5.9 \times 4.6$ 225.262 **84.** $7.2 \times 3.1 \times 1.6$ 35.712

85. $9.1 \times 7.5 \times 4.7$ 320.775 **86.** $6.3 \times 5.8 \times 4.2$ 153.468 **87.** $3.6 \times 0.4 \times 1.8$ 2.592

88. $15.3 \times 14.1 \times 7.2$ 1553.256 **89.** $18.9 \times 14.6 \times 10.1$ 2786.994 **90.** $15.4 \times 13.7 \times 12.9$ 2721.642

CHAPTER

2 APPLYING METRIC MEASURES

ESSENTIAL SKILLS/APPLICATIONS

CAREER APPLICATION

Electrician

2-1 Metric Units of Length

See the Teacher's Manual for the objectives.

This table shows the most commonly used units of length in the metric system.

One **millimeter** (abbreviated: **mm**) is about the thickness of a dime.

One **centimeter** (abbreviated: **cm**) is about the width of this paper clip.

One **meter** (abbreviated: **m**) is about the width of a door.

One **kilometer** (abbreviated: **km**) is about the length of ten football fields.

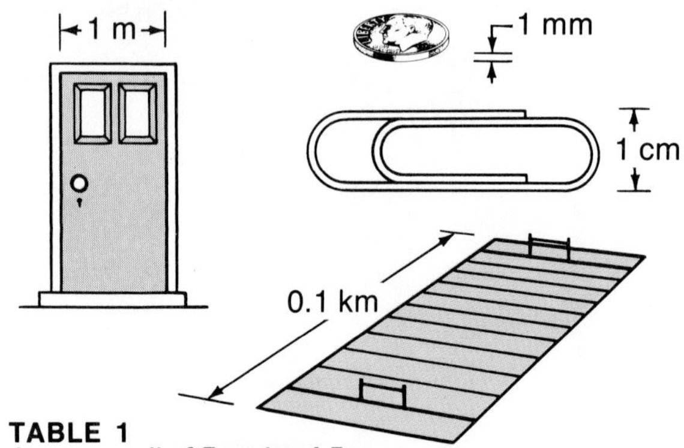

TABLE 1

After studying Table 1, you may wish to have students do some or all of Exercises 1-5.

The meter is the base unit of length. The table below shows how some of the other units are related to the meter.

TABLE 2

Units of Length	*Prefix*	*Meaning*
1 millimeter (mm) = 0.001 meter (m)	milli-	$\frac{1}{1000}$, or 0.001
1 centimeter (cm) = 0.01 meter	centi-	$\frac{1}{100}$, or 0.01
1 decimeter (dm) = 0.1 meter	deci-	$\frac{1}{10}$, or 0.1
1 dekameter (dam) = 10 meters	deka-	10
1 hectometer (hm) = 100 meters	hecto-	100
1 kilometer (km) = 1000 meters	kilo-	1000

You can use Table 2 to help change units of length.

PROCEDURE To change to a smaller metric unit, multiply by 10, by 100, or by 1000, and so on.

To change to a larger metric unit, multiply by 0.1, by 0.01, or by 0.001, and so on.

EXAMPLE

a. 5 km = __?__ m

b. 42 mm = __?__ cm

c. 6 m = __?__ cm

d. 640 cm = __?__ m

Solutions:

Larger to smaller

a. 5 km = (5 × 1000) m
= **5000 m**

c. 6 m = (6 × 100) cm
= **600 cm**

Smaller to larger

b. 42 mm = (42 × 0.1) cm
= **4.2 cm**

d. 640 cm = (640 × 0.01) m
= **6.4 m**

EXERCISES

Choose the most suitable measure. Choose a, b, or c. (Table 1)

1. The width of a nickel b — **a.** 20 cm **b.** 20 mm **c.** 20 m
2. The length of a pencil a — **a.** 18 cm **b.** 18 km **c.** 18 m
3. The length of a key c — **a.** 5.1 mm **b.** 5.1 m **c.** 5.1 cm
4. The distance from Miami to Baltimore a — **a.** 1544 km **b.** 1544 m **c.** 1544 cm
5. The height of a desk b — **a.** 1 km **b.** 1 m **c.** 1 mm

For Exercises 6–10, complete the table. Check the number by which to multiply. The first one is done for you. (Example)

	From	To	Multiply by 0.1	0.01	0.001	10	100	1000
6.	meters	centimeters					✓	
7.	meters	millimeters						✓
8.	meters	kilometers			✓			
9.	kilometers	meters						✓
10.	millimeters	centimeters	✓					

Choose the equivalent measure. Choose a, b, c, or d. (Example)

11. 15 meters a — **a.** 1500 cm **b.** 150 cm **c.** 1.5 cm **d.** 0.15 cm
12. 20 kilometers c — **a.** 200 m **b.** 2000 m **c.** 20,000 m **d.** 2 m
13. 54 centimeters b — **a.** 5.4 m **b.** 0.54 m **c.** 540 m **d.** 5400 m
14. 6.8 centimeters d — **a.** 6800 mm **b.** 680 mm **c.** 0.68 mm **d.** 68 mm
15. 724 meters c — **a.** 72.4 km **b.** 7.24 km **c.** 0.724 km **d.** 7240 km

Complete. (Example)

16. 65 m = ___?___ cm 6500
17. 346 mm = ___?___ m 0.346
18. 6.7 km = ___?___ m 6700
19. 12.2 cm = ___?___ m 0.122
20. 289 m = ___?___ km 0.289
21. 5m = ___?___ cm 500
22. 1.6 m = ___?___ mm 1600
23. 64 m = ___?___ km 0.064
24. 26 mm = ___?___ m 0.026
25. 28 m = ___?___ mm 28,000
26. 629 cm = ___?___ m 6.29
27. 31 km = ___?___ m 31,000

These word problems apply the skills taught in the lesson.

APPLICATIONS: Using Metric Length

28. A steel bar is 6.06 meters long. How many centimeters long is the bar? 606 cm
29. The length of a picture frame is 320 millimeters. How many centimeters is this? 32 cm
30. The length of a plank is 3.2 meters. How many millimeters is this? 3200 mm
31. A shelf is 241 centimeters long. How many meters is this? 2.41 m

2-2 Perimeter

See the Teacher's Manual for the objectives.

The **perimeter** of a figure is the distance around it.

PROCEDURE To find the perimeter of a figure, add the lengths of its sides.

EXAMPLE 1 Find the perimeter of each figure.

a. Triangle

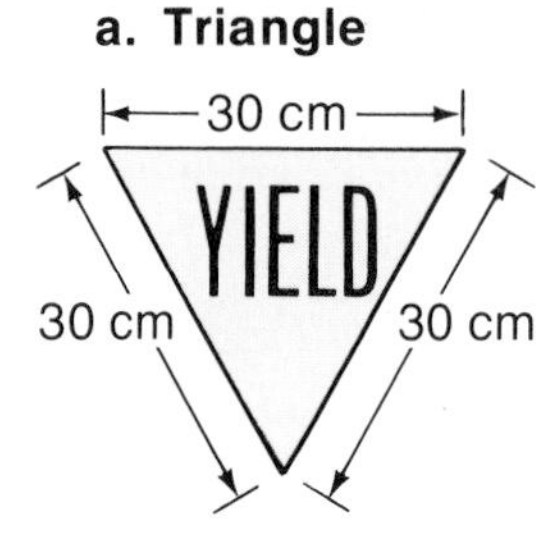

b. Rectangle

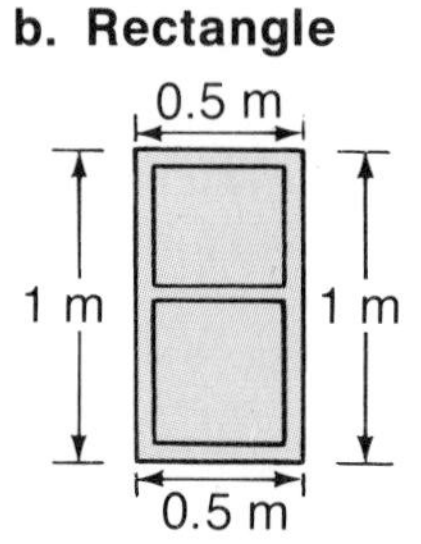

c. Octagon

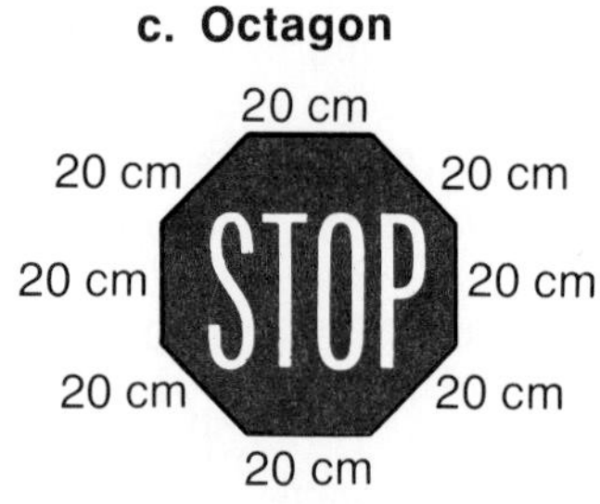

Solutions:

a. $P = 30 + 30 + 30$

$P =$ **90 centimeters**

b. $P = 0.5 + 1 + 0.5 + 1$

$P =$ **3 meters**

c. $P = 20 + 20 + 20 + 20 + 20 + 20 + 20 + 20$

$P =$ **160 centimeters**

After completing Example 1, you may wish to have students do some or all of Exercises 1-3.

You can use a **formula** to find the perimeter of a rectangle.

The opposite sides of a **rectangle** *are equal in length.*

$$P = 2(l + w)$$

***P* = perimeter**
***l* = length**
***w* = width**

EXAMPLE 2 An envelope is 24 centimeters long and 10.5 centimeters wide. Find the perimeter.

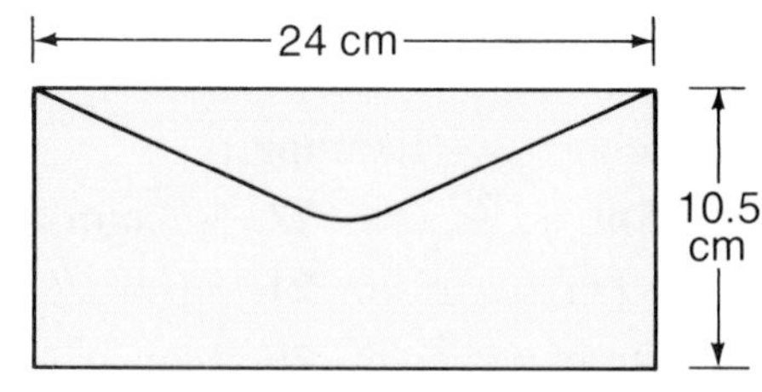

Solution: $P = 2(l + w)$ ***l* = 24 cm, *w* = 10.5 cm**

$P = 2(24 + 10.5)$

$P = 2(34.5)$

$P = \mathbf{69}$

The perimeter is **69 centimeters.**

The sides of a **square** *have equal lengths.*

To find the perimeter of a square, you use the formula

$$P = 4 \times s$$

where s represents the length of a side.

EXERCISES

Find the perimeter of each figure. (Example 1)

1. Postage Stamp 8.8 cm

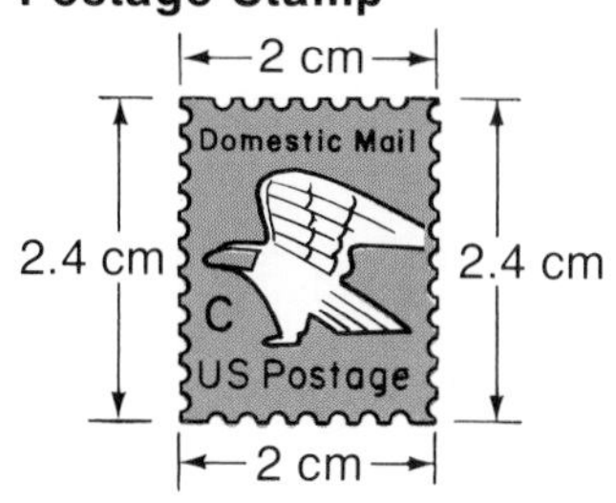

2. Garden 64.8 m

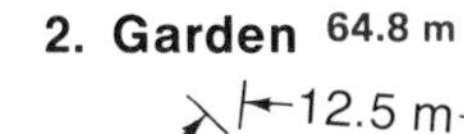
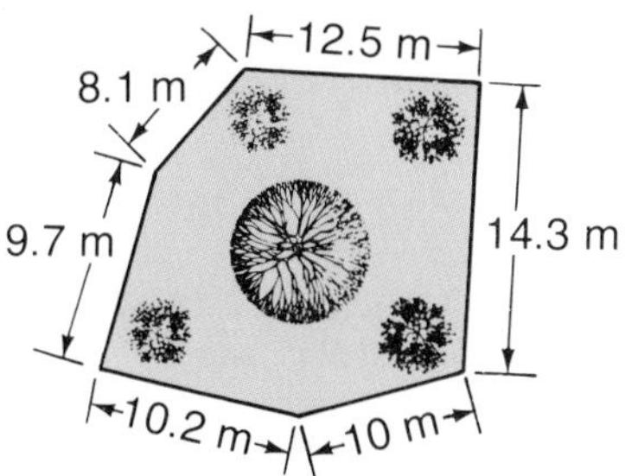

Hexagon: 6 sides

3. Pendant 95 mm

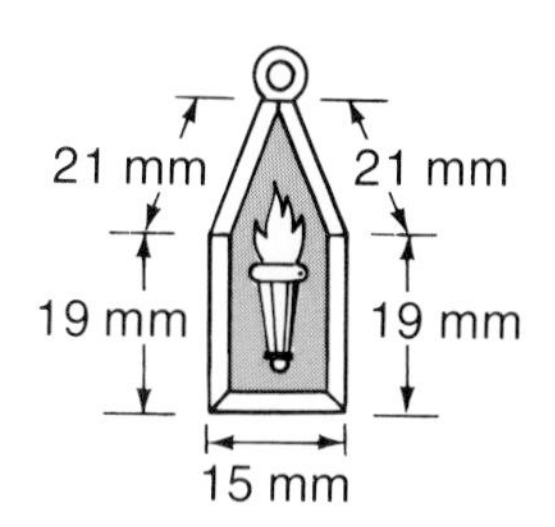

Pentagon: 5 sides

Use the formula $P = 4 \times s$ or $P = 2(l + w)$ to find the perimeter of each figure in Exercises 4–12. (Example 2)

4. Picture Frame 116 cm

5. Desk Top 4.0 m

6. Sheet of Paper 50 cm

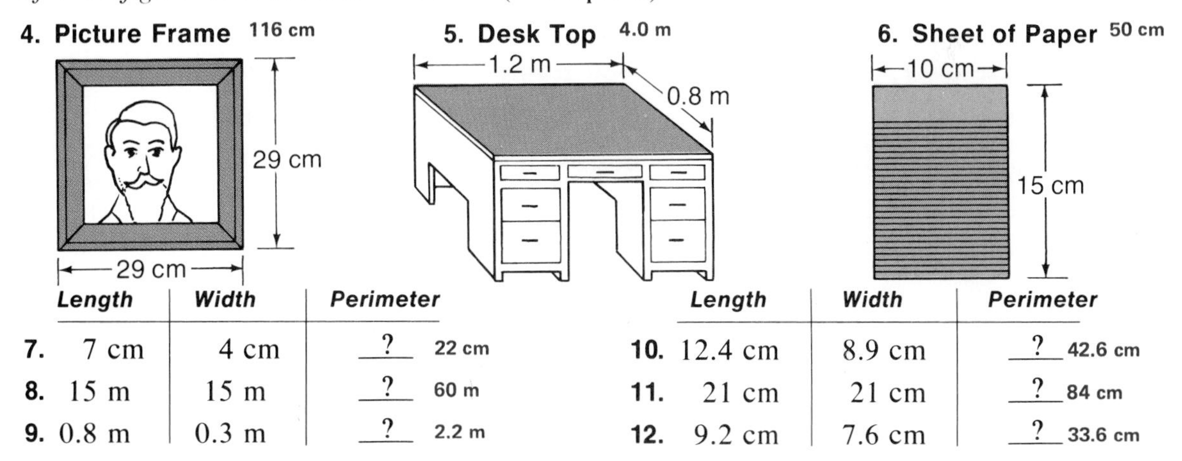

	Length	Width	Perimeter
7.	7 cm	4 cm	? 22 cm
8.	15 m	15 m	? 60 m
9.	0.8 m	0.3 m	? 2.2 m
10.	12.4 cm	8.9 cm	? 42.6 cm
11.	21 cm	21 cm	? 84 cm
12.	9.2 cm	7.6 cm	? 33.6 cm

APPLICATIONS: Using Perimeter These word problems apply the skills taught in the lesson.

For Exercises 13–18, first draw a rectangle or a square. Use the information in the problem to label the lengths of the sides. Then solve the problem.

13. A football field has a rectangular shape. It is 110 meters long and 49 meters wide. Find the perimeter of the field. 318 m

14. The goal area on a soccer field is a rectangle. It is 18 meters long and 5.5 meters wide. Find its perimeter. 47 m

15. A tablecloth is in the shape of a square. Each side is 2.3 meters long. What is its perimeter? 9.2 m

16. A rectangular yard is 16.7 meters long and 10 meters wide. Find its perimeter. 53.4 m

17. A rectangular billboard is 3.2 meters wide and 5.4 meters high. What is its perimeter? 17.2 m

18. A bookcase shelf is a rectangle. It is 0.26 meters wide and 0.86 meters long. Find its perimeter. 2.24 m

2-3 Metric Units of Mass

See the Teacher's Manual for the objectives.

The **kilogram** is the base unit of mass in the metric system. (Strictly speaking, *mass* is not equivalent to *weight*. However, in everyday use, the difference is usually ignored.)

The table below shows the most commonly used units of mass.

TABLE The mass of the wing of a bee is about 1 milligram (abbreviated: **mg**).

The mass of a paper clip is about 1 gram (abbreviated: **g**).

The mass of a pair of shoes (adult size) is about 1 kilogram (abbreviated: **kg**).

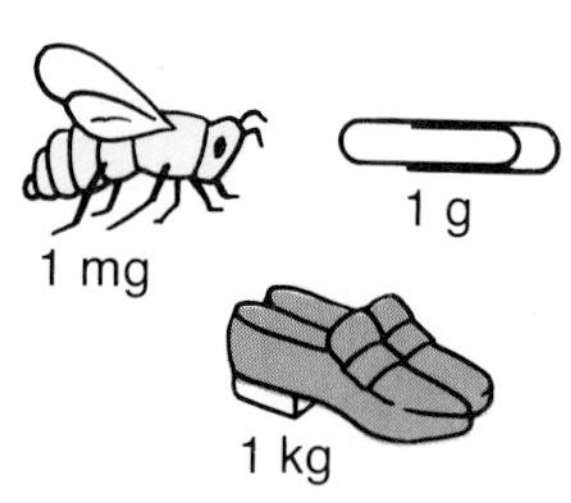

After studying the table, you may wish to have students do some or all of Exercises 1-12.

The following relationships are useful in changing units.

1 kilogram = 1000 grams **1 gram = 1000 milligrams**

PROCEDURE To change from kilograms to grams, multiply by 1000.
To change from grams to kilograms, multiply by 0.001.

To change from grams to milligrams, multiply by 1000.
To change from milligrams to grams, multiply by 0.001.

EXAMPLE

a. 62 kg = __?__ g **b.** 3700 g = __?__ kg

c. 32.7 g = __?__ mg **d.** 540 mg = __?__ g

Solutions:

Larger to smaller

a. 62 kg = (62 × 1000) g
= **62,000 g**

c. 32.7 g = (32.7 × 1000) mg
= **32,700 mg**

Smaller to larger

b. 3700 g = (3700 × 0.001) kg
= **3.7 kg**

d. 540 mg = (540 × 0.001) g
= **0.54 g**

EXERCISES

Choose the most suitable unit. Choose a, b, or c. (Table)

1. A slice of bread b — **a.** kilogram **b.** gram **c.** milligram
2. A paper clip b — **a.** kilogram **b.** gram **c.** milligram
3. A basketball a — **a.** kilogram **b.** gram **c.** milligram
4. A person a — **a.** kilogram **b.** gram **c.** milligram

Choose the most suitable measure. Choose a, b, or c. (Table)

5. Drop of water a

a. 200 mg
b. 200 g
c. 200 kg

6. Baseball b

a. 142 mg
b. 142 g
c. 142 kg

7. Book a

a. 980 g
b. 98 mg
c. 98 kg

8. Potted Plant c

a. 2 mg
b. 2 g
c. 2 kg

9. Pencil a

a. 3 g
b. 3 kg
c. 30 kg

10. Desk c

a. 40 mg
b. 40 g
c. 40 kg

11. Telephone a

a. 2 kg
b. 20 kg
c. 200 kg

12. Dime a

a. 2 g
b. 2 mg
c. 2 kg

Complete. (Example)

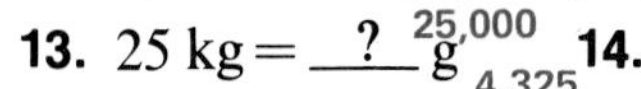

13. 25 kg = __?__ g 25,000
14. 363 kg = __?__ g 363,000
15. 4.2 kg = __?__ g 4200
16. 0.3 kg = __?__ g 300
17. 4325 g = __?__ kg 4.325
18. 264 g = __?__ kg 0.264
19. 3.8 g = __?__ kg 0.0038
20. 0.4 g = __?__ kg 0.0004
21. 25 g = __?__ mg 25,000
22. 6 g = __?__ mg 6000
23. 21.8 g = __?__ mg 21,800
24. 7.6 g = __?__ mg 7600
25. 6421 mg = __?__ g 6.421
26. 86 mg = __?__ g 0.086
27. 4.81 mg = __?__ g 0.00481
28. 0.7 mg = __?__ g 0.0007
29. 25 g = __?__ kg 0.025
30. 28 kg = __?__ g 28,000
31. 67.5 mg = __?__ g 0.0675
32. 2.21 g = __?__ mg 2210
33. 35 g = __?__ mg 35,000
34. 2130 g = __?__ kg 2.130
35. 0.16 kg = __?__ g 160
36. 46.2 mg = __?__ g 0.0462

APPLICATIONS: Using Units of Mass

These word problems apply the skills taught in the lesson.

37. A certain four-engine jet carries 259 passengers. An average person has a mass of 68 kilograms. Find the total mass of the passengers on the plane. 17,612 kg

38. An elevator can carry a total mass of 1088 kilograms. An average person has a mass of 68 kilograms. How many persons can the elevator hold? 16

39. A plane carrying 198 passengers has a maximum takeoff mass of 131,940 kilograms. Suppose that each passenger has a mass of 68 kilograms. What is the difference between the maximum takeoff mass and the total mass of the people? 118,476 kg

40. A tablespoon of whole, shelled almonds contains 0.42 milligram of iron, 1.6 milligrams of protein, and 21 milligrams of calcium. Find the total mass of iron, protein, and calcium in 1 cup (16 tablespoons) of whole, shelled almonds. 368.32 mg

2-4 Metric Units of Capacity

See the Teacher's Manual for the objectives.

The amount a container will hold is called **capacity.** In the metric system, the most commonly used units of capacity are the **milliliter** (abbreviated: mL) and the **liter** (abbreviated: L).

TABLE An eyedropper holds about 1 milliliter of liquid.

A milk carton (one–quart size) contains a little less than 1 liter.

You use this relationship to change liters to milliliters and milliliters to liters.

1000 milliliters = 1 liter

After studying the table, you may wish to have students do some or all of Exercises 1-18.

PROCEDURE To change from liters to milliliters, multiply by 1000.

To change from milliliters to liters, multiply by 0.001.

EXAMPLE **a.** 5 L = _?_ mL **b.** 13.7 mL = _?_ L

Solutions:

Larger to smaller

a. 5 L = (5 × 1000) mL
= **5000 mL**

Smaller to larger

b. 13.7 mL = (13.7 × 0.001) L
= **0.0137 L**

EXERCISES

For Exercises 1–10, choose the most suitable measure. Choose a or b. (Table)

1. A spoonful of vanilla a — **a.** milliliter **b.** liter
2. A tea pot b — **a.** milliliter **b.** liter
3. A casserole bowl b — **a.** milliliter **b.** liter
4. A small jar of mustard a — **a.** milliliter **b.** liter
5. A large pitcher of milk b — **a.** milliliter **b.** liter
6. A glass of orange juice a — **a.** milliliter **b.** liter
7. A cup of tea a — **a.** milliliter **b.** liter
8. A spoonful of vinegar a — **a.** milliliter **b.** liter
9. A large bottle of fruit juice b — **a.** milliliter **b.** liter
10. A large can of paint b — **a.** milliliter **b.** liter

Choose the most suitable measure. Choose a, b, or c. (Table)

11. Glass of milk b

a. 240 L
b. 240 mL
c. 2.4 L

12. Flower Vase a

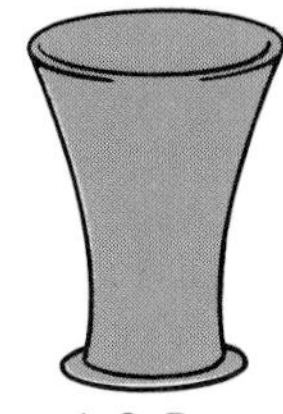

a. 1.2 L
b. 1.2 mL
c. 12 mL

13. Soup Bowl b

a. 4 L
b. 400 mL
c. 400 L

14. Can of juice b

a. 10 L
b. 1 L
c. 10 mL

15. Coffee pot c

a. 25 mL
b. 2.5 mL
c. 2.5 L

16. Swimming Pool a

a. 75,000 L
b. 75 L
c. 75 mL

17. Stew Pot a

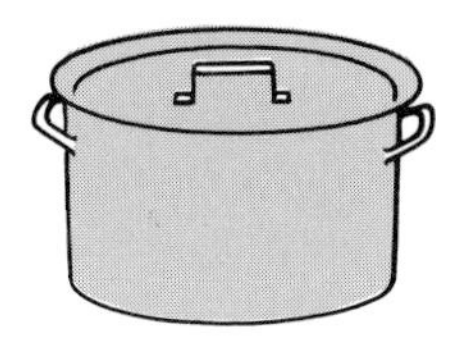

a. 6 L
b. 6 mL
c. 600 mL

18. Can of oil b

a. 100 L
b. 1 L
c. 1 mL

Complete. (Example)

19. 37 L = ? mL 37,000
20. 47 L = ? mL 47,000
21. 321 L = ? mL 321,000
22. 229 L = ? mL 229,000
23. 3.4 L = ? mL 3400
24. 5.8 L = ? mL 5800
25. 22.3 L = ? mL 22,300
26. 36.8 L = ? mL 36,800
27. 2478 mL = ? L 2.478
28. 3829 mL = ? L 3.829
29. 386 mL = ? L 0.386
30. 792 mL = ? L 0.792
31. 22 mL = ? L 0.022
32. 16 mL = ? L 0.016
33. 5 mL = ? L 0.005
34. 3 mL = ? L 0.003
35. 6.8 mL = ? L 0.0068
36. 7.2 mL = ? L 0.0072
37. 0.8 L = ? mL 800
38. 0.2 L = ? mL 200
39. 0.04 L = ? mL 40
40. 0.005 L = ? mL 5
41. 21 mL = ? L 0.021
42. 300 mL = ? L 0.3

These word problems apply the skills taught in the lesson.

APPLICATIONS: Using Units of Capacity

43. One teaspoon contains 5 milliliters. How many teaspoons are in a bottle containing 0.35 liter? 70

44. One tablespoon contains 15 milliliters. How many tablespoons can be poured from a bottle of medicine containing 0.45 liter? 30

45. A drinking glass contains 250 milliliters. How many glasses can be poured from a 1-liter container of milk? 4

46. Pharmacists use a *minim* glass to measure liquids. A **minim** is about the size of a drop. One milliliter contains 15 minims. How many minims are in 2.6 milliliters? 39

A Minim Glass

2-5 Area and Volume

See the Teacher's Manual for the objectives.

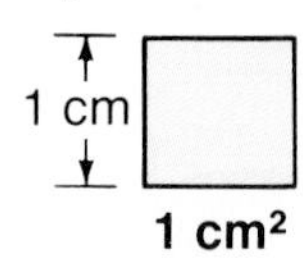

Each side of this square is 1 centimeter long. Its area is 1×1, or 1 **square centimeter** (abbreviated: 1 cm²).

Area is measured in **square units.** You can use a formula to find the area of some figures.

PROCEDURE To find the area of a rectangle multiply the length and the width.

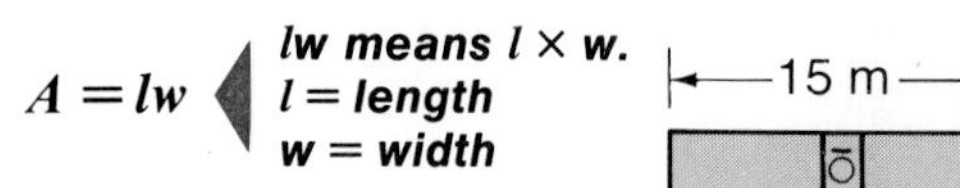

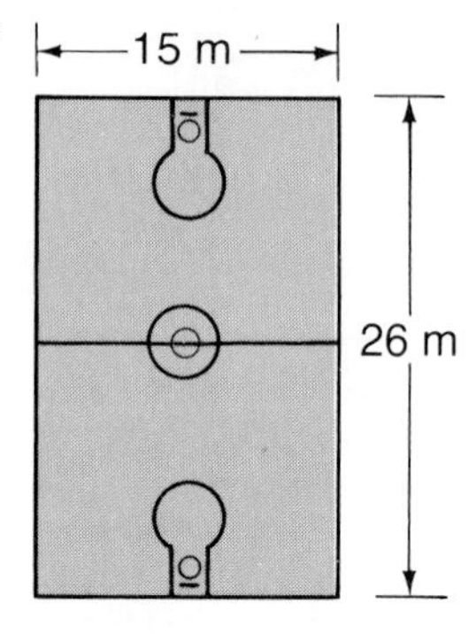

EXAMPLE 1 A basketball court is 26 meters long and 15 meters wide. Find the area of the court.

Solution: $A = lw$ ◀ *l = 26 m, w = 15 m*

$A = 26 \times 15$

$A = \mathbf{390}$ The area is **390 m²**.

After completing Example 1, you may wish to have students do some or all of Exercises 1-3.

A **rectangular prism** is a solid such as the filing cabinet at the right. The **volume** of a rectangular prism is the amount of space it contains. Volume is measured in **cubic units.**

PROCEDURE To find the volume of a rectangular prism, find the product of the length, width, and height.

$V = lwh$ ◀ *lwh means $l \times w \times h$.*

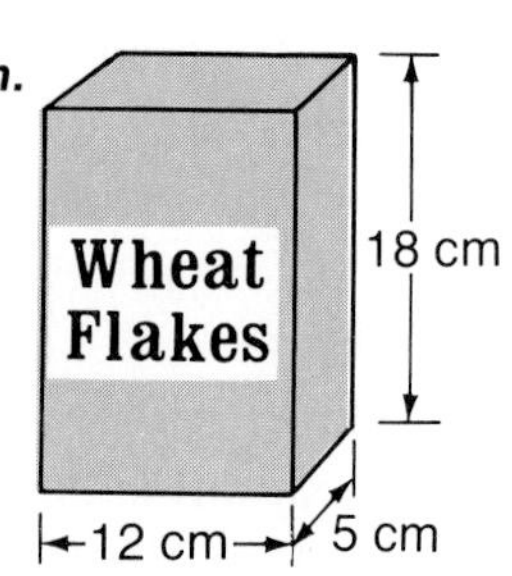

EXAMPLE 2 Find the volume of this box of cereal.

Solution: $V = lwh$ ◀ *l = 12 cm; w = 5 cm; h = 18 cm*

$V = 12 \times 5 \times 18$

$V = \mathbf{1080}$ The volume is **1080 cm³**.

EXERCISES

For Exercises 1–7, find the area of each rectangle. (Example 1)

1. Check 10,500 mm²

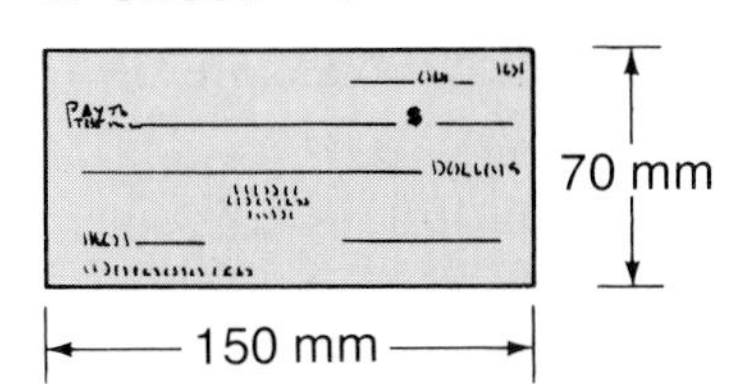

2. Photograph 500 cm² **3. Rug** 17.64 m²

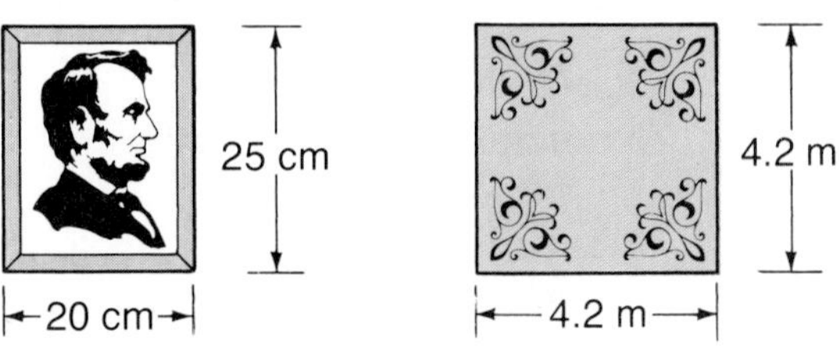

	Length	Width	Area	
4.	14 cm	8 cm	?	112 cm²
5.	3 m	1.5 m	?	4.5 m²

	Length	Width	Area	
6.	25 mm	18 mm	?	450 mm²
7.	1.2 m	1.2 m	?	1.44 m²

For Exercises 8–14, find the volume of each rectangular prism. (Example 2)

8. Briefcase 11,020 cm³ **9. Trunk** 0.63 m³ **10. Shoe Box** 6480 cm³

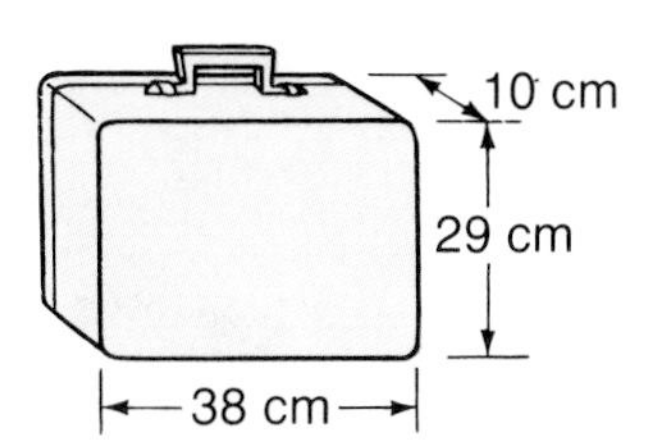

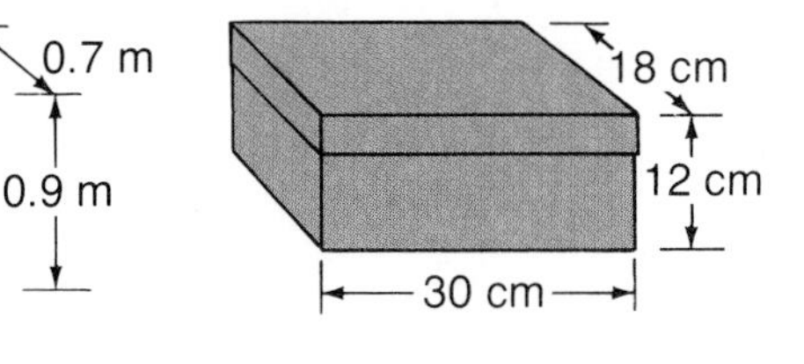

	Length	Width	Height	
11.	6 m	4 m	10 m	240 m³
12.	21 cm	15 cm	5 cm	1575 cm³

	Length	Width	Height	
13.	2.4 m	1.8 m	6.3 m	27.216 m³
14.	12 cm	12 cm	12 cm	1728 cm³

APPLICATIONS: Using Area and Volume

These word problems apply the skills taught in the lesson.

15. A movie screen is 125 centimeters long and 100 centimeters wide. Find its area. 12,500 cm²

16. A rectangular curtain is 1.5 meters long and 1.2 meters wide. Find its area. 1.8 m²

17. Each base of the two towers in New York City's World Trade Center is a square. Each base measures 62.7 meters on a side. Find the area of one base. 3931.29 m²

18. A storage cabinet is 1.6 meters long, 0.9 meters wide and 2.1 meters high. Find its volume. 3.024 m³

19. A jewelry box is 24 centimeters long, 8 centimeters wide and 5 centimeters high. Find its volume. 960 cm³

New York City's World Trade Center

2-6 Temperature

See the Teacher's Manual for the objectives.

In the metric system, the **Celsius** thermometer is used to measure temperature.

It may be helpful to memorize the temperatures and the information in the following table.

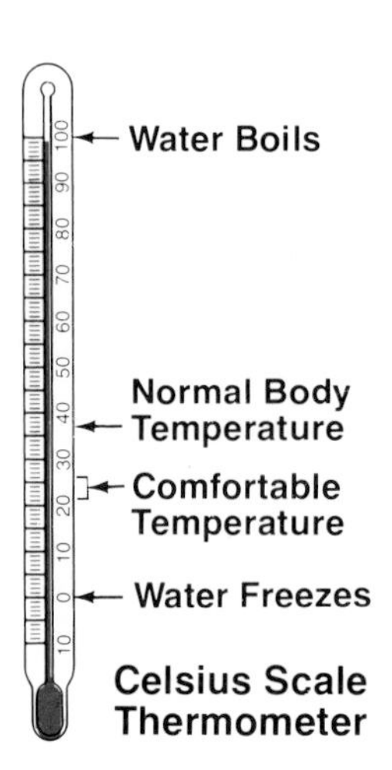

Celsius Scale Thermometer

Temperature	Meaning
100°C	Water boils
37°C	Normal body temperature
35°C	Hot summer day
22°C–26°C	Comfortable room temperature
0°C	Water freezes

PROCEDURE To determine a suitable temperature, compare with the temperatures above.

EXERCISES

Choose the most suitable temperature. Choose a, b, or c.

		a.	b.	c.
1.	The temperature of a hot cup of soup c	**a.** 10°C	**b.** 25°C	**c.** 75°C
2.	The temperature of a cool fall day b	**a.** 0°C	**b.** 11°C	**c.** 40°C
3.	The temperature of a glass of ice water a	**a.** 0°C	**b.** 10°C	**c.** 20°C
4.	The temperature of a comfortable room a	**a.** 21°C	**b.** 31°C	**c.** 41°C
5.	The temperature of a person with a fever b	**a.** 25°C	**b.** 38°C	**c.** 45°C
6.	The temperature of a cold winter day a	**a.** 4°C	**b.** 14°C	**c.** 24°C
7.	The temperature of a warm summer day b	**a.** 5°C	**b.** 28°C	**c.** 43°C
8.	The temperature of a cold glass of milk a	**a.** 3°C	**b.** 10°C	**c.** 20°C
9.	The temperature for sunbathing b	**a.** 0°C	**b.** 30°C	**c.** 50°C
10.	The temperature of a snowball a	**a.** 1°C	**b.** 10°C	**c.** 20°C

11. The outdoor temperature is 2°C. Is this warm enough for you to go sunbathing? No

12. The outdoor temperature is 30°C. Would you go to the beach or to a ski resort? beach

13. The room temperature is 15°C. Would you turn the air conditioning on or turn the heat on? the heat

14. The room temperature is 30°C. Would you need to wear a woolen sweater? No

ELECTRICIAN

career

Career lessons are optional.
This lesson applies the skills of using a formula and multiplication of decimals.

The **watt, volt,** and **ampere** are units of electrical measure in the metric system. These are common terms to Beth Gomez, an **electrician.**

When Beth plans the wiring for a house, she uses the following formula, which relates the number of watts (the amount of electrical power) and the area of the space being wired.

$W = 32.3 \times A$ ◀ *W = power in watts*
A = floor area in square meters

EXAMPLE Beth is wiring a house with a floor area of 139.35 square meters. Find the number of watts needed. Round each answer to the nearest hundred watts.

Solution: $W = 32.3 \times A$ ◀ $A = 139.35$

$W = 32.3 \times 139.35$ ◀ *Use paper and pencil or use a calculator.*

 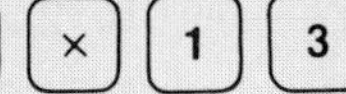   3 5 = 4501.005

The house requires **4500 watts.**

Note that Exercises 1–6 are non-verbal.

For Exercises 1–10, find the number of watts needed for the given area. Round each answer to the nearest hundred watts.

1. 125 square meters 4000
2. 42.6 square meters 1400
3. 8.75 square meters 300
4. 150 square meters 4800
5. 206.24 square meters 6700
6. 145.78 square meters 4700
7. Dan is wiring a house with a floor area of 200 square meters. 6500
8. Anna is wiring a building with a floor area of 208 square meters. 6700
9. Peg is wiring a building with a floor area of 142.25 square meters. 4600
10. Masahiro is wiring a building with a floor area of 420.8 square meters. 13,600

Chapter Review

These exercises review the vocabulary, skills and applications presented in the chapter as a preparation for the chapter test.

Part 1: VOCABULARY

For Exercises 1–8, choose from the box at the right the word(s) or number(s) that completes each statement.

100
capacity
perimeter
1000
length
liter
mass
volume
Celsius
area

1. The meter is the base unit of __?__ length in the metric system. (Pages 28–29)
2. The distance around a figure is called its __?__ perimeter. (Pages 30–31)
3. The kilogram is the base unit of __?__ mass in the metric system. (Pages 32–33)
4. One kilogram is the same as __?__ 1000 grams. (Pages 32–33)
5. The amount a container will hold is called its __?__ capacity. (Pages 34–35)
6. A common unit of capacity is the __?__ liter. (Pages 34–35)
7. A cubic centimeter is a unit of __?__ volume in the metric system. (Pages 36–37)
8. The thermometer used in the metric system is the __?__ Celsius thermometer. (Page 38)

Part 2: SKILLS

Choose the most suitable measure. Choose a, b, or c. (Pages 28–29)

9. The length of a postage stamp b — **a.** 3 mm **b.** 3 cm **c.** 3 m
10. The length of a door b — **a.** 2.6 cm **b.** 2.6 m **c.** 2.6 km
11. The length of a bicycle c — **a.** 1.2 mm **b.** 1.2 cm **c.** 1.2 m

Complete. (Pages 28–29)

12. 7 km = __?__ m 7000
13. 430 m = __?__ km 0.43
14. 23 cm = __?__ m 0.23
15. 5 m = __?__ mm 5000
16. 8.7 cm = __?__ mm 87
17. 423 mm = __?__ m 0.423

Find the perimeter of each figure. (Pages 30–31)

18. Pennant 106 cm

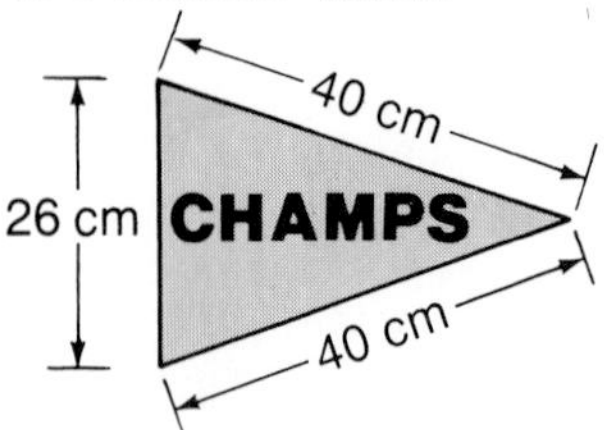

19. Rug 12 m

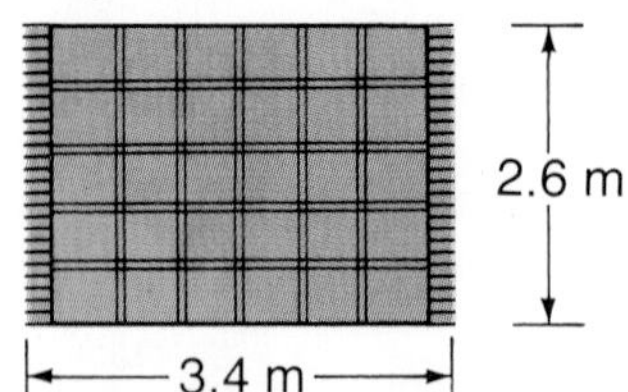

20. Wall Safe 70.4 cm

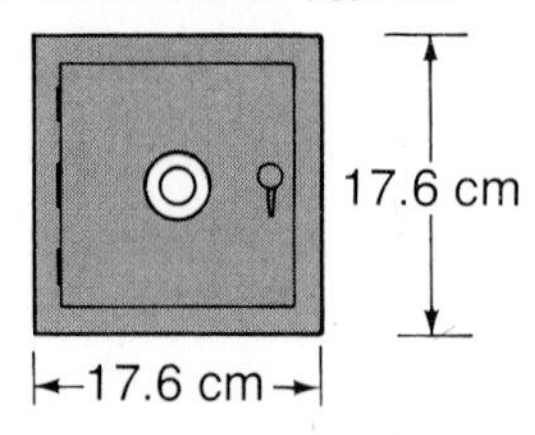

Choose the most suitable measure. Choose a, b, or c. (Pages 32–33)

21. Raisin a — **a.** 1 g **b.** 1 kg **c.** 1 mg
22. Common pin a — **a.** 380 mg **b.** 380 g **c.** 380 kg
23. Automobile c — **a.** 1000 mg **b.** 1000 g **c.** 1000 kg

Complete. (Pages 32–33)

24. 12 kg = ? g 12,000 **25.** 5212 g = ? kg 5.212 **26.** 25.4 g = ? mg 25,400

27. 43 mg = ? g 0.043 **28.** 729 mg = ? g 0.729 **29.** 14 kg = ? g 14,000

Choose the most suitable measure. Choose a, b, or c.
(Pages 34–35)

30. Tube of toothpaste b **a.** 150 mL **b.** 15 mL **c.** 1 L

31. Mug of soup a **a.** 150 mL **b.** 1.5 L **c.** 1.5 mL

32. Barrel of oil a **a.** 400 L **b.** 400 mL **c.** 4000 mL

Complete. (Pages 34–35)

33. 120 mL = ? L 0.120 **34.** 742 mL = ? L 0.742 **35.** 15 L = ? mL 15,000

36. 72 L = ? mL 72,000 **37.** 19.2 mL = ? L 0.0192 **38.** 4.2 L = ? mL 4200

In Exercises 39–47, find the area of each rectangle.
(Pages 36–37)

39. Poster 0.19 m^2 **40. Calendar Page** 816 cm^2 **41. Newspaper** 910 cm^2

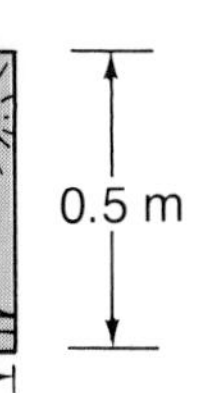

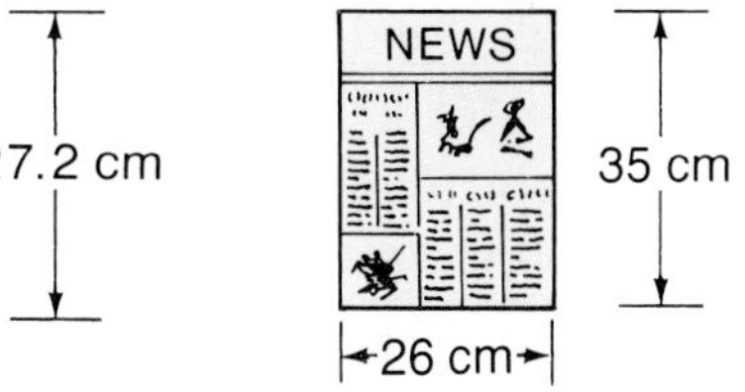

	Length	Width	Area
42.	5 m	3 m	? 15 m^2
43.	10 cm	8 cm	? 80 cm^2
44.	6.7 m	2.4 m	? 16.08 m^2

	Length	Width	Area
45.	36 mm	18 mm	? 648 mm^2
46.	10 m	10 m	? 100 m^2
47.	22.3 cm	20.4 cm	? 454.92 cm^2

In Exercises 48–56, find the volume of each rectangular prism. (Pages 36–37)

48. Suitcase 29,280 cm^3 **49. Match Box** 30 cm^3 **50. Paper Weight** 39,600 mm^3

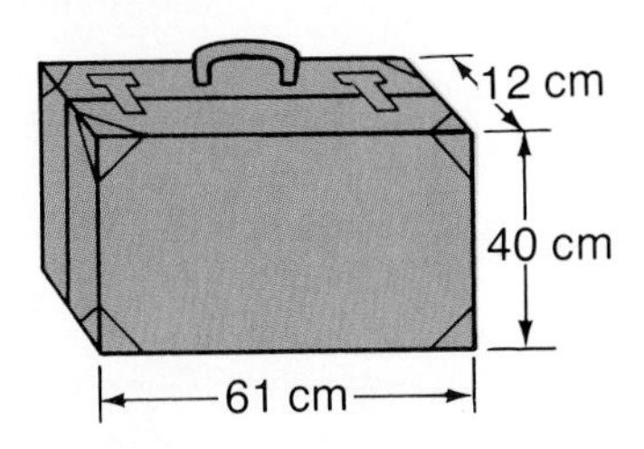

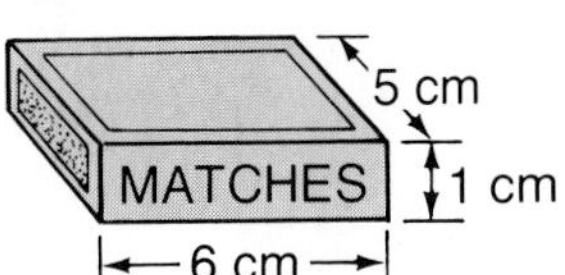

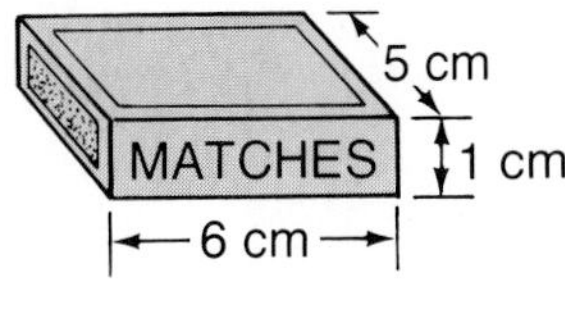

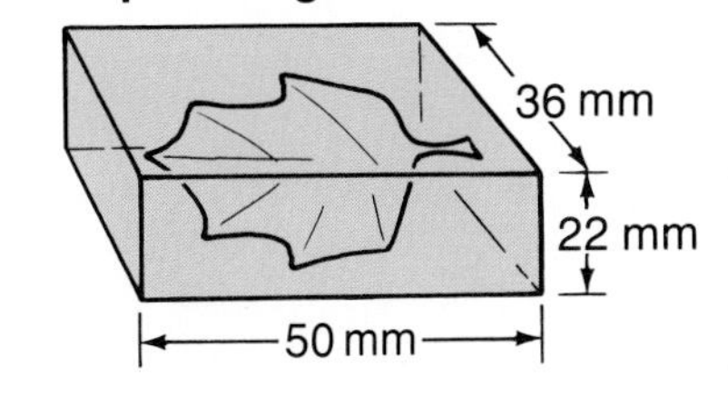

	Length	Width	Height	
51.	4 m	3 m	6 m	72 m^3
52.	8 m	8 m	8 m	512 m^3
53.	21 cm	12 cm	10 cm	2520 cm^3

	Length	Width	Height	
54.	4.6 m	3.2 m	5 m	73.6 m^3
55.	25 cm	10 cm	30 cm	7500 cm^3
56.	2.8 m	1.9 m	0.6 m	3.192 m^3

The word problems covered in this chapter are presented here in a mixed setting.

Part 3: APPLICATIONS

Note: each problem is referenced to the related page(s).

57. A rectangular table top is 1.3 meters long and 0.9 meters wide. Find the perimeter of the table top. (Pages 30–31) **4.4 m**

58. An elevator is carrying 12 people. The average mass of each person is 70 kilograms. Find the total mass. (Pages 32–33) **840 kg**

59. An *artist's print* is 60 centimeters long and 45 centimeters wide. Find its area. (Pages 36–37) **2700 cm²**

60. A mug contains 150 milliliters. How many mugs can be filled from a pitcher containing 0.6 liters? **4** (Pages 34–35)

61. The side of a bulletin board is 110 centimeters long. How many meters is this? (Pages 28–29) **1.1 m**

62. A stand-up freezer is 0.8 meters long, 0.6 meters wide, and 1.9 meters high. Find its volume. (Pages 36–37) **0.912 m³**

63. The outdoor temperature is 5°C. Would you go to a football game with or without a jacket? (Page 38) **with**

64. A rectangular scarf is 1.1 meters long and 0.6 meters wide. Find its perimeter. (Pages 30–31) **3.4 m**

65. The American flag shown below hangs in the Cleveland Arcade. It is about 18 meters long and 12 meters wide. What is its area? (Pages 36–37) **216 m²**

S. Sagiatuk is making an artist's print (copy).

66. A fish tank is 45 centimeters long, 24 centimeters wide, and 30 centimeters high. Find its volume. (Pages 36–37) **32,400 cm³**

Chapter Test The Teacher's Resource Book contains two forms of each Chapter Test.

Choose the most suitable measure. Choose a, b, or c.

1. The mass of a toothbrush b — **a.** 5 mg **b.** 5 g **c.** 5 kg
2. The capacity of a fuel tank in a car c — **a.** 4.3 mL **b.** 4.3 L **c.** 43 L
3. The length of a ballpoint pen b — **a.** 13 mm **b.** 13 cm **c.** 13 m
4. The length of a room c — **a.** 3 cm **b.** 3 km **c.** 3 m
5. The temperature of a cup of hot soup c — **a.** 0°C **b.** 20°C **c.** 90°C

Complete.

6. 9 km = __?__ m 9000
7. 23 cm = __?__ m 0.23
8. 4 kg = __?__ g 4000
9. 43.8 mg = __?__ g 0.0438
10. 3.2 L = __?__ ml 3200
11. 1481 mL = __?__ L 1.481

Find the perimeter of each figure.

12. Road Sign 160 cm

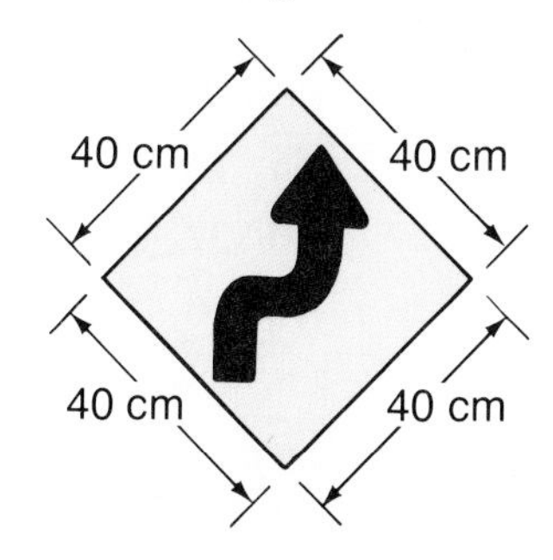

13. Parking Lot 350 m

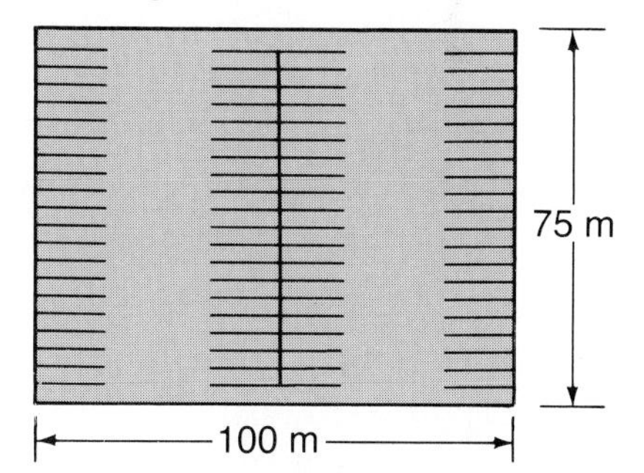

Find the area of each rectangle.

	Length	Width	Area
14.	5 m	3 m	__?__ 15 m^2
15.	2.8 m	1.9 m	__?__ 5.32 m^2

Find the volume of each prism.

	Length	Width	Height
16.	6 m	4 m	5 m 120 m^3
17.	20 cm	10 cm	3 cm 600 cm^3

Solve.

18. A glass contains 220 milliliters. How many glasses of this size can be filled from a 2.2-liter bottle of apple juice? 10

19. A bus is carrying 38 people. The average mass of each person is 70 kilograms. Find the total mass of the people. 2660 kg

20. The United States Navy uses **semaphore flags** to send messages from ship to ship. The flags are squares measuring 45 centimeters on each side. Find the area of a semaphore flag. 2025 cm^2

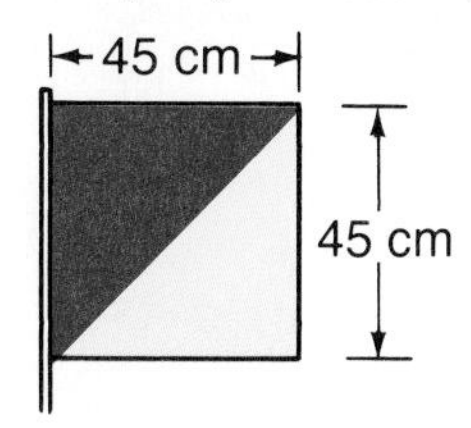

REVIEW OF RELATED SKILLS FOR CHAPTER 3

We suggest that some or all of this page be reviewed before proceeding with the chapter.

Divide. (Pages 12–13)

1. $18 \div 6$ 3 **2.** $24 \div 4$ 6 **3.** $75 \div 5$ 15 **4.** $32 \div 8$ 4 **5.** $14 \div 14$ 1

6. $51 \div 3$ 17 **7.** $68 \div 4$ 17 **8.** $42 \div 3$ 14 **9.** $75 \div 3$ 25 **10.** $27 \div 9$ 3

11. $35 \div 7$ 5 **12.** $56 \div 4$ 14 **13.** $90 \div 9$ 10 **14.** $64 \div 4$ 16 **15.** $48 \div 3$ 16

16. $48 \div 16$ 3 **17.** $42 \div 14$ 3 **18.** $75 \div 25$ 3 **19.** $64 \div 16$ 4 **20.** $96 \div 12$ 8

21. $108 \div 12$ 9 **22.** $132 \div 11$ 12 **23.** $80 \div 16$ 5 **24.** $92 \div 23$ 4 **25.** $81 \div 27$ 3

26. $76 \div 19$ 4 **27.** $72 \div 24$ 3 **28.** $72 \div 18$ 4 **29.** $114 \div 19$ 6 **30.** $115 \div 23$ 5

31. $94 \div 13$ 7 r 3 **32.** $75 \div 12$ 6 r 3 **33.** $78 \div 25$ 3 r 3 **34.** $95 \div 10$ 9 r 5 **35.** $100 \div 11$ 9 r 1

Add. (Pages 2–3)

36. $13 + 11$ 24 **37.** $14 + 19$ 33 **38.** $25 + 10$ 35 **39.** $42 + 36$ 78 **40.** $15 + 17$ 32

41. $25 + 19$ 44 **42.** $15 + 23$ 38 **43.** $36 + 47$ 83 **44.** $51 + 49$ 100 **45.** $27 + 34$ 61

46. $16 + 41$ 57 **47.** $25 + 18$ 43 **48.** $18 + 19$ 37 **49.** $23 + 17$ 40 **50.** $19 + 25$ 44

51. $27 + 33$ 60 **52.** $56 + 18$ 74 **53.** $29 + 42$ 71 **54.** $42 + 27$ 69 **55.** $16 + 49$ 65

56. $18 + 21$ 39 **57.** $16 + 25$ 41 **58.** $17 + 38$ 55 **59.** $29 + 59$ 88 **60.** $21 + 18$ 39

61. $16 + 38$ 54 **62.** $59 + 44$ 103 **63.** $81 + 10$ 91 **64.** $30 + 74$ 104 **65.** $16 + 13$ 29

Subtract. (Pages 2–3)

66. $11 - 9$ 2 **67.** $24 - 12$ 12 **68.** $72 - 27$ 45 **69.** $66 - 18$ 48 **70.** $44 - 28$ 16

71. $21 - 10$ 11 **72.** $60 - 8$ 52 **73.** $74 - 16$ 58 **74.** $35 - 18$ 17 **75.** $22 - 19$ 3

76. $19 - 10$ 9 **77.** $24 - 18$ 6 **78.** $33 - 27$ 6 **79.** $55 - 46$ 9 **80.** $36 - 27$ 9

81. $28 - 19$ 9 **82.** $42 - 36$ 6 **83.** $31 - 28$ 3 **84.** $46 - 28$ 18 **85.** $51 - 29$ 22

86. $64 - 38$ 26 **87.** $46 - 38$ 8 **88.** $72 - 64$ 8 **89.** $81 - 54$ 27 **90.** $90 - 81$ 9

91. $76 - 48$ 28 **92.** $52 - 27$ 25 **93.** $30 - 19$ 11 **94.** $44 - 38$ 6 **95.** $75 - 68$ 7

Multiply. (Pages 6–7)

96. 8×5 40 **97.** 9×6 54 **98.** 12×4 48 **99.** 11×7 77 **100.** 21×3 63

101. 16×3 48 **102.** 11×5 55 **103.** 21×7 147 **104.** 9×27 243 **105.** 14×8 112

106. 18×9 162 **107.** 3×26 78 **108.** 8×15 120 **109.** 24×3 72 **110.** 19×6 114

111. 17×18 306 **112.** 13×10 130 **113.** 14×11 154 **114.** 23×12 276 **115.** 18×14 252

116. 13×17 221 **117.** 24×14 336 **118.** 19×15 285 **119.** 21×22 462 **120.** 13×24 312

121. 16×36 576 **122.** 25×18 450 **123.** 32×21 672 **124.** 22×31 682 **125.** 15×19 285

126. 18×27 486 **127.** 42×15 630 **128.** 31×19 589 **129.** 16×15 240 **130.** 17×12 204

CHAPTER

3 FRACTIONS

ESSENTIAL SKILLS/APPLICATIONS

3-1 Fractions: Mixed Numbers and Lowest Terms

3-2 Addition and Subtraction: Like Fractions

3-3 Addition: Unlike Fractions and Mixed Numbers

3-4 Subtraction: Unlike Fractions/Mixed Numbers

3-5 Multiplication: Fractions and Mixed Numbers

3-6 Division: Fractions and Mixed Numbers

3-7 Rounding and Estimation

CAREER APPLICATIONS

Travel Agent

Air Conditioning Technician

3-1 Fractions: Mixed Numbers and Lowest Terms

See the Teacher's Manual for the objectives.

A fraction greater than 1 can be written as a **mixed number.**

PROCEDURE To write a mixed number for a fraction greater than 1:

[1] Divide the numerator by the denominator.

[2] Write a fraction for the remainder.

EXAMPLE 1 Write a mixed number for $\frac{17}{3}$.

Solution: [1] $\frac{17}{3}$ means $17 \div 3$. ⟶ $3\overline{)17}$ with quotient 5; 15; remainder 2

[2] Quotient: **5 r 2**, or $5\frac{2}{3}$ ⟵ *Remainder* (2), ⟵ *Divisor* (3)

Thus, $\frac{17}{3} = 5\frac{2}{3}$ ◀ *Mixed number*

After completing Example 1, you may wish to have students do some or all of Exercises 1-64.

A fraction is in **lowest terms** when the numerator and the denominator cannot be divided by the same number except one.

PROCEDURE To write a fraction in lowest terms:

[1] Divide the numerator and the denominator by a number that will divide evenly into both.

[2] Repeat Step 1 until the numerator and denominator cannot be divided evenly by the same number except 1.

EXAMPLE 2 Write in lowest terms. Then write a mixed number for any fraction greater than 1.

a. $\frac{42}{48}$

b. $\frac{54}{36}$

Solutions:

a. $\frac{42}{48} = \frac{42 \div 2}{48 \div 2}$

$= \frac{21}{24}$ ◀ *Not in lowest terms*

$= \frac{21 \div 3}{24 \div 3}$

$= \frac{7}{8}$ ◀ *Lowest terms*

b. $\frac{54}{36} = \frac{54 \div 9}{36 \div 9}$

$= \frac{6}{4}$ ◀ *Not in lowest terms*

$= \frac{6 \div 2}{4 \div 2}$

$= \frac{3}{2}$ ◀ *Write as a mixed number.*

$= 1\frac{1}{2}$

EXERCISES

Write a mixed number for each fraction. (Example 1)

1. $\frac{9}{5}$ $1\frac{4}{5}$ 2. $\frac{12}{7}$ $1\frac{5}{7}$ 3. $\frac{7}{3}$ $2\frac{1}{3}$ 4. $\frac{16}{9}$ $1\frac{7}{9}$ 5. $\frac{12}{5}$ $2\frac{2}{5}$ 6. $\frac{19}{6}$ $3\frac{1}{6}$ 7. $\frac{21}{8}$ $2\frac{5}{8}$ 8. $\frac{18}{7}$ $2\frac{4}{7}$

9. $\frac{13}{4}$ $3\frac{1}{4}$ 10. $\frac{15}{8}$ $1\frac{7}{8}$ 11. $\frac{20}{11}$ $1\frac{9}{11}$ 12. $\frac{17}{7}$ $2\frac{3}{7}$ 13. $\frac{19}{11}$ $1\frac{8}{11}$ 14. $\frac{25}{3}$ $8\frac{1}{3}$ 15. $\frac{37}{12}$ $3\frac{1}{12}$ 16. $\frac{43}{12}$ $3\frac{7}{12}$

17. $\frac{97}{21}$ $4\frac{13}{21}$ 18. $\frac{64}{3}$ $21\frac{1}{3}$ 19. $\frac{38}{13}$ $2\frac{12}{13}$ 20. $\frac{27}{19}$ $1\frac{8}{19}$ 21. $\frac{43}{9}$ $4\frac{7}{9}$ 22. $\frac{89}{12}$ $7\frac{5}{12}$ 23. $\frac{11}{6}$ $1\frac{5}{6}$ 24. $\frac{47}{15}$ $3\frac{2}{15}$

25. $\frac{8}{5}$ $1\frac{3}{5}$ 26. $\frac{17}{6}$ $2\frac{5}{6}$ 27. $\frac{13}{8}$ $1\frac{5}{8}$ 28. $\frac{51}{14}$ $3\frac{9}{14}$ 29. $\frac{64}{15}$ $4\frac{4}{15}$ 30. $\frac{29}{17}$ $1\frac{12}{17}$ 31. $\frac{81}{11}$ $7\frac{4}{11}$ 32. $\frac{16}{5}$ $3\frac{1}{5}$

33. $\frac{17}{3}$ $5\frac{2}{3}$ 34. $\frac{19}{2}$ $9\frac{1}{2}$ 35. $\frac{21}{4}$ $5\frac{1}{4}$ 36. $\frac{37}{3}$ $12\frac{1}{3}$ 37. $\frac{64}{13}$ $4\frac{12}{13}$ 38. $\frac{83}{22}$ $3\frac{17}{22}$ 39. $\frac{88}{15}$ $5\frac{13}{15}$ 40. $\frac{13}{3}$ $4\frac{1}{3}$

41. $\frac{29}{11}$ $2\frac{7}{11}$ 42. $\frac{85}{16}$ $5\frac{5}{16}$ 43. $\frac{74}{23}$ $3\frac{5}{23}$ 44. $\frac{92}{13}$ $7\frac{1}{13}$ 45. $\frac{67}{11}$ $6\frac{1}{11}$ 46. $\frac{77}{24}$ $3\frac{5}{24}$ 47. $\frac{62}{17}$ $3\frac{11}{17}$ 48. $\frac{91}{12}$ $7\frac{7}{12}$

49. $\frac{63}{19}$ $3\frac{6}{19}$ 50. $\frac{67}{13}$ $5\frac{2}{13}$ 51. $\frac{57}{14}$ $4\frac{1}{14}$ 52. $\frac{79}{21}$ $3\frac{16}{21}$ 53. $\frac{83}{31}$ $2\frac{21}{31}$ 54. $\frac{27}{7}$ $3\frac{6}{7}$ 55. $\frac{94}{27}$ $3\frac{13}{27}$ 56. $\frac{55}{12}$ $4\frac{7}{12}$

57. $\frac{16}{7}$ $2\frac{2}{7}$ 58. $\frac{47}{11}$ $4\frac{3}{11}$ 59. $\frac{34}{9}$ $3\frac{7}{9}$ 60. $\frac{85}{18}$ $4\frac{13}{18}$ 61. $\frac{95}{14}$ $6\frac{11}{14}$ 62. $\frac{10}{3}$ $3\frac{1}{3}$ 63. $\frac{68}{13}$ $5\frac{3}{13}$ 64. $\frac{29}{14}$ $2\frac{1}{14}$

Write in lowest terms. Then write a whole number or a mixed number for any fraction greater than one. (Example 2)

65. $\frac{8}{24}$ $\frac{1}{3}$ 66. $\frac{9}{27}$ $\frac{1}{3}$ 67. $\frac{3}{27}$ $\frac{1}{9}$ 68. $\frac{6}{30}$ $\frac{1}{5}$ 69. $\frac{17}{68}$ $\frac{1}{4}$ 70. $\frac{12}{48}$ $\frac{1}{4}$ 71. $\frac{16}{60}$ $\frac{4}{15}$ 72. $\frac{18}{45}$ $\frac{2}{5}$

73. $\frac{60}{90}$ $\frac{2}{3}$ 74. $\frac{11}{33}$ $\frac{1}{3}$ 75. $\frac{50}{12}$ $4\frac{1}{6}$ 76. $\frac{68}{24}$ $2\frac{5}{6}$ 77. $\frac{16}{32}$ $\frac{1}{2}$ 78. $\frac{15}{40}$ $\frac{3}{8}$ 79. $\frac{6}{36}$ $\frac{1}{6}$ 80. $\frac{24}{16}$ $1\frac{1}{2}$

81. $\frac{50}{75}$ $\frac{2}{3}$ 82. $\frac{81}{27}$ 3 83. $\frac{66}{30}$ $2\frac{1}{5}$ 84. $\frac{11}{44}$ $\frac{1}{4}$ 85. $\frac{17}{51}$ $\frac{1}{3}$ 86. $\frac{7}{35}$ $\frac{1}{5}$ 87. $\frac{28}{16}$ $1\frac{3}{4}$ 88. $\frac{25}{15}$ $1\frac{2}{3}$

89. $\frac{40}{12}$ $3\frac{1}{3}$ 90. $\frac{65}{13}$ 5 91. $\frac{38}{18}$ $2\frac{1}{9}$ 92. $\frac{16}{54}$ $\frac{8}{27}$ 93. $\frac{28}{32}$ $\frac{7}{8}$ 94. $\frac{9}{30}$ $\frac{3}{10}$ 95. $\frac{24}{18}$ $1\frac{1}{3}$ 96. $\frac{9}{57}$ $\frac{3}{19}$

97. $\frac{200}{40}$ 5 98. $\frac{80}{24}$ $3\frac{1}{3}$ 99. $\frac{95}{38}$ $2\frac{1}{2}$ 100. $\frac{27}{60}$ $\frac{9}{20}$ 101. $\frac{400}{1200}$ $\frac{1}{3}$ 102. $\frac{49}{63}$ $\frac{7}{9}$ 103. $\frac{98}{144}$ $\frac{49}{72}$ 104. $\frac{180}{600}$ $\frac{3}{10}$

105. $\frac{13}{78}$ $\frac{1}{6}$ 106. $\frac{29}{58}$ $\frac{1}{2}$ 107. $\frac{65}{130}$ $\frac{1}{2}$ 108. $\frac{81}{18}$ $4\frac{1}{2}$ 109. $\frac{63}{27}$ $2\frac{1}{3}$ 110. $\frac{54}{42}$ $1\frac{2}{7}$ 111. $\frac{88}{44}$ 2 112. $\frac{90}{15}$ 6

113. $\frac{21}{63}$ $\frac{1}{3}$ 114. $\frac{76}{125}$ $\frac{76}{125}$ 115. $\frac{4}{76}$ $\frac{1}{19}$ 116. $\frac{27}{72}$ $\frac{3}{8}$ 117. $\frac{84}{30}$ $2\frac{4}{5}$ 118. $\frac{9}{39}$ $\frac{3}{13}$ 119. $\frac{38}{24}$ $1\frac{7}{12}$ 120. $\frac{360}{150}$ $2\frac{2}{5}$

121. $\frac{64}{60}$ $1\frac{1}{15}$ 122. $\frac{6}{42}$ $\frac{1}{7}$ 123. $\frac{33}{30}$ $1\frac{1}{10}$ 124. $\frac{8}{56}$ $\frac{1}{7}$ 125. $\frac{27}{45}$ $\frac{3}{5}$ 126. $\frac{16}{56}$ $\frac{2}{7}$ 127. $\frac{8}{99}$ $\frac{8}{99}$ 128. $\frac{200}{6}$ $33\frac{1}{3}$

These word problems apply the skills taught in the lesson.

APPLICATIONS: Using Fractions

Write a mixed number for each fraction.

129. In 1980, the cost of white bread was $\frac{9}{5}$ times the cost in 1970. $1\frac{4}{5}$

130. In 1980, the cost of a pair of shoes was $\frac{7}{4}$ times the cost in 1970. $1\frac{3}{4}$

131. In 1980, the cost of bacon was $\frac{7}{3}$ times the cost in 1970. $2\frac{1}{3}$

132. In 1980, the cost of local bus fare was $\frac{17}{10}$ times the cost in 1970. $1\frac{7}{10}$

3-2 Addition and Subtraction: Like Fractions

See the Teacher's Manual for the objectives.

Fractions such as $\frac{7}{9}$ and $\frac{8}{9}$ are **like fractions** because they have a **common denominator,** 9.

PROCEDURE To add or subtract like fractions:

[1] Add or subtract the numerators.

[2] Write the sum or difference over the common denominator.

[3] Write the answer in lowest terms.

EXAMPLE 1 a. $\frac{1}{8}+\frac{3}{8}=$ ___?___ b. $\frac{5}{9}-\frac{2}{9}=$ ___?___

Solutions:

a. $\frac{1}{8}+\frac{3}{8}=\frac{4}{8}=\frac{1}{2}$ ◀ *Lowest Terms*

b. $\frac{5}{9}-\frac{2}{9}=\frac{3}{9}=\frac{1}{3}$ ◀ *Lowest Terms*

After completing Example 1, you may wish to have students do some or all of Exercises 1-28.

Fractions such as $\frac{7}{8}$ and $\frac{5}{6}$ are **unlike fractions** because their denominators are not the same. To write like fractions for unlike fractions, you first find the **least common denominator** (abbreviated: LCD).

PROCEDURE To write like fractions for unlike fractions:

[1] Find the LCD of the denominators.

[2] Multiply both the numerator and denominator of each fraction by a number that will make the denominator equal to the LCD.

EXAMPLE 2 Write like fractions for $\frac{7}{8}$ and $\frac{5}{6}$.

Solutions: [1] To find the LCD, write multiples of 8 until you reach a number that is also a multiple of 6.

$8 \times 1 = 8$ $8 \times 2 = 16$ $8 \times 3 = 24$ ◀ *Stop! 24 is also a multiple of 6.*

LCD: **24**

[2] $\frac{7}{8}=\frac{7 \times 3}{8 \times 3}$ $\frac{5}{6}=\frac{5 \times 4}{6 \times 4}$

$\frac{7}{8}=\frac{\mathbf{21}}{\mathbf{24}}$ $\frac{5}{6}=\frac{\mathbf{20}}{\mathbf{24}}$

Like fractions

EXERCISES

Add or subtract. Write each answer in lowest terms. (Example 1)

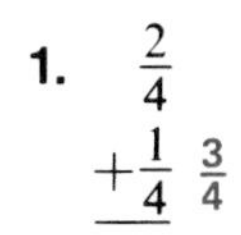

1. $\frac{2}{4} + \frac{1}{4}$ $\frac{3}{4}$
2. $\frac{5}{8} - \frac{1}{8}$ $\frac{1}{2}$
3. $\frac{3}{7} + \frac{1}{7}$ $\frac{4}{7}$
4. $\frac{8}{9} - \frac{3}{9}$ $\frac{5}{9}$
5. $\frac{2}{13} + \frac{5}{13}$ $\frac{7}{13}$
6. $\frac{7}{12} + \frac{3}{12}$ $\frac{5}{6}$
7. $\frac{3}{5} + \frac{2}{5}$ 1
8. $\frac{5}{6} - \frac{3}{6}$ $\frac{1}{3}$
9. $\frac{11}{15} - \frac{8}{15}$ $\frac{1}{5}$
10. $\frac{13}{21} + \frac{1}{21}$ $\frac{2}{3}$
11. $\frac{8}{35} - \frac{3}{35}$ $\frac{1}{7}$
12. $\frac{6}{19} + \frac{1}{19}$ $\frac{7}{19}$
13. $\frac{11}{12} - \frac{5}{12}$ $\frac{1}{2}$
14. $\frac{7}{10} - \frac{5}{10}$ $\frac{1}{5}$
15. $\frac{11}{14} - \frac{4}{14}$ $\frac{1}{2}$
16. $\frac{29}{30} - \frac{15}{30}$ $\frac{7}{15}$
17. $\frac{6}{25} + \frac{9}{25}$ $\frac{3}{5}$
18. $\frac{8}{27} + \frac{10}{27}$ $\frac{2}{3}$
19. $\frac{4}{5} - \frac{3}{5}$ $\frac{1}{5}$
20. $\frac{7}{9} - \frac{4}{9}$ $\frac{1}{3}$
21. $\frac{5}{12} + \frac{1}{12}$ $\frac{1}{2}$
22. $\frac{3}{13} + \frac{1}{13}$ $\frac{4}{13}$
23. $\frac{7}{8} - \frac{1}{8}$ $\frac{3}{4}$
24. $\frac{17}{20} + \frac{1}{20}$ $\frac{9}{10}$
25. $\frac{18}{35} + \frac{7}{35}$ $\frac{5}{7}$
26. $\frac{24}{42} - \frac{3}{42}$ $\frac{1}{2}$
27. $\frac{16}{50} + \frac{4}{50}$ $\frac{2}{5}$
28. $\frac{13}{18} - \frac{5}{18}$ $\frac{4}{9}$

Find the LCD for each pair of fractions. (Example 2, step 1)

29. $\frac{1}{2}$ and $\frac{1}{3}$ 6
30. $\frac{1}{3}$ and $\frac{5}{6}$ 6
31. $\frac{3}{4}$ and $\frac{7}{8}$ 8
32. $\frac{1}{5}$ and $\frac{3}{4}$ 20
33. $\frac{5}{6}$ and $\frac{1}{4}$ 12
34. $\frac{3}{8}$ and $\frac{2}{5}$ 40
35. $\frac{3}{4}$ and $\frac{2}{3}$ 12
36. $\frac{5}{6}$ and $\frac{3}{5}$ 30
37. $\frac{3}{8}$ and $\frac{1}{2}$ 8
38. $\frac{7}{8}$ and $\frac{5}{9}$ 72
39. $\frac{1}{4}$ and $\frac{2}{7}$ 28
40. $\frac{3}{5}$ and $\frac{2}{3}$ 15
41. $\frac{3}{7}$ and $\frac{1}{2}$ 14
42. $\frac{5}{8}$ and $\frac{2}{3}$ 24
43. $\frac{7}{9}$ and $\frac{1}{4}$ 36
44. $\frac{5}{12}$ and $\frac{5}{6}$ 12
45. $\frac{3}{7}$ and $\frac{2}{14}$ 14
46. $\frac{5}{9}$ and $\frac{2}{3}$ 9
47. $\frac{1}{6}$ and $\frac{4}{7}$ 42
48. $\frac{5}{8}$ and $\frac{2}{7}$ 56

Write like fractions for each pair of fractions. (Example 2)

49. $\frac{1}{2}$ and $\frac{2}{3}$ $\frac{3}{6}, \frac{4}{6}$
50. $\frac{4}{9}$ and $\frac{3}{6}$ $\frac{8}{18}, \frac{9}{18}$
51. $\frac{3}{4}$ and $\frac{2}{3}$ $\frac{9}{12}, \frac{8}{12}$
52. $\frac{1}{5}$ and $\frac{3}{10}$ $\frac{2}{10}, \frac{3}{10}$
53. $\frac{7}{16}$ and $\frac{3}{12}$ $\frac{21}{48}, \frac{12}{48}$
54. $\frac{5}{8}$ and $\frac{2}{3}$ $\frac{15}{24}, \frac{16}{24}$
55. $\frac{5}{12}$ and $\frac{3}{4}$ $\frac{5}{12}, \frac{9}{12}$
56. $\frac{9}{16}$ and $\frac{1}{2}$ $\frac{9}{16}, \frac{8}{16}$
57. $\frac{2}{3}$ and $\frac{4}{7}$ $\frac{14}{21}, \frac{12}{21}$
58. $\frac{5}{8}$ and $\frac{1}{9}$ $\frac{45}{72}, \frac{8}{72}$
59. $\frac{2}{5}$ and $\frac{3}{4}$ $\frac{8}{20}, \frac{15}{20}$
60. $\frac{1}{22}$ and $\frac{3}{4}$ $\frac{2}{44}, \frac{33}{44}$
61. $\frac{8}{9}$ and $\frac{5}{12}$ $\frac{32}{36}, \frac{15}{36}$
62. $\frac{1}{14}$ and $\frac{2}{3}$ $\frac{3}{42}, \frac{28}{42}$
63. $\frac{17}{25}$ and $\frac{3}{10}$ $\frac{34}{50}, \frac{15}{50}$

These word problems apply the skills taught in the lesson.

APPLICATIONS: Fractions and Customary Measures

64. Jeanne ran $\frac{1}{4}$ mile on Thursday, $\frac{3}{4}$ mile on Friday, and $\frac{3}{4}$ mile on Saturday. How many miles did she run in all? $1\frac{3}{4}$ miles
65. Last Monday Sue jogged $\frac{7}{8}$ mile. Joe jogged $\frac{3}{8}$ mile. Find the difference. $\frac{1}{2}$ mile
66. On Sunday, Ramon walked $\frac{1}{5}$ mile. That same day, Kim walked $\frac{4}{5}$ mile. How much farther did Kim walk? $\frac{3}{5}$ mile
67. Tom jogged $\frac{3}{5}$ mile on Saturday and $\frac{4}{5}$ mile on Sunday. How far did he jog on the weekend? $1\frac{2}{5}$ miles

3-3 Addition: Unlike Fractions and Mixed Numbers

See the Teacher's Manual for the objectives.

Write like fractions for any unlike fractions before you add.

PROCEDURE To add unlike fractions:

1. Find the LCD (least common denominator).
2. Use the LCD to write like fractions.
3. Add.
4. Write your answer in lowest terms.

EXAMPLE 1 a. $\frac{5}{6} + \frac{1}{10} = \underline{\ ?\ }$ b. $\frac{3}{4} + \frac{1}{3} = \underline{\ ?\ }$

Solution: a. **LCD: 30**

$$\frac{5}{6} = \frac{25}{30} \quad \frac{5 \times 5}{6 \times 5}$$
$$+\frac{1}{10} = +\frac{3}{30} \quad \frac{1 \times 3}{10 \times 3}$$
$$\frac{28}{30} = \frac{14}{15} \quad \text{Lowest terms}$$

b. **LCD: 12**

$$\frac{3}{4} = \frac{9}{12} \quad \frac{3 \times 3}{4 \times 3}$$
$$+\frac{1}{3} = +\frac{4}{12} \quad \frac{1 \times 4}{3 \times 4}$$
$$\frac{13}{12} = 1\frac{1}{12}$$

After completing Example 1, you may wish to have students do some or all of Exercises 1-22.

Adding mixed numbers is similar to adding fractions.

PROCEDURE To add mixed numbers:

1. Write like fractions for any unlike fractions.
2. Add the fractional parts.
3. Add the whole numbers.
4. Write the answer in lowest terms.

EXAMPLE 2 a. $3\frac{1}{2} + 7\frac{2}{3} = \underline{\ ?\ }$ b. $2\frac{3}{8} + 4\frac{2}{5} = \underline{\ ?\ }$

Solution: a. **LCD: 6**

$$3\frac{1}{2} = 3\frac{3}{6}$$
$$+7\frac{2}{3} = +7\frac{4}{6}$$
$$10\frac{7}{6} = 10 + 1\frac{1}{6} \quad \frac{7}{6} = 1\frac{1}{6}$$
$$= 11\frac{1}{6}$$

b. **LCD: 40**

$$2\frac{3}{8} = 2\frac{15}{40}$$
$$+4\frac{2}{5} = +4\frac{16}{40}$$
$$6\frac{31}{40}$$

EXERCISES

Add. Write each answer in lowest terms. (Example 1)

1. $\frac{5}{8} + \frac{1}{4}$ $\frac{7}{8}$
2. $\frac{5}{6} + \frac{1}{3}$ $1\frac{1}{6}$
3. $\frac{11}{15} + \frac{2}{3}$ $1\frac{2}{5}$
4. $\frac{3}{5} + \frac{1}{3}$ $\frac{14}{15}$
5. $\frac{2}{9} + \frac{1}{6}$ $\frac{7}{18}$
6. $\frac{13}{16} + \frac{1}{12}$ $\frac{43}{48}$
7. $\frac{5}{8} + \frac{1}{3}$ $\frac{23}{24}$
8. $\frac{3}{20} + \frac{2}{5}$ $\frac{11}{20}$
9. $\frac{5}{12} + \frac{3}{8}$ $\frac{19}{24}$
10. $\frac{2}{7} + \frac{1}{5}$ $\frac{17}{35}$
11. $\frac{2}{3} + \frac{1}{10}$ $\frac{23}{30}$
12. $\frac{7}{8} + \frac{2}{5}$ $1\frac{11}{40}$
13. $\frac{4}{5} + \frac{1}{4}$ $1\frac{1}{20}$
14. $\frac{2}{9} + \frac{4}{15}$ $\frac{22}{45}$
15. $\frac{5}{7} + \frac{2}{3}$ $1\frac{8}{21}$
16. $\frac{1}{8} + \frac{1}{6}$ $\frac{7}{24}$
17. $\frac{1}{12} + \frac{3}{4}$ $\frac{5}{6}$
18. $\frac{5}{6} + \frac{1}{4}$ $1\frac{1}{12}$
19. $\frac{2}{3} + \frac{1}{2}$ $1\frac{1}{6}$
20. $\frac{1}{16} + \frac{3}{5}$ $\frac{53}{80}$
21. $\frac{2}{9} + \frac{1}{5}$ $\frac{19}{45}$
22. $\frac{11}{14} + \frac{5}{21}$ $1\frac{1}{42}$

(Example 2)

23. $3\frac{1}{4} + 2\frac{1}{2}$ $5\frac{3}{4}$
24. $6\frac{3}{10} + 2\frac{2}{5}$ $8\frac{7}{10}$
25. $3\frac{5}{8} + 2\frac{5}{6}$ $6\frac{11}{24}$
26. $4\frac{2}{3} + 5\frac{1}{5}$ $9\frac{13}{15}$
27. $3\frac{1}{7} + 2\frac{2}{3}$ $5\frac{17}{21}$
28. $1\frac{5}{6} + 2\frac{1}{4}$ $4\frac{1}{12}$
29. $7\frac{1}{2} + \frac{2}{3}$ $8\frac{1}{6}$
30. $3\frac{1}{4} + \frac{2}{9}$ $3\frac{17}{36}$
31. $2\frac{11}{12} + 3\frac{1}{8}$ $6\frac{1}{24}$
32. $4\frac{2}{15} + 3\frac{4}{5}$ $7\frac{14}{15}$
33. $6\frac{2}{5} + \frac{1}{4}$ $6\frac{13}{20}$
34. $3\frac{4}{9} + \frac{1}{5}$ $3\frac{29}{45}$
35. $\frac{1}{3} + 2\frac{1}{8}$ $2\frac{11}{24}$
36. $4\frac{1}{12} + 2\frac{3}{4}$ $6\frac{5}{6}$
37. $15\frac{1}{2} + 6\frac{3}{5}$ $22\frac{1}{10}$
38. $9\frac{2}{7} + 3\frac{1}{14}$ $12\frac{5}{14}$
39. $51\frac{3}{8} + 2\frac{1}{5}$ $53\frac{23}{40}$
40. $16\frac{4}{9} + 2\frac{1}{6}$ $18\frac{11}{18}$
41. $1\frac{4}{11} + 2\frac{1}{2}$ $3\frac{19}{22}$
42. $11\frac{1}{3} + 3\frac{5}{16}$ $14\frac{31}{48}$

APPLICATIONS: Using Fractions and Customary Measures

These problems apply the skills taught in the lesson.

For Exercises 43–46, find the total length of each object. The symbol " means inch.

43. Rivet (Hint: $\frac{7}{16} + \frac{1}{4} + \frac{7}{8} = $ __?__ ") $1\frac{9}{16}$"

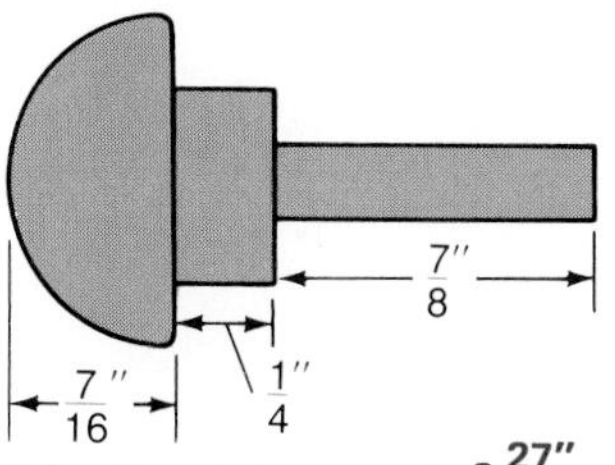

44. Pin (Hint: $\frac{1}{4} + \frac{13}{16} + \frac{5}{8} + \frac{1}{2} + \frac{1}{8} = $ __?__ ") $2\frac{5}{16}$"

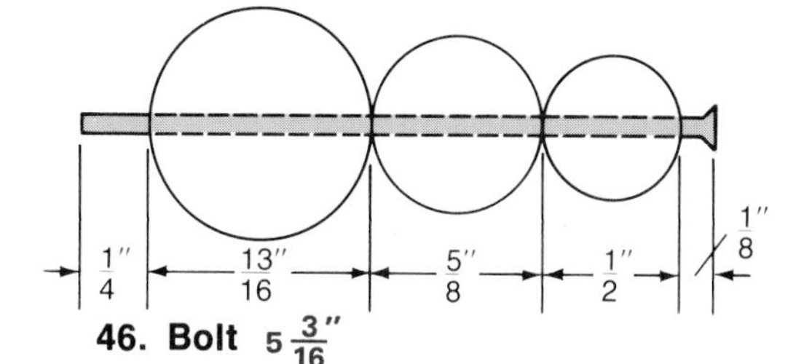

45. Machine part $8\frac{27}{32}$"

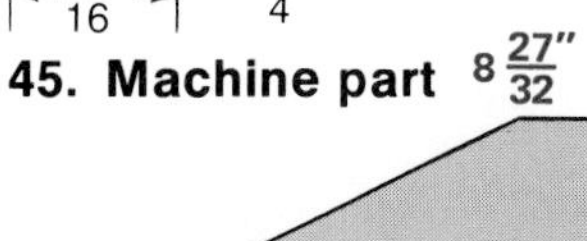

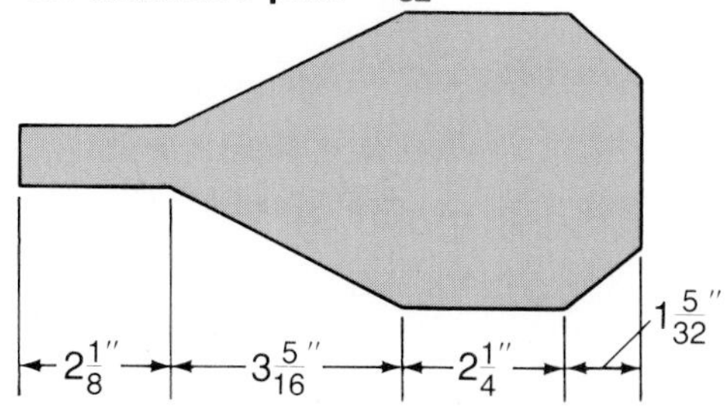

46. Bolt $5\frac{3}{16}$"

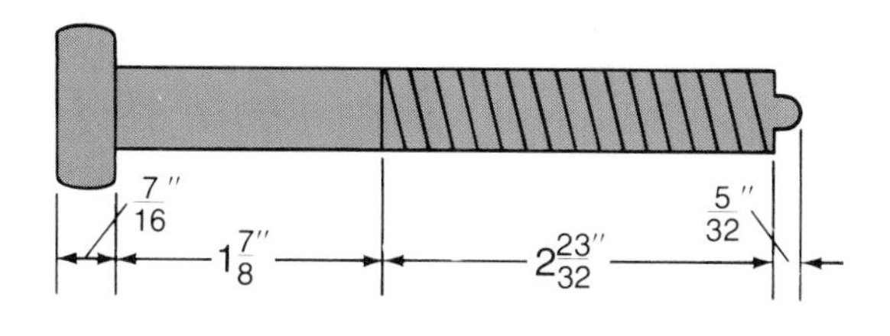

3-4 Subtraction: Unlike Fractions/Mixed Numbers

See the Teacher's Manual for the objectives.

Subtraction of unlike fractions is similar to addition of unlike fractions.

PROCEDURE To subtract unlike fractions:

1. Find the LCD.
2. Use the LCD to write like fractions.
3. Subtract.
4. Write your answer in lowest terms.

EXAMPLE 1 a. $\frac{7}{8} - \frac{1}{5} = \underline{\ ?\ }$ b. $3\frac{8}{9} - 1\frac{3}{4} = \underline{\ ?\ }$

Solutions: a. LCD: 40 b. LCD: 36

$$\begin{array}{rcr} \frac{7}{8} & = & \frac{35}{40} \\ -\frac{1}{5} & = & -\frac{8}{40} \\ \hline & & \frac{27}{40} \end{array} \qquad \begin{array}{rcr} 3\frac{8}{9} & = & 3\frac{32}{36} \\ -1\frac{3}{4} & = & -1\frac{27}{36} \\ \hline & & 2\frac{5}{36} \end{array}$$

After completing Example 1, you may wish to have students do some or all of Exercises 1-26.

When subtracting with mixed numbers, it is sometimes necessary to "borrow" from the whole number.

PROCEDURE To subtract with mixed numbers:

1. Find the LCD.
2. Use the LCD to write like fractions. "Borrow" from the whole number when necessary.
3. Subtract the fractions and whole numbers.
4. Write the answer in lowest terms.

EXAMPLE 2 $3\frac{1}{4} - 1\frac{5}{8} = \underline{\ ?\ }$

Solution: LCD: 8

$$\begin{array}{rcr} 3\frac{1}{4} & = & 3\frac{2}{8} \\ -1\frac{5}{8} & = & -1\frac{5}{8} \\ \hline \end{array}$$

Since $\frac{2}{8}$ is less than $\frac{5}{8}$, borrow 1, or $\frac{8}{8}$, from 3. ⟶

$$\begin{array}{rcr} 3\frac{1}{4} & = & 2\frac{10}{8} \\ -1\frac{5}{8} & = & -1\frac{5}{8} \\ \hline & & 1\frac{5}{8} \end{array}$$

$\frac{2}{8} + \frac{8}{8} = \frac{10}{8}$

EXERCISES

Subtract. Write each answer in lowest terms. (Example 1)

1. $\frac{3}{5} - \frac{1}{3}$ $\frac{4}{15}$
2. $\frac{7}{12} - \frac{1}{2}$ $\frac{1}{12}$
3. $\frac{5}{9} - \frac{2}{5}$ $\frac{7}{45}$
4. $\frac{6}{7} - \frac{1}{4}$ $\frac{17}{28}$
5. $\frac{11}{13} - \frac{2}{3}$ $\frac{7}{39}$
6. $\frac{5}{8} - \frac{2}{5}$ $\frac{9}{40}$
7. $\frac{4}{5} - \frac{3}{10}$ $\frac{1}{2}$
8. $\frac{7}{9} - \frac{1}{5}$ $\frac{26}{45}$
9. $\frac{6}{7} - \frac{2}{5}$ $\frac{16}{35}$
10. $\frac{7}{12} - \frac{1}{4}$ $\frac{1}{3}$
11. $\frac{9}{14} - \frac{3}{7}$ $\frac{3}{14}$
12. $\frac{8}{9} - \frac{4}{5}$ $\frac{4}{45}$
13. $3\frac{5}{9} - 1\frac{3}{8}$ $2\frac{13}{72}$
14. $2\frac{11}{15} - 1\frac{2}{3}$ $1\frac{1}{15}$
15. $7\frac{4}{7} - 3\frac{1}{3}$ $4\frac{5}{21}$
16. $6\frac{9}{10} - 2\frac{1}{4}$ $4\frac{13}{20}$
17. $5\frac{2}{3} - 1\frac{1}{4}$ $4\frac{5}{12}$
18. $6\frac{4}{5} - 2\frac{1}{4}$ $4\frac{11}{20}$
19. $7\frac{1}{2} - 4\frac{1}{3}$ $3\frac{1}{6}$
20. $5\frac{7}{12} - 3\frac{1}{4}$ $2\frac{1}{3}$
21. $12\frac{7}{15} - 8\frac{1}{3}$ $4\frac{2}{15}$
22. $3\frac{7}{8} - 2\frac{2}{3}$ $1\frac{5}{24}$
23. $11\frac{1}{2} - 4\frac{1}{9}$ $7\frac{7}{18}$
24. $11\frac{5}{7} - 2\frac{1}{6}$ $9\frac{23}{42}$
25. $3\frac{7}{12} - 2\frac{1}{9}$ $1\frac{17}{36}$
26. $12\frac{9}{16} - 3\frac{5}{12}$ $9\frac{7}{48}$

(Example 2)

27. $3\frac{1}{9} - 2\frac{3}{4}$ $\frac{13}{36}$
28. $7\frac{1}{6} - 2\frac{2}{3}$ $4\frac{1}{2}$
29. $8\frac{3}{5} - 5\frac{3}{4}$ $2\frac{17}{20}$
30. $7\frac{3}{8} - 5\frac{7}{12}$ $1\frac{19}{24}$
31. $8\frac{1}{7} - 4\frac{2}{3}$ $3\frac{10}{21}$
32. $11\frac{1}{2} - 2\frac{5}{8}$ $8\frac{7}{8}$
33. $6\frac{1}{12} - 3\frac{1}{4}$ $2\frac{5}{6}$
34. $2\frac{1}{15} - 1\frac{1}{10}$ $\frac{29}{30}$
35. $6 - 3\frac{1}{12}$ $2\frac{11}{12}$
36. $18\frac{3}{16} - 4\frac{5}{8}$ $13\frac{9}{16}$
37. $13\frac{3}{10} - \frac{3}{4}$ $12\frac{11}{20}$
38. $41\frac{2}{11} - 3\frac{1}{3}$ $37\frac{28}{33}$
39. $14 - 9\frac{2}{3}$ $4\frac{1}{3}$
40. $19\frac{2}{5} - 4\frac{3}{4}$ $14\frac{13}{20}$
41. $7\frac{1}{3} - 3\frac{5}{9}$ $3\frac{7}{9}$
42. $28 - 14\frac{3}{4}$ $13\frac{1}{4}$
43. $10 - 2\frac{1}{8}$ $7\frac{7}{8}$
44. $36 - 5\frac{4}{5}$ $30\frac{1}{5}$
45. $6\frac{5}{9} - 4\frac{7}{12}$ $1\frac{35}{36}$
46. $11\frac{3}{8} - 2\frac{2}{3}$ $8\frac{17}{24}$
47. $17\frac{1}{12} - 3\frac{3}{10}$ $13\frac{47}{60}$
48. $9\frac{2}{7} - 3\frac{2}{3}$ $5\frac{13}{21}$
49. $8\frac{1}{3} - 4\frac{7}{12}$ $3\frac{3}{4}$
50. $13\frac{3}{16} - 7\frac{2}{3}$ $5\frac{25}{48}$
51. $4\frac{3}{8} - 1\frac{5}{9}$ $2\frac{59}{72}$
52. $16\frac{2}{5} - 11\frac{5}{6}$ $4\frac{17}{30}$

These word problems apply the skills taught in the lesson.

APPLICATIONS: Using Subtraction of Fractions

53. A strip of wood is 5 inches wide. The carpenter cuts off $\frac{3}{8}$ inch. What is the new width? $4\frac{5}{8}$ inches
54. Mr. Lane has a piece of lumber $5\frac{1}{2}$ feet long. He cuts off $3\frac{5}{8}$ feet. How much is left? $1\frac{7}{8}$ feet
55. Find the missing length in the drawing. $2\frac{7}{8}$ inches

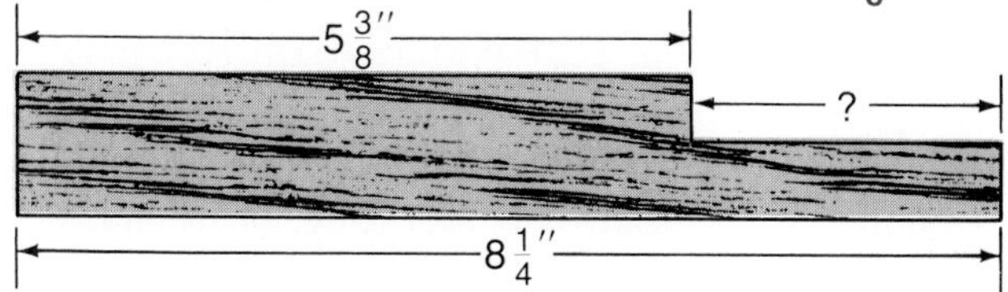

Mid–Chapter Review

This reviews all the skills presented in Sections 3-1, 3-2, 3-3, and 3-4.

Write a mixed number for each fraction. (Pages 46–47)

1. $\frac{8}{3}$ $2\frac{2}{3}$ **2.** $\frac{11}{8}$ $1\frac{3}{8}$ **3.** $\frac{5}{4}$ $1\frac{1}{4}$ **4.** $\frac{17}{6}$ $2\frac{5}{6}$ **5.** $\frac{13}{7}$ $1\frac{6}{7}$ **6.** $\frac{21}{5}$ $4\frac{1}{5}$ **7.** $\frac{12}{11}$ $1\frac{1}{11}$ **8.** $\frac{39}{10}$ $3\frac{9}{10}$

9. $\frac{17}{5}$ $2\frac{1}{8}$ **10.** $\frac{19}{2}$ $9\frac{1}{2}$ **11.** $\frac{15}{4}$ $3\frac{3}{4}$ **12.** $\frac{35}{12}$ $2\frac{11}{12}$ **13.** $\frac{47}{10}$ $4\frac{7}{10}$ **14.** $\frac{18}{7}$ $2\frac{4}{7}$ **15.** $\frac{23}{6}$ $3\frac{5}{6}$ **16.** $\frac{53}{20}$ $2\frac{13}{20}$

Write in lowest terms. Then write a mixed number for any fraction greater than one. (Pages 46–47)

17. $\frac{5}{15}$ $\frac{1}{3}$ **18.** $\frac{7}{21}$ $\frac{1}{3}$ **19.** $\frac{8}{40}$ $\frac{1}{5}$ **20.** $\frac{4}{6}$ $\frac{2}{3}$ **21.** $\frac{9}{12}$ $\frac{3}{4}$ **22.** $\frac{6}{15}$ $\frac{2}{5}$ **23.** $\frac{2}{8}$ $\frac{1}{4}$ **24.** $\frac{3}{18}$ $\frac{1}{6}$

25. $\frac{21}{6}$ $3\frac{1}{2}$ **26.** $\frac{35}{25}$ $1\frac{2}{5}$ **27.** $\frac{18}{12}$ $1\frac{1}{2}$ **28.** $\frac{42}{20}$ $2\frac{1}{10}$ **29.** $\frac{27}{18}$ $1\frac{1}{2}$ **30.** $\frac{8}{6}$ $1\frac{1}{3}$ **31.** $\frac{15}{10}$ $1\frac{1}{2}$ **32.** $\frac{28}{16}$ $1\frac{3}{4}$

Add or subtract. Write each answer in lowest terms. (Pages 48–49)

33. $\frac{3}{5} + \frac{1}{5}$ $\frac{4}{5}$ **34.** $\frac{2}{7} + \frac{4}{7}$ $\frac{6}{7}$ **35.** $\frac{9}{16} - \frac{1}{16}$ $\frac{1}{2}$ **36.** $\frac{13}{25} - \frac{8}{25}$ $\frac{1}{5}$ **37.** $\frac{16}{33} - \frac{5}{33}$ $\frac{1}{3}$

38. $\frac{7}{16} + \frac{5}{16}$ $\frac{3}{4}$

Write like fractions for each pair of fractions. (Pages 48–49)

39. $\frac{2}{5}$ and $\frac{1}{3}$ $\frac{6}{15}, \frac{5}{15}$ **40.** $\frac{3}{10}$ and $\frac{1}{4}$ $\frac{6}{20}, \frac{5}{20}$ **41.** $\frac{1}{6}$ and $\frac{3}{4}$ $\frac{2}{12}, \frac{9}{12}$ **42.** $\frac{1}{5}$ and $\frac{4}{15}$ $\frac{3}{15}, \frac{4}{15}$ **43.** $\frac{5}{8}$ and $\frac{3}{5}$ $\frac{25}{40}, \frac{24}{40}$

Add or subtract. Write each answer in lowest terms. (Pages 50–51, 52–53)

44. $\frac{2}{7} + \frac{3}{4}$ $1\frac{1}{28}$ **45.** $\frac{7}{12} + \frac{3}{4}$ $1\frac{1}{3}$ **46.** $\frac{9}{14} + \frac{3}{7}$ $1\frac{1}{14}$ **47.** $3\frac{1}{5} + 2\frac{2}{3}$ $5\frac{13}{15}$ **48.** $2\frac{1}{8} + 3\frac{3}{4}$ $5\frac{7}{8}$

49. $7\frac{1}{2} + 3\frac{1}{16}$ $10\frac{9}{16}$

50. $\frac{5}{8} - \frac{1}{4}$ $\frac{3}{8}$ **51.** $\frac{4}{9} - \frac{2}{15}$ $\frac{14}{45}$ **52.** $\frac{5}{12} - \frac{1}{4}$ $\frac{1}{6}$ **53.** $3\frac{1}{2} - 2\frac{1}{3}$ $1\frac{1}{6}$ **54.** $2\frac{4}{5} - 1\frac{1}{3}$ $1\frac{7}{15}$

55. $3\frac{5}{8} - 1\frac{1}{3}$ $2\frac{7}{24}$

56. $4\frac{1}{5} - 2\frac{1}{4}$ $1\frac{19}{20}$ **57.** $6\frac{1}{3} - 2\frac{5}{9}$ $3\frac{7}{9}$ **58.** $8 - 7\frac{9}{10}$ $\frac{1}{10}$ **59.** $16 - 8\frac{3}{4}$ $7\frac{1}{4}$ **60.** $12\frac{4}{15} - 3\frac{7}{10}$ $8\frac{17}{30}$

61. $7\frac{5}{12} - 4\frac{5}{8}$ $2\frac{19}{24}$

62. Find the total width of this piece of wood. (Pages 50–51) $12\frac{13}{24}$ inches

63. Find the height of the book at the bottom of the pile. (Pages 52–53) $1\frac{3}{8}$ inches

64. Maria walked $1\frac{1}{2}$ miles, $2\frac{3}{8}$ miles, and $2\frac{1}{4}$ miles last week. How much did she walk in all? (Pages 50–51) $6\frac{1}{8}$ miles

65. Tomas cuts $3\frac{1}{4}$ feet off a board that is 7 feet long. How many feet are left? (Pages 52–53) $3\frac{3}{4}$ feet

TRAVEL AGENT

career

Career lessons are optional.
This lesson combines the skill of reading a table with addition and subtraction of whole numbers.

Travel agents use tables such as the one below to compute airline distances in miles between two cities. A box with no entry means that the airline has no direct service between the cities. Distances in the table are rounded to the nearest ten miles.

	Cleveland	Hartford	Indianapolis	Los Angeles	Phoenix	Pittsburgh	St. Louis	Washington, D.C.
Cleveland	—	—	260	2050	1740	—	490	—
Hartford	—	—	730	2530	2210	410	960	330
Indianapolis	260	730	—	1810	1490	330	230	480
Los Angeles	2050	2530	1810	—	370	2140	1590	2290
Phoenix	1740	2210	1490	370	—	1810	1260	1960
Pittsburgh	—	410	330	2140	1810	—	550	—
St. Louis	490	960	230	1590	1260	550	—	700
Washington, D.C.	—	330	480	2290	1960	—	700	—

EXAMPLE Use the table to find the distance from Hartford to Phoenix by way of Pittsburgh.

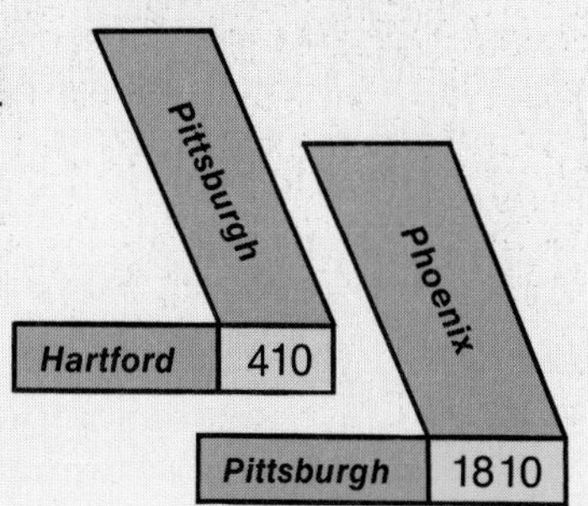

Solution: In the table, find the city of departure in the left column.
Look to the right to find the distance under the city of arrival.

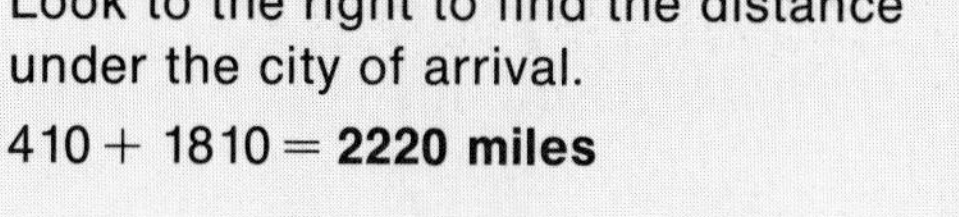

410 + 1810 = **2220 miles**

EXERCISES

In Exercises 1–4, find the total distance for each trip.

1. From Los Angeles to St. Louis 1590 miles
2. From Phoenix to Cleveland 1740 miles
3. From Hartford to Los Angeles by way of St. Louis 2550 miles
4. From Phoenix to Indianapolis by way of St. Louis. 1490 miles
5. Justine flew from Cleveland to Los Angeles by way of St. Louis. How much shorter would her trip have been if she had taken the direct flight? 30 miles
6. Riccardo flew from Hartford to Phoenix by way of Washington, D.C. Susan flew from Hartford to Phoenix by way of Indianapolis. How much farther did Riccardo travel? 70 miles

3-5 Multiplication: Fractions and Mixed Numbers

See the Teacher's Manual for the objectives.

When multiplying with fractions, you multiply the numerators and then multiply the denominators.

PROCEDURE To multiply with fractions:

[1] Multiply the numerators and multiply the denominators.

[2] Write the answer in lowest terms.

Sometimes you can divide a numerator and denominator by the same number before you multiply. (See Example 1b.)

EXAMPLE 1 **a.** $\frac{3}{5} \times \frac{11}{15} = \underline{\ ?\ }$ **b.** $\frac{5}{6} \times \frac{12}{13} = \underline{\ ?\ }$

Solutions: **a.** [1] $\frac{3}{5} \times \frac{11}{15} = \frac{3 \times 11}{5 \times 15}$

$= \frac{33}{75}$ ◀ *Write in lowest terms.*

[2] $= \frac{11}{25}$

b. Divide 6 and 12 by 6.

$\frac{5}{6} \times \frac{12}{13} = \frac{5}{\not{6}_1} \times \frac{\not{12}^2}{13}$

[1] $= \frac{5 \times 2}{1 \times 13}$

[2] $= \frac{10}{13}$

After completing Example 1, you may wish to have students do some or all of Exercises 1-24.

Writing a fraction for each mixed number is the first step in multiplying with mixed numbers.

Mixed Number	PROCEDURE		
	[1] Multiply the denominator and the whole number.	[2] Add this product to the numerator.	[3] Write this sum over the denominator.
$5\frac{3}{4}$	$4 \times 5 = 20$	$20 + 3 = 23$	$\frac{23}{4}$ ◀ $5\frac{3}{4} = \frac{23}{4}$

TABLE

PROCEDURE To multiply with mixed numbers:

[1] Write a fraction for each mixed number.

[2] Multiply the fractions.

[3] Write the answer in lowest terms.

EXAMPLE 2 a. $5 \times 3\frac{7}{10} = \underline{\ ?\ }$ b. $2\frac{2}{5} \times 3\frac{1}{8} = \underline{\ ?\ }$

Solutions: a. [1] $5 \times 3\frac{7}{10} = \frac{5}{1} \times \frac{37}{10}$

[2] $= \frac{\cancel{5}^{1}}{1} \times \frac{37}{\cancel{10}_{2}}$

$= \frac{37}{2}$ ◀ $\frac{1 \times 37}{1 \times 2}$

$= 18\frac{1}{2}$

b. [1] $2\frac{2}{5} \times 3\frac{1}{8} = \frac{12}{5} \times \frac{25}{8}$

[2] $= \frac{\cancel{12}^{3}}{\cancel{5}_{1}} \times \frac{\cancel{25}^{5}}{\cancel{8}_{2}}$

$= \frac{15}{2}$ ◀ $\frac{3 \times 5}{1 \times 2}$

[3] $= 7\frac{1}{2}$

EXERCISES

Multiply. Write each answer in lowest terms. (Example 1a)

1. $\frac{1}{5} \times \frac{1}{3}$ $\frac{1}{15}$ **2.** $\frac{3}{5} \times \frac{3}{8}$ $\frac{9}{40}$ **3.** $\frac{2}{3} \times \frac{5}{7}$ $\frac{10}{21}$ **4.** $\frac{3}{8} \times \frac{1}{5}$ $\frac{3}{40}$ **5.** $\frac{7}{15} \times \frac{1}{2}$ $\frac{7}{30}$ **6.** $\frac{3}{4} \times \frac{5}{7}$ $\frac{15}{28}$

7. $\frac{1}{12} \times \frac{3}{4}$ $\frac{1}{16}$ **8.** $\frac{3}{8} \times \frac{1}{7}$ $\frac{3}{56}$ **9.** $\frac{6}{13} \times \frac{3}{5}$ $\frac{18}{65}$ **10.** $\frac{3}{11} \times \frac{8}{10}$ $\frac{12}{55}$ **11.** $\frac{3}{8} \times \frac{11}{20}$ $\frac{33}{160}$ **12.** $\frac{8}{15} \times \frac{4}{9}$ $\frac{32}{135}$

(Example 1b)

13. $\frac{4}{7} \times \frac{3}{8}$ $\frac{3}{14}$ **14.** $\frac{3}{5} \times \frac{5}{7}$ $\frac{3}{7}$ **15.** $\frac{1}{12} \times \frac{2}{7}$ $\frac{1}{42}$ **16.** $\frac{8}{9} \times \frac{15}{32}$ $\frac{5}{12}$ **17.** $\frac{5}{21} \times \frac{3}{8}$ $\frac{5}{56}$ **18.** $\frac{2}{9} \times \frac{18}{25}$ $\frac{4}{25}$

19. $\frac{3}{11} \times \frac{22}{39}$ $\frac{2}{13}$ **20.** $\frac{6}{7} \times \frac{21}{23}$ $\frac{18}{23}$ **21.** $\frac{8}{17} \times \frac{34}{45}$ $\frac{16}{45}$ **22.** $\frac{4}{5} \times \frac{10}{16}$ $\frac{1}{2}$ **23.** $\frac{7}{50} \times \frac{25}{49}$ $\frac{1}{14}$ **24.** $\frac{8}{15} \times \frac{45}{56}$ $\frac{3}{7}$

Write a fraction for each mixed number. (Table)

25. $4\frac{7}{8}$ $\frac{39}{8}$ **26.** $3\frac{2}{3}$ $\frac{11}{3}$ **27.** $5\frac{1}{8}$ $\frac{41}{8}$ **28.** $7\frac{2}{5}$ $\frac{37}{5}$ **29.** $6\frac{5}{7}$ $\frac{47}{7}$ **30.** $3\frac{4}{9}$ $\frac{31}{9}$ **31.** $2\frac{1}{4}$ $\frac{9}{4}$

32. $3\frac{7}{9}$ $\frac{34}{9}$ **33.** $4\frac{1}{7}$ $\frac{29}{7}$ **34.** $8\frac{1}{3}$ $\frac{25}{3}$ **35.** $2\frac{5}{8}$ $\frac{21}{8}$ **36.** $11\frac{1}{2}$ $\frac{23}{2}$ **37.** $4\frac{3}{4}$ $\frac{19}{4}$ **38.** $3\frac{7}{10}$ $\frac{37}{10}$

Multiply. Write each answer in lowest terms. (Example 2)

39. $7 \times 2\frac{1}{2}$ $17\frac{1}{2}$ **40.** $8 \times 6\frac{1}{3}$ $50\frac{2}{3}$ **41.** $12\frac{1}{3} \times 1\frac{4}{5}$ $22\frac{1}{5}$ **42.** $2\frac{2}{3} \times 4\frac{1}{2}$ 12 **43.** $12\frac{1}{3} \times 1\frac{1}{8}$ $13\frac{7}{8}$

44. $16\frac{1}{2} \times 2\frac{1}{3}$ $38\frac{1}{2}$ **45.** $6\frac{3}{5} \times \frac{10}{11}$ 6 **46.** $5\frac{1}{8} \times \frac{1}{41}$ $\frac{1}{8}$ **47.** $\frac{2}{5} \times 3\frac{1}{3}$ $1\frac{1}{3}$ **48.** $4\frac{2}{7} \times 49$ 210

49. $7\frac{1}{3} \times 12$ 88 **50.** $\frac{1}{8} \times 4\frac{3}{4}$ $\frac{19}{32}$ **51.** $1\frac{3}{7} \times 2\frac{1}{5}$ $3\frac{1}{7}$ **52.** $6\frac{1}{2} \times 2\frac{1}{3}$ $15\frac{1}{6}$ **53.** $1\frac{5}{8} \times 3\frac{1}{2}$ $5\frac{11}{16}$

APPLICATIONS: Using Multiplication of Fractions These word problems apply the skills taught in the lesson.

Use this recipe for Exercises 54–56.

54. How many cups of olive oil are needed for three times this recipe? $1\frac{1}{2}$

55. How many cups of salad oil are needed to make $\frac{3}{4}$ of the amount of dressing? $1\frac{1}{8}$

56. How many tablespoons of toasted sesame seeds are needed to make $4\frac{1}{2}$ times this recipe? $13\frac{1}{2}$

Curry-Sesame Dressing

1½ cups salad oil	1 teaspoon curry powder
½ cup olive oil	Nutmeg
¼ cup lemon juice	2 tablespoons sherry
1 tablespoon brown mustard	3 tablespoons toasted sesame seeds
2 packets seasoning and broth	

In a blender, combine all ingredients except sesame seeds. Process until blended. Add sesame seeds.

Use cooked broccoli flowerettes, green beans and zucchini, with raw sliced mushrooms and halved cherry tomatoes for salad.

3-6 Division: Fractions and Mixed Numbers

See the Teacher's Manual for the objectives.

Two numbers whose product is one are **reciprocals** of each other.

$\frac{4}{9} \times \frac{9}{4} = 1$ **Reciprocals:** $\frac{4}{9}$ and $\frac{9}{4}$ $7 \times \frac{1}{7} = 1$ **Reciprocals:** 7 and $\frac{1}{7}$

Dividing by a number is the same as multiplying by its reciprocal.

PROCEDURE To divide with fractions:

1. Use the reciprocal of the divisor to write the corresponding multiplication problem.
2. Multiply.
3. Write the answer in lowest terms.

EXAMPLE 1 a. $\frac{3}{7} \div \frac{9}{14} = \underline{\ ?\ }$ b. $\frac{5}{9} \div 15 = \underline{\ ?\ }$

Solutions:

a. [1] $\frac{3}{7} \div \frac{9}{14} = \frac{3}{7} \times \frac{14}{9}$ ◀ *The reciprocal of $\frac{9}{14}$ is $\frac{14}{9}$.*

[2] $= \frac{\overset{1}{\cancel{3}}}{\underset{1}{\cancel{7}}} \times \frac{\overset{2}{\cancel{14}}}{\underset{3}{\cancel{9}}}$

[3] $= \frac{2}{3}$

b. [1] $\frac{5}{9} \div 15 = \frac{5}{9} \times \frac{1}{15}$ ◀ *The reciprocal of 15 is $\frac{1}{15}$.*

[2] $= \frac{\overset{1}{\cancel{5}}}{9} \times \frac{1}{\underset{3}{\cancel{15}}}$

[3] $= \frac{1}{27}$

After completing Example 1, you may wish to have students do some or all of Exercises 1-46.

PROCEDURE To divide with mixed numbers:

1. Write a fraction for each mixed number.
2. Divide the fractions.
3. Write the answer in lowest terms.

EXAMPLE 2 a. $7\frac{3}{4} \div 7\frac{1}{2} = \underline{\ ?\ }$ b. $12 \div 2\frac{4}{7} = \underline{\ ?\ }$

Solutions:

a. [1] $7\frac{3}{4} \div 7\frac{1}{2} = \frac{31}{4} \div \frac{15}{2}$

[2] $= \frac{31}{4} \times \frac{2}{15}$ ◀ *The reciprocal of $\frac{15}{2}$ is $\frac{2}{15}$.*

$= \frac{31}{\underset{2}{\cancel{4}}} \times \frac{\overset{1}{\cancel{2}}}{15}$

$= \frac{31}{30}$ ◀ *Write a mixed number for $\frac{31}{30}$.*

[3] $= 1\frac{1}{30}$

b. [1] $12 \div 2\frac{4}{7} = \frac{12}{1} \div \frac{18}{7}$

[2] $= \frac{12}{1} \times \frac{7}{18}$

$= \frac{\overset{2}{\cancel{12}}}{1} \times \frac{7}{\underset{3}{\cancel{18}}}$

$= \frac{14}{3}$

[3] $= 4\frac{2}{3}$

EXERCISES

Write the reciprocal of each number.

1. $\frac{2}{3}$ $\frac{3}{2}$ **2.** $\frac{3}{5}$ $\frac{5}{3}$ **3.** $\frac{9}{7}$ $\frac{7}{9}$ **4.** 2 $\frac{1}{2}$ **5.** 4 $\frac{1}{4}$ **6.** $\frac{5}{8}$ $\frac{8}{5}$ **7.** $\frac{6}{7}$ $\frac{7}{6}$ **8.** $\frac{5}{3}$ $\frac{3}{5}$

9. 15 $\frac{1}{15}$ **10.** 8 $\frac{1}{8}$ **11.** $\frac{3}{2}$ $\frac{2}{3}$ **12.** $\frac{7}{12}$ $\frac{12}{7}$ **13.** $\frac{8}{13}$ $\frac{13}{8}$ **14.** $\frac{2}{11}$ $\frac{11}{2}$ **15.** $\frac{6}{13}$ $\frac{13}{6}$ **16.** 18 $\frac{1}{18}$

Divide. (Example 1)

17. $\frac{1}{4} \div \frac{1}{3}$ $\frac{3}{4}$ **18.** $\frac{3}{8} \div 3$ $\frac{1}{8}$ **19.** $\frac{2}{7} \div \frac{1}{8}$ $2\frac{2}{7}$ **20.** $\frac{4}{5} \div \frac{16}{25}$ $1\frac{1}{4}$ **21.** $\frac{7}{10} \div 14$ $\frac{1}{20}$ **22.** $\frac{4}{9} \div 16$ $\frac{1}{36}$

23. $6 \div \frac{1}{4}$ 24 **24.** $12 \div \frac{3}{5}$ 20 **25.** $\frac{1}{18} \div \frac{2}{45}$ $1\frac{1}{4}$ **26.** $\frac{1}{2} \div 6$ $\frac{1}{12}$ **27.** $6 \div \frac{3}{7}$ 14 **28.** $\frac{4}{7} \div \frac{2}{3}$ $\frac{6}{7}$

29. $\frac{9}{10} \div \frac{3}{5}$ $1\frac{1}{2}$ **30.** $81 \div \frac{9}{11}$ 99 **31.** $\frac{7}{6} \div \frac{5}{3}$ $\frac{7}{10}$ **32.** $\frac{2}{9} \div \frac{1}{3}$ $\frac{2}{3}$ **33.** $7 \div \frac{7}{12}$ 12 **34.** $16 \div \frac{8}{13}$ 26

35. $\frac{7}{22} \div 14$ $\frac{1}{44}$ **36.** $\frac{9}{10} \div 15$ $\frac{3}{50}$ **37.** $\frac{1}{5} \div \frac{1}{10}$ 2 **38.** $4 \div \frac{1}{4}$ 16 **39.** $18 \div \frac{2}{9}$ 81 **40.** $8 \div \frac{1}{2}$ 16

41. $\frac{3}{5} \div \frac{15}{20}$ $\frac{4}{5}$ **42.** $\frac{2}{9} \div \frac{20}{27}$ $\frac{3}{10}$ **43.** $18 \div \frac{1}{3}$ 54 **44.** $\frac{2}{5} \div \frac{1}{25}$ 10 **45.** $\frac{3}{8} \div \frac{6}{16}$ 1 **46.** $\frac{1}{7} \div 21$ $\frac{1}{147}$

(Example 2)

47. $7\frac{1}{2} \div 15$ $\frac{1}{2}$ **48.** $2\frac{1}{2} \div 3\frac{1}{3}$ $\frac{3}{4}$ **49.** $8\frac{2}{5} \div 4\frac{1}{5}$ 2 **50.** $9\frac{3}{4} \div 13$ $\frac{3}{4}$ **51.** $2\frac{4}{5} \div 7$ $\frac{2}{5}$

52. $9\frac{2}{3} \div 4\frac{1}{6}$ $2\frac{8}{25}$ **53.** $8\frac{1}{2} \div 3\frac{2}{5}$ $2\frac{1}{2}$ **54.** $12 \div 1\frac{1}{2}$ 8 **55.** $4 \div 1\frac{1}{3}$ 3 **56.** $7\frac{1}{5} \div 2\frac{2}{5}$ 3

57. $4\frac{5}{9} \div \frac{5}{18}$ $16\frac{2}{5}$ **58.** $3 \div 7\frac{1}{2}$ $\frac{2}{5}$ **59.** $33 \div 4\frac{1}{8}$ 8 **60.** $2\frac{1}{2} \div 2\frac{1}{2}$ 1 **61.** $4\frac{3}{4} \div 3\frac{1}{4}$ $1\frac{6}{13}$

62. $8\frac{4}{5} \div \frac{11}{15}$ 12 **63.** $12\frac{3}{8} \div 1\frac{3}{8}$ 9 **64.** $2\frac{1}{12} \div \frac{5}{6}$ $2\frac{1}{2}$ **65.** $4\frac{8}{9} \div 2\frac{2}{3}$ $1\frac{5}{6}$ **66.** $10\frac{2}{5} \div 3\frac{1}{5}$ $3\frac{1}{4}$

67. $14 \div 1\frac{2}{5}$ 10 **68.** $21 \div 3\frac{3}{7}$ $6\frac{1}{8}$ **69.** $5\frac{1}{3} \div 8$ $\frac{2}{3}$ **70.** $1\frac{1}{3} \div 2$ $\frac{2}{3}$ **71.** $4\frac{1}{6} \div 6\frac{1}{4}$ $\frac{2}{3}$

72. $2\frac{1}{4} \div 3\frac{3}{8}$ $\frac{2}{3}$ **73.** $7\frac{1}{2} \div 1\frac{1}{4}$ 6 **74.** $\frac{3}{4} \div 4\frac{1}{12}$ $\frac{9}{49}$ **75.** $4\frac{6}{7} \div 8\frac{1}{2}$ $\frac{4}{7}$ **76.** $\frac{5}{12} \div 60$ $\frac{1}{144}$

These word problems apply the skills taught in the lesson.

APPLICATIONS: Using Division of Fractions

77. A stack of magazines weighs 20 pounds. Each magazine weighs $\frac{5}{8}$ pound. How many magazines are in the stack? 32

78. A carton of 12 cans of peaches weighs $24\frac{3}{4}$ pounds. How much does each can weigh? $2\frac{1}{16}$ pounds

79. A crate of apples weighs $21\frac{1}{4}$ pounds. Each apple weighs about $\frac{1}{8}$ pound. How many apples are in the crate? 170

80. A box of books weighs $52\frac{1}{2}$ pounds. Each book weighs $3\frac{1}{2}$ pounds. How many books are in the box? 15

3-7 Rounding and Estimation

See the Teacher's Manual for the objectives.

The rules for rounding mixed numbers can help you to estimate answers. You may wish to review comparing fractions.

PROCEDURE To round a mixed number, look at the fractional part.

a. If the fraction is less than $\frac{1}{2}$, round <u>down</u> to the nearest whole number.

b. If the fraction is greater than or equal to $\frac{1}{2}$, round <u>up</u> to the next whole number.

EXAMPLE

a. $4\frac{1}{3}$ rounded to the nearest whole number is **4.**

b. $8\frac{1}{2}$ rounded to the nearest whole number is **9.**

c. $12\frac{7}{8}$ rounded to the nearest whole number is **13.**

EXERCISES

Round to the nearest whole number. (Example)

1. $3\frac{1}{3}$ 3 **2.** $7\frac{7}{8}$ 8 **3.** $2\frac{2}{9}$ 2 **4.** $4\frac{11}{12}$ 5 **5.** $15\frac{1}{2}$ 16 **6.** $6\frac{3}{5}$ 7 **7.** $11\frac{13}{25}$ 12

8. $2\frac{9}{16}$ 3 **9.** $3\frac{3}{4}$ 4 **10.** $4\frac{5}{7}$ 5 **11.** $6\frac{3}{13}$ 6 **12.** $1\frac{1}{7}$ 1 **13.** $5\frac{4}{9}$ 5 **14.** $8\frac{3}{8}$ 8

15. $4\frac{2}{11}$ 4 **16.** $6\frac{13}{18}$ 7 **17.** $6\frac{5}{11}$ 6 **18.** $8\frac{6}{12}$ 9 **19.** $3\frac{9}{17}$ 4 **20.** $18\frac{3}{10}$ 18 **21.** $2\frac{4}{7}$ 3

Choose the best estimate. Choose a, b, c, or d.

22. $2\frac{8}{9} + 3\frac{1}{10}$ a **a.** $3 + 3$ **b.** $2 + 3$ **c.** $3 + 4$ **d.** $2 + 2$

23. $112\frac{1}{8} + 5\frac{4}{5}$ c **a.** $113 + 6$ **b.** $111 + 5$ **c.** $112 + 6$ **d.** $112 + 5$

24. $21\frac{7}{8} - 17\frac{1}{8}$ c **a.** $21 - 17$ **b.** $21 - 18$ **c.** $22 - 17$ **d.** $20 - 18$

25. $7\frac{1}{5} \div 6\frac{1}{8}$ c **a.** $7 \div 7$ **b.** $8 \div 5$ **c.** $7 \div 6$ **d.** $8 \div 6$

26. $14\frac{8}{9} \div 5\frac{1}{12}$ a **a.** $15 \div 5$ **b.** $14 \div 5$ **c.** $14 \div 6$ **d.** $15 \div 6$

27. $21\frac{1}{8} \times 14\frac{9}{10}$ d **a.** 22×15 **b.** 21×14 **c.** 22×14 **d.** 21×15

28. $\frac{9}{10} \times 10\frac{2}{11}$ a **a.** 10 **b.** 12 **c.** 13 **d.** 14

29. $6\frac{1}{5} \div 1\frac{1}{10}$ b **a.** 4 **b.** 6 **c.** 8 **d.** 10

30. $74\frac{9}{10} - 15\frac{1}{7}$ c **a.** 40 **b.** 50 **c.** 60 **d.** 70

31. $12\frac{1}{8} - 4\frac{6}{7}$ d **a.** 10 **b.** 9 **c.** 8 **d.** 7

32. $16\frac{3}{5} + 2\frac{1}{5}$ b **a.** 16 **b.** 19 **c.** 17 **d.** 21

APPLICATIONS: Using Estimation

Choose the best estimate. Choose a, b, c, or d.

33. Sue walked $3\frac{1}{8}$ miles on Saturday and $4\frac{5}{6}$ miles on Sunday. Estimate how many miles she walked on both days. d

a. 5 **b.** 6 **c.** 7 **d.** 8

34. A carpenter cuts $3\frac{7}{8}$ inches from a board that is $15\frac{1}{4}$ inches long. Estimate the new length of the board in inches. b

a. 10 **b.** 11 **c.** 12 **d.** 13

35. A recipe calls for $2\frac{1}{8}$ cups of milk. Estimate how many cups of milk are necessary for a recipe $3\frac{3}{4}$ times as large. c

a. 6 **b.** 7 **c.** 8 **d.** 9

36. A box of 1–quart cans of motor oil weighs $47\frac{4}{5}$ pounds. There are 24 cans in the box. About how many pounds does each one weigh? b

a. 1 **b.** 2 **c.** 3 **d.** 4

37. A box of books weighs $48\frac{1}{4}$ pounds. There are 16 books in the box. Estimate how many pounds each book weighs. c

a. 1 **b.** 2 **c.** 3 **d.** 4

38. Mike ran $4\frac{1}{3}$ miles on Saturday and $2\frac{7}{8}$ miles on Sunday. Estimate how many more miles he ran on Saturday than on Sunday. b

a. 2 **b.** 1 **c.** 3 **d.** 0

Calculator exercises are optional.

MULTIPLYING AND DIVIDING FRACTIONS

You can use a calculator to multiply and divide with fractions. The calculator gives the answer as an equivalent decimal.

EXAMPLE: $\frac{4}{25} \times \frac{9}{40} \div \frac{3}{5} = \underline{\ ?\ }$

Solution: 1 Write the reciprocal of the divisor.

$\frac{4}{25} \times \frac{9}{40} \div \frac{3}{5} = \frac{4}{25} \times \frac{9}{40} \times \frac{5}{3}$

2 Multiply the denominators. Enter the products in the memory.

2 5 × 4 0 × 3 = M+ — 3000.

3 Multiply the numerators. Then divide.

4 × 9 × 5 ÷ MR = — 0.06

EXERCISES

Use a calculator to find each answer.

1. $\frac{42}{100} \times \frac{25}{7} \div \frac{6}{20}$ 5

2. $\frac{14}{25} \times \frac{5}{2} \div \frac{7}{8}$ 1.6

3. $\frac{21}{50} \times \frac{10}{12} \div \frac{7}{15}$ 0.75

4. $\frac{15}{22} \times \frac{11}{5} \div \frac{30}{44}$ 2.2

5. $\frac{14}{45} \times \frac{9}{7} \div \frac{4}{5}$ 0.5

6. $\frac{8}{17} \times \frac{51}{56} \div \frac{3}{7}$ 1

7. $\frac{9}{23} \times \frac{46}{81} \div \frac{4}{27}$ 1.5

8. $\frac{7}{27} \times \frac{54}{70} \div \frac{1}{10}$ 2

AIR CONDITIONING TECHNICIAN

Career lessons are optional.
This lesson applies the skills of using a formula and reading a table.

In addition to installing and repairing air conditioners, Juan Moreno helps his customers to select the right size air conditioners.

The size (cooling capacity) is indicated by the number of **Btu's (British Thermal Units).** To do this, he used the

WHILE divided by 60

formula along with certain rules.

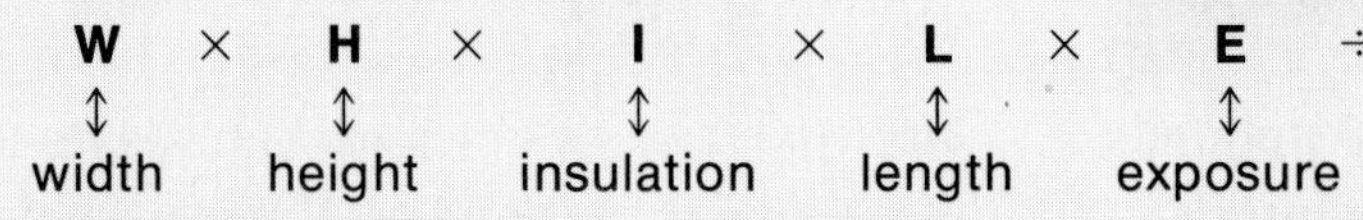

W × **H** × **I** × **L** × **E** ÷ **60** = **Btu per hour**

width, height, insulation, length, exposure

INSULATION RULES	If the room is well insulated, use 10 for **I.** If the room is not insulated, use 18 for **I.**
EXPOSURE RULES	If the longest wall faces: ① north, use 16 for **E.** ② east, use 17 for **E.** ③ south, use 18 for **E.** ④ west, use 20 for **E.**

EXAMPLE

How many Btu's per hour are needed to cool a room that is 15 feet wide, 8 feet high, and 20 feet long? The room is well insulated, and the 20–foot wall faces south.

Solution:

1 Identify the values.

W = 15, **H** = 8, **I** = 10, **L** = 20, **E** = 18

2 Replace the letters in the formula.

W × H × I × L × E ÷ 60

↕ ↕ ↕ ↕ ↕

15 × 8 × 10 × 20 × 18 ÷ 60

3 Use paper and pencil or use a calculator to compute the answer.

1 5 × 8 × 1 0 ×

2 0 × 1 8 ÷ 6 0 = 7200.

The size of the air conditioner should be at least **7200 Btu's.**

EXERCISES

Note that Exercises 1–6 are non-verbal.

For Exercises 1–6, use the formula W × H × I × L × E ÷ 60 to complete the table.

	Width of Room	Height of Room	Insulation?	Length of Room	Exposure	Cooling Capacity
1.	10 ft	10 ft	Yes	20 ft	South	? 6000 Btu's
2.	15 ft	9 ft	No	20 ft	West	? 16,200 Btu's
3.	12 ft	10 ft	Yes	15 ft	West	? 6000 Btu's
4.	10 ft	10 ft	Yes	30 ft	East	? 8500 Btu's
5.	15 ft	10 ft	No	40 ft	North	? 28,800 Btu's
6.	12 ft	8 ft	Yes	35 ft	South	? 10,080 Btu's

7. A rectangular room 20 feet by 12 feet is 9 feet high. The room is not insulated, and faces north. Find the number of Btu's per hour needed to cool the room. 10,368 Btu's

8. An insulated room with a western exposure is 25 feet long, 8 feet wide, and 12 feet high. How many Btu's per hour are needed to cool the room? 8000 Btu's

9. If the room in Exercise 7 faced east, how many Btu's per hour would be needed to cool the room? 11,016 Btu's

10. An insulated room is 30 feet long, $12\frac{1}{2}$ feet wide, and 8 feet high. The room faces north. Find the number of Btu's per hour needed to cool the room. 8000 Btu's

11. Suppose that the room in Exercise 10 were not insulated. How many Btu's per hour would be needed to cool the room? 14,400 Btu's

12. Suppose that the room in Exercise 10 faced west instead of north. Find the number of Btu's per hour needed to cool the room. 10,000 Btu's

13. If the room in Exercise 10 were not insulated and faced west, how many Btu's per hour would be needed to cool the room? 18,000 Btu's

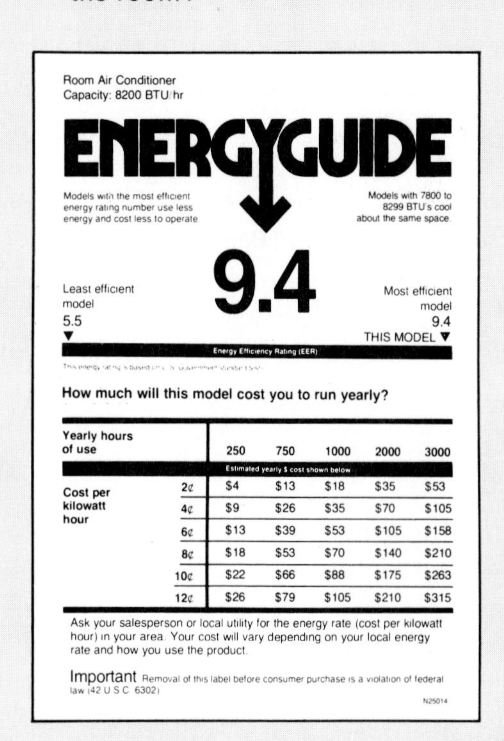

Room Air Conditioner
Capacity: 8200 BTU/hr

ENERGYGUIDE

Models with the most efficient energy rating number use less energy and cost less to operate

Models with 7800 to 8299 BTU's cool about the same space.

9.4

Least efficient model 5.5

Most efficient model 9.4

THIS MODEL

Energy Efficiency Rating (EER)

How much will this model cost you to run yearly?

Yearly hours of use		250	750	1000	2000	3000
		Estimated yearly $ cost shown below				
Cost per kilowatt hour	2¢	$4	$13	$18	$35	$53
	4¢	$9	$26	$35	$70	$105
	6¢	$13	$39	$53	$105	$158
	8¢	$18	$53	$70	$140	$210
	10¢	$22	$66	$88	$175	$263
	12¢	$26	$79	$105	$210	$315

Ask your salesperson or local utility for the energy rate (cost per kilowatt hour) in your area. Your cost will vary depending on your local energy rate and how you use the product.

Important Removal of this label before consumer purchase is a violation of federal law (42 U S C 6302)

N25014

Chapter Review

These exercises review the vocabulary, skills and applications presented in the chapter, as preparation for the chapter test.

Part 1: VOCABULARY

For Exercises 1–6, choose from the box at the right the word(s) that completes each statement.

lowest terms
reciprocals
mixed number
like fractions
fractions
LCD

1. You can write a fraction greater than 1 as a __?__. mixed number (Pages 46–47)
2. When the numerator and denominator of a fraction cannot be divided by the same number except 1, it is in __?__. lowest terms (Pages 46--47)
3. Fractions that have the same denominator are called __?__. (Pages 48–49) like fractions
4. When you write like fractions for unlike fractions, you first find the __?__. (Pages 48–49) LCD
5. Before you multiply mixed numbers you change the mixed numbers to __?__. (Pages 56–57) fractions
6. Numbers such as $\frac{3}{5}$ and $\frac{5}{3}$ are __?__. (Pages 58–59) reciprocals

Part 2: SKILLS

Write a mixed number for each fraction. (Pages 46–47)

7. $\frac{18}{13}$ $1\frac{5}{13}$ 8. $\frac{7}{4}$ $1\frac{3}{4}$ 9. $\frac{16}{9}$ $1\frac{7}{9}$ 10. $\frac{21}{5}$ $4\frac{1}{5}$ 11. $\frac{30}{11}$ $2\frac{8}{11}$ 12. $\frac{14}{5}$ $2\frac{4}{5}$ 13. $\frac{38}{23}$ $1\frac{15}{23}$ 14. $\frac{17}{7}$ $2\frac{3}{7}$

Write in lowest terms. Then write a mixed number for any fraction greater than 1. (Pages 46–47)

15. $\frac{8}{12}$ $\frac{2}{3}$ 16. $\frac{18}{24}$ $\frac{3}{4}$ 17. $\frac{25}{10}$ $2\frac{1}{2}$ 18. $\frac{8}{16}$ $\frac{1}{2}$ 19. $\frac{5}{20}$ $\frac{1}{4}$ 20. $\frac{66}{36}$ $1\frac{5}{6}$ 21. $\frac{21}{15}$ $1\frac{2}{5}$ 22. $\frac{18}{40}$ $\frac{9}{20}$

Add or subtract. Write each answer in lowest terms. (Pages 48–49)

23. $\frac{3}{7} + \frac{2}{7}$ $\frac{5}{7}$ 24. $\frac{9}{16} - \frac{7}{16}$ $\frac{1}{8}$ 25. $\frac{11}{25} + \frac{4}{25}$ $\frac{3}{5}$ 26. $\frac{7}{12} - \frac{1}{12}$ $\frac{1}{2}$ 27. $\frac{8}{15} + \frac{2}{15}$ $\frac{2}{3}$
28. $\frac{3}{5} - \frac{2}{5}$ $\frac{1}{5}$

Write like fractions for each pair of fractions. (Pages 48–49)

29. $\frac{2}{5}$ and $\frac{1}{4}$ $\frac{8}{20}, \frac{5}{20}$ 30. $\frac{9}{10}$ and $\frac{3}{4}$ $\frac{18}{20}, \frac{15}{20}$ 31. $\frac{2}{3}$ and $\frac{1}{8}$ $\frac{16}{24}, \frac{3}{24}$ 32. $\frac{3}{5}$ and $\frac{1}{2}$ $\frac{6}{10}, \frac{5}{10}$ 33. $\frac{5}{12}$ and $\frac{3}{8}$ $\frac{10}{24}, \frac{9}{24}$

Add. Write each answer in lowest terms. (Pages 50–51)

34. $\frac{7}{12} + \frac{3}{4}$ $1\frac{1}{3}$ 35. $\frac{9}{10} + \frac{3}{5}$ $1\frac{1}{2}$ 36. $\frac{7}{15} + \frac{2}{3}$ $1\frac{2}{15}$ 37. $1\frac{9}{11} + 2\frac{1}{2}$ $4\frac{7}{22}$ 38. $7\frac{3}{7} + 6\frac{1}{14}$ $13\frac{1}{2}$
39. $2\frac{5}{6} + 1\frac{1}{2}$ $4\frac{1}{3}$

Subtract. Write each answer in lowest terms. (Pages 52–53)

40. $\frac{7}{12} - \frac{1}{3}$ $\frac{1}{4}$ **41.** $\frac{5}{14} - \frac{1}{7}$ $\frac{3}{14}$ **42.** $7\frac{8}{9} - 3\frac{2}{3}$ $4\frac{2}{9}$ **43.** $1\frac{3}{8} - \frac{1}{6}$ $1\frac{5}{24}$ **44.** $\frac{9}{16} - \frac{1}{6}$ $\frac{19}{48}$

45. $4\frac{1}{11} - 3\frac{1}{2}$ $\frac{13}{22}$

46. $4\frac{3}{8} - 1\frac{1}{2}$ $2\frac{7}{8}$ **47.** $7\frac{2}{9} - 1\frac{5}{6}$ $5\frac{7}{18}$ **48.** $6\frac{3}{5} - 4\frac{7}{10}$ $1\frac{9}{10}$ **49.** $9\frac{1}{4} - 2\frac{1}{3}$ $6\frac{11}{12}$ **50.** $6\frac{5}{18} - 3\frac{4}{9}$ $2\frac{5}{6}$

51. $17\frac{2}{5} - 8\frac{3}{4}$ $8\frac{13}{20}$

Multiply. Write each answer in lowest terms. (Pages 56–57)

52. $\frac{2}{7} \times \frac{3}{10}$ $\frac{3}{35}$ **53.** $\frac{5}{8} \times \frac{2}{15}$ $\frac{1}{12}$ **54.** $\frac{4}{21} \times \frac{7}{10}$ $\frac{2}{15}$ **55.** $\frac{6}{7} \times \frac{3}{5}$ $\frac{18}{35}$ **56.** $\frac{5}{9} \times \frac{3}{4}$ $\frac{5}{12}$

57. $7 \times \frac{3}{14}$ $1\frac{1}{2}$ **58.** $18 \times \frac{5}{6}$ 15 **59.** $2 \times \frac{4}{7}$ $1\frac{1}{7}$ **60.** $\frac{3}{5} \times 6$ $3\frac{3}{5}$ **61.** $\frac{7}{10} \times 15$ $10\frac{1}{2}$

Write a fraction for each mixed number. (Pages 56–57)

62. $1\frac{7}{8}$ $\frac{15}{8}$ **63.** $4\frac{2}{3}$ $\frac{14}{3}$ **64.** $16\frac{3}{4}$ $\frac{67}{4}$ **65.** $5\frac{2}{5}$ $\frac{27}{5}$ **66.** $9\frac{1}{2}$ $\frac{19}{2}$ **67.** $4\frac{1}{4}$ $\frac{17}{4}$ **68.** $7\frac{3}{10}$ $\frac{73}{10}$

Multiply. Write the answer in lowest terms. (Pages 56–57)

69. $3\frac{1}{2} \times 7$ $24\frac{1}{2}$ **70.** $2\frac{3}{4} \times \frac{5}{11}$ $1\frac{1}{4}$ **71.** $7\frac{3}{5} \times \frac{5}{19}$ 2 **72.** $8 \times 2\frac{4}{5}$ $22\frac{2}{5}$ **73.** $16 \times 7\frac{3}{8}$ 118

74. $2\frac{2}{3} \times 1\frac{1}{8}$ 3 **75.** $4\frac{5}{7} \times 3\frac{1}{3}$ $15\frac{5}{7}$ **76.** $\frac{3}{5} \times 1\frac{2}{3}$ 1 **77.** $8\frac{1}{6} \times \frac{3}{7}$ $3\frac{1}{2}$ **78.** $4\frac{5}{8} \times \frac{1}{2}$ $2\frac{5}{16}$

Write the reciprocal of each number. (Pages 58–59)

79. $\frac{3}{8}$ $\frac{8}{3}$ **80.** $\frac{2}{7}$ $\frac{7}{2}$ **81.** 5 $\frac{1}{5}$ **82.** 11 $\frac{1}{11}$ **83.** $\frac{3}{2}$ $\frac{2}{3}$ **84.** $\frac{1}{13}$ $\frac{13}{1}$, or 13 **85.** 4 $\frac{1}{4}$

Divide. (Pages 58–59)

86. $\frac{2}{3} \div \frac{2}{9}$ 3 **87.** $\frac{5}{8} \div \frac{3}{4}$ $\frac{5}{6}$ **88.** $\frac{1}{16} \div 2$ $\frac{1}{32}$ **89.** $4 \div \frac{1}{2}$ 8 **90.** $15 \div \frac{3}{5}$ 25

91. $1\frac{3}{5} \div \frac{4}{5}$ 2 **92.** $2\frac{1}{2} \div 2$ $1\frac{1}{4}$ **93.** $16\frac{1}{3} \div 7$ $2\frac{1}{3}$ **94.** $8\frac{1}{2} \div 8\frac{1}{2}$ 1 **95.** $5\frac{2}{3} \div \frac{5}{6}$ $6\frac{4}{5}$

Round to the nearest whole number. (Pages 60–61)

96. $2\frac{3}{5}$ 3 **97.** $4\frac{9}{16}$ 5 **98.** $7\frac{7}{12}$ 8 **99.** $1\frac{3}{8}$ 1 **100.** $3\frac{2}{11}$ 3 **101.** $16\frac{3}{4}$ 17 **102.** $17\frac{12}{25}$ 17

Choose the best estimate. Choose a, b, c, or d. (Pages 60–61)

103. $4\frac{6}{7} + 12\frac{1}{8}$ b	**a.** $4 + 12$	**b.** $5 + 12$	**c.** $5 + 13$	**d.** $4 + 11$
104. $9\frac{1}{8} - 4\frac{7}{9}$ c	**a.** $9 - 4$	**b.** $10 - 4$	**c.** $9 - 5$	**d.** $10 - 5$
105. $3\frac{9}{10} \times 6\frac{1}{10}$ c	**a.** 3×7	**b.** 3×6	**c.** 4×6	**d.** 4×7
106. $6\frac{1}{10} \div 2\frac{7}{8}$ a	**a.** $6 \div 3$	**b.** $6 \div 2$	**c.** $7 \div 3$	**d.** $7 \div 2$
107. $3\frac{4}{5} + 8\frac{1}{10}$ c	**a.** 10	**b.** 11	**c.** 12	**d.** 13
108. $7\frac{1}{7} - 2\frac{9}{11}$ d	**a.** 6	**b.** 5	**c.** 3	**d.** 4
109. $\frac{7}{8} \times 12\frac{1}{4}$ a	**a.** 12	**b.** 26	**c.** 24	**d.** 13
110. $25\frac{1}{8} \div 4\frac{7}{8}$ b	**a.** 6	**b.** 5	**c.** 4	**d.** 7

The word problems covered in this chapter are presented here in a mixed setting.

Part 3: APPLICATIONS

Note: each problem is referenced to the related page(s).

111. A welder joins three pieces of pipe together. Their lengths are: $1\frac{1}{3}$ feet, $1\frac{1}{4}$ feet, and $\frac{7}{8}$ foot. How long will the finished pipe be? (Pages 50–51) $3\frac{11}{24}$ feet

112. Three pieces of wood are placed on top of each other. They are $1\frac{5}{8}$ inches, $2\frac{1}{4}$ inches, and $\frac{1}{2}$ inch thick. Find the total thickness of the stack. (Pages 50–51) $4\frac{3}{8}$ inches

113. Juan walked $4\frac{7}{8}$ miles last week and $5\frac{4}{5}$ miles this week. About how many miles did he walk? (Pages 60–61) b

a. 10 **b.** 11 **c.** 12 **d.** 9

114. A stack of wooden blocks weighs $2\frac{5}{8}$ pounds. There are 7 blocks in the stack. How much does each block weigh? (Pages 58–59) $\frac{3}{8}$ pound

115. A soup recipe calls for $\frac{3}{4}$ teaspoon of salt. How many teaspoons are needed for 4 times the recipe? (Pages 56–57) 3 teaspoons

116. A recipe calls for $1\frac{1}{3}$ cups of flour. How much flour is needed to make the recipe $3\frac{1}{2}$ times as large? (Pages 56–57) $4\frac{2}{3}$ cups

117. One cubic foot of water weighs $62\frac{1}{2}$ pounds. How many cubic feet of water weigh 250 pounds? (Pages 58–59) 4 cubic feet

118. A carpenter is making a bread board. She wants it to be 9 inches wide. It is only $7\frac{1}{2}$ inches wide now. How wide a strip must she add? (Pages 52–53) $1\frac{1}{2}$ inches

119. Find the missing length. $1\frac{1}{2}$ inches (Pages 52–53)

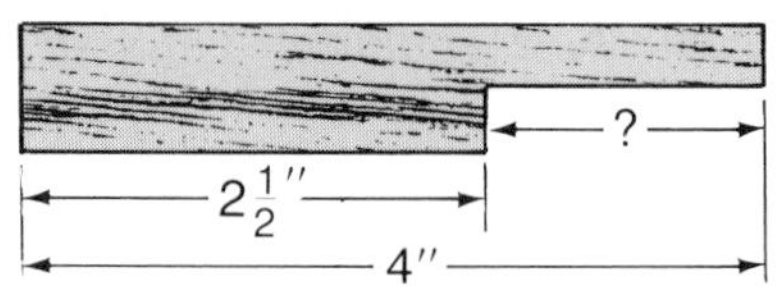

120. A case of canned apricots weighs $23\frac{7}{8}$ pounds. There are 8 cans in the case. About how many pounds does each can weigh? (Pages 60–61) d

a. 5 **b.** 2 **c.** 4 **d.** 3

Chapter Test

The Teacher's Resource Book contains two forms of each chapter test.

1. Write a fraction for $1\frac{1}{2}$. $\frac{3}{2}$

2. Write a fraction for $6\frac{3}{5}$. $\frac{33}{5}$

3. Find the LCD of $\frac{2}{3}$ and $\frac{1}{2}$. 6

4. Find the LCD of $\frac{3}{8}$ and $\frac{5}{12}$. 24

Perform the indicated operation. Write each answer in lowest terms.

5. $\frac{3}{5} + \frac{1}{5}$ $\frac{4}{5}$

6. $\frac{7}{16} + \frac{5}{8}$ $1\frac{1}{16}$

7. $\frac{11}{12} - \frac{5}{12}$ $\frac{1}{2}$

8. $\frac{5}{8} - \frac{1}{7}$ $\frac{27}{56}$

9. $7\frac{1}{2} + 9\frac{2}{15}$ $16\frac{19}{30}$

10. $4\frac{5}{8} + 1\frac{1}{10}$ $5\frac{29}{40}$

11. $6\frac{3}{5} - 2\frac{1}{3}$ $4\frac{4}{15}$

12. $6\frac{2}{3} - 4\frac{13}{15}$ $1\frac{4}{5}$

13. $\frac{1}{7} \times \frac{3}{5}$ $\frac{3}{35}$

14. $\frac{3}{8} \times \frac{5}{18}$ $\frac{5}{48}$

15. $6\frac{1}{2} \times \frac{5}{13}$ $2\frac{1}{2}$

16. $3\frac{5}{7} \times 1\frac{3}{4}$ $6\frac{1}{2}$

17. $\frac{4}{8} \div \frac{1}{3}$ $1\frac{1}{2}$

18. $7\frac{1}{2} \div 5$ $1\frac{1}{2}$

19. $3\frac{1}{6} \div 1\frac{1}{3}$ $2\frac{3}{8}$

20. $\frac{1}{5} \div 5\frac{1}{2}$ $\frac{2}{55}$

Solve.

21. A recipe calls for $2\frac{1}{2}$ teaspoons of vinegar. How much vinegar is needed for a recipe that is 4 times as large? 10 teaspoons

22. A box of washers weighs $17\frac{1}{2}$ ounces. Each washer weighs about $\frac{7}{8}$ of an ounce. How many washers are in the box? 20

23. Tim jogs three days a week. Last week he jogged $2\frac{1}{2}$ miles, $3\frac{1}{4}$ miles, and $4\frac{1}{3}$ miles. How much did he jog in all? $10\frac{1}{12}$ miles

24. Find the missing height in this brick wall. $2\frac{2}{3}$ feet

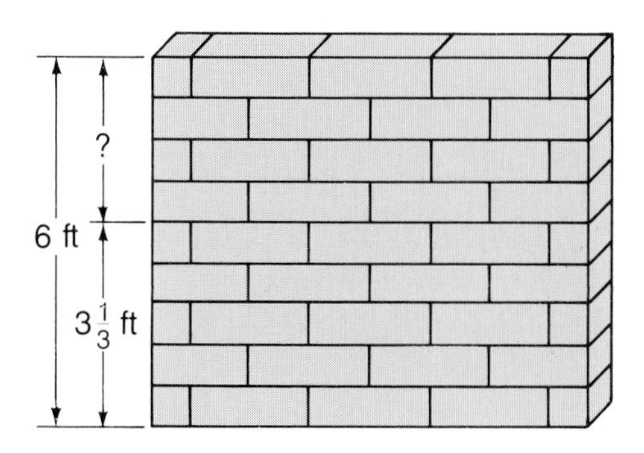

25. A carpenter cuts $2\frac{7}{8}$ feet off a board that is 6 feet long. Estimate how many feet are left. c

a. 1 **b.** 2 **c.** 3 **d.** 4

Cumulative Review: Chapters 1–3

Choose the correct answer. Choose a, b, c, or d.

1. Add: $63 + 27 + 295 + 4037$ d

a. 15,987 **b.** 7077
c. 5022 **d.** 4422

2. Subtract: b $\begin{array}{r} 6834 \\ -2918 \\ \hline \end{array}$

a. 3853 **b.** 3916
c. 9752 **d.** 3565

3. Multiply: c $\begin{array}{r} 735 \\ \times\ 27 \\ \hline \end{array}$

a. 752 **b.** 762
c. 19,845 **d.** 19,745

4. Divide: $37\overline{)7358}$ a

a. 198 r 32 **b.** 272,245
c. 19 r 32 **d.** 19 r 328

5. Round 6396 to the nearest hundred. b

a. 6300 **b.** 6400
c. 6390 **d.** 6000

6. Subtract: $12.93 - 4.07$ a

a. 8.86 **b.** 8.23 **c.** 17 **d.** 7.86

7. Add: $3.297 + 14.861 + 2.81$ b

a. 22.366 **b.** 20.968
c. 24.166 **d.** 24.895

8. How many meters are in the perimeter of this scarf? a

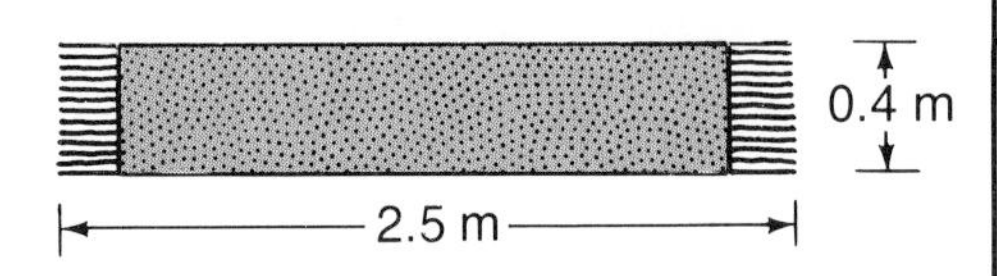

a. 5.8 **b.** 2.9 **c.** 1 **d.** 0.8

9. Divide: $28.89 \div 54$ a

a. 0.535 **b.** 5.35
c. 0.53 **d.** 0.534

10. Multiply: 293×0.17 a

a. 49.81 **b.** 23.44
c. 4.981 **d.** 2.344

11. Write the approximate capacity of an automobile gas tank in liters. c

a. 0.05 **b.** 5
c. 50 **d.** 500

12. Complete: 25 kg = __?__ g d

a. 2.5 **b.** 25
c. 250 **d.** 25,000

13. Choose the most suitable temperature for a cold winter day. a

a. 2°C **b.** 36°C **c.** 25°C **d.** 90°C

14. A tablespoon contains 15 milliliters. How many tablespoons are there in a bottle containing 1050 milliliters? a

a. 70 **b.** 20 **c.** 50 **d.** 10

15. A box of washers weighs 21 ounces. Each washer weighs about $\frac{7}{8}$ of an ounce. How many washers are in the box? c

a. 18 **b.** 20 **c.** 24 **d.** 28

16. Beef costs \$2.98 per pound. Estimate the cost of 3.9 pounds. d

a. \$15 **b.** \$9
c. \$24 **d.** \$12

17. Add. Write the answer in lowest terms. a

$$\frac{3}{7} + \frac{1}{7} + \frac{2}{7}$$

a. $\frac{6}{7}$ **b.** $\frac{6}{21}$ **c.** $\frac{2}{7}$ **d.** $\frac{5}{7}$

18. Write the least common denominator of $\frac{2}{5}$ and $\frac{5}{8}$. c

a. 10 **b.** 13 **c.** 40 **d.** 20

19. Add. Write the answer in lowest terms. c

$$2\frac{2}{5} + 3\frac{1}{10}$$

a. $8\frac{1}{2}$ **b.** $5\frac{3}{15}$ **c.** $5\frac{1}{2}$ **d.** $5\frac{1}{5}$

20. Subtract. Write the answer in lowest terms. b

$$2\frac{3}{8} - 1\frac{5}{8}$$

a. $1\frac{3}{4}$ **b.** $\frac{3}{4}$ **c.** $1\frac{1}{4}$ **d.** $\frac{1}{4}$

21. Round $3\frac{9}{16}$ to the nearest whole number. b

a. 3 **b.** 4 **c.** 39 **d.** 316

22. Write the reciprocal of $4\frac{2}{3}$. a

a. $\frac{3}{14}$ **b.** $\frac{14}{3}$ **c.** $\frac{3}{24}$ **d.** $\frac{24}{3}$

23. Find the volume in cubic meters of this filing cabinet. b

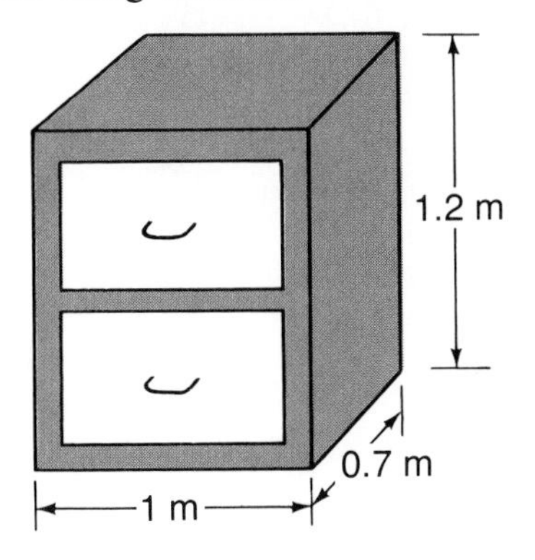

a. 2.9 **b.** 0.84
c. 0.78 **d.** 1.9

24. Multiply. Write the answer in lowest terms. d

$$\frac{6}{7} \times \frac{5}{12}$$

a. $\frac{72}{35}$ **b.** $\frac{2}{35}$ **c.** $\frac{30}{19}$ **d.** $\frac{5}{14}$

25. Divide. Write the answer in lowest terms. a

$$3\frac{1}{8} \div 2\frac{3}{16}$$

a. $1\frac{3}{7}$ **b.** $5\frac{5}{16}$ **c.** $1\frac{1}{16}$ **d.** $10\frac{1}{7}$

26. Divide. Write the answer in lowest terms. a

$$\frac{3}{7} \div \frac{9}{14}$$

a. $\frac{2}{3}$ **b.** $1\frac{2}{3}$ **c.** $1\frac{1}{14}$ **d.** $\frac{27}{98}$

27. Multiply. Write the answer in lowest terms. b

$$7\frac{1}{8} \times 24$$

a. 161 **b.** 171
c. $168\frac{1}{8}$ **d.** $168\frac{3}{8}$

28. Write a fraction for $7\frac{2}{5}$. b

a. $\frac{14}{5}$ **b.** $\frac{37}{5}$ **c.** $\frac{70}{5}$ **d.** $\frac{17}{5}$

29. Write $\frac{54}{7}$ as a mixed number. c

a. $5\frac{4}{7}$ **b.** $8\frac{2}{7}$ **c.** $7\frac{5}{7}$ **d.** $6\frac{9}{7}$

30. How many square centimeters are in the area of the drawing board below? b

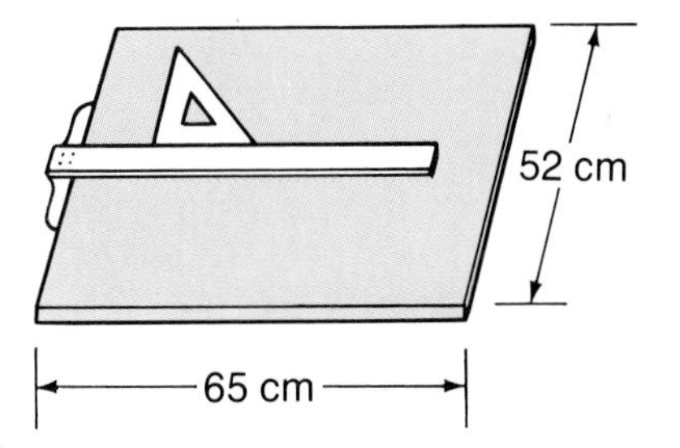

a. 3300 **b.** 3380
c. 3400 **d.** 3480

REVIEW OF RELATED SKILLS FOR CHAPTER 4

We suggest that some or all of this page be reviewed before proceeding with the chapter.

Subtract. (Pages 2–3, 4–5)

1. 25 − 19 6 **2.** 28 − 18 10 **3.** 47 − 38 9 **4.** 36 − 17 19 **5.** 53 − 46 7

6. 106 − 98 8 **7.** 300 − 256 44 **8.** 100 − 87 13 **9.** 205 − 148 57 **10.** 604 − 465 139

11. 402 − 136 266 **12.** 312 − 97 215 **13.** 153 − 86 67 **14.** 372 − 96 276 **15.** 400 − 83 317

16. 4.8 − 1.7 3.1 **17.** 8.3 − 6.7 1.6 **18.** 21.7 − 16.9 4.8 **19.** 46.5 − 3.8 42.7

20. 10.9 − 3.4 7.5 **21.** 16.3 − 11.7 4.6 **22.** 14.2 − 8.6 5.6 **23.** 25.3 − 19.6 5.7

24. 14.2 − 9.6 4.6 **25.** 21.8 − 13.9 7.9 **26.** 27.4 − 9.4 18.0 **27.** 36.2 − 27.8 8.4

Add. (Pages 2–3, 4–5)

28. 15 + 13 28 **29.** 17 + 36 53 **30.** 29 + 18 47 **31.** 43 + 12 55 **32.** 81 + 43 124

33. 96 + 42 138 **34.** 85 + 68 153 **35.** 73 + 88 161 **36.** 102 + 96 198 **37.** 236 + 47 283

38. 72 + 98 170 **39.** 46 + 66 112 **40.** 95 + 78 173 **41.** 412 + 42 454 **42.** 357 + 98 455

43. 8.3 + 2.7 11.0 **44.** 4.3 + 11.9 16.2 **45.** 2.6 + 18.3 20.9 **46.** 6.3 + 9.4 15.7

47. 16.2 + 4.8 21.0 **48.** 9.6 + 12.8 22.4 **49.** 23.7 + 18.9 42.6 **50.** 15.8 + 7.9 23.7

51. 18.3 + 7.9 26.2 **52.** 8.7 + 10.9 19.6 **53.** 42.8 + 16.7 59.5 **54.** 38.4 + 6.8 45.2

Divide. (Pages 12–13)

55. 14 ÷ 7 2 **56.** 24 ÷ 8 3 **57.** 96 ÷ 4 24 **58.** 81 ÷ 3 27 **59.** 126 ÷ 18 7

60. 78 ÷ 13 6 **61.** 48 ÷ 16 3 **62.** 135 ÷ 9 15 **63.** 192 ÷ 8 24 **64.** 90 ÷ 15 6

65. 72 ÷ 24 3 **66.** 105 ÷ 35 3 **67.** 140 ÷ 14 10 **68.** 138 ÷ 23 6 **69.** 142 ÷ 71 2

(Pages 14–15)

70. 14 ÷ 2.8 5 **71.** 32 ÷ 1.6 20 **72.** 42 ÷ 4.2 10 **73.** 60 ÷ 1.5 40

74. 6.4 ÷ 1.6 4 **75.** 4.8 ÷ 2.4 2 **76.** 0.72 ÷ 1.8 0.4 **77.** 5.4 ÷ 0.6 9

Multiply. (Pages 6–7)

78. 16 × 8 128 **79.** 40 × 5 200 **80.** 72 × 16 1152 **81.** 134 × 21 2814 **82.** 70 × 100 7000

83. 21 × 9 189 **84.** 13 × 12 156 **85.** 48 × 14 672 **86.** 64 × 15 960 **87.** 96 × 21 2016

88. 13 × 14 182 **89.** 25 × 14 350 **90.** 64 × 23 1472 **91.** 72 × 24 1728 **92.** 36 × 26 936

(Pages 8–9)

93. 1.3 × 10 13.0 **94.** 4.2 × 3 12.6 **95.** 16 × 4.5 72.0 **96.** 2.1 × 3.7 7.77

97. 4.6 × 2.3 10.58 **98.** 6.9 × 3.4 23.46 **99.** 10.2 × 9.1 92.82 **100.** 12.3 × 4.6 56.58

Write each fraction in lowest terms. (Pages 46–47)

101. $\frac{14}{28}$ $\frac{1}{2}$ **102.** $\frac{15}{60}$ $\frac{1}{4}$ **103.** $\frac{8}{15}$ $\frac{8}{15}$ **104.** $\frac{18}{20}$ $\frac{9}{10}$ **105.** $\frac{16}{28}$ $\frac{4}{7}$ **106.** $\frac{14}{35}$ $\frac{2}{5}$ **107.** $\frac{24}{60}$ $\frac{2}{5}$ **108.** $\frac{22}{55}$ $\frac{2}{5}$

CHAPTER

4 EQUATIONS/RATIO/PROPORTION

ESSENTIAL SKILLS/APPLICATIONS

CAREER APPLICATION

Nurse

4-1 Equations: Addition/Subtraction

See the Teacher's Manual for the objectives.

An **equation** is a sentence that uses "=". Here are some examples of equations.

$n + 17 = 21$ $\quad n - 2.3 = 6.5$ $\quad 14 + n = 25$

The letter n is called a **variable.** To solve an equation for n, you have to get **n alone on one side of the equation.**

PROCEDURE To solve an **addition equation** such as $n + 9 = 17$, *subtract* 9 from each side of the equation.

EXAMPLE 1 Solve and check: **a.** $n + 7 = 15$ **b.** $16 + n = 25$

Solutions: **a.** $n + 7 = 15$ *Subtract 7 from each side.*

$n + 7 - \mathbf{7} = 15 - \mathbf{7}$

$n = \mathbf{8}$

b. $16 + n = 25$ *Subtract 16 from each side.*

$16 - \mathbf{16} + n = 25 - \mathbf{16}$

$n = \mathbf{9}$

Check: $n + 7 = 15$ *Replace n with 8.*

$8 + 7 \stackrel{?}{=} 15$

$15 \stackrel{?}{=} 15$ Yes ✔

Check: $16 + n = 25$ *Replace n with 9.*

$16 + 9 \stackrel{?}{=} 25$

$25 \stackrel{?}{=} 25$ Yes ✔

After completing Example 1, you may wish to have students do some or all of Exercises 1-28.

PROCEDURE To solve a **subtraction equation** such as $n - 13 = 21$, *add* 13 to each side of the equation.

EXAMPLE 2 Solve and check: $n - 36 = 25$

Solution: $n - 36 = 25$ *Add 36 to each side.*

$n - 36 + \mathbf{36} = 25 + \mathbf{36}$

$n = 61$

Check: $n - 36 = 25$ *Replace n with 61.*

$61 - 36 \stackrel{?}{=} 25$

$25 = 25$ Yes ✔

EXERCISES

Solve and check. (Example 1)

1. $n + 8 = 13$ 5	**2.** $n + 5 = 9$ 4	**3.** $n + 11 = 20$ 9	**4.** $n + 4 = 6$ 2
5. $n + 18 = 37$ 19	**6.** $n + 34 = 38$ 4	**7.** $n + 55 = 62$ 7	**8.** $n + 29 = 38$ 9
9. $n + 11 = 23$ 12	**10.** $n + 29 = 34$ 5	**11.** $n + 18 = 23$ 5	**12.** $n + 15 = 30$ 15
13. $14 + n = 27$ 13	**14.** $38 + n = 51$ 13	**15.** $42 + n = 80$ 38	**16.** $18 + n = 95$ 77

17. $26 + n = 32$ 6
18. $51 + n = 68$ 17
19. $26 + n = 43$ 17
20. $35 + n = 54$ 19
21. $84 + n = 108$ 24
22. $57 + n = 100$ 43
23. $55 + n = 121$ 66
24. $79 + n = 117$ 38
25. $n + 1.2 = 3.4$ 2.2
26. $n + 3.7 = 11.2$ 7.5
27. $4.6 + n = 8.4$ 3.8
28. $6.5 + n = 12.3$ 5.8

Solve and check. (Example 2)

29. $n - 6 = 11$ 17
30. $n - 5 = 4$ 9
31. $n - 3 = 8$ 11
32. $n - 16 = 20$ 36
33. $n - 29 = 8$ 37
34. $n - 7 = 49$ 56
35. $n - 8 = 31$ 39
36. $n - 27 = 5$ 32
37. $n - 14 = 74$ 88
38. $n - 24 = 36$ 60
39. $n - 16 = 12$ 28
40. $n - 26 = 37$ 63
41. $n - 13 = 42$ 55
42. $n - 84 = 93$ 177
43. $n - 64 = 27$ 91
44. $n - 29 = 18$ 47
45. $n - 24 = 63$ 87
46. $n - 42 = 37$ 79
47. $n - 45 = 57$ 102
48. $n - 18 = 38$ 56
49. $n - 87 = 22$ 109
50. $n - 34 = 69$ 103
51. $n - 63 = 27$ 90
52. $n - 14 = 98$ 112
53. $n - 3.2 = 6.1$ 9.3
54. $n - 7.5 = 8.4$ 15.9
55. $n - 1.6 = 8$ 9.6
56. $n - 5 = 7.3$ 12.3

Mixed Practice The Mixed Practice contains exercises that relate to both Examples 1 and 2.

Solve and check.

57. $n + 6 = 21$ 15
58. $n + 8 = 46$ 38
59. $n - 5 = 19$ 24
60. $n - 6 = 12$ 18
61. $n - 25 = 16$ 41
62. $14 + n = 23$ 9
63. $17 + n = 26$ 9
64. $n - 14 = 16$ 30
65. $n - 72 = 12$ 84
66. $n - 46 = 18$ 64
67. $n + 64 = 120$ 56
68. $n + 39 = 74$ 35
69. $n - 58 = 96$ 154
70. $n - 38 = 14$ 52
71. $n + 48 = 63$ 15
72. $n + 53 = 81$ 28
73. $60 + n = 122$ 62
74. $n - 14 = 39$ 53
75. $n - 27 = 46$ 73
76. $81 + n = 126$ 45
77. $n - 64 = 88$ 152
78. $n + 75 = 110$ 35
79. $32 + n = 140$ 108
80. $n - 78 = 12$ 90
81. $n + 3.4 = 7$ 3.6
82. $5.9 + n = 10$ 4.1
83. $n - 6.3 = 8$ 14.3
84. $n - 4.7 = 10$ 14.7

APPLICATIONS: Using Equations in Business

These word problems apply the skills taught in the lesson.

In order to make a profit and to cover expenses, an amount called the ***markup*** *is added to the dealer's cost. Use the following equation, or formula, to find the markup in Exercises 85–88.*

markup + dealer's cost = selling price or $m + c = s$

85. The selling price of a blouse is \$18.98. It cost the store \$12.50. \$6.48
86. The selling price of a certain shirt at Royal Clothing is \$14.99. The shirt cost the store \$10.98. \$4.01
87. A certain golf club cost Front Line Sports \$75.00. The selling price is \$94.99. \$19.99
88. A certain radio cost City Audio \$26.00. The selling price is \$39.95. \$13.95

4-2 Equations: Multiplication/Division

See the Teacher's Manual for the objectives.

An equation such as $3n = 81$ is a **multiplication equation.** Note that $3n$ means $3 \times n$.

PROCEDURE To solve a **multiplication equation** such as $3n = 81$, *divide* each side by 3.

EXAMPLE 1 Solve and check: **a.** $5n = 20$ **b.** $36 = 4n$

Solutions:

a. $5n = 20$ ◀ *Divide each side by 5.*

$$\frac{5n}{5} = \frac{20}{5}$$

$$n = \mathbf{4}$$

Check: $5n = 20$ ◀ *Replace n with 4.*

$$5 \times 4 \stackrel{?}{=} 20$$

$$20 \stackrel{?}{=} 20 \quad \text{Yes} \checkmark$$

b. $36 = 4n$ ◀ *Divide each side by 4.*

$$\frac{36}{4} = \frac{4n}{4}$$

$$\mathbf{9} = n$$

Check: $36 = 4n$ ◀ *Replace n with 9.*

$$36 \stackrel{?}{=} 4 \times 9$$

$$36 \stackrel{?}{=} 36 \quad \text{Yes} \checkmark$$

You can write $n \div 8$ as $\frac{n}{8}$. After completing Example 1, you may wish to have students do some or all of Exercises 1-35.

PROCEDURE To solve a **division equation** such as $\frac{n}{4} = 21$, *multiply* each side by 4.

EXAMPLE 2 Solve and check: **a.** $\frac{n}{3} = 75$ **b.** $8 = \frac{n}{7}$

Solutions:

a. $\frac{n}{3} = 75$ ◀ *Multiply each side by 3.*

$$\frac{n}{3} \times \mathbf{3} = 75 \times \mathbf{3}$$

$$n = \mathbf{225}$$

Check: $\frac{n}{3} = 75$ ◀ *Replace n with 225.*

$$\frac{225}{3} \stackrel{?}{=} 75$$

$$75 \stackrel{?}{=} 75 \quad \text{Yes} \checkmark$$

b. $8 = \frac{n}{7}$ ◀ *Multiply each side by 7.*

$$8 \times \mathbf{7} = \frac{n}{7} \times \mathbf{7}$$

$$\mathbf{56} = n$$

Check: $8 = \frac{n}{7}$ ◀ *Replace n with 56.*

$$8 \stackrel{?}{=} \frac{56}{7}$$

$$8 \stackrel{?}{=} 8 \quad \text{Yes} \checkmark$$

EXERCISES

Solve and check (Example 1)

1. $7n = 42$ 6 **2.** $8n = 32$ 4 **3.** $11n = 88$ 8 **4.** $25n = 100$ 4 **5.** $6n = 30$ 5

6. $6n = 156$ 26 **7.** $5n = 820$ 164 **8.** $12n = 288$ 24 **9.** $7n = 98$ 14 **10.** $13n = 104$ 8

11. $37n = 74$ 2 **12.** $41n = 123$ 3 **13.** $71n = 284$ 4 **14.** $21n = 105$ 5 **15.** $19n = 95$ 5

16. $38 = 19n$ 2 **17.** $115 = 5n$ 23 **18.** $96 = 16n$ 6 **19.** $112 = 28n$ 4 **20.** $350 = 14n$ 25

21. $340 = 17n$ 20 **22.** $221 = 13n$ 17 **23.** $130 = 26n$ 5 **24.** $120 = 15n$ 8 **25.** $144 = 24n$ 6

26. $756 = 21n$ 36 **27.** $104 = 13n$ 8 **28.** $216 = 24n$ 9 **29.** $126 = 18n$ 7 **30.** $126 = 14n$ 9

31. $0.8n = 9.6$ 12 **32.** $0.5n = 2.5$ 5 **33.** $0.2n = 1.8$ 9 **34.** $57.6 = 2.4n$ 24 **35.** $39.6 = 3.3n$ 12

(Example 2)

36. $\frac{n}{7} = 2$ 14 **37.** $\frac{n}{3} = 18$ 54 **38.** $\frac{n}{5} = 20$ 100 **39.** $\frac{n}{3} = 11$ 33 **40.** $\frac{n}{10} = 16$ 160

41. $\frac{n}{8} = 8$ 64 **42.** $\frac{n}{15} = 10$ 150 **43.** $\frac{n}{4} = 2$ 8 **44.** $\frac{n}{11} = 5$ 55 **45.** $\frac{n}{2} = 27$ 54

46. $\frac{n}{4} = 20$ 80 **47.** $\frac{n}{18} = 9$ 162 **48.** $\frac{n}{9} = 8$ 72 **49.** $\frac{n}{12} = 4$ 48 **50.** $\frac{n}{8} = 5$ 40

51. $14 = \frac{n}{6}$ 84 **52.** $24 = \frac{n}{4}$ 96 **53.** $13 = \frac{n}{7}$ 91 **54.** $41 = \frac{n}{6}$ 246 **55.** $25 = \frac{n}{7}$ 175

56. $13 = \frac{n}{9}$ 117 **57.** $8 = \frac{n}{11}$ 88 **58.** $12 = \frac{n}{20}$ 240 **59.** $18 = \frac{n}{13}$ 234 **60.** $24 = \frac{n}{12}$ 288

61. $16 = \frac{n}{18}$ 288 **62.** $10 = \frac{n}{24}$ 240 **63.** $21 = \frac{n}{20}$ 420 **64.** $25 = \frac{n}{14}$ 350 **65.** $19 = \frac{n}{10}$ 190

66. $\frac{n}{4} = 1.2$ 4.8 **67.** $\frac{n}{3} = 18.7$ 56.1 **68.** $\frac{n}{5.5} = 5$ 27.5 **69.** $4.7 = \frac{n}{20}$ 94 **70.** $6.4 = \frac{n}{1.7}$ 10.88

Mixed Practice The Mixed Practice contains exercises that relate to both Examples 1 and 2.

71. $\frac{n}{8} = 25$ 200 **72.** $\frac{n}{3} = 29$ 87 **73.** $6 = \frac{n}{22}$ 132 **74.** $13 = \frac{n}{8}$ 104 **75.** $\frac{n}{7} = 31$ 217

76. $84 = 7n$ 12 **77.** $63 = 7n$ 9 **78.** $25n = 375$ 15 **79.** $21n = 42$ 2 **80.** $18n = 270$ 15

81. $144 = 72n$ 2 **82.** $120 = 24n$ 5 **83.** $300 = 15n$ 20 **84.** $27n = 108$ 4 **85.** $35n = 140$ 4

86. $\frac{n}{27} = 15$ 405 **87.** $\frac{n}{16} = 34$ 544 **88.** $87 = \frac{n}{10}$ 870 **89.** $11 = \frac{n}{11}$ 121 **90.** $\frac{n}{19} = 28$ 532

APPLICATIONS: The Distance Formula

These word problems apply the skills taught in the lesson.

When you know the speed, or rate, and the distance traveled, you can use the following formula to find the time.

distance = rate × time, or $d = r \times t$

Use this formula for Exercises 91–93.

91. An elephant can run at a rate of 31 feet per second. At that rate, how long will it take the elephant to run 465 feet? 15 seconds

92. A house cat can run at a rate of 13.5 meters per second. The cat ran 283.5 meters. How long did it take? 21 seconds

93. An ostrich can run at a rate of 18 meters per second. At that rate, how long will it take the ostrich to run 216 meters? 12 seconds

4-3 Solving Equations

See the Teacher's Manual for the objectives.

Sometimes you use more than one operation to solve an equation.

PROCEDURE To solve an equation:

1. Add or subtract the same number from each side of the equation when necessary.
2. Multiply or divide each side of the equation by the same number (except zero) when necessary.

EXAMPLE 1 Solve and check: $24n + 7 = 55$

Solution: $24n + 7 = 55$ ◀ ***Subtract 7 from each side.***

1. $24n + 7 - \mathbf{7} = 55 - \mathbf{7}$

$24n = 48$ ◀ ***Divide each side by 24.***

2. $\frac{24n}{\mathbf{24}} = \frac{48}{\mathbf{24}}$

$n = 2$

Check:

$24n + 7 = 55$ ◀ ***Replace n by 2.***

$24 \times 2 + 7 \stackrel{?}{=} 55$

$48 + 7 \stackrel{?}{=} 55$

$55 \stackrel{?}{=} 55$ Yes ✓

After completing Example 1, you may wish to have students do some or all of Exercises 1-27.

EXAMPLE 2 Solve and check: $\frac{n}{3} - 4 = 12$

Solution: $\frac{n}{3} - 4 = 12$ ◀ ***Add 4 to each side.***

1. $\frac{n}{3} - 4 + \mathbf{4} = 12 + \mathbf{4}$

$\frac{n}{3} = 16$ ◀ ***Multiply each side by 3.***

2. $\frac{n}{3} \times \mathbf{3} = 16 \times \mathbf{3}$

$n = \mathbf{48}$

Check:

$\frac{n}{3} - 4 = 12$ ◀ ***Replace n with 48.***

$\frac{48}{3} - 4 \stackrel{?}{=} 12$

$16 - 4 \stackrel{?}{=} 12$

$12 \stackrel{?}{=} 12$ Yes ✓

EXERCISES

In Exercises 1–9 write the first step you would use to solve the equation. Write "Subtract 5 from each side," "Add 3 to each side," and so on. (Examples 1 and 2, step 1)

1. $2n + 4 = 12$ Subtract 4 from each side.

2. $4n + 18 = 30$ Subtract 18 from each side.

3. $18n - 9 = 27$ Add 9 to each side.

4. $25n - 40 = 15$ Add 40 to each side.

5. $6n - 8 = 4$ Add 8 to each side.

6. $14n - 12 = 20$ Add 12 to each side.

7. $4n - 50 = 150$ Add 50 to each side.

8. $28n + 27 = 55$ Subtract 27 from each side.

9. $26n + 65 = 70$ Subtract 65 from each side.

Solve and check. (Example 1)

10. $13n + 6 = 32$ 2
11. $5n + 11 = 36$ 5
12. $11n + 5 = 115$ 10
13. $8n - 5 = 59$ 8
14. $7n - 9 = 40$ 7
15. $12n - 10 = 122$ 11
16. $5n + 16 = 96$ 16
17. $4n + 28 = 68$ 10
18. $21n + 6 = 111$ 5
19. $18n - 7 = 83$ 5
20. $13n - 5 = 60$ 5
21. $12n - 3 = 33$ 3
22. $4n + 0.6 = 5.4$ 1.2
23. $2n + 0.3 = 2.9$ 1.3
24. $12n + 1.7 = 4.1$ 0.2
25. $3n - 2.4 = 2.4$ 1.6
26. $7n + 0.7 = 29.4$ 4.1
27. $16n + 2.9 = 52.5$ 3.1

(Example 2)

28. $\frac{n}{2} + 9 = 18$ 18
29. $\frac{n}{3} + 5 = 12$ 21
30. $\frac{n}{8} - 5 = 5$ 80
31. $\frac{n}{6} - 5 = 0$ 30
32. $\frac{n}{2} + 8 = 11$ 6
33. $\frac{n}{7} + 14 = 20$ 42
34. $\frac{n}{8} - 4 = 6$ 80
35. $\frac{n}{3} - 6 = 2$ 24
36. $\frac{n}{4} - 3 = 3$ 24
37. $\frac{n}{8} + 5 = 10$ 40
38. $\frac{n}{3} - 7 = 7$ 42
39. $\frac{n}{13} - 5 = 8$ 169
40. $\frac{n}{2} + \frac{1}{12} = \frac{7}{12}$ 1
41. $\frac{n}{9} + \frac{5}{9} = \frac{7}{9}$ 2
42. $\frac{n}{10} - \frac{1}{5} = \frac{3}{5}$ 8
43. $\frac{n}{6} - \frac{1}{4} = \frac{7}{12}$ 5
44. $\frac{n}{9} + \frac{1}{6} = \frac{11}{18}$ 4
45. $\frac{n}{25} + \frac{1}{5} = \frac{2}{5}$ 5

Mixed Practice The Mixed Practice contains exercises that relate to both Examples 1 and 2.

46. $4n - 11 = 9$ 5
47. $5n - 5 = 50$ 11
48. $2n + 38 = 60$ 11
49. $8n + 17 = 265$ 31
50. $4n - 84 = 12$ 24
51. $15n + 18 = 228$ 14
52. $\frac{n}{8} + 1 = 3$ 16
53. $\frac{n}{11} - 16 = 1$ 187
54. $\frac{n}{4} - 5 = 100$ 420
55. $\frac{n}{3} + 4 = 28$ 72
56. $\frac{n}{8} + 7 = 32$ 200
57. $\frac{n}{9} - 3 = 46$ 441
58. $18n + 12 = 102$ 5
59. $7n - 8 = 62$ 10
60. $2n + 50 = 100$ 25
61. $0.3n + 4 = 5.5$ 5
62. $1.9n + 6 = 17.4$ 6
63. $3.2n - 4 = 12$ 5

APPLICATIONS: Using Equations

These problems apply the skills taught in the lesson.

You can use the formula $F = 1.8C + 32$ *to change Fahrenheit degrees to Celsius degrees. Use this formula to complete Exercises 64–69.*

64. 50°F = __?__ °C 10
65. 77°F = __?__ °C 25
66. 59°F = __?__ °C 15
67. 41°F = __?__ °C 5
68. 68°F = __?__ °C 20
69. 86°F = __?__ °C 30

The formula $t = \frac{n}{7} + 4$ *relates the number of times a cricket chirps in one minute, n, to the Celsius temperature, t. Use this formula to find the rate of chirping at the given temperature in Exercises 70–75.*

70. 10°C 42
71. 15°C 77
72. 5°C 7
73. 21°C 119
74. 18°C 98
75. 30°C 182

4-4 Ratio

See the Teacher's Manual for the objectives.

A **ratio** is a way to compare numbers. You can write a ratio as a fraction.

TABLE

Ratio	Written as a Fraction
5 to 17	$\frac{5}{17}$
3 to 100	$\frac{3}{100}$
27 to 45	$\frac{27}{45} = \frac{3}{5}$ ◀ **Lowest terms**

Ratios such as $\frac{27}{45}$ and $\frac{3}{5}$ are **equivalent ratios.** They are equal.

PROCEDURE To tell whether two ratios are equivalent:

1. Find the cross-products.
2. Compare the cross-products. Equivalent ratios have equal cross-products.

EXAMPLE Determine whether the ratios are equivalent.

a. $\frac{3}{7}$ and $\frac{12}{28}$

b. $\frac{5}{12}$ and $\frac{4}{11}$

Solutions: **a.** $\frac{3}{7} \stackrel{?}{=} \frac{12}{28}$ ◀ ***The loop shows the cross-product.***

$3 \times 28 \stackrel{?}{=} 7 \times 12$

$84 \stackrel{?}{=} 84$ Yes ✔

The cross-products are equal. So the ratios are **equivalent.**

b. $\frac{5}{12} \stackrel{?}{=} \frac{4}{11}$

$5 \times 11 \stackrel{?}{=} 12 \times 4$

$55 \stackrel{?}{=} 48$ No

The cross-products are not equal. So the ratios are **not equivalent.**

EXERCISES

Write a fraction in lowest terms for each ratio. (Table)

1. 5 to 9 $\frac{5}{9}$ **2.** 4 to 11 $\frac{4}{11}$ **3.** 6 to 15 $\frac{2}{5}$ **4.** 8 to 18 $\frac{4}{9}$

5. 20 to 50 $\frac{2}{5}$ **6.** 30 to 25 $\frac{6}{5}$ **7.** 8 to 6 $\frac{4}{3}$ **8.** 3 to 12 $\frac{1}{4}$

9. 4 to 14 $\frac{2}{7}$ **10.** 7 to 21 $\frac{1}{3}$ **11.** 5 to 15 $\frac{1}{3}$ **12.** 10 to 15 $\frac{2}{3}$

13. 6 to 19 $\frac{6}{19}$ **14.** 18 to 27 $\frac{2}{3}$ **15.** 4 to 3 $\frac{4}{3}$ **16.** 11 to 22 $\frac{1}{2}$

17. 3 to 27 $\frac{1}{9}$ **18.** 5 to 40 $\frac{1}{8}$ **19.** 1 to 11 $\frac{1}{11}$ **20.** 81 to 162 $\frac{1}{2}$

21. 6 to 54 $\frac{1}{9}$ **22.** 9 to 81 $\frac{1}{9}$ **23.** 7 to 56 $\frac{1}{8}$ **24.** 3 to 48 $\frac{1}{16}$

25. 12 to 60 $\frac{1}{5}$ 26. 5 to 25 $\frac{1}{5}$ 27. 3 to 3 $\frac{1}{1}$ 28. 9 to 54 $\frac{1}{6}$

29. 6 to 84 $\frac{1}{14}$ 30. 3 to 1 $\frac{3}{1}$ 31. 12 to 3 $\frac{4}{1}$ 32. 18 to 9 $\frac{2}{1}$

Determine whether the ratios are equivalent. Answer Yes or No.

33. $\frac{3}{5}$ and $\frac{9}{15}$ Yes 34. $\frac{2}{3}$ and $\frac{3}{4}$ No 35. $\frac{8}{12}$ and $\frac{10}{15}$ Yes 36. $\frac{18}{3}$ and $\frac{12}{2}$ Yes

37. $\frac{7}{8}$ and $\frac{12}{16}$ No 38. $\frac{1}{5}$ and $\frac{7}{49}$ No 39. $\frac{2}{7}$ and $\frac{6}{21}$ Yes 40. $\frac{1}{3}$ and $\frac{17}{61}$ No

41. $\frac{9}{12}$ and $\frac{18}{25}$ No 42. $\frac{7}{13}$ and $\frac{21}{39}$ Yes 43. $\frac{6}{7}$ and $\frac{24}{21}$ No 44. $\frac{3}{5}$ and $\frac{21}{35}$ Yes

45. $\frac{3}{5}$ and $\frac{36}{60}$ Yes 46. $\frac{4}{6}$ and $\frac{20}{24}$ No 47. $\frac{9}{8}$ and $\frac{36}{32}$ Yes 48. $\frac{3}{10}$ and $\frac{22}{80}$ No

49. $\frac{4}{1}$ and $\frac{28}{7}$ Yes 50. $\frac{2}{5}$ and $\frac{18}{45}$ Yes 51. $\frac{39}{26}$ and $\frac{3}{2}$ Yes 52. $\frac{1}{8}$ and $\frac{17}{136}$ Yes

53. $\frac{3}{4}$ and $\frac{15}{21}$ No 54. $\frac{5}{8}$ and $\frac{15}{25}$ No 55. $\frac{7}{6}$ and $\frac{42}{36}$ Yes 56. $\frac{5}{8}$ and $\frac{10}{16}$ Yes

57. $\frac{11}{13}$ and $\frac{44}{52}$ Yes 58. $\frac{3}{7}$ and $\frac{20}{49}$ No 59. $\frac{5}{9}$ and $\frac{30}{45}$ No 60. $\frac{8}{13}$ and $\frac{39}{24}$ No

61. $\frac{4}{5}$ and $\frac{64}{80}$ Yes 62. $\frac{2}{11}$ and $\frac{33}{6}$ No 63. $\frac{1}{8}$ and $\frac{5}{40}$ Yes 64. $\frac{3}{4}$ and $\frac{24}{32}$ Yes

65. $\frac{3}{4}$ and $\frac{9}{16}$ No 66. $\frac{7}{8}$ and $\frac{49}{56}$ Yes 67. $\frac{21}{25}$ and $\frac{3}{5}$ No 68. $\frac{18}{30}$ and $\frac{3}{5}$ Yes

69. $\frac{22}{66}$ and $\frac{1}{3}$ Yes 70. $\frac{37}{29}$ and $\frac{18}{15}$ No 71. $\frac{2}{5}$ and $\frac{30}{75}$ Yes 72. $\frac{13}{14}$ and $\frac{28}{26}$ No

73. $\frac{2}{7}$ and $\frac{1}{14}$ No 74. $\frac{3}{8}$ and $\frac{9}{16}$ No 75. $\frac{5}{12}$ and $\frac{25}{144}$ No 76. $\frac{2}{17}$ and $\frac{6}{50}$ No

77. $\frac{5}{12}$ and $\frac{10}{24}$ Yes 78. $\frac{1}{22}$ and $\frac{22}{484}$ Yes 79. $\frac{9}{5}$ and $\frac{45}{25}$ Yes 80. $\frac{81}{16}$ and $\frac{9}{4}$ No

81. $\frac{75}{30}$ and $\frac{10}{4}$ Yes 82. $\frac{18}{81}$ and $\frac{2}{9}$ Yes 83. $\frac{25}{49}$ and $\frac{5}{7}$ No 84. $\frac{63}{7}$ and $\frac{9}{1}$ Yes

APPLICATIONS: Using Ratios

These word problems apply the skills taught in the lesson.

For Exercises 85–87, write your answers in lowest terms.

85. During a certain time of the day, commercial advertising uses 8 minutes of every 30 minutes of broadcast time on television. Find the ratio of advertising time to the total broadcast time. $\frac{4}{15}$

86. Tom completed 14 out of 20 passes last Saturday. What is the ratio of completed passes to pass attempts? $\frac{7}{10}$

87. The state of Alaska has about 20,000 square miles of inland water. Its total area is 590,000 square miles. What is the ratio of inland water to the total area? $\frac{2}{59}$

4-5 Proportions

See the Teacher's Manual for the objectives.

A **proportion** is an equation that shows equivalent ratios.

$\frac{n}{7} = \frac{4}{14}$ and $\frac{2}{n} = \frac{12}{24}$ are examples of proportions.

Solving a proportion is similar to solving a multiplication equation.

PROCEDURE To solve a proportion for n:

1. Write the cross-products.
2. Solve the multiplication equation for n.

EXAMPLE 1 Solve the proportion for n.

a. $\frac{n}{6} = \frac{20}{30}$

b. $\frac{7}{5} = \frac{21}{n}$

Solutions:

a. $\frac{n}{6} = \frac{20}{30}$

1. $n \times 30 = 6 \times 20$

   $30n = 120$

2. $\frac{30n}{\mathbf{30}} = \frac{120}{\mathbf{30}}$

   $n = \mathbf{4}$

Check: $\frac{n}{6} = \frac{20}{30}$ ◀ *Replace n with 4.*

$\frac{4}{6} \stackrel{?}{=} \frac{20}{30}$

$4 \times 30 \stackrel{?}{=} 6 \times 20$

$120 \stackrel{?}{=} 120$ Yes ✓

b. $\frac{7}{5} = \frac{21}{n}$

1. $7 \times n = 5 \times 21$

   $7n = 105$

2. $\frac{7n}{\mathbf{7}} = \frac{105}{\mathbf{7}}$

   $n = 15$

Check: $\frac{7}{5} = \frac{21}{n}$ ◀ *Replace n with 15.*

$\frac{7}{5} \stackrel{?}{=} \frac{21}{15}$

$7 \times 15 \stackrel{?}{=} 5 \times 21$

$105 \stackrel{?}{=} 105$ Yes ✓

EXERCISES

Solve each proportion for n. (Example 1a)

1. $\frac{n}{8} = \frac{3}{24}$ 1
2. $\frac{n}{2} = \frac{5}{10}$ 1
3. $\frac{n}{7} = \frac{6}{42}$ 1
4. $\frac{n}{4} = \frac{9}{12}$ 3
5. $\frac{n}{5} = \frac{21}{35}$ 3

6. $\frac{n}{10} = \frac{35}{50}$ 7
7. $\frac{n}{16} = \frac{3}{8}$ 6
8. $\frac{n}{9} = \frac{24}{54}$ 4
9. $\frac{n}{18} = \frac{2}{3}$ 12
10. $\frac{n}{3} = \frac{10}{15}$ 2

11. $\frac{n}{27} = \frac{5}{9}$ 15
12. $\frac{n}{81} = \frac{2}{27}$ 6
13. $\frac{n}{4} = \frac{11}{44}$ 1
14. $\frac{n}{6} = \frac{60}{72}$ 5
15. $\frac{n}{18} = \frac{15}{90}$ 3

16. $\frac{n}{25} = \frac{96}{200}$ 12
17. $\frac{n}{3} = \frac{19}{57}$ 1
18. $\frac{n}{84} = \frac{3}{14}$ 18
19. $\frac{n}{20} = \frac{65}{100}$ 13
20. $\frac{n}{8} = \frac{9}{24}$ 3

21. $\frac{n}{15} = \frac{15}{75}$ 3
22. $\frac{n}{28} = \frac{2}{7}$ 8
23. $\frac{n}{60} = \frac{6}{20}$ 18
24. $\frac{n}{19} = \frac{3}{57}$ 1
25. $\frac{n}{92} = \frac{2}{23}$ 8

(Example 1b)

26. $\frac{6}{81}=\frac{2}{n}$ 27 27. $\frac{3}{12}=\frac{15}{n}$ 60 28. $\frac{7}{10}=\frac{28}{n}$ 40 29. $\frac{9}{7}=\frac{72}{n}$ 56 30. $\frac{3}{5}=\frac{21}{n}$ 35

31. $\frac{5}{8}=\frac{25}{n}$ 40 32. $\frac{7}{25}=\frac{28}{n}$ 100 33. $\frac{6}{13}=\frac{18}{n}$ 39 34. $\frac{30}{70}=\frac{6}{n}$ 14 35. $\frac{9}{10}=\frac{45}{n}$ 50

36. $\frac{16}{25}=\frac{48}{n}$ 75 37. $\frac{17}{20}=\frac{85}{n}$ 100 38. $\frac{2}{3}=\frac{26}{n}$ 39 39. $\frac{3}{4}=\frac{45}{n}$ 60 40. $\frac{11}{33}=\frac{1}{n}$ 3

41. $\frac{18}{25}=\frac{36}{n}$ 50 42. $\frac{11}{24}=\frac{33}{n}$ 72 43. $\frac{5}{9}=\frac{70}{n}$ 126 44. $\frac{8}{13}=\frac{32}{n}$ 52 45. $\frac{1}{8}=\frac{24}{n}$ 192

46. $\frac{26}{52}=\frac{13}{n}$ 26 47. $\frac{5}{8}=\frac{20}{n}$ 32 48. $\frac{2}{3}=\frac{54}{n}$ 81 49. $\frac{7}{10}=\frac{84}{n}$ 120 50. $\frac{3}{4}=\frac{9}{n}$ 12

51. $\frac{3}{8}=\frac{45}{n}$ 120 52. $\frac{50}{350}=\frac{1}{n}$ 7 53. $\frac{9}{7}=\frac{54}{n}$ 42 54. $\frac{63}{21}=\frac{9}{n}$ 3 55. $\frac{15}{16}=\frac{75}{n}$ 80

Mixed Practice The Mixed Practice contains exercises that relate to both Examples 1a and 1b.

56. $\frac{n}{7}=\frac{14}{49}$ 2 57. $\frac{n}{21}=\frac{8}{84}$ 2 58. $\frac{7}{9}=\frac{28}{n}$ 36 59. $\frac{25}{75}=\frac{5}{n}$ 15 60. $\frac{80}{240}=\frac{5}{n}$ 15

61. $\frac{n}{21}=\frac{3}{7}$ 9 62. $\frac{n}{6}=\frac{25}{30}$ 5 63. $\frac{17}{63}=\frac{34}{n}$ 126 64. $\frac{4}{29}=\frac{12}{n}$ 87 65. $\frac{n}{16}=\frac{35}{80}$ 7

66. $\frac{n}{35}=\frac{8}{70}$ 4 67. $\frac{11}{50}=\frac{33}{n}$ 150 68. $\frac{9}{12}=\frac{3}{n}$ 4 69. $\frac{n}{18}=\frac{35}{90}$ 7 70. $\frac{n}{2}=\frac{67}{134}$ 1

71. $\frac{n}{5}=\frac{90}{150}$ 3 72. $\frac{n}{12}=\frac{15}{36}$ 5 73. $\frac{14}{20}=\frac{42}{n}$ 60 74. $\frac{7}{25}=\frac{35}{n}$ 125 75. $\frac{3}{2}=\frac{18}{n}$ 12

76. $\frac{81}{75}=\frac{27}{n}$ 25 77. $\frac{12}{n}=\frac{9}{12}$ 16 78. $\frac{13}{n}=\frac{26}{48}$ 24 79. $\frac{12}{17}=\frac{48}{n}$ 68 80. $\frac{5}{27}=\frac{15}{n}$ 81

81. $\frac{1}{n}=\frac{6}{42}$ 7 82. $\frac{20}{n}=\frac{5}{9}$ 36 83. $\frac{12}{n}=\frac{6}{50}$ 100 84. $\frac{20}{n}=\frac{4}{24}$ 120 85. $\frac{43}{200}=\frac{129}{n}$ 600

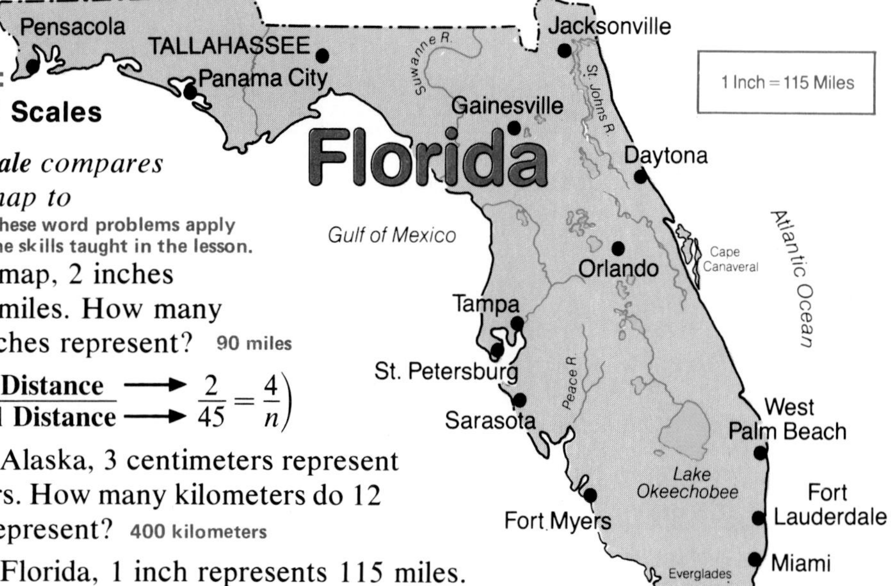

APPLICATIONS: Proportions and Scales

*On a map, the **scale** compares distance on the map to actual distance.* These word problems apply the skills taught in the lesson.

86. On a certain map, 2 inches represent 45 miles. How many miles do 4 inches represent? 90 miles

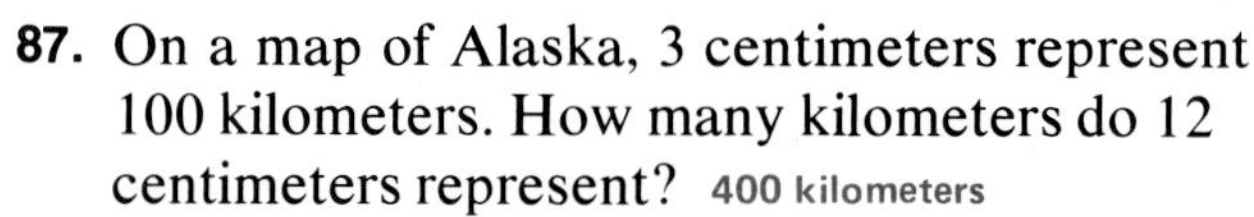
(Hint: Map Distance → / Actual Distance → $\frac{2}{45}=\frac{4}{n}$)

87. On a map of Alaska, 3 centimeters represent 100 kilometers. How many kilometers do 12 centimeters represent? 400 kilometers

88. On a map of Florida, 1 inch represents 115 miles. How many inches represent 230 miles? 2 inches

89. On a certain map, 2.5 centimeters represent 40 kilometers. How many centimeters represent 200 kilometers? 12.5 centimeters

NURSE

Career lessons are optional.
This lesson applies the skills presented in Section 4–5.

Registered nurses must be able to follow a doctor's orders and give patients medicine in prescribed doses. A knowledge of measurement and proportions is important for nurses.

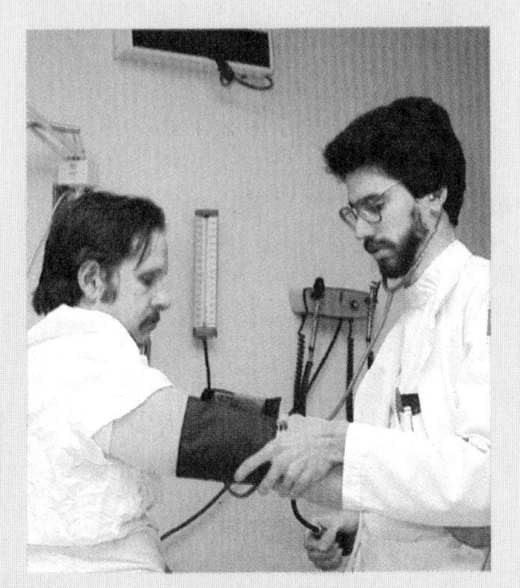

EXAMPLE Dr. Miklos has prescribed a dose of 25 milligrams of medicine for a patient. Tom Benson, a nurse, has a solution of 215 milligrams of the medicine in 40 milliliters of solution. Find the number of milliliters of solution Tom should give the patient. Round the answer to the nearest tenth.

Solution: Use pencil and paper or use a calculator.

Amount of medicine → $\frac{215}{40} = \frac{25}{n}$ ← *Amount of medicine*
Amount of solution → ← *Amount of solution*

$$215 \times n = 40 \times 25$$

$$n = \frac{40 \times 25}{215}$$

4 0 × 2 5 ÷ 2 1 5 = 4.6511628

Tom should give the patient **4.7 mL** of solution.

EXERCISES

Note that Exercises 1–10 are non-verbal.

For Exercises 1–10, find the amount of solution needed. Round each answer to the nearest tenth.

	Medicine on Hand	*Prescribed Dose*	*Amount of Solution Needed*
1.	300 mg in 100 mL of solution	30 mg	? 10 mL
2.	225 mg in 45 mL of solution	25 mg	? 5 mL
3.	500 mg in 100 mL of solution	50 mg	? 10 mL
4.	1000 mg in 100 mL of solution	20 mg	? 2 mL
5.	400 mg in 40 mL of solution	25 mg	? 2.5 mL
6.	800 mg in 75 mL of solution	30 mg	? 2.8 mL

	Medicine on Hand	Prescribed Dose	Amount of Solution Needed
7.	100 mg in 30 mL of solution	15 mg	? 4.5 mL
8.	215 mg in 30 mL of solution	35 mg	? 4.9 mL
9.	325 mg in 65 mL of solution	30 mg	? 6 mL
10.	435 mg in 55 mL of solution	20 mg	? 2.5 mL

For Exercises 11–16, round the answer to the nearest tenth.

11. A doctor prescribed 24 milligrams of a liquid antacid. The nurse on duty has a solution of 500 milligrams of the antacid in 45 milliliters of solution. How many milliliters of the solution should the nurse give the patient? 2.2 mL

12. Dr. Rosner has prescribed a dose of 30 milligrams of medicine for a patient. Nurse Carolis has a solution of 315 milligrams of the medicine in 50 milliliters of solution. How many milliliters of the solution should Nurse Carolis give the patient? 4.8 mL

13. Dr. Falk prescribed a dose of 30 milligrams of medicine. The nurse has a solution of 300 milligrams of the medicine in 60 milliliters of solution. How many milliliters of solution should the nurse give? 6 mL

14. Dr. Blaine prescribed a dose of 25 milligrams of medicine for Jenny. The nurse has a solution of 315 milligrams of the medicine in 65 milliliters of solution. How many milliliters of solution should the nurse give Jenny? 5.2 mL

15. Dr. Garcia prescribed 30 milligrams of medicine for a patient. The nurse has a solution of 150 milligrams of the medicine in 40 milliliters of solution. Find the number of milliliters of solution the nurse should give the patient. 8 mL

16. A doctor orders 0.2 milligrams of medicine for a patient. The nurse has a solution of 0.6 milligrams in 1 milliliter of solution. How many milliliters of solution should the nurse give the patient? 0.3 mL

Chapter Review

These exercises review the vocabulary, skills and applications presented in the chapter, as a preparation for the chapter test.

Part 1: VOCABULARY

For Exercises 1–6, choose from the box at the right the word(s) that completes each statement.

equivalent
division
equation
add 4 to
proportion
subtract 4 from
fraction

1. A sentence that uses "=" is an __?__. (Pages 72–73) equation
2. The first step in solving an equation such as $n + 4 = 8$ is to __?__ both sides of the equation. (Pages 72–73) subtract 4 from
3. The first step in solving an equation such as $n - 4 = 2$ is to __?__ both sides of the equation. (Pages 72–73) add 4 to
4. You can write a ratio as a __?__. (Pages 78–79) fraction
5. Ratios such as $\frac{3}{5}$ and $\frac{9}{15}$ are __?__. (Pages 78–79) equivalent
6. An equation that shows equivalent ratios is a __?__. proportion (Pages 80–81)

Part 2: SKILLS

Solve for n. Check each answer. (Pages 72–73)

7. $n + 4 = 18$ 14
8. $n + 8 = 29$ 21
9. $n - 16 = 4$ 20
10. $n - 13 = 4$ 17
11. $n - 7 = 6$ 13
12. $n - 18 = 41$ 59
13. $n + 11 = 20$ 9
14. $n + 6 = 88$ 82
15. $n + 73 = 82$ 9
16. $n + 17 = 184$ 167
17. $n - 39 = 14$ 53
18. $n - 48 = 62$ 110
19. $n - 25 = 112$ 137
20. $n + 34 = 61$ 27
21. $n + 78 = 110$ 32
22. $n - 57 = 29$ 86
23. $n - 8.6 = 17.4$ 26.0
24. $n - 11.7 = 11.7$ 23.4
25. $n + 13.6 = 18$ 4.4
26. $n + 17.1 = 25$ 7.9
27. $n + 3.4 = 20.4$ 17.0
28. $n - 5.2 = 6.5$ 11.7
29. $n - 18.6 = 22$ 40.6
30. $n + 3.5 = 12$ 8.5

(Pages 74–75)

31. $6n = 24$ 4
32. $7n = 56$ 8
33. $10n = 80$ 8
34. $30n = 270$ 9
35. $9n = 117$ 13
36. $12n = 156$ 13
37. $19n = 76$ 4
38. $36n = 144$ 4
39. $5n = 27.5$ 5.5
40. $8n = 64.8$ 8.1
41. $3.2n = 6.4$ 2
42. $1.6n = 4.8$ 3
43. $\frac{n}{12} = 4$ 48
44. $\frac{n}{15} = 6$ 90
45. $\frac{n}{23} = 2$ 46
46. $\frac{n}{4} = 80$ 320
47. $\frac{n}{12} = 8.3$ 99.6
48. $\frac{n}{2} = 6.6$ 13.2
49. $\frac{n}{3} = 18.4$ 55.2
50. $\frac{n}{5} = 6.7$ 33.5

(Pages 76–77)

51. $6n - 3 = 39$ 7
52. $3n + 11 = 29$ 6
53. $11n + 20 = 119$ 9
54. $3n - 5 = 40$ 15
55. $5n + 4 = 29$ 5
56. $6n + 4 = 40$ 6
57. $2n + 1.5 = 4.5$ 1.5
58. $3n - 7.6 = 1.4$ 3
59. $0.2n - 6 = 12$ 90
60. $0.3n - 11 = 22$ 110
61. $4.1n + 6.4 = 14.6$ 2
62. $5.4n + 3.1 = 19.3$ 3

63. $\frac{n}{5}+13=14$ 5

64. $\frac{n}{3}+8=16$ 24

65. $\frac{n}{4}-6=0$ 24

66. $\frac{n}{7}-12=8$ 140

67. $\frac{n}{2}-1.8=2.3$ 8.2

68. $\frac{n}{5}-6.3=1.5$ 39.0

Write a fraction in lowest terms for each ratio. (Pages 78–79)

69. 13 to 26 $\frac{1}{2}$

70. 4 to 6 $\frac{2}{3}$

71. 7 to 28 $\frac{1}{4}$

72. 81 to 27 $\frac{3}{1}$

73. 14 to 21 $\frac{2}{3}$

74. 9 to 27 $\frac{1}{3}$

75. 3 to 30 $\frac{1}{10}$

76. 6 to 15 $\frac{2}{5}$

77. 12 to 30 $\frac{2}{5}$

78. 7 to 21 $\frac{1}{3}$

79. 5 to 35 $\frac{1}{7}$

80. 42 to 6 $\frac{7}{1}$

81. 54 to 9 $\frac{6}{1}$

82. 72 to 12 $\frac{6}{1}$

83. 14 to 40 $\frac{7}{20}$

84. 12 to 66 $\frac{2}{11}$

Determine whether the ratios are equivalent. Answer Yes or No. (Pages 78–79)

85. $\frac{2}{7}$ and $\frac{3}{8}$ No

86. $\frac{5}{9}$ and $\frac{15}{27}$ Yes

87. $\frac{8}{25}$ and $\frac{32}{100}$ Yes

88. $\frac{7}{6}$ and $\frac{9}{11}$ No

89. $\frac{4}{5}$ and $\frac{16}{25}$ No

90. $\frac{7}{42}$ and $\frac{4}{24}$ Yes

91. $\frac{15}{20}$ and $\frac{9}{12}$ Yes

92. $\frac{6}{40}$ and $\frac{9}{70}$ No

93. $\frac{2}{5}$ and $\frac{5}{10}$ No

94. $\frac{16}{24}$ and $\frac{10}{15}$ Yes

95. $\frac{18}{25}$ and $\frac{40}{100}$ No

96. $\frac{16}{80}$ and $\frac{5}{25}$ Yes

97. $\frac{4}{7}$ and $\frac{16}{49}$ No

98. $\frac{8}{10}$ and $\frac{32}{40}$ Yes

99. $\frac{6}{13}$ and $\frac{12}{39}$ No

100. $\frac{5}{12}$ and $\frac{25}{60}$ Yes

Solve each proportion for n. (Pages 80–81)

101. $\frac{n}{8}=\frac{7}{14}$ 4

102. $\frac{n}{12}=\frac{5}{30}$ 2

103. $\frac{6}{15}=\frac{30}{n}$ 75

104. $\frac{11}{20}=\frac{44}{n}$ 80

105. $\frac{n}{12}=\frac{10}{15}$ 8

106. $\frac{9}{7}=\frac{81}{n}$ 63

107. $\frac{n}{9}=\frac{2}{6}$ 3

108. $\frac{18}{24}=\frac{75}{n}$ 100

109. $\frac{4}{13}=\frac{24}{n}$ 78

110. $\frac{5}{9}=\frac{20}{n}$ 36

111. $\frac{n}{4}=\frac{27}{36}$ 3

112. $\frac{n}{72}=\frac{4}{12}$ 24

113. $\frac{8}{n}=\frac{40}{25}$ 5

114. $\frac{2}{n}=\frac{14}{21}$ 3

115. $\frac{3}{8}=\frac{n}{72}$ 27

116. $\frac{72}{144}=\frac{n}{12}$ 6

117. $\frac{24}{32}=\frac{n}{8}$ 6

118. $\frac{1}{3}=\frac{n}{45}$ 15

119. $\frac{1}{n}=\frac{4}{52}$ 13

120. $\frac{5}{n}=\frac{15}{75}$ 25

Part 3: APPLICATIONS

The word problems covered in this chapter are presented here in a mixed setting. Note: each problem is referenced to the related page(s).

121. The selling price of a pair of shoes at Murdock Booting is \$45.50. The shoes cost the store \$29.98. Use the formula

$$m+c=s$$

to find the markup. (Pages 72–73) \$15.52

122. A gazelle can run at a rate of 66 feet per second. Use the formula

$$d=r\times t$$

to find how long it will take a gazelle to run 990 feet. (Pages 74–75) 15 seconds

123. At Falcon Clothing, the selling price of a suit is \$249.99. It cost the store \$170.00. Use the formula $m + c = s$ to find the markup. (Pages 72–73) \$79.99

124. One hot summer day the temperature was 95°F. Use the formula $F = 1.8C + 32$ to change this temperature to Celsius degrees. (Pages 76–77) 35° C

125. The outside temperature is 25°C. Use the formula $t = \frac{n}{7} + 4$ to find how many times (n) a cricket will chirp per minute at this temperature (t). (Pages 76–77) 147

126. A lion can run at a rate of 15.5 meters per second. The lion ran 93 meters. How long did it take? Use the formula $d = r \times t$. (Pages 74–75) 6 seconds

127. On a map of Hilltown, 4 centimeters represent 5 kilometers. How many kilometers do 6 centimeters represent? (Pages 80–81) 7.5 kilometers

128. On a certain map, 1.5 centimeters represent 30 meters. How many centimeters represent 90 meters? (Pages 80–81) 4.5 centimeters

129. A certain basketball cost Sports Inc. \$16.00. The selling price is \$24.50. Use the formula $m + c = s$ to find the markup. (Pages 72–73) \$8.50

130. The shortest distance of the planet Mars from the sun is 206,000,000 kilometers. Its longest distance from the sun is 250,000,000 kilometers. What is the ratio of its shortest distance to its longest distance from the sun? (Pages 78–79) $\frac{103}{125}$

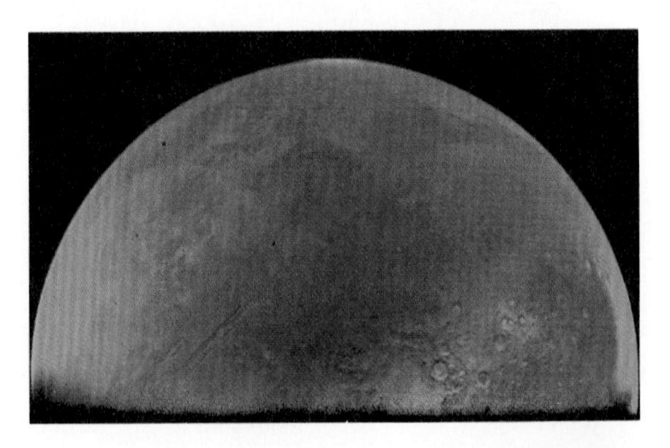

Chapter Test

The Teacher's Resource Book contains two forms of each chapter test.

Solve and check.

1. $n + 11 = 20$ 9 **2.** $n - 9 = 6$ 15 **3.** $3n = 36$ 12 **4.** $n + 1.9 = 3.9$ 2.0

5. $n - 3.4 = 8.7$ 12.1 **6.** $2.7n = 8.1$ 3 **7.** $2n + 6 = 18$ 6 **8.** $5n - 11 = 44$ 11

Write a fraction in lowest terms for each ratio.

9. 18 to 20 $\frac{9}{10}$ **10.** 9 to 5 $\frac{9}{5}$ **11.** 72 to 80 $\frac{9}{10}$ **12.** 15 to 75 $\frac{1}{5}$

Determine whether the ratios are equivalent. Answer Yes *or* No.

13. $\frac{3}{4}$ and $\frac{9}{16}$ No **14.** $\frac{5}{17}$ and $\frac{15}{51}$ Yes **15.** $\frac{2}{7}$ and $\frac{2}{61}$ No **16.** $\frac{7}{5}$ and $\frac{45}{35}$ No

Solve each proportion.

17. $\frac{n}{7} = \frac{35}{49}$ 5 **18.** $\frac{n}{20} = \frac{15}{100}$ 3 **19.** $\frac{2}{7} = \frac{6}{n}$ 21 **20.** $\frac{5}{8} = \frac{40}{n}$ 64

Solve.

21. A certain 10-speed bicycle cost Cycles Unlimited \$65.00. The selling price is \$94.99. Use the formula $m + c = s$ to find the markup. \$29.99

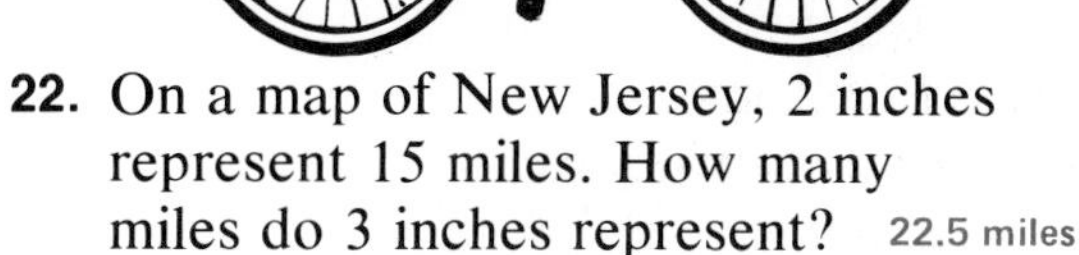

22. On a map of New Jersey, 2 inches represent 15 miles. How many miles do 3 inches represent? 22.5 miles

23. On a map of Fieldston, 2 centimeters represent 5 kilometers. How many centimeters represent 30 kilometers? 12 centimeters

24. A house cat can run at a rate of 13.5 meters per second. Use the formula $r \times t = d$ to find how long it will take a cat to run 67.5 meters at that rate. 5 seconds

25. The outside temperature is 77°F. Use the formula $F = 1.8C + 32$ to find the Celsius temperature. 25°C

REVIEW OF RELATED SKILLS FOR CHAPTER 5

We suggest that some or all of this page be reviewed before proceeding with the chapter.

Write each fraction in lowest terms. (Pages 46–47)

1. $\frac{6}{100}$ $\frac{3}{50}$ **2.** $\frac{42}{100}$ $\frac{21}{50}$ **3.** $\frac{15}{100}$ $\frac{3}{20}$ **4.** $\frac{18}{100}$ $\frac{9}{50}$ **5.** $\frac{65}{100}$ $\frac{13}{20}$ **6.** $\frac{58}{100}$ $\frac{29}{50}$

Multiply or divide. Write each answer in lowest terms. (Pages 56–57, 58–59)

7. $\frac{1}{4} \times \frac{1}{100}$ $\frac{1}{400}$ **8.** $\frac{3}{5} \times \frac{1}{100}$ $\frac{3}{500}$ **9.** $\frac{7}{8} \times \frac{1}{100}$ $\frac{7}{800}$ **10.** $33\frac{1}{3} \times \frac{1}{100}$ $\frac{1}{3}$ **11.** $87\frac{1}{2} \times \frac{1}{100}$ $\frac{7}{8}$

12. $400 \times \frac{1}{5}$ 80 **13.** $500 \times \frac{1}{4}$ 125 **14.** $64 \times \frac{1}{2}$ 32 **15.** $72 \times \frac{1}{3}$ 24 **16.** $48 \times \frac{1}{6}$ 8

17. $\frac{2}{3} \div 100$ $\frac{1}{150}$ **18.** $\frac{5}{7} \div 100$ $\frac{1}{140}$ **19.** $\frac{2}{9} \div 100$ $\frac{1}{450}$ **20.** $\frac{1}{3} \div 100$ $\frac{1}{300}$ **21.** $\frac{2}{7} \div 100$ $\frac{1}{350}$

22. $\frac{4}{9} \div 100$ $\frac{1}{225}$ **23.** $\frac{3}{5} \div 100$ $\frac{3}{500}$ **24.** $\frac{5}{6} \div 100$ $\frac{1}{120}$ **25.** $\frac{5}{8} \div 100$ $\frac{1}{160}$ **26.** $\frac{4}{5} \div 100$ $\frac{1}{125}$

Write a fraction for each mixed number. (Pages 56–57)

27. $3\frac{1}{3}$ $\frac{10}{3}$ **28.** $2\frac{1}{2}$ $\frac{5}{2}$ **29.** $1\frac{7}{8}$ $\frac{15}{8}$ **30.** $37\frac{1}{2}$ $\frac{75}{2}$ **31.** $66\frac{2}{3}$ $\frac{200}{3}$ **32.** $11\frac{1}{9}$ $\frac{100}{9}$

Divide. Carry the division to two decimal places. (Pages 14–15)

33. $3 \div 5$ 0.60 **34.** $7 \div 8$ $0.87\frac{1}{2}$ **35.** $4 \div 9$ $0.44\frac{4}{9}$ **36.** $7 \div 10$ 0.70 **37.** $24 \div 28$ $0.85\frac{6}{7}$

Multiply. (Pages 8–9)

38. 0.14×42 5.88 **39.** 0.58×16 9.28 **40.** 0.44×28 12.32 **41.** 0.39×150 58.5

42. 25×0.04 1 **43.** 64×0.05 3.2 **44.** 220×0.47 103.4 **45.** 316×0.65 205.4

Solve each equation. (Pages 74–75)

46. $5n = 30$ 6 **47.** $6n = 48$ 8 **48.** $12n = 96$ 8 **49.** $25n = 400$ 16

50. $0.6n = 72$ 120 **51.** $0.8n = 16$ 20 **52.** $0.25n = 40$ 160 **53.** $0.55n = 110$ 200

54. $\frac{n}{4} = 96$ 384 **55.** $\frac{n}{3} = 102$ 306 **56.** $\frac{n}{5} = 75$ 375 **57.** $\frac{n}{8} = 12$ 96

58. $\frac{n}{7} = 48$ 336 **59.** $\frac{n}{5} = 27$ 135 **60.** $\frac{n}{4} = 49$ 196 **61.** $\frac{n}{2} = 76$ 152

Divide. (Pages 14–15)

62. $40 \div 0.8$ 50 **63.** $200 \div 0.4$ 500 **64.** $64 \div 0.16$ 400 **65.** $80 \div 0.25$ 320 **66.** $100 \div 0.32$ 312.5

Round each number as indicated. (Pages 12–13)

67. 472; to the nearest ten 470

68. 4655; to the nearest thousand 5000

69. 381; to the nearest hundred 400

70. 12,730; to the nearest ten thousand 10,000

(Pages 16–17)

71. 55.46; to the nearest whole number 55

72. 0.567; to the nearest hundredth 0.57

73. 48.72; to the nearest tenth 48.7

74. 0.8384; to the nearest thousandth 0.838

CHAPTER

5 PER CENT

ESSENTIAL SKILLS/APPLICATIONS

CAREER APPLICATION

Photographer

5-1 Per Cents, Decimals, and Fractions

See the Teacher's Manual for the objectives.

Per cent means **hundredths** or **per hundred.**

8% means 8 hundredths or 0.08.

11% means 11 per hundred or $\frac{11}{100}$.

You can write a decimal or a fraction for a per cent.

PROCEDURE To write a decimal for a per cent, move the decimal point two places to the left.

EXAMPLE 1 Write a decimal for each per cent.

a. 28% **b.** 5% **c.** 148%

Solutions: **a.** 28% = 0.28 **b.** 05% = 0.05 **c.** 148% = 1.48

Insert one zero.

After completing Example 1, you may wish to have students do some or all of Exercises 1-42.

PROCEDURE To write a fraction for a per cent:

1 Write a fraction with a denominator of 100 for the per cent.

2 Write the fraction in lowest terms.

EXAMPLE 2 Write a fraction for each per cent.

a. 17% **b.** 20% **c.** $\frac{1}{2}$% **d.** $33\frac{1}{3}$%

Solutions:

a. $17\% = \frac{17}{100}$ *Lowest terms*

b. $20\% = \frac{20}{100} = \frac{1}{5}$ *Write in lowest terms*

c. $\frac{1}{2}\% = \frac{\frac{1}{2}}{100}$ *$\frac{1}{2}$% means $\frac{1}{2}$ per hundred.*

$= \frac{1}{2} \div 100$

$= \frac{1}{2} \times \frac{1}{100}$

$= \frac{1}{200}$

d. $33\frac{1}{3}\% = \frac{33\frac{1}{3}}{100}$

$= 33\frac{1}{3} \div 100$

$= 33\frac{1}{3} \times \frac{1}{100}$

$= \frac{\cancel{100}^{1}}{3} \times \frac{1}{\cancel{100}_{1}}$

$= \frac{1}{3}$

EXERCISES

Write a decimal for each per cent. (Example 1)

1. 36% 0.36 **2.** 42% 0.42 **3.** 85% 0.85 **4.** 49% 0.49 **5.** 34% 0.34 **6.** 24% 0.24

7. 25% 0.25 **8.** 16% 0.16 **9.** 46% 0.46 **10.** 58% 0.58 **11.** 83% 0.83 **12.** 74% 0.74

13. 44% 0.44 **14.** 67% 0.67 **15.** 98% 0.98 **16.** 43% 0.43 **17.** 51% 0.51 **18.** 12% 0.12

19. 56% 0.56 **20.** 21% 0.21 **21.** 73% 0.73 **22.** 29% 0.29 **23.** 53% 0.53 **24.** 82% 0.82

25. 6% 0.06 **26.** 8% 0.08 **27.** 4% 0.04 **28.** 9% 0.09 **29.** 3% 0.03 **30.** 2% 0.02

31. 121% 1.21 **32.** 156% 1.56 **33.** 373% 3.73 **34.** 438% 4.38 **35.** 129% 1.29 **36.** 364% 3.64

37. $33\frac{1}{3}\%$ $0.33\frac{1}{3}$ **38.** $12\frac{1}{2}\%$ $0.12\frac{1}{2}$ **39.** $16\frac{2}{3}\%$ $0.16\frac{2}{3}$ **40.** $37\frac{1}{2}\%$ $0.37\frac{1}{2}$ **41.** $11\frac{1}{9}\%$ $0.11\frac{1}{9}$ **42.** $14\frac{2}{7}\%$ $0.14\frac{2}{7}$

Write a fraction for each per cent. (Example 2)

43. 19% $\frac{19}{100}$ **44.** 21% $\frac{21}{100}$ **45.** 37% $\frac{37}{100}$ **46.** 53% $\frac{53}{100}$ **47.** 50% $\frac{1}{2}$ **48.** 20% $\frac{1}{5}$

49. 30% $\frac{3}{10}$ **50.** 45% $\frac{9}{20}$ **51.** 25% $\frac{1}{4}$ **52.** 80% $\frac{4}{5}$ **53.** 75% $\frac{3}{4}$ **54.** 60% $\frac{3}{5}$

55. 42% $\frac{21}{50}$ **56.** 85% $\frac{17}{20}$ **57.** 56% $\frac{14}{25}$ **58.** 38% $\frac{19}{50}$ **59.** 48% $\frac{12}{25}$ **60.** 15% $\frac{3}{20}$

61. 65% $\frac{13}{20}$ **62.** 22% $\frac{11}{50}$ **63.** 78% $\frac{39}{50}$ **64.** 95% $\frac{19}{20}$ **65.** 14% $\frac{7}{50}$ **66.** 34% $\frac{17}{50}$

67. $\frac{1}{3}\%$ $\frac{1}{300}$ **68.** $\frac{1}{4}\%$ $\frac{1}{400}$ **69.** $\frac{1}{8}\%$ $\frac{1}{800}$ **70.** $\frac{1}{5}\%$ $\frac{1}{500}$ **71.** $\frac{1}{10}\%$ $\frac{1}{1000}$ **72.** $\frac{1}{12}\%$ $\frac{1}{1200}$

73. $\frac{2}{3}\%$ $\frac{1}{150}$ **74.** $\frac{3}{4}\%$ $\frac{3}{400}$ **75.** $66\frac{2}{3}\%$ $\frac{2}{3}$ **76.** $37\frac{1}{2}\%$ $\frac{3}{8}$ **77.** $62\frac{1}{2}\%$ $\frac{5}{8}$ **78.** $87\frac{1}{2}\%$ $\frac{7}{8}$

APPLICATIONS: From Per Cents to Decimals and Fractions

These word problems apply the skills taught in the lesson.

For Exercises 79–80, write a decimal for each per cent.

79. In a recent year, about 16% of the electricity in the United States was produced from oil. 0.16

80. In a recent year, about 44% of the electricity in the United States was produced from coal. 0.44

For Exercises 81–84, write a fraction for each per cent.

81. In a recent year, Texas produced about 25% of all the minerals produced in the United States. $\frac{1}{4}$

82. In a recent year, Louisiana produced about 14% of all the minerals produced in the United States. $\frac{7}{50}$

83. In a recent year, West Virginia produced about 4% of all the minerals produced in the United States. $\frac{1}{25}$

84. In a recent year, California produced about 6% of all the minerals produced in the United States. $\frac{3}{50}$

5-2 Writing Per Cents for Decimals and Fractions

See the Teacher's Manual for the objectives.

You can write a per cent for a decimal or a fraction.

PROCEDURE To write a per cent for a decimal, move the decimal point <u>two</u> places to the right.

EXAMPLE 1 Write a per cent for each decimal.

a. 0.48 **b.** 0.225 **c.** $0.12\frac{1}{2}$

Solutions: **a.** 0.48 = **48%** **b.** 0.225 = **22.5%** **c.** $0.12\frac{1}{2} = \mathbf{12\frac{1}{2}\%}$

After completing Example 1, you may wish to have students do some or all of Exercises 1-54.

PROCEDURE To write a per cent for a fraction:

1. Divide the numerator of the fraction by the denominator. Carry the division to two decimal places.
2. Write a per cent for the decimal.

EXAMPLE 2 Write a per cent for each fraction.

a. $\frac{3}{4}$ **b.** $\frac{3}{8}$

Solutions:

a. $\frac{3}{4}$ means $3 \div 4$.

1. $4\overline{)3.00}$ = 0.75
2. 0.75 = **75%**

b. $\frac{3}{8}$ means $3 \div 8$.

1. $8\overline{)3.00}$; 24; 60; 56; 4 — $0.37\frac{4}{8} = 0.37\frac{1}{2}$ ◀ *Lowest terms*
2. $0.37\frac{1}{2} = \mathbf{37\frac{1}{2}\%}$

To write a per cent for a mixed number, you first write the mixed number as a fraction.

$$1\frac{1}{5} = \frac{6}{5} = 1.20 = 120\%$$

EXERCISES

Write a per cent for each decimal. (Example 1)

1. 0.37 37% **2.** 0.29 29% **3.** 0.32 32% **4.** 0.37 37% **5.** 0.41 41% **6.** 0.25 25%

7. 0.28 28% **8.** 0.39 39% **9.** 0.91 91% **10.** 0.99 99% **11.** 0.33 33% **12.** 0.27 27%

13. 0.04 4% **14.** 0.09 9% **15.** 0.03 3% **16.** 0.02 2% **17.** 0.15 15% **18.** 0.62 62%

19. 1.32 132% **20.** 4.65 465% **21.** 11.02 1102% **22.** 9.03 903% **23.** 7.15 715% **24.** 1.54 154%

25. 0.224 22.4% **26.** 0.185 18.5% **27.** 0.575 57.5% **28.** 0.282 28.2% **29.** 0.443 44.3% **30.** 0.916 91.6%

31. 1.346 134.6% **32.** 5.428 542.8% **33.** 7.199 719.9% **34.** 2.048 204.8% **35.** 3.264 326.4% **36.** 4.533 453.3%

37. 0.002 0.2% **38.** 0.003 0.3% **39.** 0.005 0.5% **40.** 1.004 100.4% **41.** 2.008 200.8% **42.** 0.007 0.7%

43. $0.37\frac{1}{2}$ $37\frac{1}{2}\%$ **44.** $0.33\frac{1}{3}$ $33\frac{1}{3}\%$ **45.** $0.62\frac{1}{2}$ $62\frac{1}{2}\%$ **46.** $0.11\frac{1}{9}$ $11\frac{1}{9}\%$ **47.** $0.66\frac{2}{3}$ $66\frac{2}{3}\%$ **48.** $0.86\frac{2}{3}$ $86\frac{2}{3}\%$

49. $0.28\frac{1}{4}$ $28\frac{1}{4}\%$ **50.** $0.37\frac{1}{3}$ $37\frac{1}{3}\%$ **51.** $0.44\frac{5}{8}$ $44\frac{5}{8}\%$ **52.** $0.75\frac{1}{2}$ $75\frac{1}{2}\%$ **53.** $0.27\frac{1}{4}$ $27\frac{1}{4}\%$ **54.** $0.19\frac{3}{4}$ $19\frac{3}{4}\%$

Write a per cent for each fraction or mixed number. (Example 2)

55. $\frac{3}{10}$ 30% **56.** $\frac{7}{10}$ 70% **57.** $\frac{4}{50}$ 8% **58.** $\frac{7}{25}$ 28% **59.** $\frac{9}{25}$ 36% **60.** $\frac{6}{40}$ 15%

61. $\frac{3}{5}$ 60% **62.** $\frac{1}{2}$ 50% **63.** $\frac{2}{8}$ 25% **64.** $\frac{1}{5}$ 20% **65.** $\frac{1}{4}$ 25% **66.** $\frac{4}{5}$ 80%

67. $\frac{9}{10}$ 90% **68.** $\frac{27}{50}$ 54% **69.** $\frac{11}{20}$ 55% **70.** $\frac{2}{5}$ 40% **71.** $\frac{8}{40}$ 20% **72.** $\frac{6}{12}$ 50%

73. $\frac{13}{20}$ 65% **74.** $\frac{17}{25}$ 68% **75.** $\frac{33}{50}$ 66% **76.** $\frac{18}{40}$ 45% **77.** $\frac{6}{20}$ 30% **78.** $\frac{23}{25}$ 92%

79. $\frac{2}{3}$ $66\frac{2}{3}\%$ **80.** $\frac{5}{8}$ $62\frac{1}{2}\%$ **81.** $\frac{7}{12}$ $58\frac{1}{3}\%$ **82.** $\frac{3}{8}$ $37\frac{1}{2}\%$ **83.** $\frac{1}{40}$ $2\frac{1}{2}\%$ **84.** $\frac{15}{16}$ $93\frac{3}{4}\%$

85. $\frac{1}{12}$ $8\frac{1}{3}\%$ **86.** $\frac{7}{8}$ $87\frac{1}{2}\%$ **87.** $\frac{1}{7}$ $14\frac{2}{7}\%$ **88.** $\frac{5}{6}$ $83\frac{1}{3}\%$ **89.** $\frac{2}{9}$ $22\frac{2}{9}\%$ **90.** $\frac{4}{11}$ $36\frac{4}{11}\%$

91. $\frac{1}{3}$ $33\frac{1}{3}\%$ **92.** $\frac{3}{40}$ $7\frac{1}{2}\%$ **93.** $\frac{3}{16}$ $18\frac{3}{4}\%$ **94.** $\frac{1}{6}$ $16\frac{2}{3}\%$ **95.** $\frac{7}{16}$ $43\frac{3}{4}\%$ **96.** $\frac{4}{7}$ $57\frac{1}{7}\%$

97. $3\frac{9}{10}$ 390% **98.** $5\frac{1}{10}$ 510% **99.** $8\frac{3}{20}$ 815% **100.** $7\frac{2}{5}$ 740% **101.** $5\frac{4}{5}$ 580% **102.** $10\frac{3}{4}$ 1075%

103. $2\frac{5}{6}$ $283\frac{1}{3}\%$ **104.** $1\frac{11}{12}$ $191\frac{2}{3}\%$ **105.** $5\frac{5}{8}$ $562\frac{1}{2}\%$ **106.** $16\frac{1}{3}$ $1633\frac{1}{3}\%$ **107.** $12\frac{1}{8}$ $1212\frac{1}{2}\%$ **108.** $5\frac{1}{9}$ $511\frac{1}{9}\%$

109. $4\frac{1}{5}$ 420% **110.** $6\frac{3}{4}$ 675% **111.** $5\frac{7}{10}$ 570% **112.** $4\frac{1}{4}$ 425% **113.** $3\frac{4}{5}$ 380% **114.** $8\frac{9}{20}$ 845%

These word problems apply the skills taught in the lesson.

APPLICATIONS: From Decimals and Fractions to Per Cents

For Exercises 115–120, write a per cent for each decimal or fraction.

115. The sale price of a shirt is 0.75 times the original price. 75%

116. The sale price of a television is 0.8 times the original price. 80%

117. The price of a pair of shoes was reduced by $\frac{1}{5}$ of the original price. 20%

118. The price of a pair of slacks was reduced by $\frac{1}{4}$ of the original price. 25%

119. The price of a baseball bat was reduced by 0.25 times the original price. 25%

120. The sale price of a coat is $\frac{4}{5}$ of the original price. 80%

5-3 Finding a Per Cent of a Number

See the Teacher's Manual for the objectives.

You can use a decimal or a fraction to find a per cent of a number. The table below shows some common fraction and per cent equivalents.

TABLE

EQUIVALENT FRACTIONS AND PER CENTS			
$\frac{1}{4} = 25\%$	$\frac{1}{2} = 50\%$	$\frac{3}{4} = 75\%$	
$\frac{1}{5} = 20\%$	$\frac{2}{5} = 40\%$	$\frac{3}{5} = 60\%$	$\frac{4}{5} = 80\%$
$\frac{1}{6} = 16\frac{2}{3}\%$	$\frac{1}{3} = 33\frac{1}{3}\%$	$\frac{2}{3} = 66\frac{2}{3}\%$	$\frac{5}{6} = 83\frac{1}{3}\%$
$\frac{1}{8} = 12\frac{1}{2}\%$	$\frac{3}{8} = 37\frac{1}{2}\%$	$\frac{5}{8} = 62\frac{1}{2}\%$	$\frac{7}{8} = 87\frac{1}{2}\%$

PROCEDURE To find a per cent of a number:

[1] Write an equation.

[2] Write a decimal or fraction for the per cent.

[3] Solve the equation.

After completing Example 1a, you may wish to have students do some or all of Exercises 1-36.

EXAMPLE 1 **a.** What number is 12% of 750? **b.** What number is $37\frac{1}{2}\%$ of 64?

Solutions: **a.** What number is 12% of 750?

[1] $n = 12\% \times 750$

[2] $n = 0.12 \times 750$

[3] $n = \mathbf{90}$

Thus, 12% of 750 = **90.**

b. What number is $37\frac{1}{2}\%$ of 64?

$n = 37\frac{1}{2}\% \times 64$

$n = \frac{3}{8} \times 64$

$n = \frac{3}{\not{8}_1} \times \frac{\not{64}^{8}}{1}$

$n = \mathbf{24}$

Thus, $37\frac{1}{2}\%$ of 64 = **24.**

EXERCISES

Find each answer. Write a decimal for the per cent. (Example 1a)

1. 70% of 63 44.1 **2.** 18% of 90 16.2 **3.** 25% of 16 4 **4.** 40% of 82 32.8

5. 28% of 60 16.8 **6.** 7% of 25 1.75 **7.** 11% of 50 5.5 **8.** 17% of 100 17

9. 95% of 20 19 **10.** 36% of 40 14.4 **11.** 4% of 83 3.32 **12.** 9% of 72 6.48

13. 63% of 80 50.4 **14.** 17% of 400 68 **15.** 30% of 28 8.4 **16.** 27% of 900 243

17. 5% of 20 1 | **18.** 8% of 120 9.6 | **19.** 6% of 50 3 | **20.** 3% of 400 12

21. 12% of 36 4.32 | **22.** 14% of 18 2.52 | **23.** 21% of 42 8.82 | **24.** 43% of 100 43

25. 85% of 50 42.5 | **26.** 74% of 300 222 | **27.** 28% of 500 140 | **28.** 32% of 56 17.92

29. 10.1% of 16 1.616 | **30.** 30.4% of 400 121.6 | **31.** 19.5% of 60 11.7 | **32.** 21.2% of 800 169.6

33. 14.5% of 600 87 | **34.** 15.5% of 200 31 | **35.** 87.5% of 120 105 | **36.** 32.5% of 64 20.8

Find each answer. Write a fraction for the per cent. (Example 1b)

37. 60% of 45 27 | **38.** $83\frac{1}{3}$% of 66 55 | **39.** $37\frac{1}{2}$% of 56 21 | **40.** 50% of 90 45

41. $12\frac{1}{2}$% of 88 11 | **42.** 75% of 44 33 | **43.** $33\frac{1}{3}$% of 72 24 | **44.** $16\frac{2}{3}$% of 84 14

45. $66\frac{2}{3}$% of 120 80 | **46.** 20% of 65 13 | **47.** 25% of 76 19 | **48.** $87\frac{1}{2}$% of 96 84

49. 40% of 75 30 | **50.** 50% of 86 43 | **51.** 80% of 70 56 | **52.** 75% of 400 300

53. $12\frac{1}{2}$% of 80 10 | **54.** $87\frac{1}{2}$% of 48 42 | **55.** $62\frac{1}{2}$% of 96 60 | **56.** $33\frac{1}{3}$% of 51 17

57. 40% of 60 24 | **58.** 80% of 25 20 | **59.** 25% of 80 20 | **60.** 50% of 110 55

61. $33\frac{1}{3}$% of 27 9 | **62.** $87\frac{1}{2}$% of 64 56 | **63.** $16\frac{2}{3}$% of 54 9 | **64.** $37\frac{1}{2}$% of 96 36

65. 75% of 28 21 | **66.** 60% of 120 72 | **67.** 20% of 15 3 | **68.** 35% of 40 14

69. $66\frac{2}{3}$% of 33 22 | **70.** $83\frac{1}{3}$% of 60 50 | **71.** $12\frac{1}{2}$% of 72 9 | **72.** $33\frac{1}{3}$% of 54 18

Mixed Practice The Mixed Practice contains exercises that relate to both Examples 1a and 1b.

73. 25% of 40 10 | **74.** 60% of 45 27 | **75.** 7% of 40 2.8 | **76.** 9% of 62 5.58

77. 67% of 80 53.6 | **78.** 42% of 50 21 | **79.** $12\frac{1}{2}$% of 48 6 | **80.** $83\frac{1}{3}$% of 96 80

81. 5% of 78 3.9 | **82.** 3% of 84 2.52 | **83.** 13% of 29 3.77 | **84.** 28% of 46 12.88

85. $37\frac{1}{2}$% of 64 24 | **86.** $66\frac{2}{3}$% of 72 48 | **87.** 40% of 80 32 | **88.** 30% of 90 27

APPLICATIONS: Using Per Cents

These word problems apply the skills taught in the lesson.

The table on the right shows eight blood types and the per cent of the population with each type. Use this table for Exercises 89–92.

89. Out of a total population of 5000, about how many people would you expect to have type A positive blood? 1900

90. Out of a total population of 5000, about how many people would you expect to have type A negative blood? 300

91. Out of a total population of 12,400, about how many people would you expect to have type AB positive blood? 434

92. Out of a total population of 12,400, about how many people would you expect to have type O positive blood? 4464

Type	Per Cent
A positive	38
O positive	36
B positive	8
O negative	6
A negative	6
AB positive	3.5
B negative	2
AB negative	0.5

5-4 Finding What Per Cent A Number is of Another

See the Teacher's Manual for the objectives.

PROCEDURE To find what per cent one number is of another:

1. Write an equation.
2. Solve the equation for n.
3. Write a per cent for n.

After completing Example 1a, you may wish to have the students do some or all of Exercise 1-4, 9-12, and 13-30.

EXAMPLE 1 **a.** What per cent of 15 is 12? **b.** 30 is what per cent of 48?

Solutions:

a. [1] What per cent of 15 is 12?

$n \times 15 = 12$, or $15n = 12$

[2] $15n = 12$

$\frac{15n}{\mathbf{15}} = \frac{12}{\mathbf{15}}$

$n = \frac{12}{15}$, or $\frac{4}{5}$

[3] $\frac{4}{5} = \mathbf{80\%}$ ◀ *From the table*

b. [1] 30 is what per cent of 48?

$30 = n \times 48$

$30 = 48n$

[2] $48n = 30$ ◀ ***30 = 48n is the same as 48n = 30.***

$\frac{48n}{\mathbf{48}} = \frac{30}{\mathbf{48}}$

$n = \frac{30}{48}$, or $\frac{5}{8}$

[3] $\frac{5}{8} \longrightarrow 8\overline{)5.00}$, $0.62\frac{4}{8} = 0.62\frac{1}{2}$

$0.62\frac{1}{2} = \mathbf{62\frac{1}{2}\%}$

EXERCISES

Write an equation for each exercise. (Example 1, step 1)

1. What per cent of 20 is 14? $n \times 20 = 14$
2. What per cent of 90 is 45? $n \times 90 = 45$
3. What per cent of 70 is 35? $n \times 70 = 35$
4. What per cent of 50 is 37? $n \times 50 = 37$
5. 20 is what per cent of 80? $20 = n \times 80$
6. 75 is what per cent of 225? $75 = n \times 225$
7. 17 is what per cent of 68? $17 = n \times 68$
8. 15 is what per cent of 90? $15 = n \times 90$
9. What per cent of 80 is 32? $n \times 8 = 32$
10. What per cent of 72 is 27? $n \times 72 = 27$
11. What per cent of 200 is 150? $n \times 200 = 150$
12. What per cent of 110 is 11? $n \times 110 = 11$

Solve. (Example 1a)

13. What per cent of 8 is 2? 25%
14. What per cent of 16 is 4? 25%
15. What per cent of 25 is 15? 60%
16. What per cent of 15 is 3? 20%
17. What per cent of 63 is 27? $42\frac{6}{7}\%$
18. What per cent of 14 is 7? 50%
19. What per cent of 120 is 30? 25%
20. What per cent of 12 is 4? $33\frac{1}{3}\%$
21. What per cent of 80 is 16? 20%
22. What per cent of 6 is 3? 50%

23. What per cent of 40 is 30? 75%

24. What per cent of 90 is 15? $16\frac{2}{3}\%$

25. What per cent of 50 is 20? 40%

26. What per cent of 75 is 25? $33\frac{1}{3}\%$

27. What per cent of 24 is 3? $12\frac{1}{2}\%$

28. What per cent of 65 is 26? 40%

29. What per cent of 120 is 80? $66\frac{2}{3}\%$

30. What per cent of 240 is 180? 75%

(Example 1b)

31. 18 is what per cent of 90? 20%

32. 16 is what per cent of 64? 25%

33. 75 is what per cent of 300? 25%

34. 36 is what per cent of 108? $33\frac{1}{3}\%$

35. 25 is what per cent of 200? $12\frac{1}{2}\%$

36. 70 is what per cent of 420? $16\frac{2}{3}\%$

37. 12 is what per cent of 96? $12\frac{1}{2}\%$

38. 65 is what per cent of 130? 50%

39. 50 is what per cent of 250? 20%

40. 27 is what per cent of 162? $16\frac{2}{3}\%$

41. 36 is what per cent of 90? 40%

42. 81 is what per cent of 324? 25%

43. 11 is what per cent of 55? 20%

44. 13 is what per cent of 78? $16\frac{2}{3}\%$

45. 25 is what per cent of 40? $62\frac{1}{2}\%$

46. 6 is what per cent of 60? 10%

47. 75 is what per cent of 225? $33\frac{1}{3}\%$

48. 5 is what per cent of 500? 1%

Mixed Practice The Mixed Practice contains exercises that relate to both Examples 1a and 1b.

49. What per cent of 10 is 3? 30%

50. What per cent of 4 is 1? 25%

51. 18 is what per cent of 54? $33\frac{1}{3}\%$

52. 7 is what per cent of 56? $12\frac{1}{2}\%$

53. 30 is what per cent of 40? 75%

54. 25 is what per cent of 150? $16\frac{2}{3}\%$

55. What per cent of 24 is 8? $33\frac{1}{3}\%$

56. What per cent of 64 is 48? 75%

57. What per cent of 38 is 19? 50%

58. What per cent of 200 is 56? 28%

These word problems apply the skills taught in the lesson.

APPLICATIONS: Using Per Cents in Sports

59. Luis completed 11 out of 20 passing attempts. What per cent did he complete? 55%

60. Jennie won 5 out of 25 races she ran last year. What per cent did she win? 20%

61. The Blue Sox won 20 out of the 30 games they played. What per cent did they win? $66\frac{2}{3}\%$

62. Out of 25 times at bat, Thomas hit safely 17 times. What per cent is this? 68%

63. Marita made 20 of her last 25 foul shots. What per cent did she make? 80%

64. Out of 40 field goal attempts, Jim scored 18 times. What per cent is that? 45%

65. Jeanine is a field hockey goalie. She has been scored on only 3 times out of 20 attempts. What per cent is this? 15%

PHOTOGRAPHER

Career lessons are optional. This lesson applies the skills of solving a proportion, writing a ratio as a per cent and using a formula.

Photographers must be able to reduce and enlarge photographs. To do this, a photographer must know how to use proportions.

Artist, Ruth Gordon

EXAMPLE 1

Cindy Clayton, a photographer, has to reduce a photograph 12 centimeters long and 8 centimeters wide to fit a space 7 centimeters long. Find the width of the reduced photograph to the nearest tenth.

Solution:

$$\frac{\textbf{Length of Original}}{\textbf{Width of Original}} = \frac{\textbf{Length of Copy}}{\textbf{Width of Copy}}$$

$$\frac{12}{8} = \frac{7}{n}$$

$$12 \times n = 8 \times 7$$

$$12n = 56$$

$$n = 4.667$$

The width is about **4.7 centimeters.**

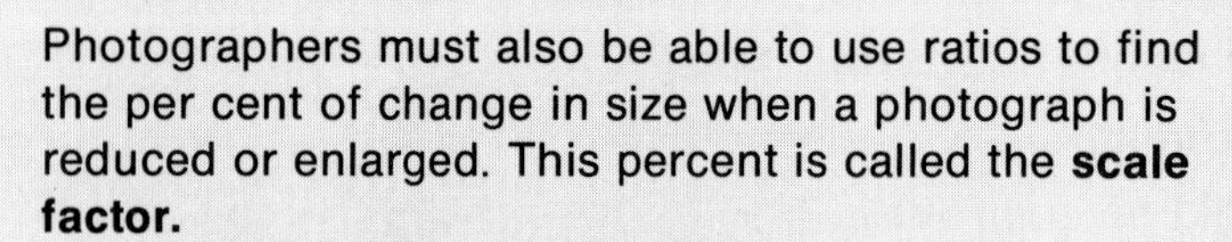

Photographers must also be able to use ratios to find the per cent of change in size when a photograph is reduced or enlarged. This percent is called the **scale factor.**

The photographer will set an enlarging camera at the per cent needed, and make a copy of the original that is the correct size.

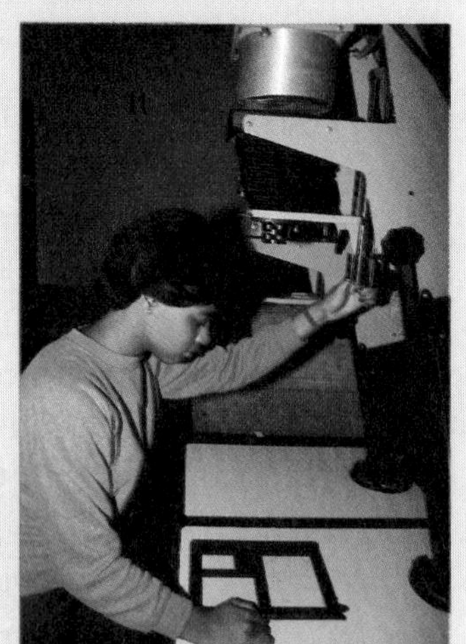

EXAMPLE 2

Find the scale factor for the copy Cindy needs in Example 1.

Solution:

$$\textbf{Scale Factor} = \frac{\textbf{Length of Copy}}{\textbf{Length of Original}}$$

$$= \frac{7}{12}$$

$$= 0.583 = \mathbf{58.3\%}$$

Rounded to the nearest whole per cent

The scale factor is about **58%.**

EXERCISES

Note that Exercises 1–16 are non-verbal.

For Exercises 1–8, complete the table. Round each answer to the nearest tenth. (Example 1)

	Length of Original	Width of Original	Length of Copy	Width of Copy
1.	12 cm	8 cm	6 cm	? 4 cm
2.	15 cm	7 cm	12 cm	? 5.6 cm
3.	16 cm	8 cm	? 8 cm	4 cm
4.	27 cm	15 cm	11 cm	? 6.1 cm
5.	30 cm	12 cm	? 25 cm	10 cm
6.	60 cm	55 cm	12 cm	? 11 cm
7.	62 cm	25 cm	15 cm	? 6.0 cm
8.	37 cm	27 cm	? 15.1 cm	11 cm

For Exercises 9–16, complete the table. (Example 2)

	Length of Copy	Length of Original	Scale Factor
9.	12 cm	8 cm	? 150%
10.	18 cm	27 cm	? $66\frac{2}{3}\%$
11.	6 cm	18 cm	? $33\frac{1}{3}\%$
12.	24 cm	9 cm	? $266\frac{2}{3}\%$

	Length of Copy	Length of Original	Scale Factor
13.	36 cm	48 cm	? 75%
14.	60 cm	50 cm	? 120%
15.	85 cm	100 cm	? 85%
16.	40 cm	100 cm	? 40%

17. A photograph 15 centimeters long and 12 centimeters wide has to be reduced to fit in a space 10 centimeters long. Find the width of the reduced photograph. 8 cm (Example 1)

18. A picture 25 centimeters long and 20 centimeters wide has to be enlarged to fit in a frame 30 centimeters long. Find the width of the enlarged photograph. (Example 1) 24 cm

For Exercises 19–20, round each answer to the nearest whole per cent. (Example 2)

19. Find the scale factor for the copy of the photograph in Exercise 18. 120%

20. One newspaper has advertising space that is 5 centimeters wide. The original design for an ad is 18 centimeters wide. Find the scale factor. 28%

5-5 Finding a Number Given a Per Cent

See the Teacher's Manual for the objectives.

PROCEDURE To find a number when a per cent of it is known:

1. Write an equation.
2. Solve the equation.

EXAMPLE 1 30 is 60% of what number?

Solution: 30 is 60% of what number?

1. $30 = 0.60 \times n$

$0.60n = 30$ ◀ ***30 = 0.60n is the same as 0.60n = 30.***

2. $\frac{0.60n}{\mathbf{0.60}} = \frac{30}{\mathbf{0.60}}$

$n = \mathbf{50}$ 30 is 60% of **50.**

After completing Example 1, you may wish the students to do some or all of Exercises 1, 2, 4, 6, 7, 10, 11-28.

Sometimes it is convenient to write a fraction for the per cent.

EXAMPLE 2 72 is $33\frac{1}{3}\%$ of what number?

Solution: 72 is $33\frac{1}{3}\%$ of what number ◀ $\mathbf{33\frac{1}{3}\% = \frac{1}{3}}$

1. $72 = \frac{1}{3} \times n$, or $72 = \frac{1}{3}n$

$\frac{n}{3} = 72$ ◀ $\mathbf{\frac{1}{3}n = \frac{n}{3}}$

2. $\frac{n}{3} \times \mathbf{\frac{3}{1}} = 72 \times \mathbf{3}$

$n = \mathbf{216}$ 72 is $33\frac{1}{3}\%$ of **216.**

EXERCISES

Write an equation for each exercise. (Examples 1 and 2, step 1)

1. 60 is 25% of what number? $60 = 0.25 \times n$

2. 11 is 20% of what number? $11 = 0.20 \times n$

3. 15 is $33\frac{1}{3}\%$ of what number? $15 = \frac{1}{3} \times n$

4. 5 is 10% of what number? $5 = 0.10 \times n$

5. 7 is $16\frac{2}{3}\%$ of what number? $7 = \frac{1}{6} \times n$

6. 20 is 20% of what number? $20 = 0.20 \times n$

7. 32 is 40% of what number? $32 = 0.40 \times n$

8. 12 is $33\frac{1}{3}\%$ of what number?

9. 9 is $12\frac{1}{2}\%$ of what number? $9 = \frac{1}{8} \times n$

10. 60 is 30% of what number? $60 = 0.30 \times n$

8. $12 = \frac{1}{3} \times n$

Solve. (Example 1)

11. 9 is 20% of what number? 45
12. 24 is 50% of what number? 48
13. 6 is 40% of what number? 15
14. 21 is 35% of what number? 60
15. 16 is 80% of what number? 20
16. 9 is 5% of what number? 180
17. 81 is 27% of what number? 300
18. 45 is 30% of what number? 150
19. 99 is 18% of what number? 550
20. 90 is 15% of what number? 600
21. 14 is 25% of what number? 56
22. 195 is 65% of what number? 300
23. 55 is 22% of what number? 250
24. 70 is 28% of what number? 250
25. 234 is 52% of what number? 450
26. 204 is 85% of what number? 240
27. 54 is 45% of what number? 120
28. 18 is 24% of what number? 75

Solve. Use a fraction for the per cent. (Example 2)

29. 9 is 50% of what number? 18
30. 14 is 25% of what number? 56
31. 73 is 10% of what number? 730
32. 14 is 40% of what number? 35
33. 24 is $37\frac{1}{2}$% of what number? 64
34. 8 is 25% of what number? 32
35. 17 is $16\frac{2}{3}$% of what number? 102
36. 42 is 60% of what number? 70
37. 60 is $83\frac{1}{3}$% of what number? 72
38. 30 is $62\frac{1}{2}$% of what number? 48
39. 4 is $12\frac{1}{2}$% of what number? 32
40. 45 is 25% of what number? 180

These word problems apply the skills taught in the lesson.

APPLICATIONS: Using Per Cents

Find the 1981 population.

41. By 1991, it is projected that the population of Alaska will be 40,000 more than the population in 1981. This is 10% of the 1981 population. 400,000

42. By 1991, the population of Texas is projected to be 2,600,000 more than it was in 1981. This is 20% of the population in 1981. 13,000,000

43. It is projected that by 1991 the population of South Carolina will be 450,000 more than in 1981. This is 15% of the population in 1981. 3,000,000

44. By 1991, it is projected that the population of Vermont will be 60,000 more than the population in 1981. This is 12% of the 1981 population. 500,000

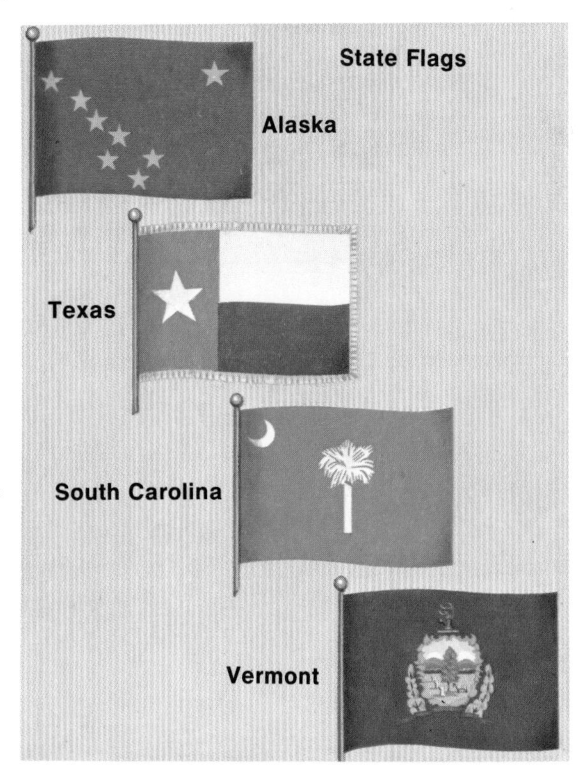

5-6 Per Cent and Estimation

See the Teacher's Manual for the objectives.

To estimate a per cent of a number, it is sometimes convenient to round the number only.

EXAMPLE 1 What number is 25% of 158?

Solution: [1] $25\% = \frac{1}{4}$

[2] Round to a convenient number; that is, to a number that is easy to multiply by $\frac{1}{4}$.

158 is close to 160.

[3] $n = \frac{1}{4} \times 160$

$n = 40$ 25% of 158 $\approx$ **40.**

After completing Example 1, you may wish to have students do some or all of Exercises 1-10.

Sometimes it is convenient to round the per cent.

EXAMPLE 2 What number is 19% of 50?

Solution: [1] Round to a convenient per cent; that is, to a per cent close to 19% and easy to multiply by 50.

19% is about 20%. $20\% = \frac{1}{5}$

[2] $n = \frac{1}{5} \times 50$

$n = 10$ 19% of 50 $\approx$ **10.**

EXERCISES

Choose the best estimate. Choose a, b, or c. (Example 1)

1. 20% of 39 c	**a.** 20% of 35	**b.** 20% of 30	**c.** 20% of 40
2. 50% of 11 a	**a.** 50% of 10	**b.** 50% of 15	**c.** 50% of 20
3. 75% of 99 c	**a.** 75% of 90	**b.** 75% of 95	**c.** 75% of 100
4. 60% of 63 a	**a.** 60% of 60	**b.** 60% of 65	**c.** 60% of 70
5. 25% of 410 b	**a.** 25% of 500	**b.** 25% of 400	**c.** 25% of 450
6. 50% of 89 b	**a.** 40	**b.** 45	**c.** 50
7. 80% of 403 b	**a.** 300	**b.** 320	**c.** 400
8. 20% of 31.98 b	**a.** 5	**b.** 6	**c.** 7
9. 25% of 47.9 b	**a.** 10	**b.** 12	**c.** 14
10. 10% of 74.7 b	**a.** 7	**b.** 7.50	**c.** 8

(Example 2)

	a.	b.	c.
11. 29% of 400 [c]	**a.** 20% of 400	**b.** 25% of 400	**c.** 30% of 400
12. 10.4% of 90 [a]	**a.** 10% of 90	**b.** 15% of 90	**c.** 20% of 90
13. 24.5% of 1200 [b]	**a.** 20% of 1200	**b.** 25% of 1200	**c.** 30% of 1200
14. 33% of 45 [b]	**a.** 30% of 45	**b.** $33\frac{1}{3}\%$ of 45	**c.** 40% of 45
15. 48% of 80 [c]	**a.** 40% of 80	**b.** 45% of 80	**c.** 50% of 80
16. 26% of 120 [b]	**a.** 25	**b.** 30	**c.** 35
17. 16% of 30 [b]	**a.** 3	**b.** 5	**c.** 7
18. 74% of 20 [a]	**a.** 15	**b.** 14	**c.** 13
19. 9.7% of 1700 [c]	**a.** 160	**b.** 165	**c.** 170
20. 38% of 64 [a]	**a.** 24	**b.** 19	**c.** 15

These word problems apply the skills taught in the lesson.

APPLICATIONS: Using Per Cent and Estimation

21. A community theater group sold \$198 worth of tickets to one of its productions. They sold 25% of the tickets to senior citizens. About how much money came from senior citizens? [c]
a. \$30 **b.** \$40 **c.** \$50

22. Ticket sales at a wildlife park totaled \$4750 in one week. Adult tickets accounted for $37\frac{1}{2}\%$ of this amount. Estimate how much money was received from adult ticket sales. [c]
a. \$1500 **b.** \$1700 **c.** \$1800

23. The price of a certain car is \$6300. The profit to the dealer is 9%. Estimate the profit. [b]
a. \$500 **b.** \$600 **c.** \$700

24. The price of a certain television is \$300. The price is reduced by 24%. Estimate the reduction. [a]
a. \$75 **b.** \$80 **c.** \$70

Calculator exercises are optional.

FINDING A PER CENT OF A NUMBER

You can use a calculator to find a per cent of a number.

EXAMPLE: Find 9% of 425.

Solution: Rewrite the problem as 425 × 9%.

[4] [2] [5] [×] [9] [%] 38.25

EXERCISES

Find each answer.

1. 4% of 28 [1.12] **2.** 7% of 40 [2.8] **3.** 15% of 20 [3] **4.** 20% of 55 [11]

5. 8% of 640 [51.2] **6.** 6% of 210 [12.6] **7.** 12% of 200 [24] **8.** 21% of 500 [105]

Chapter Review

These exercises review the vocabulary, skills and applications presented in the chapter as a preparation for the chapter test.

Part 1: VOCABULARY

For Exercises 1–5, choose from the box at the right the word(s) or number(s) that completes each statement.

left
thousandths
hundredths
right
50
100
denominator

1. Per cent means per hundred or __?__. (Pages 90–91) hundredths
2. To write a decimal for a per cent, move the decimal point two places to the __?__. (Pages 90–91) left
3. To write a fraction for a per cent, write a fraction with a denominator of __?__ for the per cent. (Pages 90–91) 100
4. To write a per cent for a fraction divide the numerator of the fraction by the __?__. (Pages 92–93) denominator
5. To write a per cent for a decimal, move the decimal point two places to the __?__. (Pages 92–93) right

Part 2: SKILLS

Write a decimal for each per cent. (Pages 90–91)

6. 43% 0.43 **7.** 58% 0.58 **8.** 44% 0.44 **9.** 21% 0.21 **10.** 16% 0.16 **11.** 95% 0.95

12. 6% 0.06 **13.** 8% 0.08 **14.** 3% 0.03 **15.** 7% 0.07 **16.** 125% 1.25 **17.** 236% 2.36

Write a fraction for each per cent. (Pages 90–91)

18. 20% $\frac{1}{5}$ **19.** 75% $\frac{3}{4}$ **20.** 10% $\frac{1}{10}$ **21.** 24% $\frac{6}{25}$ **22.** 50% $\frac{1}{2}$ **23.** 29% $\frac{29}{100}$

24. 37% $\frac{37}{100}$ **25.** 48% $\frac{12}{25}$ **26.** $\frac{3}{5}\%$ $\frac{3}{500}$ **27.** $\frac{3}{4}\%$ $\frac{3}{400}$ **28.** $28\frac{4}{7}\%$ $\frac{2}{7}$ **29.** $55\frac{5}{9}\%$ $\frac{5}{9}$

Write a per cent for each decimal. (Pages 92–93)

30. 0.27 27% **31.** 0.59 59% **32.** 0.13 13% **33.** 0.48 48% **34.** 1.41 141% **35.** 6.28 628%

36. 0.365 36.5% **37.** 0.582 58.2% **38.** 3.556 355.6% **39.** 7.268 726.8% **40.** $0.33\frac{1}{3}$ $33\frac{1}{3}\%$ **41.** $0.12\frac{1}{2}$ $12\frac{1}{2}\%$

Write a per cent for each fraction or mixed number. (Pages 92–93)

42. $\frac{7}{10}$ 70% **43.** $\frac{4}{25}$ 16% **44.** $\frac{1}{4}$ 25% **45.** $\frac{7}{20}$ 35% **46.** $\frac{1}{3}$ $33\frac{1}{3}\%$ **47.** $\frac{3}{8}$ $37\frac{1}{2}\%$

48. $\frac{5}{6}$ $83\frac{1}{3}\%$ **49.** $\frac{1}{9}$ $11\frac{1}{9}\%$ **50.** $1\frac{1}{5}$ 120% **51.** $6\frac{1}{2}$ 650% **52.** $3\frac{1}{8}$ 312.5% **53.** $1\frac{2}{3}$ $166\frac{2}{3}\%$

Find each answer. Write a decimal for each per cent. (Pages 94–95)

54. 23% of 80 = __?__ 18.4

55. 17% of 27 = __?__ 4.59

56. 25% of 60 = __?__ 15

57. 66% of 135 = __?__ 89.1

58. 16.4% of 13 = __?__ 2.132

59. 28.5% of 193 = __?__ 55.005

60. 8% of 24 = __?__ 1.92

61. 9% of 16 = __?__ 1.44

Find each answer. Write a fraction for each per cent. (Pages 94–95)

62. $33\frac{1}{3}\%$ of $18 =$ __?__ 6

63. $37\frac{1}{2}\%$ of $24 =$ __?__ 9

64. $16\frac{2}{3}\%$ of $42 =$ __?__ 7

65. 25% of $44 =$ __?__ 11

66. 40% of $65 =$ __?__ 26

67. 75% of $88 =$ __?__ 66

68. $66\frac{2}{3}\%$ of $96 =$ __?__ 64

69. $12\frac{1}{2}\%$ of $104 =$ __?__ 13

Write an equation for each exercise. (Pages 96–97)

70. What per cent of 30 is 6? $n \times 30 = 6$

71. What per cent of 90 is 75? $n \times 90 = 75$

72. 18 is what per cent of 144? $18 = n \times 144$

73. 27 is what per cent of 135? $27 = n \times 135$

Solve. (Pages 96–97)

74. 16 is what per cent of 64? 25%

75. 35 is what per cent of 210? $16\frac{2}{3}\%$

76. 9 is what per cent of 45? 20%

77. 42 is what per cent of 126? $33\frac{1}{3}\%$

78. What per cent of 92 is 23? 25%

79. What per cent of 400 is 64? 16%

80. What per cent of 87 is 29? $33\frac{1}{3}\%$

81. What per cent of 500 is 150? 30%

Write an equation for each exercise. (Pages 100–101)

82. 7 is 20% of what number? $7 = 0.20 \times n$

83. 17 is 15% of what number? $17 = 0.15 \times n$

84. 14 is $33\frac{1}{3}\%$ of what number? $14 = \frac{1}{3} \times n$

85. 56 is $12\frac{1}{2}\%$ of what number? $56 = \frac{1}{8} \times n$

Solve. (Pages 100–101)

86. 8 is 25% of what number? 32

87. 42 is 50% of what number? 84

88. 13 is 20% of what number? 65

89. 59 is 10% of what number? 590

90. 56 is 14% of what number? 400

91. 64 is 16% of what number? 400

92. 84 is 7% of what number? 1200

93. 39 is 30% of what number? 130

Choose the best estimate. Choose a, b, or c. (Pages 102–103)

94. 75% of 197 c

a. 75% of 190 **b.** 75% of 180 **c.** 75% of 200

95. 21% of 40 a

a. 20% of 40 **b.** 15% of 40 **c.** 30% of 40

96. $33\frac{1}{3}\%$ of 41 b

a. 12 **b.** 14 **c.** 16

97. 51% of 400 a

a. 200 **b.** 190 **c.** 210

98. 40% of \$71.39 a

a. \$28 **b.** \$30 **c.** \$32

The word problems covered in this chapter are presented here in a mixed setting. Note: each problem is referenced to the related page(s).

Part 3: APPLICATIONS

99. By mid–season, the New York Cosmos had won 20 out of 25 of their games. What per cent had they won? (Pages 96–97) 80%

100. The price of a certain typewriter is \$800. The salesperson receives 19% of this. Estimate the amount the salesperson receives. (Pages 102–103) c

a. \$140 **b.** \$150 **c.** \$160

101. Out of a total population of 15,000 about how many people would you expect to have type AB positive blood? Refer to the table on page 95. (Pages 94–95) 525

102. In a recent year, Pennsylvania produced about 4% of all the minerals produced in the United States. Write a fraction for this per cent. (Pages 90–91) $\frac{1}{25}$

103. In a recent year, Wyoming produced about 3% of all the minerals produced in the United States. Write a decimal for this per cent. (Pages 90–91) 0.03

104. The Braves won 85 out of 120 baseball games. What per cent did they win? Round your answer to the nearest whole per cent. (Pages 96–97) 71%

The Soccer Great, Giorgio Chinaglia

105. In a clearance sale, the sale price of an evening dress is $\frac{3}{4}$ of the original price. Write a per cent for this fraction. (Pages 92–93). 75%

106. The sale price of a stove is 0.85 times the original price. Write a per cent for this decimal. (Pages 92–93) 85%

Chapter Test

The Teacher's Resource Book contains two forms of each chapter test.

Write a per cent for each of the following.

1. 0.93 93% **2.** 0.065 6.5% **3.** $\frac{3}{5}$ 60% **4.** $\frac{5}{8}$ $62\frac{1}{2}\%$ **5.** $1\frac{1}{3}$ $133\frac{1}{3}\%$

Solve.

6. 32% of 25 = __?__ 8

7. $33\frac{1}{3}\%$ of 729 = __?__ 243

8. 27 is what per cent of 90? 30%

9. What per cent of 60 is 15? 25%

10. 7 is 50% of what number? 14

11. What per cent of 84 is 14? $16\frac{2}{3}\%$

12. 28 is $33\frac{1}{3}\%$ of what number? 84

13. 16 is 80% of what number? 20

Choose the best estimate. Choose a, b, or c.

14. 19% of 80 b **a.** 15% of 80 **b.** 20% of 80 **c.** 25% of 80

15. $33\frac{1}{3}\%$ of 242 a **a.** $33\frac{1}{3}\%$ of 240 **b.** $33\frac{1}{3}\%$ of 250 **c.** $33\frac{1}{3}\%$ of 230

16. 24.5% of 60 c **a.** 13 **b.** 14 **c.** 15

Solve.

17. It is said that 8% of the population has type B positive blood. How many people in a population of 12,000 would you expect to have type B positive blood? 960

18. In last week's football game, Philip Gordon threw 20 passes. He completed 16 of them. What per cent did he complete? 80%

19. By 1991, the population of Missouri will be 150,000 more than in 1981. This is 3% of the 1981 population. Find the 1981 population. 5,000,000

20. The price of a certain sweater is \$40. The cost of the sweater is 79% of this. Estimate the cost of the sweater. c

a. \$27 **b.** \$30 **c.** \$32 **d.** \$35

REVIEW OF RELATED SKILLS FOR CHAPTER 6

We suggest that some or all of this page be reviewed before proceeding with the chapter.

Round each number to the nearest ten. (Pages 12–13)

1. 62 60 **2.** 59 60 **3.** 41 40 **4.** 53 50 **5.** 675 680 **6.** 796 800

Round each number to the nearest hundred. (Pages 12–13)

7. 478 500 **8.** 325 300 **9.** 936 900 **10.** 588 600 **11.** 1989 2000 **12.** 1426 1400

Round each number to the nearest thousand. (Pages 12–13)

13. 6715 7000 **14.** 4280 4000 **15.** 5364 5000 **16.** 7692 8000 **17.** 10,650 11,000 **18.** 12,398 12,000

Subtract. (Pages 2–3)

19. $48 - 39$ 9 **20.** $53 - 27$ 26 **21.** $24 - 18$ 6 **22.** $62 - 54$ 8 **23.** $71 - 38$ 33 **24.** $43 - 27$ 16

25. $122 - 37$ 85 **26.** $248 - 79$ 169 **27.** $262 - 83$ 179 **28.** $227 - 89$ 138 **29.** $431 - 295$ 136 **30.** $653 - 478$ 175

31. $304 - 215$ 89 **32.** $708 - 659$ 49 **33.** $500 - 377$ 123 **34.** $400 - 265$ 135

Write a decimal for each per cent. (Pages 90–91)

35. 43% 0.43 **36.** 54% 0.54 **37.** 5% 0.05 **38.** 6% 0.06 **39.** 17.2% 0.172 **40.** 47.8% 0.478

Write a fraction for each per cent. (Pages 90–91)

41. 15% $\frac{3}{20}$ **42.** 30% $\frac{3}{10}$ **43.** 75% $\frac{3}{4}$ **44.** 48% $\frac{12}{25}$ **45.** $62\frac{1}{2}\%$ $\frac{5}{8}$ **46.** $66\frac{2}{3}\%$ $\frac{2}{3}$

Multiply. (Pages 8–9)

47. 360×0.45 162 **48.** 360×0.62 223.2 **49.** 0.15×360 54 **50.** 0.75×360 270

51. 0.81×360 291.6 **52.** 0.24×360 86.4 **53.** 360×0.18 64.8 **54.** 360×0.32 115.2

Round each number to the nearest whole number. (Pages 16–17)

55. 21.2 21 **56.** 35.4 35 **57.** 78.9 79 **58.** 63.7 64 **59.** 122.81 123 **60.** 142.39 142

Add. (Pages 2–3)

61. $625 + 436 + 899 + 742$ 2702 **62.** $863 + 471 + 994 + 836$ 3164 **63.** $345 + 267 + 109 + 448$ 1169 **64.** $566 + 598 + 544 + 529$ 2237 **65.** $824 + 762 + 950 + 648$ 3184 **66.** $480 + 763 + 548 + 622$ 2413

Divide. (Pages 12–13)

67. $144 \div 6$ 24 **68.** $315 \div 5$ 63 **69.** $294 \div 3$ 98 **70.** $392 \div 7$ 56 **71.** $768 \div 12$ 64

72. $6\overline{)342}$ 57 **73.** $8\overline{)504}$ 63 **74.** $9\overline{)459}$ 51 **75.** $3\overline{)174}$ 58 **76.** $11\overline{)209}$ 19

CHAPTER

6 STATISTICS

ESSENTIAL SKILLS / APPLICATIONS

CAREER APPLICATION

Store Manager

6-1 Bar Graphs and Applications

See the Teacher's Manual for the objectives.

A **bar graph** has two axes, a **horizontal axis** and a **vertical axis.** The length of each bar represents a number. The **scale** on one of the axes tells you how to find the number.

This bar graph shows the lengths of the five Great Lakes in kilometers.

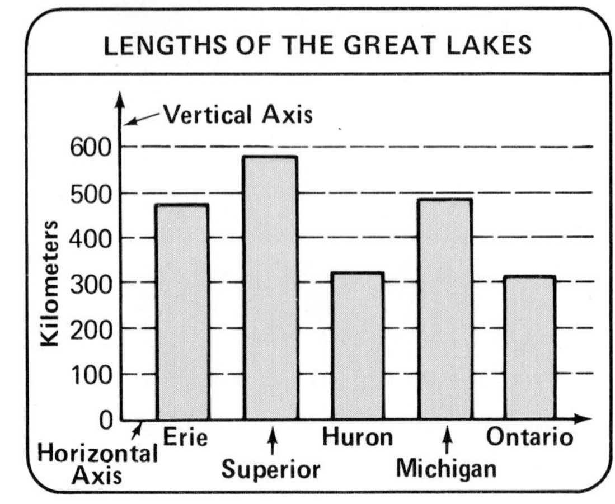

PROCEDURE To read a bar graph:

[1] Look for the number scale on one of the axes.

[2] Use the scale to interpret the graph.

EXAMPLE Use the bar graph above to answer each question.

Questions	Solutions
a. Which of the Great Lakes is the longest?	**a.** Lake Superior ◀ ***Superior has the longest bar.***
b. Which two Great Lakes are almost the same length?	**b.** Lake Huron and Lake Ontario ◀ ***The bars are equal in height.***
c. Which of the Great Lakes are longer than 400 kilometers?	**c.** Lake Superior, Lake Michigan, and Lake Erie

EXERCISES

*The **horizontal bar graph** at the right shows the number of kilograms of honey produced by 5 states in a recent year. Use this graph for Exercises 1–7.*

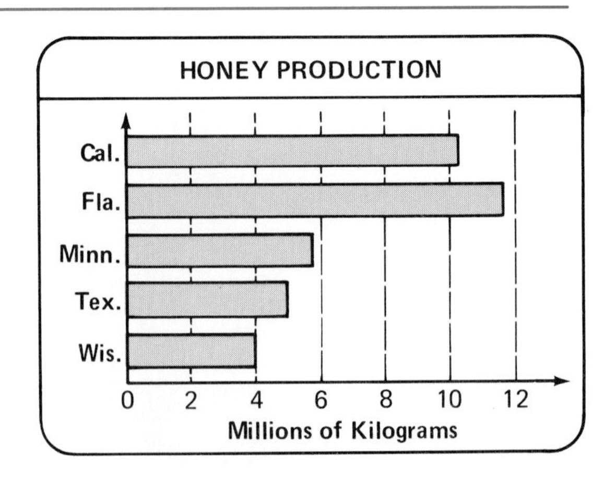

1. Which state produced the most honey? Florida
2. Which state produced the least honey? Wisconsin
3. Which states produced about 5,000,000 kilograms of honey? Texas

4. Which state produced about half as much honey as Florida? Minnesota

5. Which state produced almost three times as much honey as Wisconsin? Florida

6. Which state produced about 4,000,000 kilograms of honey? Wisconsin

7. Which states produced more than 6,000,000 kilograms of honey? California, Florida

The vertical bar graph at the right shows the results of a survey of favorite sports. Use this graph for Exercises 8–11.

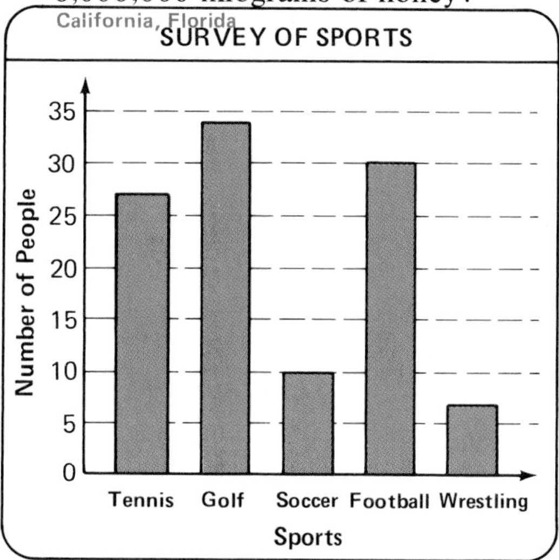

8. Which are the two most popular sports? golf, football

9. Which sport is the least popular? wrestling

10. Which sport received about 30 votes? football

11. Which sports received fewer than 15 votes? soccer, wrestling

For Exercises 12–13, use the tables to complete the bar graphs. The first bar is drawn for you.

12. **Orbit Speeds of Five Planets**

Planet	Speed in Miles per Second
Earth	18.5
Venus	22
Saturn	6
Mars	15
Mercury	30

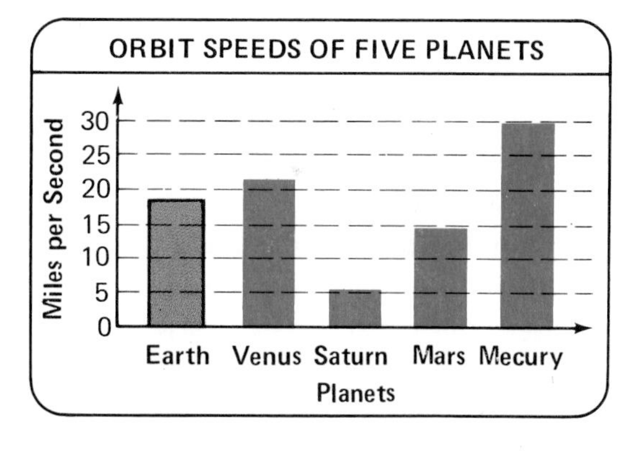

13. **Height in Meters of Six Waterfalls**

Waterfall	Height
Yosemite Lower Falls	98
Yosemite Upper Falls	436
Nevada Falls	181
Great Falls	256
Ribbon Falls	491
Silver Strand Falls	357

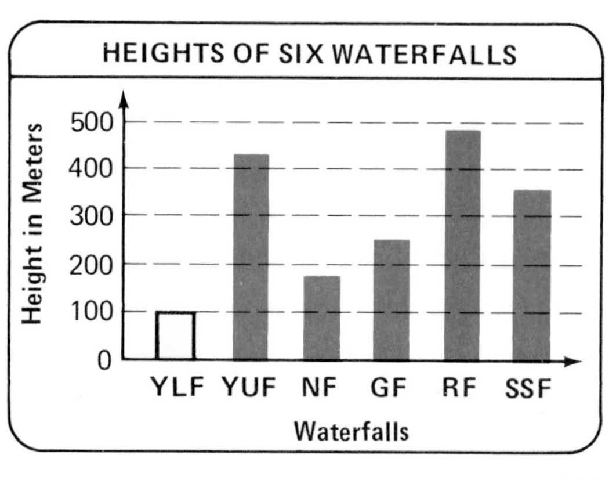

6-2 Line Graphs and Applications

See the Teacher's Manual for the objectives.

Line graphs show the amount of change over a specific period of time. A line graph has a horizontal and a vertical axis. One axis shows the period of time. The other shows the amount of change.

This line graph shows the United States' production of barley in millions of bushels from 1973 to 1980.

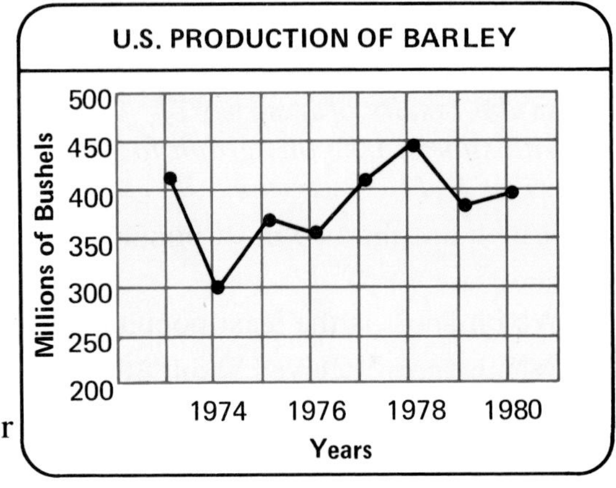

PROCEDURE To read a line graph:

1. Find the given number or time on one axis.
2. Use the second axis to find the unknown number or time.

EXAMPLE Use the line graph above to answer each question.

Questions	Solutions	
a. During which year was the production the highest?	**a.** 1978	***Highest point on graph***
b. During which year was the production the lowest?	**b.** 1974	***Lowest point on graph***
c. Between which two years was there the greatest decrease in production?	**c.** Between 1973 and 1974	***The line between the dots is the longest and steepest.***
d. Between which two years was there the least decrease in production?	**d.** Between 1975 and 1976	***The line between the dots is the shortest and least steep.***

EXERCISES

Use this graph for Exercises 1–8.

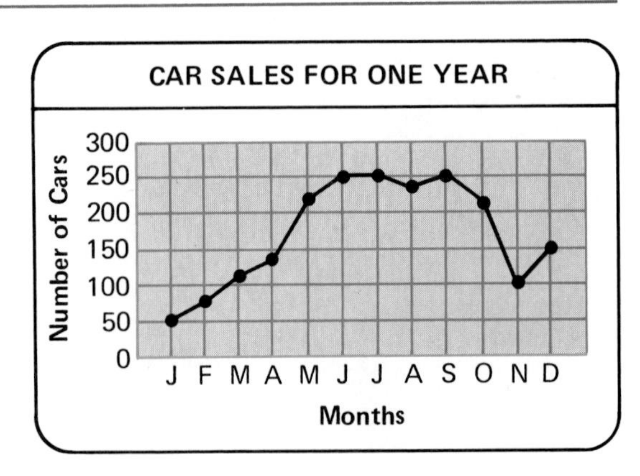

1. In which months were the same number of cars sold as in June? July, September
2. Between which two months did car sales increase the most? April-May
3. During which month was the number of cars sold the least? January
4. Between which two months did car sales decrease the least? July-August

5. For which months were fewer than 100 cars sold? January, February

6. How many cars were sold in January and November? 50; 100

7. What is the difference between the number of cars sold in January and the number sold in November? 50

8. What is the difference between the number of cars sold in July and the number sold in December? 100

This graph shows the number of cattle on farms in the United States over periods of 10 years. Use this graph for Exercises 9–12.

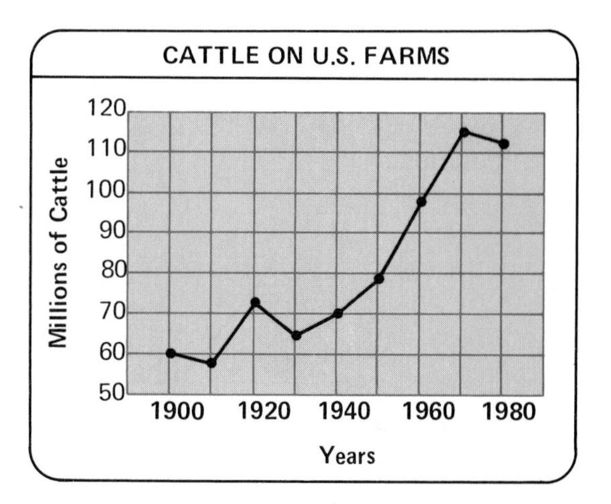

9. For which years did the number of cattle remain above 90,000,000? 1960-1980

10. During which year were there about 70,000,000 cattle? 1940

11. In which year was there the greatest number of cattle? 1970

12. In which year was there the least number of cattle? 1910

For Exercises 13–14, use the tables to complete the line graphs.

13. Normal Temperatures in Houston, Texas

Month	*Temperature*
May	76
June	81
July	83
August	83
September	79

14. Number of Books Borrowed from Farmingdale Library

Day	*Number*
Monday	62
Tuesday	85
Wednesday	60
Thursday	75
Friday	100

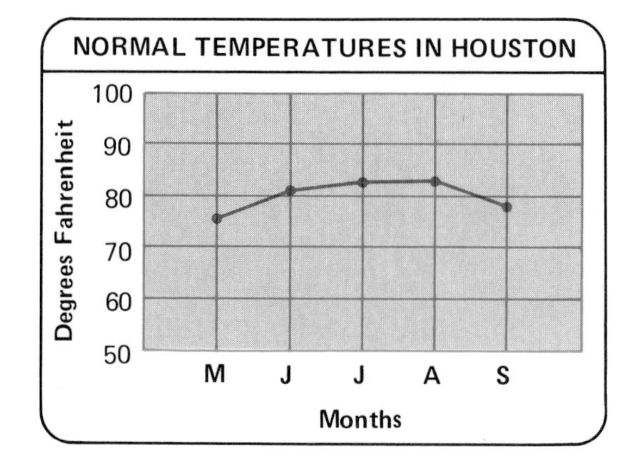

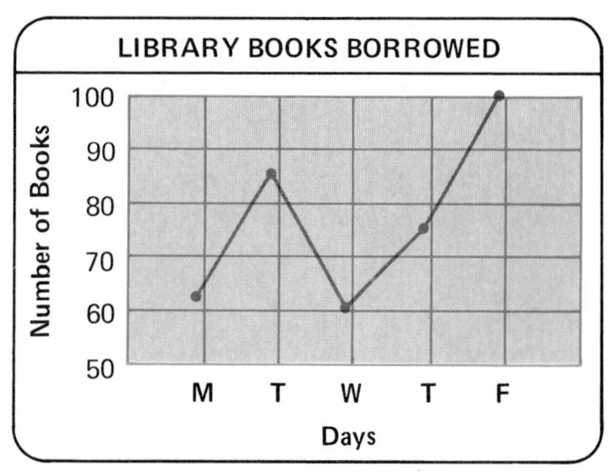

6-3 Angles

See the Teacher's Manual for the objectives.

The degree (°) is the unit of measure of an angle. You use a **protractor** to measure an angle.

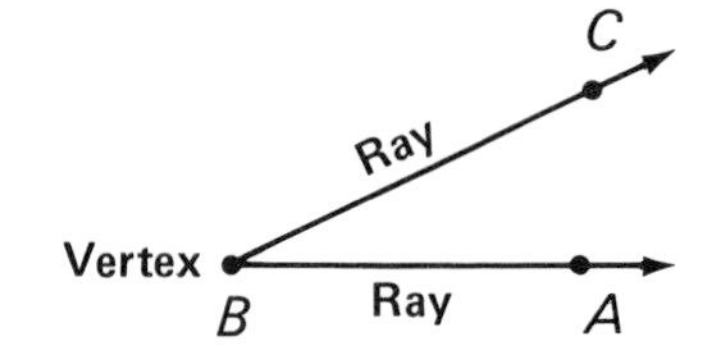

EXAMPLE Find the measures of the given angles.

a. ∠ ABC **b.** ∠ ABD **c.** ∠ ABE

Solutions:

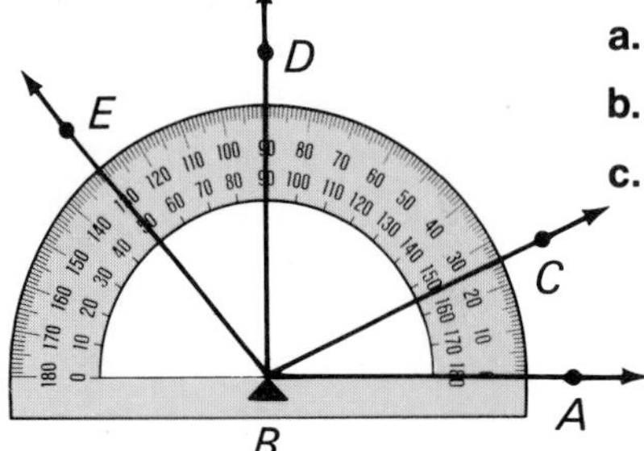

a. m ∠ ABC = 25°

b. m ∠ ABD = 90°

c. m ∠ ABE = 130°

"m" is read, "the measure of"

After completing the Example, you may wish to have students do some or all of Exercises 1-6.

Definitions:

Angle ABC is an *acute angle*. An **acute angle** has a measure of less than 90°.

Angle ABD is a *right angle*. A **right angle** has a measure of 90°.

Angle ABE is an *obtuse angle*. An **obtuse angle** has a measure of more than 90° but less than 180°.

EXERCISES

For Exercises 1–6, use the protractor to find the measure of each angle. (Example)

1. ∠ HPI 28°
2. ∠ HPJ 49°
3. ∠ HPK 90°
4. ∠ HPL 103°
5. ∠ HPM 137°
6. ∠ HPN 160°

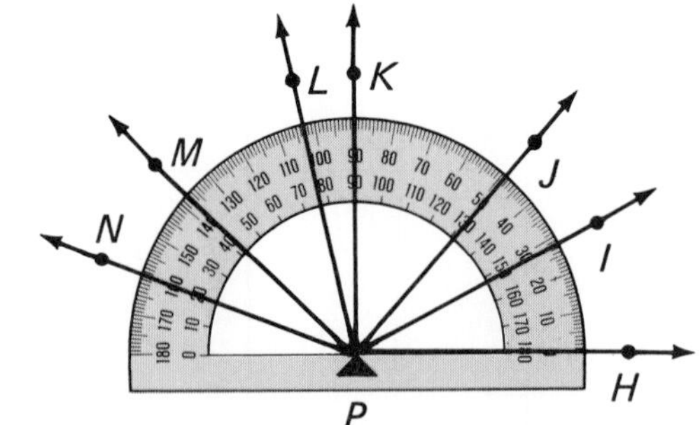

For each of Exercises 7–13, the measure of an angle is given. Tell whether the angle is acute, right, or obtuse. (Definitions)

7. 29° acute **8.** 144° obtuse **9.** 90° right **10.** 14° acute **11.** 138° obtuse **12.** 98° obtuse **13.** 86° acute

Mid–Chapter Review

This reviews all the skills presented in sections 6-1, 6-2, and 6-3.

The bar graph at the right shows how many calories the average person uses during one hour of each of four activities. Use the graph for Exercises 1–4. (Pages 110–111)

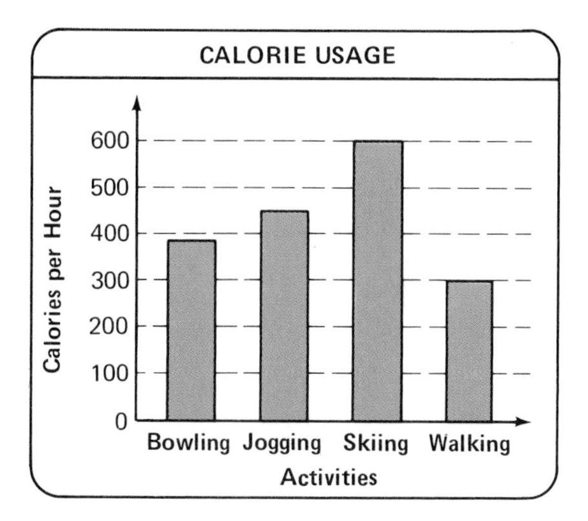

1. Which activity uses the most calories per hour? skiing
2. Which activity uses 200 fewer calories than skiing? bowling
3. Which activity uses 100 fewer calories than bowling? walking
4. How many calories does jogging use per hour? 450

The table below shows how many minutes a 68–kilogram person must run in order to use up the calories in one serving of the foods listed. Use this table to complete the bar graph. (Pages 110–111)

5.

Food	*Minutes*
Large apple	5
Ham, 2 slices	9
Pork chop	16
Hamburger	18

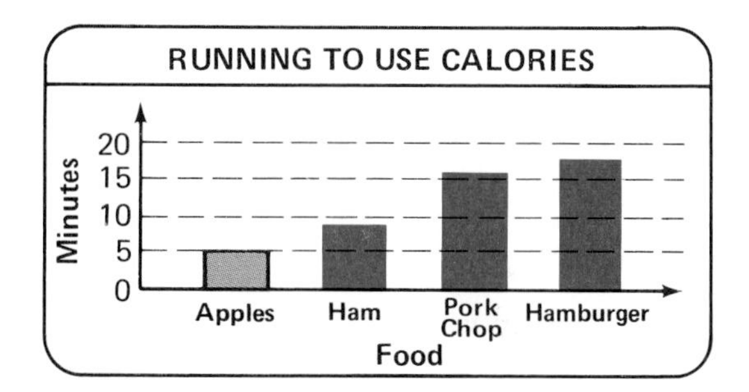

Jean Beauvoir sells shoes. The line graph on the right shows Jean's sales totals for five months. Use this graph for Exercises 6–9. (Pages 112–113)

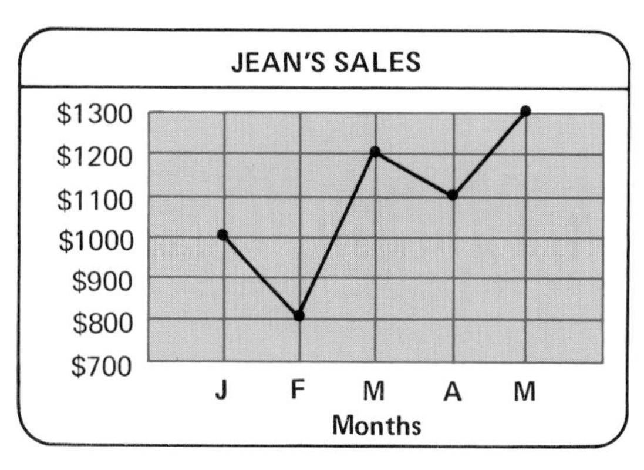

6. In which month were the sales totals the highest? May
7. Between which two months did sales increase the most? Feb.-March
8. What was the total for April? $1100
9. In which month was the total $800? Feb.

For each of Exercises 10–16, the measure of an angle is given. Tell whether the angle is acute, right, or obtuse. (Page 114)

10. 48° acute **11.** 159° obtuse **12.** 179° obtuse **13.** 90° right **14.** 27° acute **15.** 88° acute **16.** 93° obtuse

6-4 Circle Graphs and Applications

See the Teacher's Manual for the objectives.

You can use circle graphs to show information. There are 360° in a circle.

PROCEDURE To draw a circle graph:

[1] Write a decimal for each per cent.

[2] Multiply the decimal by 360°. Round your answer to the nearest degree.

[3] Use a protractor to draw the graph.

EXAMPLE This table shows the per cent of use of each of four kinds of freight vehicles in the United States in a recent year. Make a circle graph to show the data.

Freight Traffic

Type	Per Cent
Railroads	36
Inland Waterways	15
Trucks	25
Others	24

Solution:

[1] Write a decimal for each per cent.

36% = 0.36 15% = 0.15 25% = 0.25 24% = 0.24

[2] Multiply each decimal by 360°. Round to the nearest degree.

$0.36 \times 360 = 129.6$, or **130°** $0.15 \times 360 =$ **54°**

$0.25 \times 360 =$ **90°** $0.24 \times 360 = 86.4$, or **86°**

[3] Draw the graph.

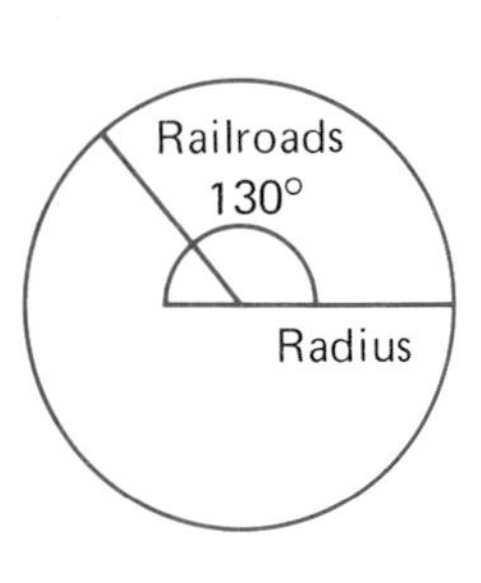

Draw a radius. Place the protractor on the radius. Draw the angle for *Railroads*.

New Radius
54°
Inland Waterways

Place the protractor on the "new" radius. Draw the angle for *Inland Waterways*.

New Radius
Trucks
90°

Place the protractor on the "new" radius. Draw the angle for *Trucks*.

FREIGHT TRAFFIC
Inland Waterways
15%
Railroads
36%
Trucks
25%
Others
24%

The remaining angle represents *Others*.

EXERCISES

For Exercises 1–6, make a circle graph to show the data.

1. Distribution of Commercial Fishing

Body of Water	Per Cent
Pacific Ocean	43 155°
Atlantic Ocean	39 140°
Indian Ocean	5 18°
Others	13 47°

2. Per Cent of Electoral Votes in 1860

Candidate	Per Cent
Lincoln	58 209°
Breckinridge	25 90°
Bell	13 47°
Douglas	4 14°

3. Monthly Budget

Item	Per Cent
Food and Shelter	45 162°
Clothing	5 18°
Medical	10 36°
Gasoline	10 36°
Miscellaneous	30 108°

4. Population by Age in U.S.

Age Group	Per Cent
Under 5	7 25°
5–17	22 79°
18–44	40 144°
45–65	20 72°
66 and over	11 40°

5. A Disc Jockey's Hour

Activity	Per Cent
Music	50 180°
Commercials	13 47°
Sports	10 36°
Chatter	7 25°
News and Weather	20 72°

6. Causes of Forest Fires

Cause	Per Cent
Lightning	34 122°
Children	17 61°
Campers	11 40°
Auto Passengers	10 36°
Others	28 101°

These word problems apply the skills taught in the lesson.

APPLICATIONS: Circle Graphs and the Human Body

7. Which material makes up the greatest part of the human body? muscle
8. Tom Holmes weighs 150 pounds. About how many pounds are muscle? 75
9. Juanita Muldoon weighs 52 kilograms. About how much of her body weight is bone? about 9 kg
10. Kim Kelly weighs 140 pounds. About how much of this weight is not fat? 112 pounds

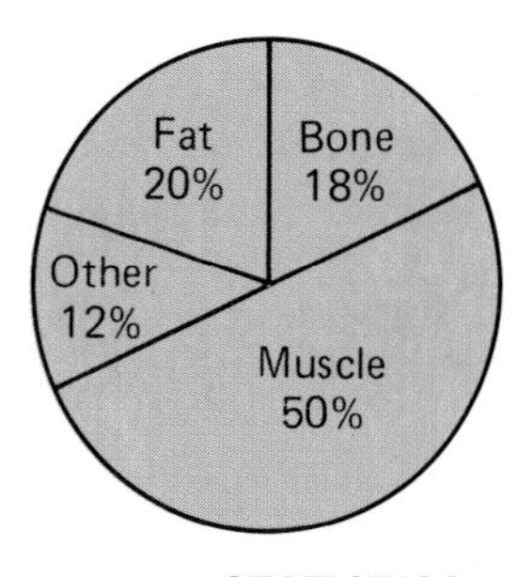

6-5 The Mean and the Mode with Applications

See the Teacher's Manual for the objectives.

Another word for *average* is **mean.**

PROCEDURE Use this formula to find the mean.

$$\textbf{Mean} = \frac{\textbf{Sum of Measures}}{\textbf{Number of Measures}}$$

EXAMPLE 1 This table shows the number of games won in a recent year by five football teams. Find the mean number of games won for the five teams.

Number of Wins	
Team	*Number*
Miami Dolphins	10
New England Patriots	9
New York Jets	8
Buffalo Bills	7
Baltimore Colts	5

Solution:

$$\text{Mean} = \frac{\text{Sum of Measures}}{\text{Number of Measures}}$$

$$= \frac{10 + 9 + 8 + 7 + 5}{5}$$

$= \frac{39}{5}$, or 7.8 The mean number of games won is **7.8.**

After completing Example 1, you may wish to have students do some or all of Exercises 1-6.

The **mode** is the measure that occurs most often. When the highest count occurs more than once, there is more than one mode.

EXAMPLE 2 This table shows the points scored by 17 basketball players in recent games. What is the mode of this data?

Points	*Count*
0–10	3
11–15	6
16–20	5
21–25	3

Solution: The greatest number of players, 6, scored between 11 and 15 points. Therefore, the mode is **11–15.**

EXERCISES

For Exercises 1–6, find the mean. (Example 1)

1. 43 **Passengers on Eight Buses**

42	45	38	56
40	41	40	42

2. \$7132 **Prices for Six Cars**

\$8441	\$7680	\$6955
\$7521	\$6250	\$5945

3. 413 **Number of Pages in Ten Books**

336	464	304	288	400
384	560	448	466	480

5572

4. Population in Eight Small Towns

4608	5479	6500	3875
4450	6291	5833	7540

5. $7\frac{1}{2}$ **Number of Hours Worked in a Day by Twelve Adults**

$7\frac{1}{2}$	8	$7\frac{1}{2}$	$8\frac{1}{2}$	7	$8\frac{1}{2}$
6	$7\frac{1}{2}$	8	$6\frac{1}{2}$	6	9

6. 1.95 **Heights in Meters of Ten Basketball Players**

2.1	1.95	2.0	1.85	1.9
2.0	2.1	1.9	1.8	1.9

For Exercises 7–8 find the mode. (Example 2)

7. 23.4 **Times in a Track Meet**

Time in Seconds	*Count*
23.9	2
23.6	4
23.4	6
22.9	3
22.1	1

$11,500

8. Annual Payroll of a Small Business

Salary	*Count*
$60,000	1
$40,000	1
$35,000	2
$20,000	3
$11,500	5

9. 85-89 **Grades of Forty Students on a Science Test**

Grade	*Count*
70–74	4
75–79	7
80–84	8
85–89	10
90–94	8
95–100	3

10. $200 **Weekly Salaries of Twenty Secretaries**

Salary	*Count*
$100	1
$150	3
$200	8
$250	5
$300	2
$350	1

4–6 P.M.

11. Customers at a Newsstand

Hours	*Count*
6–8 A.M.	30
8–10 A.M.	41
10–12 A.M.	25
12–2 P.M.	13
2–4 P.M.	26
4–6 P.M.	49

44.1–45.0 and 46.1–47.0

12. Times for the 400-Meter Run

Time in Seconds	*Count*
44.1–45.0	4
45.1–46.0	2
46.1–47.0	4
47.1–48.0	2
48.1–49.0	1
49.1–50.0	3

6-6 The Median with Applications

See the Teacher's Manual for the objectives.

Mount McKinley

In a listing of data, the **median** is the middle measure or score.

PROCEDURE To find the median:

[1] Arrange the data in order.

[2] **a.** For an **odd** number of items, the median is the middle measure listed.

b. For an **even** number of items, the median is the average of the two middle measures.

EXAMPLE 1 This table shows the speeds in kilometers per hour of five animals. Find the median speed.

Animal	*Speed*
Cheetah	112
Elephant	40
Lion	80
Reindeer	51.2
Squirrel	19.2

Solution: [1] Arrange the speeds in order.

19.2 40 51.2 80 112

[2] The number of items is odd (5). Choose the middle number.

The median speed is **51.2** kilometers per hour.

After completing Example 1, you may wish to have students do some or all of Exercises 1, 2, 5, and 6.

EXAMPLE 2 This table shows the heights in feet of six mountains in the United States. Find the median height.

Mountain	*Height*
Blackburn	16,390
Churchill	15,638
McKinley	20,320
Pike's Peak	14,110
Rainier	14,410
San Luis	14,014

Solution: [1] Arrange the heights in order.

14,014 14,110 14,410
15,638 16,390 20,320

[2] The number of items is even (6). Find the average of the two middle numbers.

$$\frac{14{,}410 + 15{,}638}{2} = \frac{30{,}048}{2}$$

$$= \mathbf{15{,}024}$$

The median height is **15,024** feet.

EXERCISES

Find the median. (Examples 1 and 2)

1. 56 **Inauguration Age of Five Presidents**

President	Age
L. Johnson	55
R. Nixon	56
G. Ford	61
J. Carter	52
R. Reagan	69

2. $445 **Prices of Several Stereos**

Brand	Price
A	$273
B	$670
C	$200
D	$445
E	$857

3. 60 **Number of Counties**

State	Counties
Arizona	14
California	58
Hawaii	4
Kansas	105
Michigan	83
New York	62

4. $7714.50 **Net Income Per Farm**

State	Farm Income
Georgia	$3700
Nebraska	$7017
Oregon	$4268
S. Dakota	$11,367
Vermont	$8412
Wisconsin	$12,105

5. 163,114 **Telephones in Five Cities**

City	Number
Albany, NY	170,643
Cambridge, MA	111,498
Lexington, KY	163,114
Lubbock, TX	161,860
San Francisco, CA	815,520

6. 3.125 **State Sales Tax Rate**

State	Per Cent
Arkansas	3.0
California	4.75
Florida	4.0
Iowa	3.0
Missouri	3.125

7. 8,601 **Points Scored in the National Football League**

Year	Total Points
1977	6,733
1978	8,213
1979	8,989
1980	9,178

8. 6.9 **Summer Costs for Several Appliances**

Appliance	Cent Per Hour
Color Television	5.1
Fan	2.1
Iron	8.7
Vacuum Cleaner	10.0

STORE MANAGER

Career lessons are optional.
This lesson applies the skills presented in Sections 6–5 and 6–6.

As the **manager** of a large department store, Roberto Filo uses the mean, median, and mode to help him make decisions. He has to decide which of these three—mean, median, or mode—he should use.

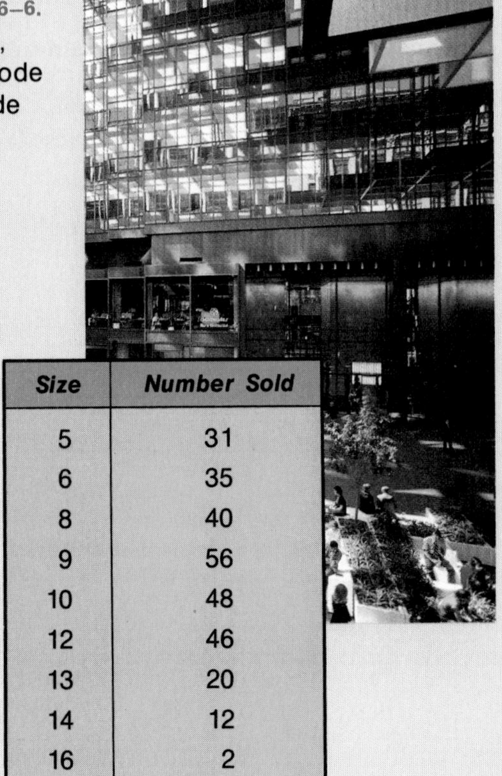

Size	Number Sold
5	31
6	35
8	40
9	56
10	48
12	46
13	20
14	12
16	2

EXERCISES

Emily Franks is manager of the dress department. Before she ordered dresses for the summer season, Emily checked her records of the sizes sold last summer.

1. What is the mode of the number of dresses sold? 56
2. What is the dress size of the mode? 9
3. What is the median of the number of dresses sold? 35
4. What is the dress size of the median? 6
5. Based on the answers to Exercises 1–4, should Emily use the median or the mode as a guide for ordering dresses? the mode

Susan Picker is manager of the department store's accounting department. To help cut expenses, she planned on reducing the number of typewriters. She included this graph along with her report to Mr. Filo on typewriter use.

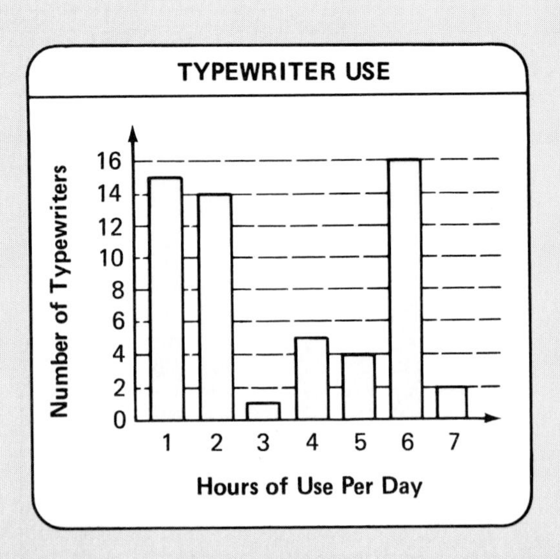

Refer to the graph to complete her report in Exercises 6–9.

6. Only __?__ typewriters are used all day (7 hours). 2
7. The average (mean) number of hours that the 57 typewriters are used is __?__ hours. 3.4

8. Half of the 57 typewriters are used only _?_ (median) hours or less a day. 2

9. The largest number are used _?_ (mode) hours each day. 6

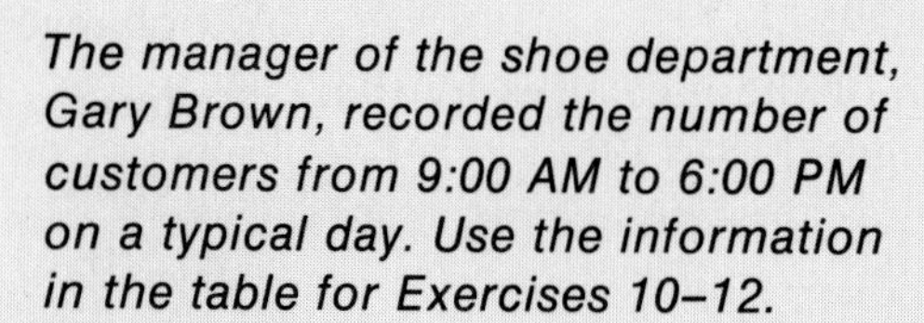

The manager of the shoe department, Gary Brown, recorded the number of customers from 9:00 AM to 6:00 PM on a typical day. Use the information in the table for Exercises 10–12.

Hours	Customers
9:00–10:00	11
10:00–11:00	24
11:00–12:00	26
12:00–1:00	48
1:00–2:00	40
2:00–3:00	31
3:00–4:00	24
4:00–5:00	27
5:00–6:00	52

10. During what hour does the mode occur? 5:00-6:00

11. Gary decided to hire part–time help for the 12:00–1:00 and 5:00–6:00 hours. Why was this a good decision? He has the most customers at those times.

Gary wants one employee on duty for every 10 customers in a given hour, as shown in the chart below. Use the information in the chart for Exercise 12.

Customers	Employees
1–10	1
11–20	2
21–30	3
31–40	4
41–50	5
51–60	6

12. Gary has three employees on duty between 10:00 AM and 6:00 PM each day. How many part–time employees should he hire to work between 12:00 and 1:00? 2

Chapter Review

These exercises review the vocabulary, skills and applications presented in the chapter as a preparation for the chapter test.

Part 1: VOCABULARY

For Exercises 1–6, choose from the box at the right the word or number that completes each statement.

median
360
width
length
number
change
mode
mean
270

1. On a bar graph, the length of the bar represents a __?__. number (Pages 110–111)
2. Line graphs show the amount of __?__ over a period of time. change (Pages 112–113)
3. A circle contains __?__ degrees. 360 (Pages 116–117)
4. The average obtained by dividing the sum of the measures by the number of the measures is the __?__. mean (Pages 118–119)
5. In a group of measures, the one that occurs most often is the __?__. mode (Pages 118–119)
6. In a listing of data, the middle measure is the __?__. median (Pages 120–121)

Part 2: SKILLS AND APPLICATIONS

The vertical bar graph at the right shows the number of calories per 100 grams of five kinds of shellfish. (Pages 110–111)

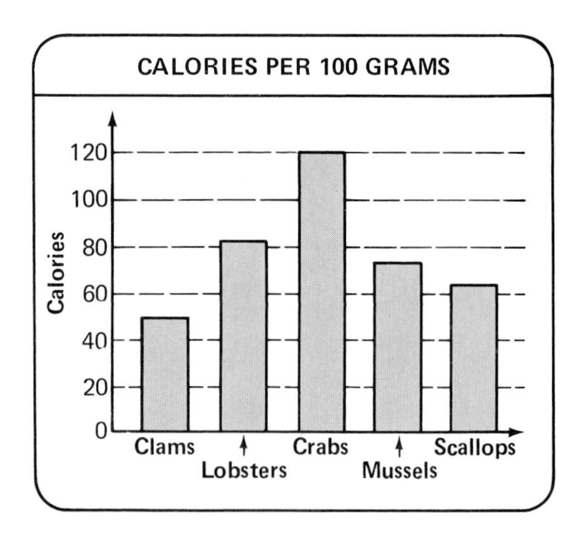

7. Which shellfish contains the most calories per 100 grams? crabs
8. Which shellfish contains the least calories per 100 grams? clams
9. Which shellfish contains about 65 calories per 100 grams? scallops
10. Which shellfish contains about 70 calories less than crab? mussels
11. Use this information to complete the bar graph. (Pages 110–111)

Absentees from Work

Day	Number
Monday	250
Tuesday	140
Wednesday	40
Thursday	90
Friday	290

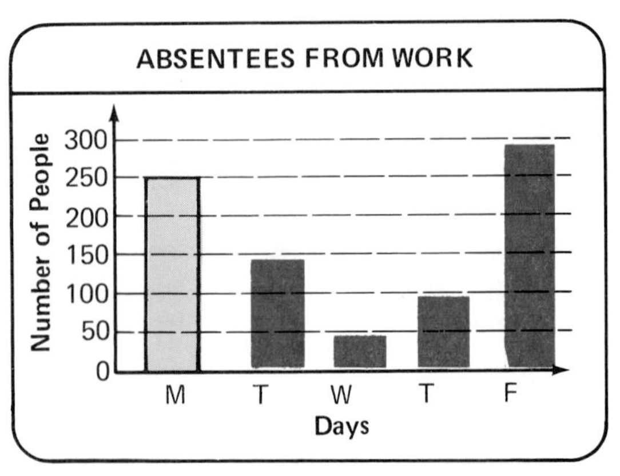

Use the line graph below for Exercises 12–16. (Pages 112–113)

12. In which year was the price for wheat the lowest? 1977
13. Between which two years did the price increase the most? 1978-79
14. For which year was the price about $3.00 per bushel? 1978
15. About how much did a farmer receive for a bushel of wheat in 1977? $2.50
16. About how much did a farmer receive for a bushel of wheat in 1980? $4.00

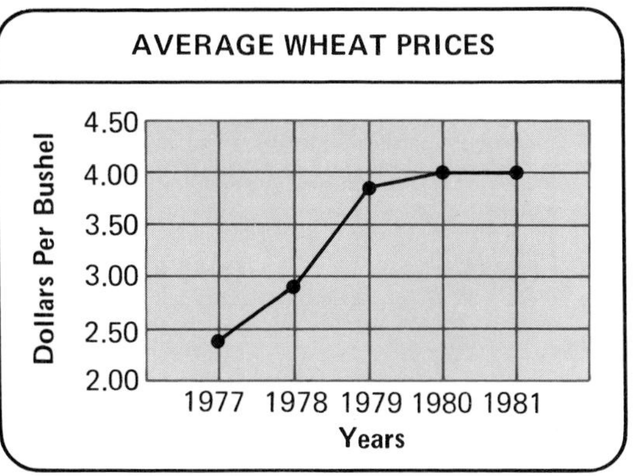

17. Use this information to complete the line graph. (Pages 112–113)

United States Cotton Production

Year	Million Bales
1977	14.4
1978	10.9
1979	14.6
1980	14.9
1981	13.7

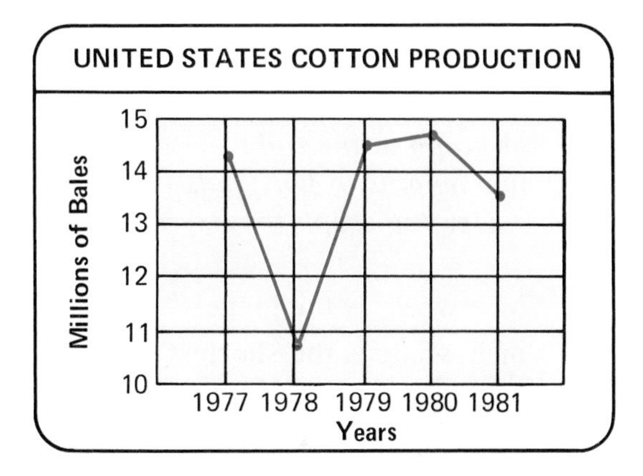

18. Use the table below to make a circle graph. (Pages 116–117)

Monthly Budget of a Recreation Center

Item	Salaries	Utilities	Repairs	Lease	Other
Per Cent	40% 144°	15% 54°	10% 36°	20% 72°	15% 54°

For Exercises 19–20, find the mean. (Pages 118–119)

19. **Weekly Wages of Eight Workers** $236.25

$125	$180	$250	$310
$225	$210	$270	$320

20. **Heights in Meters of Ten Trees** 12

13.9	11.5	12.2	14.1	10.7
9.3	12.4	13.6	10.5	11.8

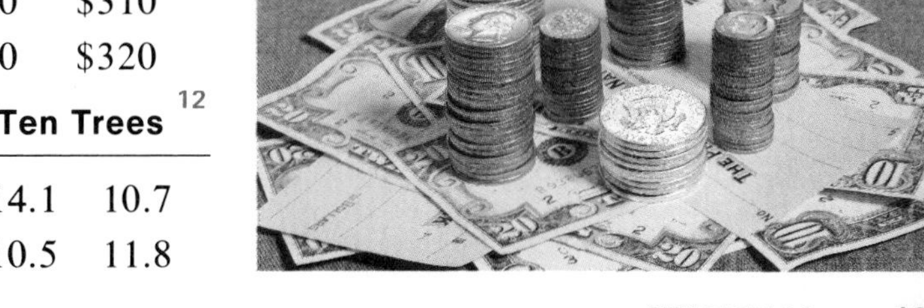

21. Find the mode. (Pages 118–119)

Customers at a Fresh Fruit Stand 12-2 P.M.

Hours	Number of People
8–10 A.M.	10
10–12 A.M.	25
12–2 P.M.	46
2–4 P.M.	27
4–6 P.M.	13

22. Find the median. (Pages 120–121)

Movie Ticket Sales at Unicorn Theater 300

Day	Number of Tickets
Monday	300
Tuesday	248
Wednesday	289
Thursday	325
Friday	560

Chapter Test

The Teacher's Resource Book contains two forms of each chapter test.

The bar graph at the right shows the maximum lengths of five kinds of whales. Use the graph for Exercises 1–3.

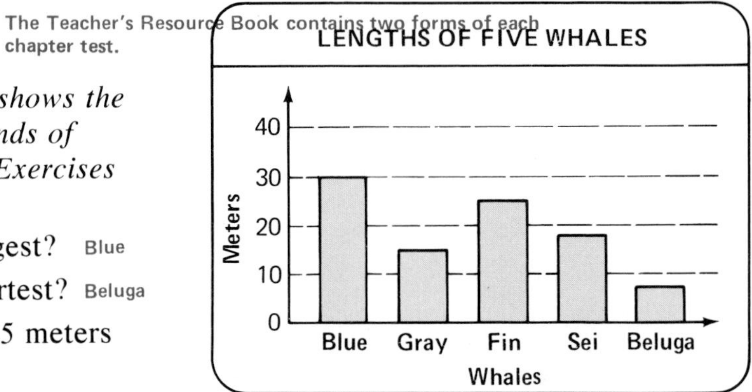

1. Which whale is the longest? Blue
2. Which whale is the shortest? Beluga
3. Which whale is about 25 meters long? Fin

The line graph below shows the normal monthly number of inches of rain or snow in Portland, Oregon. This is called precipitation. Use this graph for Exercises 4–7.

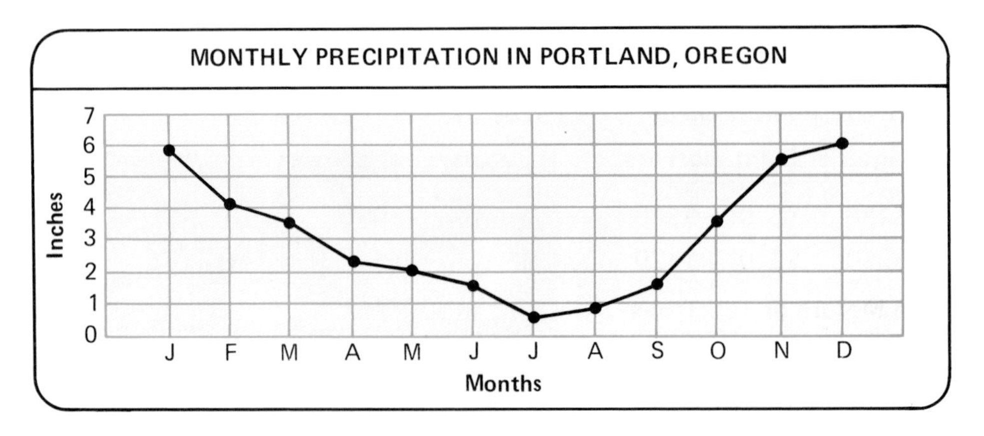

4. In which month was there the most precipitation? December

5. In which month was there the least precipitation? July

6. What is the normal precipitation in July? $\frac{1}{2}$ inch

7. What is the normal precipitation in May? 2 inches

The table below shows the jobs taken by graduates of a trade school. Use this information to construct a circle graph.

8.

Job	Per Cent
Carpenters	40 144°
Painters	20 72°
Electricians	10 36°
Plumbers	30 108°

For Exercises 9–10, find the mean.

9. 6 **Lengths of Five Wrens in Inches**

5 $5\frac{1}{2}$ $7\frac{3}{4}$ 6 $5\frac{3}{4}$

10. $10.00 **Prices of Eight Books**

$13.45	$ 8.95	$10.00	$8.50
$12.50	$10.80	$ 7.00	$8.80

11. Find the mode. Grape Ivy

Plants Sold by a Greenhouse

Plant	Number
Spider	8
Grape Ivy	14
English Ivy	11
Swedish Ivy	12
Begonia	9

12. Find the median. 1450

Length in Miles of Five Rivers

River	Length
Arkansas	1459
Colorado	1450
Columbia	1243
Fraser	850
Mississippi	2348

The Teacher's Resource Book also contains a cumulative review for Chapters 4-6.

Cumulative Review: Chapters 4–6

Choose the correct answer. Choose a, b, c, or d.

1. Solve for n. a

$$n + 5 = 11$$

a. 6 **b.** 16 **c.** $2\frac{1}{2}$ **d.** 55

2. Solve for n. d

$$n - 3 = 18$$

a. 19 **b.** 18 **c.** 5 **d.** 21

3. Solve for n. b

$$n + 0.05 = 0.11$$

a. 0.6 **b.** 0.06 **c.** 6 **d.** 0.006

4. Solve for n. c

$$7n + 2 = 44$$

a. 46 **b.** 42 **c.** 6 **d.** $6\frac{4}{7}$

5. Which ratio is equivalent to $\frac{1}{4}$? c

a. $\frac{3}{24}$ **b.** $\frac{4}{8}$ **c.** $\frac{4}{16}$ **d.** $\frac{3}{6}$

6. Solve the proportion for n. a

$$\frac{n}{16} = \frac{7}{8}$$

a. 14 **b.** $\frac{14}{16}$ **c.** $3\frac{1}{2}$ **d.** 3.5

7. All per cents may be written as a fraction with a denominator of c

a. 1 **b.** 10 **c.** 100 **d.** 1000

8. Write a decimal for 48%. a

a. 0.48 **b.** 0.0048
c. 4.8 **d.** 48.0

9. Write a per cent for 0.002. c

a. 2% **b.** 20%
c. 0.2% **d.** 0.02%

10. Write a fraction for 70%. b

a. $\frac{10}{7}$ **b.** $\frac{7}{10}$
c. $\frac{7}{100}$ **d.** $\frac{3}{4}$

11. Write a per cent for $\frac{2}{5}$. c

a. 4% **b.** 2%
c. 40% **d.** 25%

12. Find 17% of 80. a

a. 13.6 **b.** 136
c. 1.36 **d.** 80.17

13. What per cent of 90 is 27? a

a. 30% **b.** 3% **c.** 33% **d.** 300%

14. 81 is 90% of what number? d

a. 72.9 **b.** 73 **c.** 81 **d.** 90

15. Which is the best estimate of 30% of 899? a

a. 270 **b.** 240 **c.** 27 **d.** 24

16. The circle graph below shows how one family spends its income. How many degrees represent the section "Shelter"? b

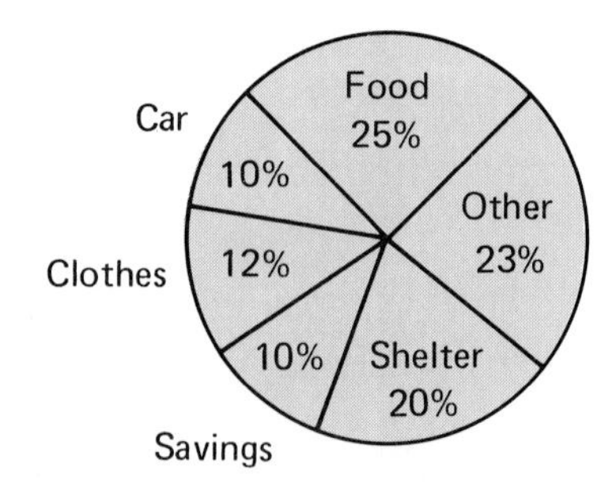

a. 90° **b.** 72° **c.** 85° **d.** 45°

17. Use the graph below to tell which state grows twice as much corn as Ohio. a

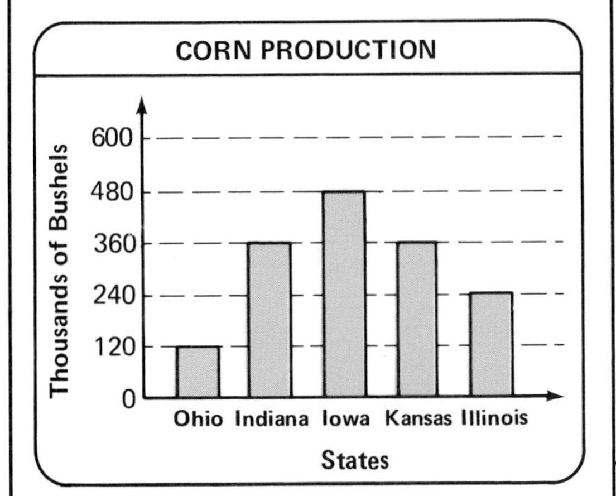

a. Illinois **b.** Iowa
c. Indiana **d.** Kansas

18. Solve for n: $3n = 27$ c

a. 24 **b.** 21 **c.** 9 **d.** 6

19. Solve the proportion for n. b

$$\frac{3}{21} = \frac{9}{n}$$

a. 27 **b.** 63 **c.** 7 **d.** 189

20. Estimate: 11% of \$700c

a. \$50 **b.** \$60 **c.** \$70 **d.** \$90

21. Three typists can type 87, 93, and 69 words per minute. Find the mean. b

a. 87 **b.** 83 **c.** 93 **d.** 90

22. John's bowling scores were 128, 135, 167, 167, 175. Find the mode. d

a. 135 **b.** 151 **c.** 154 **d.** 167

23. Mary saw the same kind of juice in 5 different stores with prices of 73¢, 78¢, 78¢, 79¢ and 82¢. What was the median price? b

a. 82¢ **b.** 78¢ **c.** 79¢ **d.** 73¢

24. How many degrees represent the section titled "Bus, Train"? c

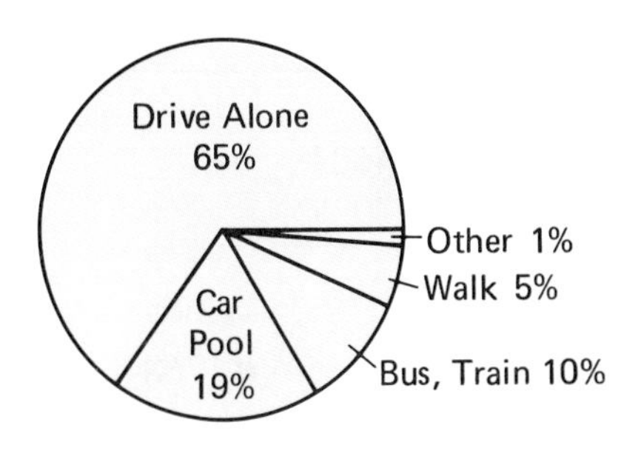

a. 45° **b.** 90° **c.** 36° **d.** 120°

25. Find the mode of these numbers. d

25 38 42 64 25 64
38 24 25 53 42 25

a. 38 **b.** 42 **c.** 64 **d.** 25

26. Solve for n: $\frac{n}{4} = 16$ a

a. 64 **b.** 4 **c.** 20 **d.** 12

27. Write a fraction for 24%. b

a. $\frac{2}{10}$ **b.** $\frac{6}{25}$ **c.** $\frac{3}{25}$ **d.** $\frac{3}{50}$

28. In lowest terms, the ratio of 15 to 45 is d

a. $\frac{15}{45}$ **b.** $\frac{3}{9}$ **c.** $\frac{1}{2}$ **d.** $\frac{1}{3}$

29. The selling price of a baseball bat is \$10.95. It cost the store \$7.50. Use the formula $m + c = s$ to find the markup. b

a. \$2.45 **b.** \$3.45
c. \$18.45 **d.** \$1.50

30. The scale on a road map is:

1 centimeter represents 50 kilometers.

350 kilometers = _?_ centimeters a

a. 7 **b.** 8 **c.** 6 **d.** 5

The Teacher's Resource Book also contains a Sample Competency Test for Chapters 1-6.

Sample Competency Test: Chapters 1–6

Choose the correct answer. Choose a, b, c, or d.

1. Subtract: c

$$\begin{array}{r} 4607 \\ -3929 \\ \hline \end{array}$$

a. 768 **b.** 688
c. 678 **d.** 768

2. Add: 71 + 129 + 38 + 4409 d

a. 4547 **b.** 687
c. 4697 **d.** 4647

3. The graph below shows the number of customers in Joe's store each day for five days. On which days were there about the same number of customers? b

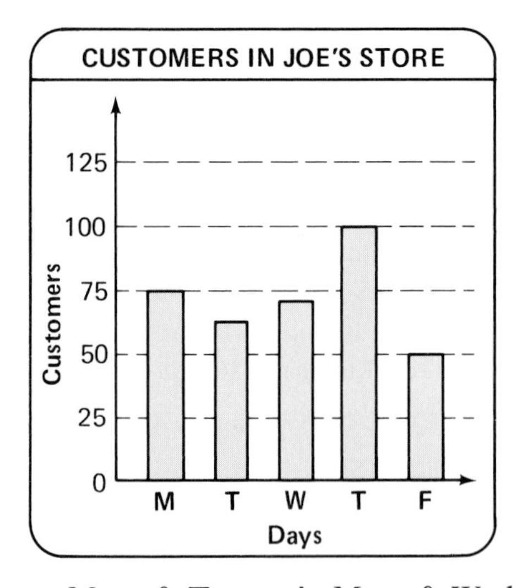

a. Mon. & Tues. **b.** Mon. & Wed.
c. Tues. & Fri. **d.** Wed. & Thurs

4. Divide: $39\overline{)15.405}$ c

a. 0.39 R 24 **b.** 395.0
c. 0.395 **d.** 39.5

5. Divide: $0.293\overline{)6.153}$ a

a. 21 **b.** 210
c. 0.021 **d.** 2.01

6. Choose the best estimate. b

14.9 − 10.1

a. 6 **b.** 5 **c.** 4 **d.** 3

7. What is the volume in cubic centimeters of this box? c

a. 33
b. 250
c. 1200
d. 1000

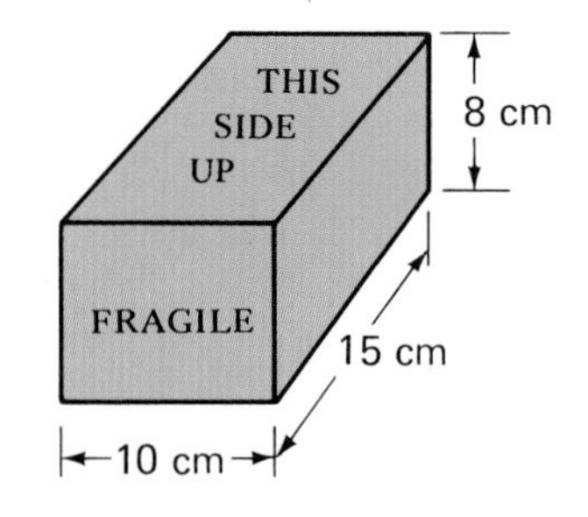

8. Choose an equivalent measure for 150 centimeters. b

a. 1500 m **b.** 1500 mm
c. 15 m **d.** 0.15 km

9. Multiply: a

$$\begin{array}{r} 609 \\ \times\ 45 \\ \hline \end{array}$$

a. 27,405 **b.** 3105
c. 2791 **d.** 654

10. Round 73,799 to the nearest thousand. c

a. 70,000 **b.** 72,000
c. 74,000 **d.** 75,000

11. The graph below shows how Jane spends her income. On which item is the most money spent? a

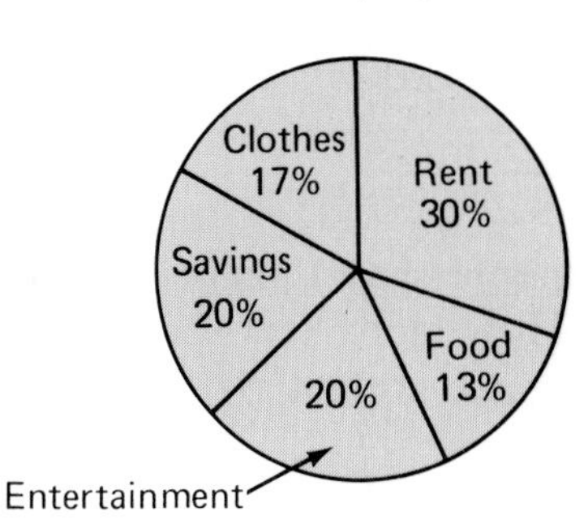

a. Rent **b.** Savings
c. Entertainment **d.** Clothes

12. Multiply: 16.09×2.3 c

a. 37 **b.** 15.87
c. 37.007 **d.** 36.007

13. Divide: $64\overline{)2964}$ a

a. 46 R 20 **b.** 4 R 40
c. 4 R 44 **d.** 46 R 24

14. What temperature is shown on the Celsius thermometer at the right? b

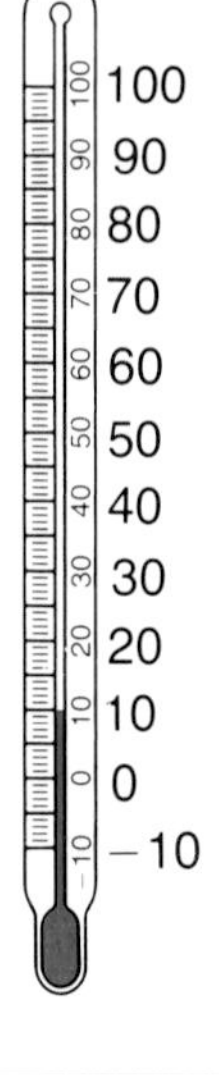

a. 20°
b. 10°
c. 0°
d. 40°

15. 75 mg of salt is equivalent to how many grams of salt? c

a. 7.5 **b.** 0.75
c. 0.075 **d.** 0.0075

16. Write a mixed number for $\frac{17}{11}$. c

a. $1\frac{7}{11}$ **b.** 17.11
c. $1\frac{6}{11}$ **d.** 1.711

17. Add. Write your answer in lowest terms. c

$$\frac{3}{10} + \frac{6}{10} + \frac{1}{10}$$

a. $\frac{1}{3}$ **b.** $\frac{10}{30}$ **c.** 1 **d.** $\frac{9}{10}$

18. Add: $7.304 + 2.9 + 5.87 + 6.225$ b

a. 14.145 **b.** 22.299
c. 22.335 **d.** 1.4145

19. Subtract: $7.34 - 5.29$ b

a. 1.05 **b.** 2.05
c. 1.50 **d.** 2.50

20. Solve for n. c

$$9n = 54$$

a. 486 **b.** 7 **c.** 6 **d.** 45

21. How many centimeters are there in the perimeter of this banner? c

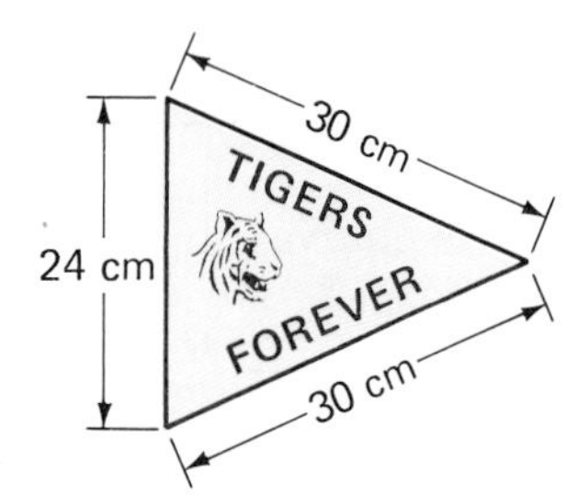

a. 720 **b.** 60 **c.** 84 **d.** 168

22. A baseball team won 15 out of 20 games it played. What per cent of its games did the team win? a

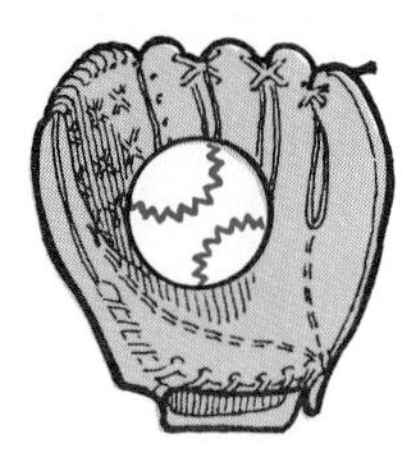

a. 75
b. 50
c. 2
d. 20

23. Round $7\frac{5}{12}$ to the nearest whole number. b

a. 6 **b.** 7 **c.** 8 **d.** $7\frac{1}{2}$

24. A graph that shows the amount of change over a specified period of time is called a __?__. d

a. bar graph **b.** circle graph
c. pictograph **d.** line graph

25. Two towns are 5 centimeters apart on a map. The scale on the map is:

1 cm represents 40 km.

What is the real distance in kilometers between the towns? b

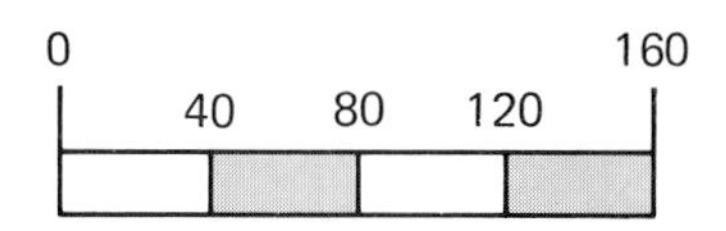

a. 45 **b.** 200 **c.** 100 **d.** 400

26. A carpenter has a plank $8\frac{1}{2}$ feet long. How many feet should be cut off to make a plank $5\frac{7}{8}$ feet long? d

a. $3\frac{3}{8}$ **b.** $2\frac{3}{8}$ **c.** $3\frac{5}{8}$ **d.** $2\frac{5}{8}$

27. The price of a certain dress is \$25. The cost of the dress is 79% of this. Estimate the cost of the dress. b

a. \$15 **b.** \$20 **c.** \$18 **d.** \$24

28. A recipe calls for $\frac{2}{3}$ cup of milk. How many cups of milk are necessary to make the recipe 3 times as large? b

a. 1 **b.** 2 **c.** $2\frac{1}{2}$ **d.** 3

29. Multiply: 6.31×1000 a

a. 6310 **b.** 0.0631
c. 631.0 **d.** 0.000631

30. In five baseball games Pete got 3, 2, 4, 1, and 2 hits. What was the mode? b

a. 1 **b.** 2 **c.** 3 **d.** 4

31. Five employees in an office make the following weekly salaries:
\$175, \$203, \$212, \$219, and \$314
What is the median salary? c

a. \$175 **b.** \$180
c. \$212 **d.** \$314

32. Choose the most suitable measure for a pitcher of milk. c

a. 20 mL **b.** 20 L
c. 2 L **d.** 100 L

33. Write a decimal for 65%. b

a. 65 **b.** 0.65 **c.** 6.5 **d.** 65.0

34. Write a fraction in lowest terms for 45%. a

a. $\frac{9}{20}$ **b.** $\frac{4}{10}$ **c.** $4\frac{5}{10}$ **d.** $4\frac{1}{2}$

35. Write a per cent for $\frac{1}{8}$. c

a. 18% **b.** 180%
c. $12\frac{1}{2}$% **d.** 8%

36. The length of a photograph is 250 millimeters. How many meters is this? c

a. 25
b. 2.5
c. 0.25
d. 0.025

37. Multiply: 16.3×0.001 b

a. 0.163 **b.** 0.0163
c. 0.00163 **d.** 1630.0

38. Divide: $\frac{3}{8} \div 1\frac{1}{4}$ a

a. $\frac{3}{10}$ **b.** $\frac{3}{4}$ **c.** $\frac{15}{32}$ **d.** $\frac{10}{3}$

39. Subtract: b

$$\begin{array}{r} 7 \\ -4\frac{1}{2} \\ \hline \end{array}$$

a. $3\frac{1}{2}$ **b.** $2\frac{1}{2}$ **c.** 3 **d.** 2

40. During what month was the average temperature the highest? b

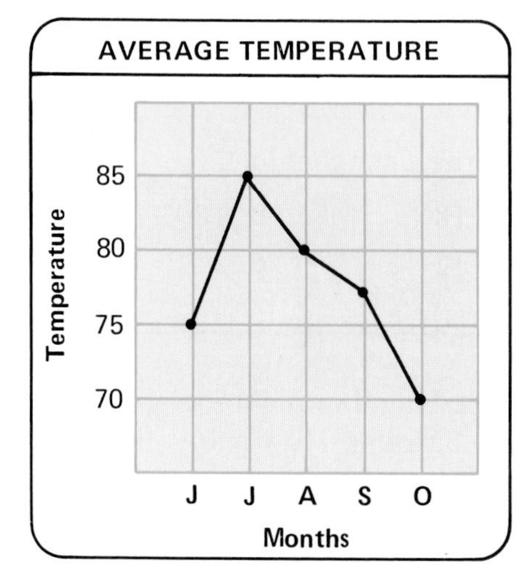

a. June **b.** July
c. August **d.** September

41. Solve for n. a

$$n + 2 = 16$$

a. 14 **b.** 15 **c.** 16 **d.** 18

42. Add: $\frac{3}{7} + \frac{5}{6}$ c

a. $\frac{2}{3}$ **b.** $\frac{8}{13}$ **c.** $1\frac{11}{42}$ **d.** 2

43. What is the least common denominator of $\frac{5}{6}$ and $\frac{3}{4}$? c

a. 6 **b.** 4 **c.** 12 **d.** 24

44. Multiply: $\frac{3}{8} \times \frac{16}{25}$ a

a. $\frac{6}{25}$ **b.** $\frac{1}{5}$ **c.** $\frac{75}{128}$ **d.** $\frac{3}{8}$

45. Solve for n. a

$$8n - 11 = 21$$

a. 4 **b.** 6 **c.** 5 **d.** 32

46. Which ratio is equivalent to $\frac{3}{5}$? d

a. $\frac{9}{10}$ **b.** $\frac{6}{15}$ **c.** $\frac{9}{25}$ **d.** $\frac{12}{20}$

47. Solve for n. b

$$\frac{1}{3} = \frac{n}{12}$$

a. 3 **b.** 4 **c.** 6 **d.** 7

48. Find the total length of this rivet in inches. a

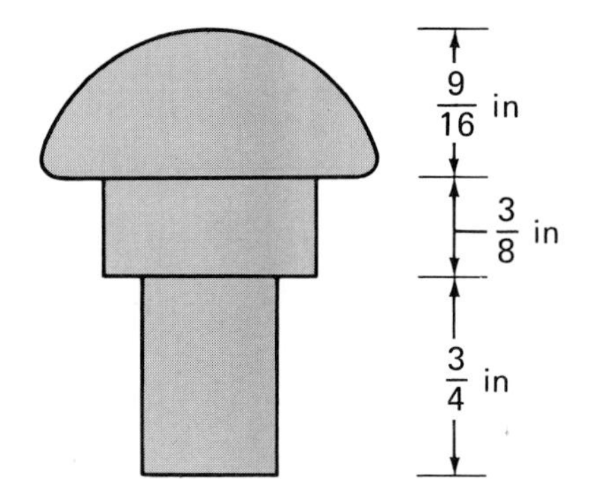

a. $1\frac{11}{16}$ **b.** $1\frac{5}{8}$
c. $1\frac{3}{4}$ **d.** $1\frac{7}{8}$

49. Subtract: c

$$\begin{array}{r} 5\frac{6}{13} \\ -2\frac{8}{13} \\ \hline \end{array}$$

a. $3\frac{2}{13}$ **b.** $2\frac{5}{13}$
c. $2\frac{11}{13}$ **d.** $10\frac{48}{169}$

50. Find 26% of 75. d

a. 26.75 **b.** 75.26

c. $2\frac{23}{26}$ **d.** 19.5

51. What per cent of 80 is 16? c

a. 80% **b.** 16% **c.** 20% **d.** 12.8%

52. 16 is 40% of what number? a

a. 40 **b.** 16 **c.** 64 **d.** 6.4

53. What is the area in square meters of this rectangular yard? b

a. 78.4
b. 382.2
c. 39.2
d. 300.4

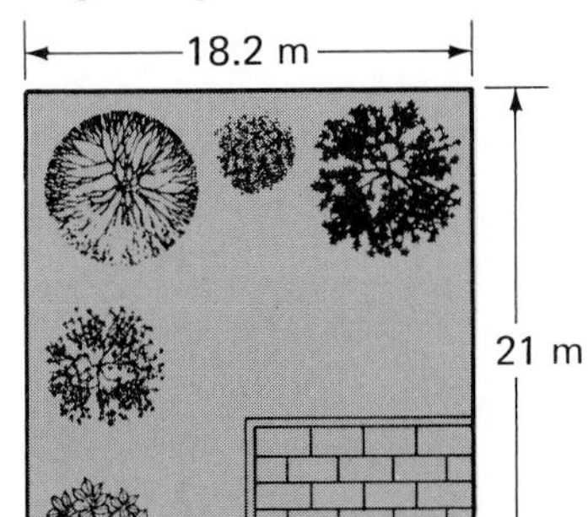

54. Round 27.39 to the nearest whole number. a

a. 27 **b.** 28 **c.** 27.3 **d.** 27.4

55. A bottle of grape juice contains 0.45 liters. How many milliliters is this? c

a. 45 **b.** 4.5 **c.** 450 **d.** 4500

56. Solve for n: $n - 1.9 = 4.8$ b

a. 5.7 **b.** 6.7 **c.** 3.9 **d.** 2.9

57. Solve for n: $2.4n = 48$ b

a. 200 **b.** 20 **c.** 2 **d.** 0.2

58. Choose the best estimate for 24% of 160. b

a. 4 **b.** 40 **c.** 320 **d.** 400

59. Choose the best estimate for 50% of 195. b

a. 50 **b.** 100 **c.** 150 **d.** 200

60. The line graph below shows the amount of steel the United States imported during the first six months of a recent year. About how many millions of tons were imported in March? b

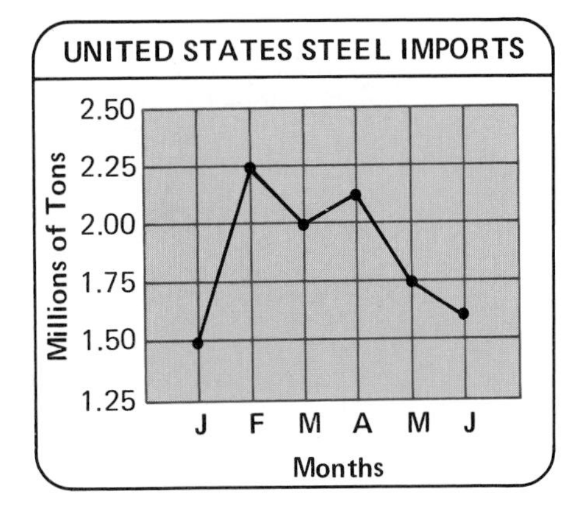

a. 1.5 **b.** 2.0 **c.** 2.2 **d.** 1.4

REVIEW OF RELATED SKILLS FOR CHAPTER 7

We suggest that some or all of this page be reviewed before proceeding with the chapter.

Multiply. (Pages 8–9, 56–57)

1. $7.35 × 25 $183.75 **2.** $6.30 × 20 $126.00 **3.** $5.50 × 28 $154.00 **4.** $4.20 × 48 $201.60

5. $16.30 × 1.5 $24.45 **6.** $12.40 × 1.5 $18.60 **7.** $7.50 × 1.5 $11.25 **8.** $11.00 × 1.5 $16.50

9. $3.00 × $12\frac{1}{2}$ $37.50 **10.** $7.50 × $7\frac{1}{2}$ $56.25 **11.** $13.00 × $6\frac{1}{2}$ $84.50 **12.** $14.00 × $10\frac{1}{2}$ $147.00

13. $6.00 × $1\frac{1}{2}$ $9.00 **14.** $8.00 × $1\frac{1}{2}$ $12.00 **15.** $10.20 × $1\frac{1}{2}$ $15.30 **16.** $7.60 × $1\frac{1}{2}$ $11.40

17. $17,500 × 0.0705 $1233.75 **18.** $18,980 × 0.0935 $1774.63 **19.** $16,480 × 0.099 $1631.52

20. $21,590 × 0.093 $2007.87 **21.** $23,450 × 0.067 $1571.15 **22.** $38,500 × 0.0705 $2714.25

Write a decimal for each per cent. (Pages 90–91)

23. 6% 0.06 **24.** 8% 0.08 **25.** 10% 0.1 **26.** 12% 0.12 **27.** $7\frac{1}{2}$% 0.075 **28.** $3\frac{1}{2}$% 0.035

29. 3.5% 0.035 **30.** 9.1% 0.091 **31.** 47.8% 0.478 **32.** 2.30% 0.023 **33.** 4.01% 0.0401 **34.** 12.33% 0.1233

35. 7.04% 0.0704 **36.** 1.9% 0.019 **37.** 21.8% 0.218 **38.** 11.2% 0.112 **39.** 6.74% 0.0674 **40.** 18.43% 0.1843

Write a fraction for each per cent. (Pages 90–91)

41. 50% $\frac{1}{2}$ **42.** 75% $\frac{3}{4}$ **43.** 10% $\frac{1}{10}$ **44.** $66\frac{2}{3}$% $\frac{2}{3}$ **45.** $12\frac{1}{2}$% $\frac{1}{8}$ **46.** 80% $\frac{4}{5}$

47. 15% $\frac{3}{20}$ **48.** 25% $\frac{1}{4}$ **49.** 30% $\frac{3}{10}$ **50.** 55% $\frac{11}{20}$ **51.** 70% $\frac{7}{10}$ **52.** 48% $\frac{12}{25}$

53. $\frac{1}{2}$% $\frac{1}{200}$ **54.** $\frac{1}{4}$% $\frac{1}{400}$ **55.** $37\frac{1}{2}$% $\frac{3}{8}$ **56.** $33\frac{1}{3}$% $\frac{1}{3}$ **57.** $62\frac{1}{2}$% $\frac{5}{8}$ **58.** $14\frac{2}{7}$% $\frac{1}{7}$

Find each answer. (Pages 94–95)

59. 8% of $1700 $136 **60.** 5% of $10,500 $525 **61.** 14% of $5700 $798

62. 12% of $3000 $360 **63.** 9% of $4500 $405 **64.** 8% of $6800 $544

65. 25% of $4800 $1200 **66.** 20% of $12,000 $2400 **67.** 50% of $10,800 $5400

68. $33\frac{1}{3}$% of $660 $220 **69.** $12\frac{1}{2}$% of $8400 $1050 **70.** $62\frac{1}{2}$% of $96,400 $60,250

Add. (Pages 4–5)

71. 7.95 + 12.80 + 17.75 38.50 **72.** 12.15 + 29.85 + 6.65 48.65 **73.** 31.25 + 63.88 + 9.87 105.00

74. 18.93 + 7.99 + 18.64 45.56 **75.** 15.27 + 14.84 + 7.83 37.94 **76.** 6.93 + 8.58 + 21.93 37.44

77. 52.48 + 21.36 + 9.87 83.71 **78.** 48.23 + 36.42 + 5.64 90.29 **79.** 27.36 + 12.04 + 5.62 45.02

80. 38.96 + 19.42 + 3.75 62.13 **81.** 56.44 + 21.79 + 12.46 90.69 **82.** 38.42 + 15.64 + 8.21 62.27

Subtract. (Pages 4–5)

83. $250.00 − $175.15 $74.85 **84.** $395.87 − $93.53 $302.34 **85.** $465.00 − $83.90 $381.10

86. $175.80 − $123.33 $52.47 **87.** $675.00 − $163.27 $511.73 **88.** $290.40 − $75.40 $215.00

89. $289.50 − $192.45 $97.05 **90.** $372.75 − $221.89 $150.86 **91.** $400.00 − $123.84 $276.16

92. $500.00 − $96.49 $403.51 **93.** $448.27 − $169.27 $279.00 **94.** $624.36 − $249.53 $374.83

CHAPTER

7 INCOME

CONSUMER SKILLS/APPLICATIONS

7-1 Hourly Wages
7-2 Commission
7-3 Deductions and Net Pay
7-4 Social Security
Rounding and Estimation

CAREER APPLICATIONS

Truck Driver
Personnel Worker

7-1 Hourly Wages

See the Teacher's Manual for the objectives.

Tom Benedict is looking for a job as a bank teller. He notices the advertisement at the right in a newspaper.

BANK TELLER

$5.50 per hour—min.
1 yr. exp. Good ref.
Call 799-0104

EXAMPLE 1 Tom applies for and gets the job. What will be his weekly income for a 40-hour week?

Solution: **Amount per Hour × Number of Hours = Amount Earned**

$\$5.50 \times 40 = \$220$ Tom's weekly income will be **$220.**

After completing Example 1, you may wish to have students do some or all of Exercises 1-6.

Alice Brown also applied for a job that was advertised in a newspaper. She asked about the overtime guarantee. Working **overtime** means that she will receive $1\frac{1}{2}$, or 1.5 times the regular hourly pay when she works more than 35 hours in a week. This is also called **time and a half.**

TRAINEE-MECHANIC
$5 per hr.—35 hrs. Time and a
half for overtime. Gd benefits.
Equal Oppty Employer. Contact Mr.

To find Alice's total weekly income, first answer the **hidden questions:**

What is the weekly pay for 35 hours of work?

What is the overtime pay?

Then you can find her total weekly income.

EXAMPLE 2 Alice worked 48 hours one week. Find her total income for that week.

Solutions:

[1] Find the pay for 35 hours.

$\$5.00 \times 35 = \$175.00$

[2] Find the overtime pay per hour.

$\$5.00 \times 1.5 = \$7.50$ ◀ *Regular Pay Per Hour × 1.5 = Overtime Pay Per Hour*

[3] Find the overtime pay for 13 hours. ◀ *48 − 35 = 13*

$\$7.50 \times 13 = \$97.50$

[4] Find the total income.

$\$175.00 + 97.50 = \$272.50$ ◀ *Regular Pay + Overtime Pay = Total Income*

Alice's total income that week was **$272.50.**

REVIEW OF RELATED SKILLS

You may wish to use these exercises before teaching the lesson.

Multiply. (Pages 8–9, 56–57)

1. $3.25 × 30 $97.50 **2.** $4.60 × 40 $184.00 **3.** $5.80 × 38 $220.40 **4.** $6.15 × 35 $215.25

5. $5.00 × $38\frac{1}{2}$ $192.50 **6.** $8.00 × $30\frac{1}{2}$ $244.00 **7.** $8.50 × $3\frac{1}{2}$ $29.75 **8.** $12.00 × $6\frac{1}{2}$ $78.00

9. $14.50 × 1.5 $21.75 **10.** $7.00 × 1.5 $10.50 **11.** $8.20 × 1.5 $12.30 **12.** $6.70 × 1.5 $10.05

13. $6.00 × $1\frac{1}{2}$ $9.00 **14.** $4.00 × $1\frac{1}{2}$ $6.00 **15.** $12.00 × $1\frac{1}{2}$ $18.00 **16.** $8.00 × $1\frac{1}{2}$ $12.00

EXERCISES

For Exercises 1–6, find the weekly income. (Example 1)

	Hourly Wage	Hours Worked	Weekly Income
1.	$4.00	40	? $160.00
2.	$5.00	38	? $190.00
3.	$5.25	40	? $210.00
4.	$3.75	25	? $93.75

5. An auto mechanic earns $8.50 per hour and works 35 hours per week. Find the weekly income. $297.50

6. A machinist earns $10 per hour and works 40 hours per week. Find the weekly income. $400.00

For Exercises 7–10, find the total income. Time and a half is paid for all hours worked over 40. (Example 2)

	Hourly Wage	Hours Worked	Total Income
7.	$7.00	42	? $301.00
8.	$5.50	44	? $253.00
9.	$5.00	$44\frac{1}{2}$	? $233.75
10.	$8.40	42	? $361.20

Use the information from the advertisements at the right to answer Exercises 11–14.

DRIVER

with own late model 4-door car or station wagon. $5 per hour. 35 hr. per wk. Time and a half for overtime. Will train. 622-0500

GUARD

$4/hr. 40 hr. week. Good benefits. Overtime guaranteed (at time and a half). No exp. required. Call for interview between 9:00 and

11. Jane Youngblood applied for the job of driver. Find her pay for a 35-hour work week. $175.00

12. One week Jane worked 43 hours. Find her total income for the week. $235.00

13. Toby Felch was just hired for the guard's position. Find his pay for a regular work week. $160.00

14. The first week Toby worked 42 hours. Find his total income for the first week. $172.00

TRUCK DRIVER

Career lessons are optional. This lesson combines the skills of reading a table and multiplication of whole numbers and decimals.

Some truck drivers are paid by the mile. This mileage chart shows the distances between some major cities.

	Birmingham, Alabama	Boston, Massachusetts	Chicago, Illinois	Dallas, Texas	Detroit, Michigan	Los Angeles, California	Memphis, Tennessee	New York, New York	Seattle, Washington
Birmingham, Alabama	–	1153	634	631	728	2006	241	949	2522
Boston, Massachusetts	1153	–	949	1752	678	2931	1298	206	2938
Chicago, Illinois	634	949	–	899	269	2039	527	811	1981
Dallas, Texas	631	1752	899	–	1127	1376	454	1549	2048
Detroit, Michigan	728	678	269	1127	–	2287	730	648	2258
Los Angeles, California	2006	2931	2039	1376	2287	–	1783	2727	1110
Memphis, Tennessee	241	1298	527	454	730	1783	–	1095	2281
New York, New York	949	206	811	1549	648	2727	1095	–	2800
Seattle, Washington	2522	2938	1981	2048	2258	1110	2281	2800	–

EXAMPLE: Karen Jackson operates an 18-wheel semi-trailer truck. She makes a round trip from Memphis, Tennessee to Detroit, Michigan for $0.25 per mile. Find the total earnings.

Solution: 1 Use the mileage chart to find the distance between the cities.

a. Find the row marked Memphis, Tennessee.

b. Look directly to the right at the box under Detroit, Michigan.

c. Read the number: 730

2 Find the round trip distance.

$2 \times 730 = \mathbf{1460}$

3 Find the total earnings.

$1460 \times \$0.25 = \mathbf{365.00}$ ◀ ***Total Miles*** × ***Rate per Mile*** = ***Total Earnings***

EXERCISES Note that Exercises 1–6 are non-verbal.

For Exercises 1–6, use the mileage chart to find the distance between the given cities. Then compute the total earnings.

	From	To	One-way Distance	Round trip Distance	Rate per Mile	Total Earnings
1.	Boston	Chicago	? miles 949	? miles 1898	$0.25	? $474.50
2.	Los Angeles	Seattle	? miles 1110	? miles 2220	$0.20	? $444.00
3.	Detroit	New York	? miles 648	? miles 1296	$0.21	? $272.16
4.	New York	Boston	? miles 206	? miles 412	$0.23	? $94.76
5.	Chicago	Memphis	? miles 527	? miles 1054	$0.24	? $252.96
6.	Dallas	Birmingham	? miles 631	? miles 1262	$0.22	? $277.64

7. Kevin Stevens makes two round trips from Boston, Massachusetts to Detroit, Michigan. He is paid $0.24 per mile. What are his total earnings? $650.88

8. Kim Yu drives a truck from New York, New York to Chicago, Illinois. She makes three round trips and is paid $0.21 per mile. Find the total earnings. $1021.86

9. Fred Thompson drives a truck from Los Angeles, California to Dallas, Texas. He then drives from Dallas to Memphis, Tennessee. He is paid $0.23 per mile. What are his total earnings? $420.90

10. Louise Beyers makes a trip from New York City to Chicago, Illinois. At Chicago, she loads more cargo and then drives to Birmingham, Alabama. She is paid $0.25 per mile. Find her total earnings. $361.25

11. A trucker makes a round trip from Detroit, Michigan to Chicago, Illinois and then drives the truck to Boston, Massachusetts. The trucker earns $0.20 per mile. Find the total earnings. $243.20

7-2 Commission

See the Teacher's Manual for the objectives.

Sometimes a salesperson's earnings are based on a fixed per cent of total sales. This per cent is called the **rate of commission.**

EXAMPLE 1 Maria Calderon's rate of commission is 8%. One week, Maria's sales total was \$2185. What was her commission that week?

Solution: **Total Sales × Rate of Commission = Commission**

\$2185 × 0.08 = \$174.80 ◀ *8% = 0.08*

Maria's commission is **\$174.80.**

After completing Example 1, you may wish to have students do some or all of Exercises 1-8.

Some salespersons receive a salary *plus* commission. To find the total income, first answer the question:

What is the amount of commission?

This is the **hidden question** in the problem. Then you can find the total income.

EXAMPLE 2 Steve Carmen accepted the job advertised at the right. In August, his sales total was \$14,750. Find his total income for August.

> **SALESPERSON**
> Good opportunity to earn high pay. \$400 per mo. + a 4% commission on sales. Car necessary. Will train. Good benefits. Equal Oppty Employer

Solution: 1 Find the amount of commission.

\$14,750 × 0.04 = \$590.00

2 Find the total income.

\$400 + \$590 = \$990 ◀ *Salary + Commission = Total Income*

Steve's total income for August was **\$990.**

REVIEW OF RELATED SKILLS

You may wish to use these exercises before teaching the lesson.

Write a decimal for each per cent. (Pages 90–91)

1. 5% 0.05 **2.** 7% 0.07 **3.** 14% 0.14 **4.** 20% 0.2 **5.** $4\frac{1}{2}$% 0.045 **6.** $10\frac{1}{2}$% 0.105

Write a fraction for each per cent. (Pages 90–91)

7. 10% $\frac{1}{10}$ **8.** 25% $\frac{1}{4}$ **9.** 5% $\frac{1}{20}$ **10.** 15% $\frac{3}{20}$ **11.** $33\frac{1}{3}$% $\frac{1}{3}$ **12.** $12\frac{1}{2}$% $\frac{1}{8}$

Find each answer. (Pages 94–95)

13. 3% of \$1500 \$45 **14.** 6% of \$12,500 \$750 **15.** 10% of \$3600 \$360 **16.** $3\frac{1}{2}$% of \$400 \$14

EXERCISES

For Exercises 1–6, find the commission. (Example 1)

	Sales	Rate of Commission	Commission
1.	$12,000	3%	? $360
2.	$18,500	4%	? $740
3.	$26,000	2%	? $520
4.	$10,500	5%	? $525

5. A real estate agent's rate of commission is 7% of all sales. What is the commission on the sale of a house valued at $90,000? $6300.00

6. Kim Lu's rate of commission is 4% of all sales. How much commission does she earn in a month in which her sales are $19,200? $768.00

7. Lisa Olafson sells books. Her rate of commission is 9% of all sales. What is her commission on $560? $50.40

8. A clerk receives a 10% rate of commission on all sales. What is the commission on sales of $954? $95.40

For Exercises 9–14, find the total income. (Example 2)

	Salary	Sales	Rate of Commission	Income
9.	$400	$10,000	7%	? $1100
10.	$275	$16,500	3%	? $770
11.	$515	$14,200	4%	? $1083
12.	$480	$2500	6%	? $630
13.	$600	$4000	20%	? $1400
14.	$525	$1600	15%	? $765

Use this advertisement for Exercises 15–17.

SALES—OFFICE SUPPLIES

No exp. necessary—will train. Salary $100/wk. + 15% commission. Exc. benefits. References.

15. Brett King was hired to sell office supplies. He sold $900 worth of supplies the first week. Find the amount of his commission. $135.00

16. Find Brett's total income for the first week. $235.00

17. Brett's sales were $1350 the second week. Find the total income for the week. $302.50

More Challenging Problems

Some people are paid by ***graduated commission.*** *The rate of commission changes as the amount of sales increases.*

18. Jules Bennington sells machinery at Acme Machine Company. The rate of commission is 6% of the first $1500 in sales and $7\frac{1}{2}$% of all sales over $1500. Find his commission on sales of $2850. $191.25

19. Elena DeTroy receives a salary of $800 per month plus commission. The rate of commission is 5% of the first $2000 and 6% on sales over $2000. Find her total income on sales of $4380. $1042.80

7-3 Deductions and Net Pay

See the Teacher's Manual for the objectives.

When Amy Harris receives her pay check, she also receives a statement of earnings.

DEPT.	EMPLOYEE	CHECK #		WEEK ENDING	GROSS PAY ❶	NET PAY ❹
07	Harris, A.	54601		8/24/--	225.00	?
❷ TAX DEDUCTIONS				PERSONAL DEDUCTIONS ❸		
FIT	FICA	STATE	LOCAL	MEDICAL	UNION DUES	OTHERS
34.27	14.96	6.85	---	4.42	----	4.00

Gross pay (see Box 1), represents the total income for the week.

Tax deductions (see Box 2), shows the taxes that are **deducted** (subtracted) from gross pay.

Personal deductions (see Box 3), shows other items deducted from gross pay.

After the taxes and personal items are deducted, or subtracted, from the gross pay, what remains is the **net pay,** or **take-home pay** (see Box 4).

EXAMPLE Find Amy's net pay.

Solution: [1] Find the total deductions.

Box 2: \$34.27 + \$14.96 + \$6.85 = \$56.08
Box 3: \$ 4.42 + \$4.00 = +\$ 8.42
Total deductions: **\$64.50**

[2] Find the net pay.

\$225.00 − \$64.50 = **\$160.50** ◀ ***Gross Pay − Total Deductions = Net Pay***

REVIEW OF RELATED SKILLS

You may wish to use these exercises before teaching the lesson.

Add or subtract as indicated. (Pages 4–5)

1. \$12.95 + \$24.60 + \$3.80 \$41.35
2. \$14.16 + \$30.81 + \$5.75 \$50.72
3. \$21.34 + \$53.16 + \$9.67 \$84.17
4. \$16.35 + \$40.85 + \$8.37 \$65.57
5. \$11.13 + \$14.25 + \$3.08 \$28.46
6. \$12.18 + \$16.70 + \$4.98 \$33.86
7. \$25.48 + \$64.35 + \$9.95 \$99.78
8. \$15.23 + \$29.48 + \$4.56 \$49.27
9. \$23.69 + \$15.98 + \$5.50 \$45.17
10. \$621.00 − \$75.98 \$545.02
11. \$784.93 − \$29.99 \$754.94
12. \$400.00 − \$87.56 \$312.44
13. \$350.00 − \$127.15 \$222.85
14. \$285.50 − \$84.36 \$201.14
15. \$254.00 − \$63.79 \$190.21
16. \$324.95 − \$98.60 \$226.35
17. \$478.00 − \$154.17 \$323.83
18. \$380.00 − \$88.95 \$291.05

EXERCISES

For Exercises 1–6, find the total deductions and the net pay.

	Gross Pay	Federal Tax	F.I.C.A. Tax	State Tax	Local Tax	Medical Insurance	Pension Plan	Total Deductions	Net Pay
1.	$250	$ 45.05	$16.93	$ 9.98	—	—	$12.50	? $84.46	? $165.54
2.	$300	$ 59.21	$19.95	$12.05	$4.12	$1.50	—	? $96.83	? $203.17
3.	$180	$ 19.10	$11.97	$ 7.20	$3.10	$0.75	—	? $42.12	? $137.88
4.	$520	$137.02	$34.08	$20.85	—	—	$35.00	? $226.95	? $293.05
5.	$600	$168.93	$39.90	$24.10	—	$3.00	$45.00	? $280.93	? $319.07
6.	$430	$102.27	$28.60	$17.15	$7.27	$4.00	$25.00	? $184.29	? $245.71

7. Joseph Ortega earned $560 last week. The deductions were: federal tax–$72.80; state tax–$14.56; F.I.C.A. tax–$37.24; life insurance–$2.50. Find the net pay. $432.90

8. Marie Kelly earned $430 last week. The deductions were: federal tax–$32.00; state tax–$12.90; F.I.C.A. tax–$28.60; pension plan–$20.00. Find the net pay. $336.50

9. Clyde Jones earned $1558 in one month. The deductions were: federal tax–$258.40; state tax–$54.20; F.I.C.A. tax–$103.61; local tax–$72.20. Find the net pay. $1069.59

10. Jean Silver Spring's monthly gross pay is $1172. The deductions are: federal tax–$275.80; state tax–$70.16; F.I.C.A. tax–$77.94; life insurance–$5.00. Find the net pay. $743.10

For Exercises 11–16, use the statement of earnings below.

THE MIDLAND CORPORATION CHARLOTTESVILLE, VIRGINIA

DEPARTMENT	LIFE NO.	MONTH	DAY	YR	LIFE INSURANCE	ACCIDENT & SICKNESS	COMMUNITY FUND	MAJOR MEDICAL	RATE
		11	24		1.14		.30		4.50

TOTAL HOURS		CREDIT UNION	BONDS	C	SPECIAL ALLOWANCE	C	MISCELLANEOUS DEDUCTIONS
40.0		25.00					

	GROSS PAY	F.I.C.A.	FEDERAL TAX	STATE INCOME TAX	PENSION	NET PAY
	180.00	11.03	22.80	2.64		117.09

YOU EARNED AND *THE MIDLAND CORPORATION* PAID YOU

SPECIAL ALLOWANCE CODES
1. SICK PAY
2. ADJUSTMENTS
3. TUITION REFUND
4. JURY DUTY
5. UNUSED SICK LEAVE
6. DEATH IN FAMILY
7. VACATION PAY
8. HOLIDAY PAY
9. MISCELLANEOUS

PLEASE DETACH AND KEEP THIS STUB FOR YOUR TAX RECORD

11. What is the hourly rate of pay? $4.50
12. What are the total hours worked? 40
13. What is the total amount of taxes? $36.47
14. Find the total deductions. $62.91
15. What is the gross pay? $180.00
16. Is the net pay correct? Yes

7-4 Social Security

See the Teacher's Manual for the objectives.

In Section 7–3, one of the amounts **withheld** (deducted) from Amy's paycheck was the **F.I.C.A.** (Federal Insurance Contribution Act) deduction. This is also called the **social security tax.**

There are two parts to the F.I.C.A. tax:

1. the tax rate, and
2. the maximum amount of income that is taxed.

This table shows the tax rate and the maximum amount of income that is taxed for the years 1982–1985. Employers must match the amount paid by workers to social security.

Year	Maximum Pay Taxed	Employee Rate
1982	\$32,700	6.70%
1983	\$33,900	6.70%
1984	\$36,000	6.70%
1985	\$43,500	7.05%

EXAMPLE Samantha earned \$35,480 in 1982. How much social security tax did she pay?

Solution: In 1982, the maximum amount that could be taxed was \$32,700. Therefore, find the tax on \$32,700.

$\$32,700 \times 0.067 = \$2190.90$ ◀ ***From the table above, the employee rate for 1982 was 6.7%, or 0.067.***

Samantha paid **\$2190.90.**

Social security withholdings are used to provide benefits for retired workers and to provide income for the families of workers who die or are disabled by illness or injury. They are also used to pay certain medical costs for workers and their families covered by Medicare.

REVIEW OF RELATED SKILLS

You may wish to use these exercises before teaching the lesson.

Write a decimal for each per cent. (Pages 90–91)

1. 6.7% 0.067 **2.** 7.2% 0.072 **3.** 9.35% 0.0935 **4.** 9.30% 0.093 **5.** 6.65% 0.0665 **6.** 7.05% 0.0705

Multiply. (Pages 8–9)

7. $\$14,300 \times 0.067$ \$958.10 **8.** $\$21,480 \times 0.0705$ \$1514.34 **9.** $\$15,460 \times 0.0705$ \$1089.93

10. $\$10,290 \times 0.067$ \$689.43 **11.** $\$22,560 \times 0.0705$ \$1590.48 **12.** $\$33,500 \times 0.067$ \$2244.50

13. $\$14,560 \times 0.067$ \$975.52 **14.** $\$23,780 \times 0.067$ \$1593.26 **15.** $\$41,700 \times 0.0705$ \$2939.85

EXERCISES

For Exercises 1–18, find the F.I.C.A. tax. Refer to the Table on page 146. Round each answer up to the next cent.

	Year	Income	F.I.C.A.		Year	Income	F.I.C.A.		Year	Income	F.I.C.A.
1.	1982	$14,381	? $963.53	**7.**	1982	$15,970	? $1069.99	**13.**	1984	$16,859	? $1129.55
2.	1985	$17,207	? $1213.09	**8.**	1985	$16,832	? $1186.66	**14.**	1982	$24,638	? $1650.75
3.	1984	$13,546	? $907.58	**9.**	1983	$42,147	? $2271.30	**15.**	1983	$45,921	? $2271.30
4.	1983	$14,261	? $955.49	**10.**	1984	$38,395	? $2412.00	**16.**	1985	$56,487	? $3066.75
5.	1985	$10,475	? $738.49	**11.**	1982	$30,434	? $2039.08	**17.**	1984	$25,432	? $1703.94
6.	1984	$12,580	? $842.86	**12.**	1985	$50,789	? $3066.75	**18.**	1982	$64,887	? $2190.90

19. In 1982, Gina Minetti earned $13,500. How much was deducted for social security? **$904.50**

20. Franz Wagner's income was $25,380 in 1983. How much was the social security deduction? **$1700.46**

21. A car salesperson estimates an income of $54,000 for 1985. What will the social security tax be? **$3066.75**

22. An airline pilot made $33,000 in 1982. What was the amount of the F.I.C.A. deduction? **$2190.90**

23. Jim Beauchamp is a welder. He expects to earn $28,490 in 1984. What will the F.I.C.A. tax be? **$1908.83**

24. Migdalia Perez is a tailor. In 1983 her total earnings were $33,500. How much is the F.I.C.A. tax? **$2244.50**

More Challenging Problems

The table below shows the tax rate for self-employed workers.

Year	Maximum Income Taxed	Rate
1982	$32,700	9.35%
1983	$33,900	9.35%
1984	$36,000	9.35%
1985	$43,500	9.90%

25. Harry Sims, who is self-employed as a cabinetmaker, expects to earn $23,400 in 1985. How much of his income will be paid for social security? **$2316.60**

26. In 1982, Michael Long's income from his self-employment was $34,850. How much did he pay for F.I.C.A. tax? **$3057.45**

PERSONNEL WORKER

Career lessons are optional.
This lesson applies the skills of reading a table and addition of decimals.

As a **personnel worker** for a large business, Philip Carey helps employees to compute their Social Security benefits. Social Security provides these types of benefits.

1. Retirement income
2. Benefits for the dependents of a worker who dies
3. Income for persons who become disabled
4. Medical costs for persons covered by Medicare

The table below shows some approximate benefits.

Examples of Monthly Social Security Retirement Payments

	Average Yearly Earnings after 1950 Covered by Social Security						
Benefits can be paid to a:	*$923 or less*	*$3000*	*$4000*	*$5000*	*$6000*	*$8000*	*$10,000**
Retired worker at 65	133.90	276.80	325.60	377.60	426.70	530.40	587.70
Retired worker at 62	107.20	221.50	260.50	302.10	341.40	424.40	470.20
Wife or husband at 65	67.00	138.40	162.80	188.80	213.40	265.20	293.90
Wife or husband at 62	50.30	103.80	122.10	141.60	160.10	198.90	220.50
Wife under 65 and one child in her care	67.00	146.40	230.80	319.00	356.00	397.80	440.80
Maximum family payment	200.90	423.10	556.40	696.60	782.60	928.20	1028.40

*Maximum earnings covered by Social Security were lower in past years and must be included in figuring your average earnings. This average determines your payment amount.

The amount of the Social Security benefits depends largely on average yearly earnings on which Social Security taxes were paid.

EXAMPLE Anna Rodriguez plans to retire at age 62. Her average yearly earnings since 1950 were $6000. Use the table to estimate the monthly benefits.

Solution: Find the row that reads: "Retired worker at 62." Look to the right under "$6000."

341.40

The monthly benefit is **$341.40.**

EXERCISES Note that Exercises 1–6 are non-verbal.

Find the approximate monthly benefit for each worker. Use the table on page 148.

1. Retired worker at 65 Average yearly earnings: $4000 $325.60
2. Wife or husband at 62 Average yearly earnings: $8000 $198.90
3. Wife under 65 and one child Average yearly earnings: $5000 $319.00
4. Retired worker at 62 Average yearly earnings: $10,000 $470.20
5. Wife or husband at 65 Average yearly earnings: $6000 $213.40
6. Maximum family payment Average yearly earnings: $10,000 $1028.40

7. Joe Carlucci is thinking about retiring. His average yearly earnings are $8000. How much more will he receive in benefits per year if he retires at age 65 rather than at age 62? $1272

8. Elaine Rotor is thinking about retiring. Her average yearly earnings are $6000. How much more will she receive in benefits over 10 years if she retires at 65 rather than at 62? $10,236

9. Emma Chin retired at age 62. Her average yearly earnings were $5000. When Emma retired, her husband was 65. Find the total of their monthly benefits.

   Retired worker at 62: ? $302.10
   Husband or wife at 65: ? $188.80
   Total: ? $490.90

10. Julio King retired at age 65. His average yearly earnings were $8000. When Julio retired, his wife was 62. Find the total of their monthly benefits.

    Retired worker at 65: ? $530.40
    Husband or wife at 62: ? $198.90
    Total: ? $729.30

11. Greg Jones has been receiving $587.70 in Social Security checks each month. In July, this amount will be increased 7% because of a cost–of–living adjustment. What will be the monthly payment after July 1? $628.84

12. Jim Katz is retiring at age 62. His average yearly earnings were $10,000. His wife is under 65 and is caring for a young child. Find the total of their monthly benefits. $911

13. The Conti family is eligible for the maximum family payment. Tim Conti's average yearly earnings were $8000. What is the monthly benefit? $928.20

Rounding and Estimation

Consumers use rounding and estimation to solve problems related to income.

EXERCISES See the Teacher's Manual for the objectives and a description of the Rounding and Estimation feature.

Skills

Choose the best estimate. Choose a, b, or c.

		a.	b.	c.
1.	3.49×20 a	3.5×20	3×20	4×20
2.	85.04×70 b	90×70	85×70	80×70
3.	5.98×38 b	6×35	6×40	5×40
4.	4.88×42 c	4×40	5×45	5×40
5.	$53.4 + 11.16 + 29.5$ c	$60 + 20 + 20$	$60 + 10 + 30$	$50 + 10 + 30$
6.	$249.20 - 172.80$ a	$250 - 170$	$240 - 170$	$250 - 180$
7.	10% of 780 b	$\frac{1}{10} \times 700$	$\frac{1}{10} \times 800$	$\frac{1}{10} \times 70$
8.	5% of 6023 c	$\frac{1}{20} \times 7000$	$\frac{1}{20} \times 70$	$\frac{1}{20} \times 6000$
9.	32% of 92 c	$\frac{2}{5} \times 90$	$\frac{4}{5} \times 90$	$\frac{3}{10} \times 90$
10.	29% of 900 c	0.25×900	0.20×900	0.30×900
11.	$9\frac{1}{2}$% of 1875 a	0.10×2000	0.10×1000	0.20×2000

Choose the best estimate. Choose a, b, c, or d.

		a.	b.	c.	d.
12.	6.98×30 c	180	21	210	18
13.	5.07×41 a	200	2000	20	250
14.	$3.95 \times 29\frac{1}{2}$ d	60	900	1200	120
15.	$48.25 + 18.14 + 31.60$ b	80	100	110	90
16.	$198.28 - 57.24$ c	160	150	140	130
17.	20% of 206 a	40	1000	100	50
18.	21% of 8004 c	2000	800	1600	1200

Applications

19. Wilma earns $4.95 per hour. Last week she worked 39 hours. Estimate the gross pay. b

a. $\$4.00 \times 40$ **b.** $\$5.00 \times 40$
c. $\$4.00 \times 30$ **d.** $\$5.00 \times 30$

20. Louis earns $221.40 per week. Total deductions are about 19% of gross pay. Estimate his total deductions. b

a. $\$230 \times \frac{1}{3}$ **b.** $\$220 \times \frac{1}{5}$
c. $\$230 \times \frac{1}{10}$ **d.** $\$230 \times \frac{1}{5}$

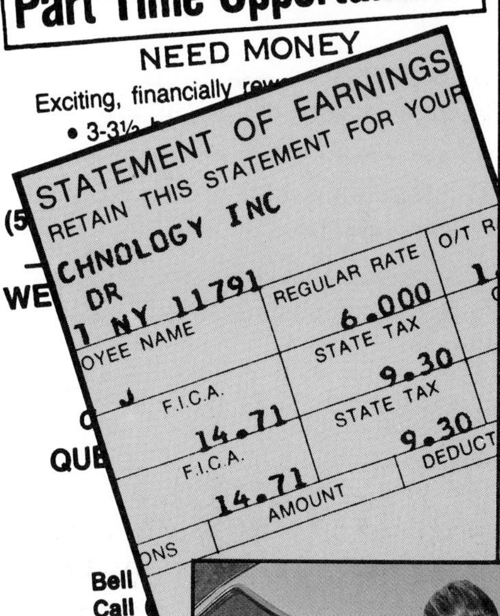

21. Gilbert receives an 8% commission on all sales. His sales last week amounted to $18,321. Estimate the amount Gilbert earned. d
    - a. $10,000 × 0.05
    - b. $10,000 × 0.01
    - c. $20,000 × 0.20
    - d. $20,000 × 0.10

22. The deductions from Leon's gross pay were: federal tax–$51.40; state tax–$10.06; F.I.C.A.–$29.30. Estimate the total deductions. b
    - a. $50.00 + $10.00 + $20.00
    - b. $50.00 + $10.00 + $30.00
    - c. $60.00 + $20.00 + $20.00
    - d. $60.00 + $20.00 + $30.00

23. Rudolph earns $5.10 per hour. This week he worked 31 hours. Estimate the gross pay. a
    - a. $150
    - b. $200
    - c. $100
    - d. $250

24. The deductions from Sam's pay were: federal tax–$67.50; state tax–$12.21; F.I.C.A.–$28.90. Estimate the total deductions. c
    - a. $100
    - b. $120
    - c. $110
    - d. $130

25. Lisa earns $196.50 per week. Total deductions are about 24% of gross pay. Estimate the total deductions. b
    - a. $40
    - b. $50
    - c. $60
    - d. $55

26. Valerie receives an 11% commission as an automobile dealer. Her total sales for a week were $15,225. Estimate the commission. d
    - a. $3000
    - b. $150
    - c. $160
    - d. $1500

Chapter Review

These exercises review the vocabulary, skills and applications presented in the chapter, as a preparation for the chapter test.

Part 1: VOCABULARY

For Exercises 1–6, choose from the box at the right the word(s) that completes each statement.

taxes
gross pay
graduated
overtime pay
net pay
deductions
commission
social security

1. Pay for working extra hours is called __?__. overtime pay (Pages 138–139)
2. A per cent of sales that a salesperson earns is called __?__. (Pages 142–143) commission
3. When the commission rate changes as the amount of sales increases, the commission is __?__. graduated (Pages 142–143)
4. The total amount a person earns at a job is __?__. gross pay (Pages 144–145)
5. After taxes and voluntary deductions are subtracted from a person's gross pay, the remaining amount is the __?__. net pay (Pages 144–145).
6. Federal Insurance Contributions Act (F.I.C.A.) taxes are also called __?__ taxes. (Pages 146–147) social security

Part 2: SKILLS

Multiply. (Pages 8–9, 56–57)

7. \$6.25 × 21 \$131.25 8. \$5.40 × 38 \$205.20 9. \$7.00 × $3\frac{1}{2}$ \$24.50 10. \$12.80 × $7\frac{1}{2}$ \$96.00

11. \$15,500 × 0.075 \$1162.50 12. \$19,960 × 0.0525 \$1047.90 13. \$17,480 × 0.0615 \$1075.02

Write a decimal for each per cent. (Pages 90–91)

14. 3% 0.03 15. 5% 0.05 16. 11.43% 0.1143 17. 7.5% 0.075 18. $3\frac{1}{2}$% 0.035 19. $16\frac{2}{3}$% $0.16\frac{2}{3}$

Write a fraction for each per cent. (Pages 90–91)

20. 25% $\frac{1}{4}$ 21. $33\frac{1}{3}$% $\frac{1}{3}$ 22. 20% $\frac{1}{5}$ 23. 50% $\frac{1}{2}$ 24. 75% $\frac{3}{4}$ 25. 10% $\frac{1}{10}$

Find each answer. (Pages 94–95)

26. 7% of \$1800 \$126 27. 5% of \$2500 \$125 28. $3\frac{1}{2}$% of \$7000 \$245 29. 10% of \$8300 \$830

Add or subtract. (Pages 4–5)

30. 3.75 + 12.50 + 18.65 34.90 31. 6.83 + 12.95 + 3.15 22.93 32. 30.51 + 17.30 + 9.20 57.01

33. 219.48 − 117.19 102.29 34. 750.00 − 219.83 530.17 35. 385.00 − 119.75 265.25

Part 3: APPLICATIONS

For Exercises 36–39, find the total income. (Pages 138–139)

	Hourly Wage	Hours Worked	Total Income
36.	$6.00	28	? $168
37.	$4.00	40	? $160
38.	$3.25	20	? $65
39.	$4.20	35	? $147

40. Donna is an electrician. She earns $10.50 per hour for a 40–hour work week, with time and a half for overtime. Find her income for a 45–hour week. (Pages 138–139) $498.75

41. Bill is a travel agent. He is paid $5.50 per hour for a 35–hour work week. What is his income for a 40-hour week if he is paid time and a half for overtime? (Pages 138–139) $233.75

42. Megan sells appliances, and is paid an 8% commission on all sales. What is her commission on $4200 in sales? (Pages 142–143) $336.00

43. Hector earns a weekly salary of $150 plus a 20% commission on sales. Find his total income on sales of $2500. (Pages 142–143) $650.00

For Exercises 44–47, use the statement of earnings below. (Pages 144–145)

DEPT.	EMPLOYEE	CHECK #	WEEK ENDING	GROSS PAY	NET PAY
12	Tynan, B.	11352	5/03/--	205.20	?

TAX DEDUCTIONS				PERSONAL DEDUCTIONS		
FIT	FICA	STATE	LOCAL	MEDICAL	UNION DUES	OTHERS
19.10	13.75	8.10	1.21	3.24	4.00	3.15

44. What is the gross pay? $205.20

45. Find the total tax deductions. $42.16

46. Find the total personal deductions. $10.39

47. Find the net pay. $152.65

For Exercises 48–51 find the F.I.C.A. tax. Refer to the table on page 146. (Pages 146–147)

	Year	Income	F.I.C.A.
48.	1985	$17,395	? $1226.35
49.	1982	$21,550	? $1443.85
50.	1983	$27,050	? $1812.35
51.	1984	$19,398	? $1299.67

52. Roger earns $5.25 per hour. He works $38\frac{1}{2}$ hours per week. Estimate his weekly gross pay. (Pages 150–151) d

a. $240 **b.** $150
c. $180 **d.** $200

53. Leona receives a $9\frac{3}{4}$% commission on all sales. Last week, her total sales were $21,250. Estimate the commission. (Pages 150–151) a

a. $2000 **b.** $200
c. $20,000 **d.** $4000

Chapter Test

The Teacher's Resource Book contains two forms of each chapter test.

Perform the indicated operation.

1. \$6.95 × 35 \$243.25 **2.** \$3.75 × 42 \$157.50 **3.** \$9600 × 0.067 \$643.20

4. 41.5 + 9.40 + 6.45 57.35 **5.** 7.04 + 12.38 + 9.16 28.58

6. 341.12 − 89.08 252.04 **7.** 259.63 − 104.19 155.44

Write a decimal for each per cent.

8. 8% 0.08 **9.** $22\frac{1}{2}\%$ 0.225

Write a fraction for each per cent.

10. 80% $\frac{4}{5}$ **11.** $37\frac{1}{2}\%$ $\frac{3}{8}$

Find each answer.

12. 12% of \$2045 \$245.40 **13.** 5% of \$9820 \$491.00 **14.** 20% of \$2608 \$521.60

15. Josh is paid \$6.20 per hour for a 35-hour week with time and a half for overtime. How much is he paid for working 40 hours one week? \$263.50

16. Jane works at a skating rink and earns \$3.50 per hour. Find her pay for a 25-hour week. \$87.50

17. A broker receives a 2.2% commission on stock sales, in addition to a weekly salary of \$250. Find the total income on weekly sales of \$8300. \$432.60

18. Juan is a sales representative, and receives a commission of 11% on total sales. Find the commission on sales of \$19,700. \$2167.00

19. Sue Ellen earned \$38,900 in 1982. The social security tax that year was 6.70%. The maximum amount taxed was \$32,700. Find her total F.I.C.A. tax. \$2190.90

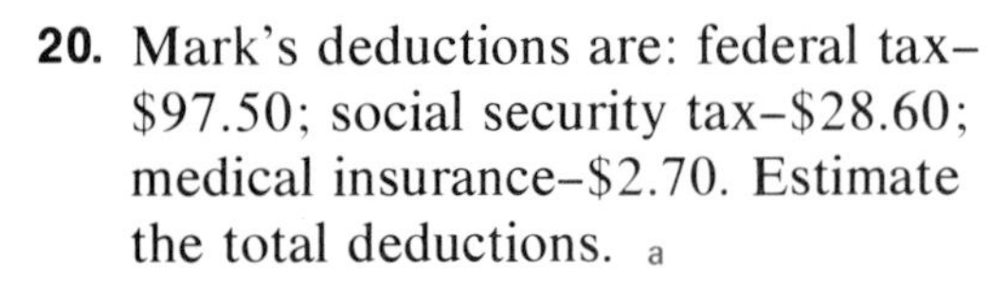

20. Mark's deductions are: federal tax–\$97.50; social security tax–\$28.60; medical insurance–\$2.70. Estimate the total deductions. a

a. \$130 **b.** \$180

c. \$200 **d.** \$100

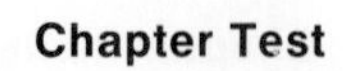

Additional Practice

You may wish to use all or some of these exercises, depending on how well students performed on the formal chapter test.

Skills

Perform the indicated operations. (Pages 4–5, 8–9)

1. \$5.83 × 31 \$180.73
2. \$7.05 × 39 \$274.95
3. \$9.15 × 42 \$384.30
4. \$3.90 × 28 \$109.20
5. 15.05 + 10.00 + 14.75 39.80
6. 4.92 + 10.69 + 16.49 32.10
7. 25.61 + 10.57 + 38.05 74.23
8. 187.55 − 119.04 68.51
9. 208.64 − 75.38 133.26
10. 504.14 − 256.77 247.37

Find each answer. (Pages 94–95)

11. 14% of \$780 \$109.20
12. 8% of \$1025 \$82.00
13. 12% of \$1563 \$187.56
14. 24% of \$3828 \$918.72

Applications

15. Jack King works as a clerk and earns \$3.50 per hour. He works 28 hours each week. Find his weekly income. (Pages 138–139) \$98.00

16. Paula Vance works as a toll collector for \$4.30 per hour. How much does she earn for a 35-hour work week? (Pages 138–139) \$150.50

For Exercises 17–20, find the total income. Time and a half is paid for overtime work. (Pages 138–139)

	Hourly Wage	Regular Hours	Hours Worked	Total Income
17.	\$3.80	35	42	? \$172.90
18.	\$5.50	40	43	? \$244.75

	Hourly Wage	Regular Hours	Hours Worked	Total Income
19.	\$6.95	40	46	? \$340.55
20.	\$7.50	30	35	? \$281.25

21. Luis Lazar receives a 9% commission on his sales. Estimate his commission on sales of \$5030. (Pages 150–151) c
    a. \$50 **b.** \$1000 **c.** \$500 **d.** \$100

22. Sue Santelli earned \$425 last week. The deductions were: federal tax–\$93.50; social security tax–\$28.48; state tax–\$31.98. Find her net pay that week. (Pages 144–145) \$271.04

23. Use the statement of earnings below to find the net pay. (Pages 144–145) \$235.56

DEPT.	EMPLOYEE	CHECK #	WEEK ENDING	GROSS PAY	NET PAY
M	Boylan, T.	347528	11/2/--	342.25	?

TAX DEDUCTIONS				PERSONAL DEDUCTIONS		
FIT	FICA	STATE	LOCAL	MEDICAL	UNION DUES	OTHERS
60.40	22.91	6.88	---	4.50	----	12.00

24. Bill Gomez earned \$25,400 in 1982. The F.I.C.A. tax rate that year was 6.70% on a maximum of \$32,700. Find the amount of tax. (Pages 146–147) \$1701.80

25. Kim Li earned \$45,300 in 1982. The F.I.C.A. tax rate was 6.70%. The maximum amount taxed was \$32,700. Find the F.I.C.A. tax. (Pages 146–147) \$2190.90

REVIEW OF RELATED SKILLS FOR CHAPTER 8

We suggest that some or all of this page be reviewed before proceeding with the chapter.

Multiply. (Pages 8–9)

1. $2.70 × 30 $81.00 **2.** $7.30 × 98 $715.40 **3.** $2.75 × 25 $68.75 **4.** $5.50 × 36 $198.00
5. $3.50 × 20 $70.00 **6.** $7.00 × 30 $210.00 **7.** $3.00 × 27 $81.00 **8.** $3.80 × 35 $133.00
9. $6.40 × 28 $179.20 **10.** $2.80 × 32 $89.60 **11.** $4.90 × 38 $186.20 **12.** $6.40 × 42 $268.80
13. $3.50 × 40 $140.00 **14.** $5.25 × 36 $189.00 **15.** $6.15 × 34 $209.10 **16.** $5.45 × 37 $201.65
17. $4.85 × 31 $150.35 **18.** $4.90 × 28 $137.20 **19.** $7.50 × 27 $202.50 **20.** $8.40 × 31 $260.40

Add. (Pages 4–5)

21. $11,375.21 + $258.39 + $1389.75 $13,023.35 **22.** $12,571.33 + $297.50 + $1385.27 $14,254.10
23. $26,435.81 + $925.31 + $2144.63 $29,505.75 **24.** $7358.39 + $798.21 + $635.91 $8792.51
25. $14,347.20 + $135.41 + $645.25 $15,127.86 **26.** $28,642.15 + $474.89 + $65.68 $29,182.72
27. $17,544.38 + $256.27 + $87.04 $17,887.69 **28.** $25,542.10 + $86.75 + $144.28 $25,773.13

Subtract. (Pages 4–5)

29. $2719.00 − $1875.00 $844.00 **30.** $1763.00 − $1693.00 $70.00 **31.** $4307.63 − $4218.50 $89.13
32. $6243.29 − $3929.88 $2313.41 **33.** $7629.80 − $6739.73 $890.07 **34.** $2175.30 − $1981.90 $193.40
35. $3850 − $267.41 $3582.59 **36.** $2483 − $1864.27 $618.73 **37.** $1348 − $1252.15 $95.85
38. $2624 − $1885.96 $738.04 **39.** $1856 − $1542.75 $313.25 **40.** $2400 − $2286.48 $113.52

Add. (Pages 2–3)

41. $22 + $35 + $146 + $1341 $1544 **42.** $58 + $75 + $108 + $1314 $1555
43. $1452 + $16 + $244 + $96 $1808 **44.** $1875 + $421 + $356 + $98 $2750

Subtract. (Pages 2–3)

45. $25,381 − $464 $24,917 **46.** $18,496 − $1348 $17,148 **47.** $19,540 − $1207 $18,333
48. $21,946 − $1508 $20,438 **49.** $36,000 − $1846 $34,154 **50.** $29,000 − $1458 $27,542

Write a decimal for each per cent. (Pages 90–91)

51. 15% 0.15 **52.** 21% 0.21 **53.** 13% 0.13 **54.** 14% 0.14 **55.** 3% 0.03 **56.** 5% 0.05
57. 8% 0.08 **58.** 9% 0.09 **59.** 3.4% 0.034 **60.** 2.9% 0.029 **61.** 4.2% 0.042 **62.** 4.7% 0.047
63. 2.1% 0.021 **64.** 5.5% 0.055 **65.** 6.5% 0.065 **66.** 7.3% 0.073 **67.** 2.4% 0.024 **68.** 3.2% 0.032

Find each answer. (Pages 94–95)

69. 12% of 48 5.76 **70.** 15% of 50 7.5 **71.** 21% of 64 13.44
72. 3% of 96 2.88 **73.** 5% of 104 5.2 **74.** 8% of 75 6
75. 4.2% of 840 35.28 **76.** 3.8% of 1008 38.304 **77.** 3.4% of 1200 40.8

CHAPTER

8 INCOME TAX

CONSUMER SKILLS/APPLICATIONS

CAREER APPLICATIONS

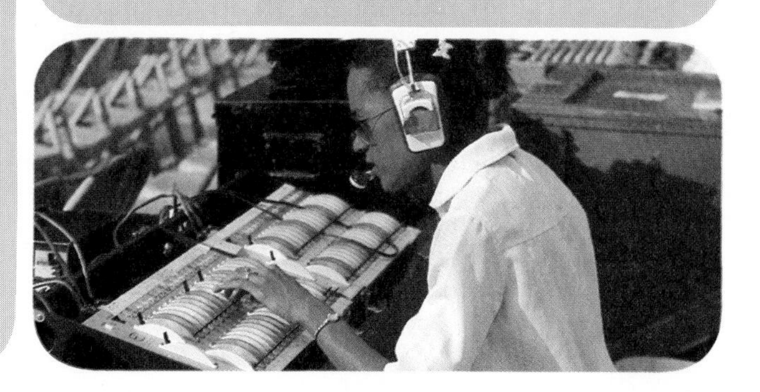

8-1 Federal Income Tax

See the Teacher's Manual for the objectives.

You saw on page 144 that $34.27 was deducted from Amy's paycheck for Federal income tax.

A table such as the one at the right was used to determine this amount. The amount to be deducted depends on:

1. Your weekly gross income
2. The number of **exemptions**

Federal Withholding Tax				
Single Persons—Weekly				
Wages		*Exemptions*		
At Least	*Less Than*	*0*	*1*	*2*
		Income Tax		
$110	$120	$14.30	$10.80	$ 7.30
$120	$130	$16.10	$12.60	$ 9.10
$130	$140	$17.90	$14.40	$10.90
$140	$150	$20.00	$16.20	$12.70
$150	$160	$22.60	$18.60	$15.00
$160	$170	$24.70	$20.70	$16.80
$170	$180	$26.80	$22.80	$18.80
$180	$190	$32.40	$29.10	$25.80

Neil Jackson is single and supports himself. He can claim one exemption—himself.

EXAMPLE 1 Neil's gross income as an apprentice plumber is $160 a week. How much Federal income tax will be deducted from his paycheck?

Solution:

1. Find $160 in the **At Least** column.
2. Look to the right across the line of $160. Stop when you reach the "1 exemption" column. Read the amount: **$20.70** ◀ *Federal income tax*

After completing Example 1, you may wish to have students do some or all of Exercises 1-10.

Wanda Lee is single and supports her mother.

EXAMPLE 2 Wanda makes $4.30 an hour as a sales clerk. Last week she worked 40 hours. How much Federal income tax will be deducted?

Solution:

1. Find the gross income. $4.30 × 40 = **$172.00**
2. Since $172 is between $170 and $180, find $170 in the **At Least** column.
3. Look at the right along the line of $170. Stop when you reach the "2 exemption" column. Read the amount: **$18.80**

REVIEW OF RELATED SKILLS

You may wish to use these exercises before teaching the lesson.

Multiply. (Pages 8–9)

1. $3.80 × 40 $152.00
2. $5.40 × 38 $205.20
3. $3.25 × 25 $81.25
4. $4.50 × 34 $153.00
5. $5.00 × 30 $150.00
6. $6.00 × 40 $240.00
7. $4.00 × 35 $140.00
8. $5.15 × 28 $144.20
9. $6.80 × 30 $204.00
10. $4.20 × 20 $84.00

EXERCISES

See the suggested assignment guide in the Teacher's Manual.

For Exercises 1–10, use the table to find the federal income tax. (Example 1)

	Gross Pay	Number of Exemptions		Gross Pay	Number of Exemptions		Gross Pay	Number of Exemptions
1.	$153	0 $22.60	3.	$175	1 $22.80	5.	$140	2 $12.70
2.	$147	0 $20.00	4.	$164	2 $16.80	6.	$160	1 $20.70

7. Laura Snell earned $125 last week. She is single and claims one exemption. $12.60
8. Elvis Green was paid $138 for a week's work. He is single and claims one exemption. $14.40
9. Billy Kent earns $164 a week. He is single and claims no exemptions. $24.70
10. Lisa Lang earns $150 per week. She is single and claims two exemptions. $15.00

For Exercises 11–14,
a. find the gross pay
b. use the table to find the federal income tax. (Example 2)

	Hours Worked	Hourly Pay	Number of Exemptions		Hours Worked	Hourly Pay	Number of Exemptions
11.	30	$4.00 a. $120.00	0 b. $16.10	13.	37	$5.00 a. $185.00	1 b. $29.10
12.	25	$5.00 a. $125.00	2 b. $9.10	14.	23	$6.05 a. $139.15	2 b. $10.90

For Exercises 15–18, find the amount of the federal income tax.

15. A stock clerk works 35 hours per week and earns $3.95 per hour. The clerk is not married and claims no exemptions. $17.90
16. Vincent Virga works part time as a gardener for $5.00 per hour. Last week he worked 24 hours. He is single and claims one exemption. $12.60
17. A chauffeur works 40 hours per week at $4.60 per hour. The chauffeur is single, and claims one exemption. $29.10
18. Jan Ludmar worked 34 hours last week at $4.20 per hour. She is not married and claims two exemptions. $12.70

8-2 Adjusted Gross Income and Deductions

See the Teacher's Manual for the objectives.

Last year Louise D'Amato's gross income as an engineering technician was $17,480. When she was preparing her federal income tax return, she found that she had to compute her **adjusted gross income.** This is the sum of all kinds of income such as wages, bonuses, commissions, tips, and so on, that a person receives during a year.

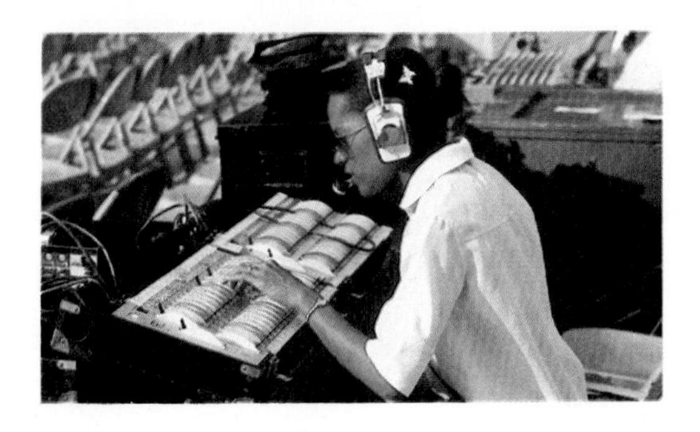

EXAMPLE 1 Louise earned $17,480 in wages last year. The interest from a savings account was $521. She also received a bonus of $2500. Find the adjusted gross income.

Solution: Add the different kinds of income.

$17,480 + $521 + $2500 = **$20,501** ◀ *Louise's adjusted gross income*

After completing Example 1, you may wish to have students do some or all of Exercises 1-10.

Louise had certain expenses, such as interest on a loan, that she could subtract from her adjusted gross income. These amounts are called **deductions.** Listing these deductions on a special tax form called Schedule A, is called **itemizing deductions.**

All taxpayers do not have to itemize deductions. To decide whether or not to itemize, Louise found the total of her possible itemized deductions. Then she consulted the table below.

TABLE

You may itemize your deductions if you are:

Married and filing jointly	**and**	your itemized deductions are more than $3400
Single, or a Head of household	**and**	your itemized deductions are more than $2300

EXAMPLE 2 Louise had deductions totaling $1735.25. Louise is not married. Should she itemize deductions?

Solution: Compare her total deductions with the amount for a single person in the table: **$1735.25 is less than $2300.**

Louise should ***not*** itemize deductions.

REVIEW OF RELATED SKILLS

You may wish to use these exercises before teaching the lesson.

Add. (Pages 4–5)

1. 10,385.21 + 249.50 + 1236.75 $11,871.46

2. 12,694.25 + 487.96 + 1346.87 $14,529.08

3. 14,739.04 + 321.70 + 2347.32 $17,408.06

4. 8759.25 + 679.32 + 1444.28 $10,882.85

5. 16,839.67 + 408.17 + 3521.75 $20,769.59

6. 4789.70 + 381.29 + 4895.37 $10,066.36

EXERCISES

For Exercises 1–8, find the adjusted gross income. (Example 1)

	Wages	Interest	Other Income	Adjusted Gross Income
1.	$9562	$34.75	$127.80	? $9724.55
2.	$10,121	$78.96	$287.63	? $10,487.59
3.	$14,263	$47.61	–	? $14,310.61
4.	$12,381	$59.72	–	? $12,440.72
5.	$11,790	–	$1342.75	? $13,132.75
6.	$15,620	–	$2178.23	? $17,798.23
7.	$20,291	$125.60	$1572.95	? $21,989.55
8.	$19,475	$468.73	$1463.29	? $21,407.02

9. Mary Pappas received $12,472 in wages last year. She also received $38.29 and $46.57 in interest from two savings accounts. Find the adjusted gross income. $12,556.86

10. Clem Forrest earned $10,478 last year. He received $1200.50 rent from a tenant and $10.23 in interest on a savings account. Find the adjusted gross income. $11,688.73

For Exercises 11–18, decide whether or not deductions should be itemized. Use the table on page 160. (Example 2)

	Total Deductions	Filing Status	
11.	$2475.62	Married filing jointly	Do not itemize
12.	$1346.08	Single	Do not itemize
13.	$3702.95	Single	Itemize
14.	$2238.79	Married filing jointly	Do not itemize
15.	$2342.43	Single	Itemize
16.	$3786.49	Married filing jointly	Itemize
17.	$1625.62	Married filing jointly	Do not itemize
18.	$1872.44	Single	Do not itemize

19. Chris Lee has deductions that total $2475. Chris is single. Should he itemize his deductions? Yes

20. Sue Jaffe and her husband are filing a joint return. Their deductions total $1342. Should they itemize? No

21. Mr. and Mrs. Johansen are filing a joint return. Their deductions total $5320. Should they itemize? Yes

career SALES CLERK

Career lessons are optional.
This lesson applies the skills of reading a table and addition of decimals.

Kevin Galway is a **sales clerk** at the Trent Book Store. He uses a table such as the one on the right to find the amount of sales tax.

To find the total cost of a purchase, you must first answer the question:

What is the amount of sales tax?

This is the **hidden question** in the problem. Then you can find the total cost.

Amount of Sale	*Tax*	*Amount of Sale*	*Tax*
0.01- 0.10	0.00	10.68-10.88	0.54
0.11- 0.25	0.01	10.89-11.10	0.55
0.26- 0.46	0.02	11.11-11.25	0.56
0.47- 0.67	0.03	11.26-11.46	0.57
0.68- 0.88	0.04	11.47-11.67	0.58
0.89- 1.10	0.05	11.68-11.88	0.59
1.11- 1.25	0.06	11.89-12.10	0.60
1.26- 1.46	0.07	12.11-12.25	0.61
1.47- 1.67	0.08	12.26-12.46	0.62
1.68- 1.88	0.09	12.47-12.67	0.63
1.89- 2.10	0.10	12.68-12.88	0.64
2.11- 2.25	0.11	12.89-13.10	0.65
2.26- 2.46	0.12	13.11-13.25	0.66
2.47- 2.67	0.13	13.26-13.46	0.67
2.68- 2.88	0.14	13.47-13.67	0.68
2.89- 3.10	0.15	13.68-13.88	0.69
3.11- 3.25	0.16	13.89-14.10	0.70
3.26- 3.46	0.17	14.11-14.25	0.71
3.47- 3.67	0.18	14.26-14.46	0.72
3.68- 3.88	0.19	14.47-14.67	0.73
3.89- 4.10	0.20	14.68-14.88	0.74
4.11- 4.25	0.21	14.89-15.10	0.75
4.26- 4.46	0.22	15.11-15.25	0.76
4.47- 4.67	0.23	15.26-15.46	0.77
4.68- 4.88	0.24	15.47-15.67	0.78
4.89- 5.10	0.25	15.68-15.88	0.79
5.11- 5.25	0.26	15.89-16.10	0.80
5.26- 5.46	0.27	16.11-16.25	0.81
5.47- 5.67	0.28	16.26-16.46	0.82
5.68- 5.88	0.29	16.47-16.67	0.83
5.89- 6.10	0.30	16.68-16.88	0.84
6.11- 6.25	0.31	16.89-17.10	0.85
6.26- 6.46	0.32	17.11-17.25	0.86
6.47- 6.67	0.33	17.26-17.46	0.87
6.68- 6.88	0.34	17.47-17.67	0.88
6.89- 7.10	0.35	17.68-17.88	0.89
7.11- 7.25	0.36	17.89-18.10	0.90
7.26- 7.46	0.37	18.11-18.25	0.91
7.47- 7.67	0.38	18.26-18.46	0.92
7.68- 7.88	0.39	18.47-18.67	0.93
7.89- 8.10	0.40	18.68-18.88	0.94
8.11- 8.25	0.41	18.89-19.10	0.95
8.26- 8.46	0.42	19.11-19.25	0.96
8.47- 8.67	0.43	19.26-19.46	0.97
8.68- 8.88	0.44	19.47-19.67	0.98
8.89- 9.10	0.45	19.68-19.88	0.99
9.11- 9.25	0.46	19.89-20.10	1.00
9.26- 9.46	0.47	20.11-20.25	1.01
9.47- 9.67	0.48	20.26-20.46	1.02
9.68- 9.88	0.49	20.47-20.67	1.03
9.89-10.10	0.50	20.68-20.88	1.04
10.11-10.25	0.51	20.89-21.10	1.05
10.26-10.46	0.52	21.11-21.25	1.06
10.47-10.67	0.53	21.26-21.46	1.07

EXAMPLE Find the total cost of a purchase of $14.75.

Solution: [1] Under "Amount of Sale" in the table, find the interval for $14.75.

$14.75 lies between these numbers. 14.68 – 14.88 | **0.74** ***Tax***

[2] Amount of Purchase: $14.75
Tax: + 0.74
Total Cost: **$15.49**

EXERCISES

Find the sales tax on each purchase.

1. $15.49 $0.78 **2.** $7.83 $0.39 **3.** $12.88 $0.64

4. $20.15 $1.01 **5.** $18.98 $0.95 **6.** $19.99 $1.00

Find the total cost for each purchase.

7. $10.25 $10.76 **8.** $13.64 $14.32 **9.** $0.89 $0.94

10. $0.54 $0.57 **11.** $7.45 $7.82 **12.** $17.46 $18.33

13. Carla bought two books, one for $12.95 and one for $3.50. Find the total cost of the purchase, including tax. $17.27

14. Melanie purchased 3 paperbacks at $2.95 each. Find the total cost of the purchase, including tax. $9.29

8-3 Form 1040A—The Short Form

See the Teacher's Manual for the objectives.

In January, Wayne Motta received this **W-2 Form** from his employer. This is a **Wage and Tax Statement.**

Control number: 22222 — WAGE AND TAX STATEMENT

Employer's name, address, and ZIP code:
BATES CONSTRUCTION CO.
1445 Main Street
Huntsville, Kansas 67520
71-4-623

Employer's identification number | Employer's State number

Stat. employee ☐ Deceased ☐ Pension plan ☐ Legal rep. ☐ 942 emp. ☐ Subtotal ☐ Correction ☐ Void ☐

Advance EIC payment

Employee's social security number	1 Federal income tax withheld	2 Wages, tips, other compensation	3 FICA tax withheld
478-12-4836	2689.00	16,482.00	1,104.29

Employee's name, address, and ZIP code:
Wayne L. Motta
345 Seabrook Road
Huntsville, Kansas 67520

4 FICA wages: 16,482.00 | 5 FICA tips

6 Employer's use

7 State income tax	8 State wages, tips, etc.	9 Name of State
1,236.15	16,482.00	KANSAS
10 Local income tax	11 Local wages, tips, etc.	12 Name of locality

The W-2 lists these totals for the previous year.

Box 1: The amount withheld (deducted) for federal income tax.

Box 2: Gross earnings which included wages, tips, and any other money that he received from the company.

Box 3: The amount withheld for F.I.C.A.

Box 4: The amount on which F.I.C.A. taxes were paid

Boxes 7 and 10: Any amounts withheld for state and city income taxes.

Each employee needs this information to prepare an income tax return for that year.

To prepare his income tax return, Wayne used **Form 1040A,** the short form, because he is single, with an adjusted gross income less than $20,000. Also, he does not itemize deductions.

The exercises on page 164 will help you to understand Form 1040A.

REVIEW OF RELATED SKILLS

You may wish to use these exercises before teaching the lesson.

Add or subtract as indicated. (Pages 4–5)

1. 7949.50 + 75.24 8024.74
2. 9094.76 + 102.93 9197.69
3. 17,812.51 + 150.66 17,963.17
4. 2020.40 − 1989.55 30.85
5. 3241.58 − 3069.12 172.46
6. 4504.28 − 4291.94 212.34

EXERCISES

For Exercises 1–4, refer to Wayne Motta's Wage and Tax Statement on page 163.

1. What is Wayne's social security number? 478-12-4836

2. How much F.I.C.A. tax was withheld (see box 3)? $1104.29

3. Was Wayne covered by a qualified pension plan (see box 5)? No

4. Find the amount of state or local tax withheld (see box 7). $1236.15

For Exercises 5–16, refer to Wayne Motta's W-2 form to complete Form 1040A on page 165.

5. **Line 1:** What is Wayne's filing status? Single

6. **Line 5:** Find the number to be entered in the top box in the right column. (Wayne wrote an X only in the box for "Yourself" on Line 5*a*.) 1

7. **Lines 5*c* and 5*d*:** How many dependents is Wayne claiming? 0

8. **Line 6:** How many exemptions is Wayne claiming? (Add the numbers in boxes 5*a* and *b*, 5*c* and 5*d*.) 1

9. **Line 7:** Find Wayne's total wages from box 2 on the W-2 form. $16,482.00

10. **Line 8*e*:** What was Wayne's income from interest? $54.00

11. **Line 10:** Find Wayne's adjusted gross income. (Add the amounts on lines 7 and 8*e*.) $16,536.00

12. **Line 12:** What is Wayne's taxable income? (Subtract line 11 from line 10.) $15,536.00

NOTE: Line 11 is $1000.00 because Wayne is claiming one exemption.

13. **Line 13*b*:** Find the total Federal income tax withheld from box 1 on the W-2 form. $2689.00

14. **Line 15*a*:** What is the actual tax on Wayne's taxable income? $2713.00

15. **Lines 17 and 18:** Find the difference between lines 14 and 16. $24

16. If line 14 is larger than line 16 you will receive a **refund.** The difference is entered on line 17. If line 16 is larger than line 14, you **owe money.** The difference is entered on line 18. On which line should Wayne write the answer to Exercise 15? line 18

For Exercises 17–25, find the amount to be refunded or the balance due.

17. Tax withheld: $694
Tax owed: $781 $87 due

18. Tax withheld: $1246
Tax owed: $1089 $157 refund

19. Tax withheld: $1523
Tax owed: $1743 $220 due

20. Tax withheld: $1409
Tax owed: $1654 $245 due

21. Tax withheld: $2135
Tax owed: $1728 $407 refund

22. Tax withheld: $1795
Tax owed: $1321 $474 refund

23. Tax withheld: $863
Tax owed: $1075 $212 due

24. Tax withheld: $978
Tax owed: $1346 $368 due

25. Tax withheld: $1249
Tax owed: $898 $351 refund

Form **1040A** Department of the Treasury—Internal Revenue Service
U.S. Individual Income Tax Return (5) OMB No. 1545–0085

Use IRS label. Otherwise, please print or type.

Your first name and initial (if joint return, also give spouse's name and initial): WAYNE L.
Last name: MOTTA
Your social security number: 478 12 4836
Present home address (Number and street, including apartment number, or rural route): 345 SEABANK ROAD
Spouse's social security no.:
City, town or post office, State and ZIP code: HUNTSVILLE, KANSAS 67520
Your occupation ▶ CARPENTER
Spouse's occupation ▶

Presidential Election Campaign ▶ Do you want $1 to go to this fund? X Yes ☐ No
If joint return, does your spouse want $1 to go to this fund? ☐ Yes ☐ No
Note: *Checking "Yes" will not increase your tax or reduce your refund.*

For Privacy Act and Paperwork Reduction Act Notice, see page 23 of Instructions

Filing Status
Check Only One Box.

1 [X] Single
2 [ ] Married filing joint return (even if only one had income)
3 [ ] Married filing separate return. Enter spouse's social security no. above and full name here ▶
4 [ ] Head of household (with qualifying person). (See page 8 of Instructions.) If he or she is your unmarried child, enter child's name ▶

Exemptions
Always check the box labeled Yourself. Check other boxes if they apply.

5a [X] Yourself [ ] 65 or over [ ] Blind
b [ ] Spouse [ ] 65 or over [ ] Blind
Enter number of boxes checked on 5a and b ▶ ?
c First names of your dependent children who lived with you ▶
Enter number of children listed on 5c ▶ 0

d Other dependents:

(1) Name	(2) Relationship	(3) Number of months lived in your home.	(4) Did dependent have income of $1,000 or more?	(5) Did you provide more than one-half of dependent's support?

Enter number of other dependents ▶ 0
Add numbers entered in boxes above ▶ ?

6 Total number of exemptions claimed

Please Attach Copy B of Forms W-2 Here

Line	Description	Sub-line	Amount		Line	Amount	
7	Wages, salaries, tips, etc. *(Attach Forms W–2. See page 10 of Instructions)*				7	?	?
8a	Interest income *(Complete page 2 if over $400 or you have any All-Savers interest)*	8a	54	00			
b	Dividends *(Complete page 2 if over $400)*	8b					
c	Total *(add lines 8a and 8b)*	8c					
d	Exclusion *(See page 11 of Instructions)*	8d					
e	Subtract line 8d from line 8c *(but not less than zero)*				8e	54	00
9a	Unemployment compensation (insurance). Total received from Form(s) 1099–UC						
b	Taxable amount, if any, from worksheet on page 12 of Instructions				9b		
10	Adjusted gross income *(add lines 7, 8e, and 9b). If under $10,000, see page 13 of Instructions on "Earned Income Credit"*				10	?	?
11	Multiply $1,000 by the total number of exemptions claimed on line 6				11	1000	00
12	Taxable income *(subtract line 11 from line 10)*				12	?	?
13a	Credit for contributions to candidates for public office. *(See page 13 of Instructions)*	13a					

IF YOU WANT IRS TO FIGURE YOUR TAX, PLEASE STOP HERE AND SIGN BELOW.

Attach Payment Here

Line	Description	Sub-line	Amount		Line	Amount	
b	Total Federal income tax withheld *(If line 7 is more than $29,700, see page 13 of Instructions)*	13b	?	?			
c	Earned income credit *(from page 14 of Instructions)*	13c					
14	Total *(add lines 13a, b, and c)*				14	?	?
15a	Tax on the amount on line 12. *(See page 15 of Instructions; then find your tax in the Tax Table on pages 17–22)*	15a	2713	00			
b	Advance earned income credit (EIC) *(from Form W–2)*	15b					
16	Total *(add lines 15a and 15b)*				16	2713	00
17	If line 14 is larger than line 16, enter amount to be **REFUNDED TO YOU** ▶				17	?	?
18	If line 16 is larger than line 14, enter **BALANCE DUE.** Attach check or money order for full amount payable to "Internal Revenue Service." Write your social security number and "Form 1040A" on it. ▶				18	?	?

Please Sign Here

Under penalties of perjury, I declare that I have examined this return, including accompanying schedules and statements, and to the best of my knowledge and belief, it is true, correct, and complete. Declaration of preparer (other than taxpayer) is based on all information of which preparer has any knowledge.

▶ *Wayne L. Motta* 1/29/8 ▶
Your signature Date Spouse's signature (if filing jointly, BOTH must sign even if only one had income)

Paid Preparer's Use Only

Preparer's signature ▶ Date Check if self-employed ▶ ☐ Preparer's social security no.
Firm's name (or yours, if self-employed) and address ▶ E.I. No. ▶ ZIP code ▶

Form **1040A**

8-4 Taxable Income and Tax Tables

See the Teacher's Manual for the objectives.

Julia Blackfoot will itemize deductions this year. She knows that she must use Form 1040 (Long Form) for her tax return. To use this form, Julia must compute taxable income.

Taxable Income = Adjusted Gross Income − (Deductions + Exemptions)

EXAMPLE 1 Julia's adjusted gross income is $22,480. She claims herself and her brother as exemptions. Her deductions are:

Medical expenses: $980 Interest expense: $1415
Contributions: $450 Miscellaneous deductions: $125

Find her taxable income.

Solution: 1 Find the total deductions.
$980 + $1415 + $450 + $125 = **$2970**

2 Find the amount for exemptions.
$1000 × 2 = **$2000**

3 Find the taxable income.

Adjusted Gross Income − (Deductions + Exemptions) = Taxable Income

$22,480 − $4970 = **$17,510**

After completing Example 1, you may wish to have students do some or all of Exercises 1-6.

To find the amount of tax, Julia reads the tax table indicated in the instruction booklet. The partial tax table at the right is for people with taxable incomes of $50,000 or less.

If taxable income is		*And you are—*			
At least	*But less than*	*Single*	*Married filling jointly*	*Married filling sepa-rately*	*Head of a house-hold*
		Your tax is—			
17,300	17,350	3,261	2,551	3,930	3,042
17,350	17,400	3,276	2,563	3,948	3,055
17,400	17,450	3,291	2,574	3,966	3,068
17,450	17,500	3,306	2,586	3,984	3,081
17,500	17,550	3,320	2,598	4,003	3,093
17,550	17,600	3,335	2,610	4,021	3,106
17,600	17,650	3,350	2,622	4,041	3,119
17,650	17,700	3,365	2,634	4,062	3,132

EXAMPLE 2 Julia is single. Use the tax table and her taxable income from Example 1 to find the amount of tax.

Solution: 1 Read down the "taxable income" column until you find

17,500 17,550 ◀ ***17,510 is between these two numbers.***

2 Read across to the column headed "Single." The amount where the lines meet is the tax. ⟶ **$3,320**

Thus Julia's federal income tax is **$3,320.**

REVIEW OF RELATED SKILLS

You may wish to use these exercises before teaching the lesson.

Add or subtract as indicated. (Pages 2–3)

1. \$43 + \$281 + \$346 + \$1218 \$1888
2. \$475 + \$64 + \$1347 + \$290 \$2176
3. \$673 + \$421 + \$92 + \$1047 \$2233
4. \$1383 + \$49 + \$112 + \$64 \$1608
5. \$43,422 − \$2840 \$40,582
6. \$28,470 − \$3128 \$25,342
7. \$19,385 − \$864 \$18,521

EXERCISES

For Exercises 1–4, complete the table. (Example 1)

	Adjusted Gross Income	Deductions				Total Deductions	Exemptions	Taxable Income
		Medical	Taxes	Interest	Other			
1.	\$19,586	\$480	\$1325	\$1440	—	\$3245 ?	2 \$14,341	?
2.	\$26,741	\$398	\$2100	\$1724	\$590	\$4812 ?	3 \$18,929	?
3.	\$14,325	\$642	\$1024	\$1210	—	\$2876 ?	1 \$10,449	?
4.	\$17,946	\$500	\$1440	—	\$675	\$2615 ?	1 \$14,331	?

5. Linda Liebman claims two exemptions. Her adjusted gross income was \$28,384 last year. Her deductions were: medical – \$1560; interest – \$1242. Find the taxable income. \$23,582

6. Irving Lyon's adjusted gross income is \$19,475. His deductions are: interest – \$1384; contributions – \$680. He claims one exemption. Find the taxable income. \$16,411

For Exercises 7–12, find the tax. Use the tax table on page 166. (Example 2)

	Taxable Income	Filing Status
7.	\$17,421	Single \$3291
8.	\$17,532	Head of a household \$3093
9.	\$17,385	Married filing jointly \$2563
10.	\$17,548	Married filing separately \$4003

11. Mr. and Mrs. Hawkins are filing together (jointly). Their taxable income is \$17,690. Find the tax. \$2634

12. Mr. and Mrs. McCourt are filing separate returns. Mrs. McCourt's taxable income is \$17,321. Find the tax. \$3930

PAYROLL CLERK

Career lessons are optional.
This lesson applies the skill of addition of mixed numbers.

Mary Deare is a **payroll clerk.** Besides computing gross pay and net pay, she also calculates deductions from wages, such as those for Social Security and income taxes.

To find weekly gross pay, Mary first computes the number of hours worked each day. The total number of hours worked per day is rounded down to the nearest quarter hour.

EXAMPLE George Kelly, a machine operator, earns \$5.75 per hour. His time card for one week is shown at the right.

DAYS	IN	OUT	IN	OUT	DAILY TOTALS
1	8:30	12:00	1:00	4:20	?
2	8:30	12:30	1:45	4:50	7
3	9:00	1:20	—	—	$4\frac{1}{4}$
4	8:30	11:30	12:30	3:45	$6\frac{1}{4}$
5	8:45	12:15	1:00	5:05	$7\frac{1}{2}$

a. Find the number of hours worked on Day 1.

b. Find the total number of hours worked for that week.

c. Find the weekly gross pay to the nearest cent.

Solutions: **a.** 8:30 – 12:00: $3\frac{1}{2}$ hours $= \ 3\frac{2}{4}$

1:00 – 4:20: $3\frac{1}{4}$ hours $= +3\frac{1}{4}$

Rounded down to the nearest quarter hour

$6\frac{3}{4}$ **hours** ◀ ***Hours worked on Day 1***

b. Add the Daily Totals.

$$\begin{aligned} 6\tfrac{3}{4} &= 6\tfrac{3}{4} \\ 7 &= 7 \\ 4\tfrac{1}{4} &= 4\tfrac{1}{4} \\ 6\tfrac{1}{4} &= 6\tfrac{1}{4} \\ +7\tfrac{1}{2} &= +7\tfrac{2}{4} \\ & \quad 30\tfrac{7}{4} = 31\tfrac{3}{4} \text{ hours} \end{aligned}$$

c. Find the gross pay. Use paper and pencil or use a calculator. Write $31\frac{3}{4}$ hours as 31.75 hours.

Amount per Hour × Number of Hours = Gross Pay

5 . 7 5 × 3 1 . 7 5 = 182.5625

The weekly gross pay is **\$182.56** (nearest cent).

EXERCISES

For Exercises 1–4, complete each time card.

1.

DAYS	IN	OUT	IN	OUT	DAILY TOTALS	
1	8:00	12:00	1:00	4:30	?	$7\frac{1}{2}$
2	8:30	12:30	2:00	5:00	?	7
3	8:30	12:30	1:30	4:45	?	$7\frac{1}{4}$
4	8:45	12:00	1:00	4:10	?	$6\frac{1}{4}$
5	9:00	1:30	—	—	?	$4\frac{1}{2}$

	HOURS	RATE	EARNINGS	
				$32\frac{1}{2}$
Regular	?	$6.25	?	$203.13

2.

DAYS	IN	OUT	IN	OUT	DAILY TOTALS	
1	8:30	11:00	1:00	4:50	?	$6\frac{1}{4}$
2	8:30	12:00	1:15	5:00	?	$7\frac{1}{4}$
3	8:30	12:30	1:45	4:40	?	$6\frac{3}{4}$
4	—	—	12:15	5:15	?	5
5	8:45	12:45	1:45	5:40	?	$7\frac{3}{4}$

	HOURS	RATE	EARNINGS	
				33
Regular	?	$5.95	?	$196.35

3.

DAYS	IN	OUT	IN	OUT	DAILY TOTALS	
1	8:00	12:00	1:00	5:00	?	8
2	8:30	12:00	1:00	5:00	?	$7\frac{1}{2}$
3	8:00	12:00	12:30	5:30	?	9
4	8:30	12:30	1:00	5:40	?	$8\frac{1}{2}$
5	8:00	12:00	1:00	5:30	?	$8\frac{1}{2}$

	HOURS	RATE	EARNINGS	
				$41\frac{1}{2}$
Regular	?	$7.50	?	$311.25

4.

DAYS	IN	OUT	IN	OUT	DAILY TOTALS	
1	8:00	12:00	1:00	5:30	?	$8\frac{1}{2}$
2	8:00	11:30	1:00	6:00	?	$8\frac{1}{2}$
3	8:30	12:30	1:15	5:30	?	$8\frac{1}{4}$
4	8:00	12:45	1:30	5:30	?	$8\frac{3}{4}$
5	8:00	12:30	1:30	5:40	?	$8\frac{1}{2}$

	HOURS	RATE	EARNINGS	
				$42\frac{1}{2}$
Regular	?	$8.25	?	$350.63

For Exercises 5–6, complete the bottom portion of each time card. Workers are paid time and a half for overtime.

5.

	HOURS	RATE	EARNINGS	
Regular	40	$6.00	?	$240
Overtime	5	?	?	$9; $45
Totals	—	—	?	$285

6.

	HOURS	RATE	EARNINGS	
Regular	40	$9.00	?	$360
Overtime	12	?	?	$13.50; $162
Totals	?	—	?	$522

7. Molly earns $5.00 an hour for each hour up to 40 hours per week. For each hour over 40 hours, she earns $7.50 per hour. Molly worked 43 hours one week. How much did she earn that week? **$222.50**

8. Louis earns $5.85 per hour. His time card for one week showed that he had worked 35 hours. What was his net pay if $51.19 was deducted for taxes? **$153.56**

8-5 State and City Income Taxes

See the Teacher's Manual for the objectives.

In addition to paying a federal income tax, Paul Price also pays a state income tax and a city income tax. A basic difference between federal and state income taxes is the tax rate. Part of a sample tax rate schedule for state income taxes is shown below.

Tax Rate Schedule

If taxable income is		
over	***but not over***	***Amount of Tax***
13,000	15,000	680 plus 9% of excess over 13,000
15,000	17,000	860 plus 10% of excess over 15,000
17,000	19,000	1,060 plus 11% of excess over 17,000
19,000	21,000	1,280 plus 12% of excess over 19,000
21,000	23,000	1,520 plus 13% of excess over 21,000
23,000		1,780 plus 14% of excess over 23,000

EXAMPLE Paul's taxable income is $17,893. Find the amount of his state income tax.

Solution: [1] In the tax table, read down the "taxable income" column until you reach

17,000 19,000 ◀ ***17,893 is between these two numbers.***

Read the tax at the right: ***1060 plus 11% of the excess over 17,000***

[2] Find the excess over 17,000: $17,893 − $17,000 = **$893**

[3] Find 11% of $893: $893 × 0.11 = **$98.23**

[4] Find the total tax: $1060 + $98.23 = **$1158.23** ◀ ***$1060 plus 11% of $893***

Paul's state income tax is **$1158.23.**

The tax rate schedule for city taxes is usually similar to that for state taxes. The procedure for computing the tax is also similar.

REVIEW OF RELATED SKILLS

You may wish to use these exercises before teaching the lesson.

Add or subtract. (Pages 2–3, 4–5)

1. $16,381 − $15,000 $1381 **2.** $18,946 − $17,000 $1946 **3.** $21,479 − $21,000 $479

4. $1060 + $86.10 $1146.10 **5.** $1520 + $103.40 $1623.40 **6.** $860 + $148.20 $1008.20

Write a decimal for each per cent. (Pages 90–91)

7. 12% 0.12 **8.** 14% 0.14 **9.** 7% 0.07 **10.** 9% 0.09 **11.** 2.3% 0.023 **12.** 4.1% 0.041

Find each answer. (Pages 94–95)

13. 9% of $642 $57.78 **14.** 13% of $1221 $158.73 **15.** 11% of $1464 $161.04

EXERCISES

For Exercises 1–10, find the state income tax. Use the schedule on page 170.

	Taxable Income	State Tax
1.	$18,400	? $1214.00
2.	$15,900	? $950.00
3.	$22,360	? $1696.80
4.	$18,900	? $1269.00
5.	$25,600	? $2144.00
6.	$28,765	? $2587.10

7. An electrician's taxable income was $20,374. $1444.88

8. A construction inspector's taxable income was $19,453. $1334.36

9. A diesel mechanic had a taxable income of $18,460 last year. $1220.60

10. A carpenter had a taxable income of $23,450 last year. $1843.00

Part of a city tax rate schedule is shown below. Use this schedule to find the tax in Exercises 11–20.

If taxable income is over	but not over	Amount of tax
19,000	21,000	449 plus 3.5% of excess over 19,000
21,000	23,000	519 plus 3.8% of excess over 21,000
23,000	25,000	595 plus 4.0% of excess over 23,000

	Taxable Income	City Tax
11.	$19,000	? $449.00
12.	$22,300	? $568.40
13.	$19,630	? $471.05
14.	$22,550	? $577.90
15.	$24,380	? $650.20
16.	$21,844	? $551.07

17. A locksmith's taxable income was $19,340 last year. $460.90

18. A chef's taxable income was $24,500 last year. $655.00

19. A welder's taxable income was $22,490 last year. $575.62

20. A drafting technician's taxable income was $21,380 last year. $533.44

Rounding and Estimation

Consumers use rounding and estimation to solve problems related to income tax.

EXERCISES See the Teacher's Manual for the objectives.

Skills

Choose the best estimate. Choose a, b, or c.

		a.	b.	c.
1. 4.95×40	b	4×40	5×40	4.5×40
2. 5.85×39	c	5×30	6×30	6×40
3. $9975 + 279$	a	$10{,}000 + 300$	$9000 + 200$	$10{,}000 + 200$
4. $10{,}042 + 193$	c	$10{,}000 + 100$	$11{,}000 + 200$	$10{,}000 + 200$
5. $14{,}125 - 3221$	b	$15{,}000 - 3000$	$14{,}000 - 3000$	$14{,}000 - 4000$
6. $21{,}963 - 5011$	b	$21{,}000 - 5000$	$22{,}000 - 5000$	$21{,}000 - 6000$
7. 12% of 1600	b	$\frac{1}{10} \times 1600$	$\frac{1}{8} \times 1600$	$\frac{1}{12} \times 1600$
8. 10% of 723	c	0.1×800	0.1×750	0.1×700

Choose the best estimate. Choose a, b, c, or d.

		a.	b.	c.	d.
9. 5.78×30	b	150	180	240	210
10. 4.05×41	a	160	200	150	180
11. $10{,}043 + 280$	d	10,100	11,000	10,200	10,300
12. $22{,}946 + 723$	b	23,000	23,700	22,000	23,900
13. $16{,}048 - 1879$	c	15,500	15,000	14,000	14,500
14. $25{,}862 - 4116$	a	22,000	21,000	23,000	20,000
15. 21% of 14,962	a	3000	4000	2000	3500

Applications

16. Saundra earned $18,960 in wages. She also received $610 as a bonus and $3425 in rent. Estimate the adjusted gross income. c

a. $18,000 + $600 + $3500

b. $19,000 + $700 + $3500

c. $19,000 + $600 + $3400

d. $18,000 + $700 + $3400

17. Dennis earned $17,050 in wages. He also received $397 in interest from a saving account. Estimate the adjusted gross income. b

a. $18,000 + $200

b. $17,000 + $400

c. $18,000 + $400

d. $17,000 + $300

18. Estimate the balance due. a

Tax withheld	$2397
Tax owed	$2820

a. $2800 − $2400
b. $2800 − $2300
c. $2900 − $2300
d. $2900 − $2400

19. Cindy's deductions last year were: medical–$1225; interest–$1589; contributions–$378. Estimate the total deductions. d

a. $1300 + $1600 + $400
b. $1300 + $1100 + $300
c. $1200 + $1500 + $300
d. $1200 + $1600 + $400

20. Julio earned $21,040 last year. He also received $689 in interest. Estimate the adjusted gross income. a

a. $21,700
b. $22,000
c. $21,000
d. $22,700

21. During one year, the federal tax withheld from Jean Chin's salary was $3110. Jean actually owed $2695 in taxes. Estimate the amount of Jean's refund. b

a. $500
b. $400
c. $600
d. $300

22. Randy Tennaro's deductions last year were: medical expenses–$920; interest–$1590; contributions–$785. Estimate the total deductions. b

a. $2500
b. $3300
c. $3500
d. $2300

23. Simone Farkle owed state tax last year on her income. The state tax was $1280 plus 12% of $1600. Estimate the income tax. c

a. $1000
b. $1200
c. $1500
d. $2000

Chapter Review

These exercises review the vocabulary, skills and applications presented in the chapter, as a preparation for the chapter test.

Part 1: VOCABULARY

For Exercises 1–5, choose from the box at the right the word(s) that complete(s) each statement.

W-2 Form
hours worked
adjusted gross income
deduction
taxable income
exemptions

1. Persons who depend on a wage earner for support can be listed on a tax return as __?__. (Pages 158–159) exemptions
2. The sum of all kinds of income such as wages, bonuses, commissions, and tips, is __?__. (Pages 160–161) adjusted gross income
3. When you subtract the interest on a loan from adjusted gross income, it is called a __?__. (Pages 160–161) deduction
4. The Wage and Tax Statement that you receive from your employer is called a __?__. (Pages 163–165) W-2 Form
5. After you subtract deductions and exemptions from the adjusted gross income, your result is called __?__. taxable income (Pages 166–167).

Part 2: SKILLS

Multiply. (Pages 8–9)

6. \$3.80 × 40 \$152.00 **7.** \$9.60 × 87 \$835.20 **8.** \$2.25 × 15 \$33.75 **9.** \$6.40 × 63 \$403.20

Add or subtract as indicated. (Pages 2–5)

10. \$86 + \$42 + \$212 + \$4107 \$4447 **11.** \$81 + \$94 + \$203 + \$1016 \$1394

12. \$13,207.91 + \$216.82 + \$540.70 \$13,965.43 **13.** \$26,417.91 + \$810.05 + \$81.27 \$27,309.23

14. \$17,498 − \$807 \$16,691 **15.** \$32,000 − \$1702 \$30,298 **16.** \$24,500 − \$2019 \$22,481

17. \$4131.00 − \$1145.00 \$2986.00 **18.** \$8813.70 − \$5902.11 \$2911.59 **19.** \$2700 − \$2317.99 \$382.01

Write a decimal for each per cent. (Pages 90–91)

20. 17% 0.17 **21.** 23% 0.23 **22.** 12% 0.12 **23.** 2% 0.02 **24.** 8.4% 0.084 **25.** 5.6% 0.056

Find each answer. (Pages 94–95)

26. 14% of 54 7.56 **27.** 6% of 201 12.06 **28.** 3.8% of 900 34.2 **29.** 4.6% of 1580 72.68

Part 3: APPLICATIONS

For Exercises 30–33 find the federal income tax. Assume that the wage earner is single. Use the table on page 158. (Pages 158–159)

	Weekly Gross Pay	Number of Exemptions	Federal Tax
30.	\$143	0	? \$20.00
31.	\$172	1	? \$22.80
32.	\$165	2	? \$16.80
33.	\$156	2	? \$15.00

For Exercises 34–37, find the adjusted gross income. (Pages 160–161)

	Yearly Wages	Interest	Other Income	
34.	$18,980	$ 562.50	—	$19,542.50
35.	$22,460	$1053.20	$987.60	$24,500.80

	Yearly Wages	Interest	Other Income	
36.	$15,960	$2305.91	$895.70	$19,161.61
37.	$24,680	$ 872.40	—	$25,552.40

For Exercises 38–39, decide whether or not deductions should be itemized. Refer to the table on page 160. (Pages 160–161)

38. The Jaffes are filing a joint return. Deductions total $3500. Itemize

39. Sue Garcia has deductions that total $2700. Sue is single. Itemize

For Exercises 40–43, find the missing amounts. (Pages 163–165)

40. Pauline Luce

Wages, salaries, tips	$18,204
Interest income	$ 2,408
Adjusted gross income	? $20,612

42.

Federal tax withheld	$ 3,386
Total tax due	$ 4,207
Refund	? 0
Balance due	? $821

41. James McAdoo

Wages, salaries, tips	$17,128
Interest income	$ 250
Adjusted gross income	? $17,378

43.

Federal tax withheld	$ 3,133
Total tax due	$ 3,008
Refund	? $125
Balance due	? 0

44. Ricardo Palmieri's taxable income was $17,465 last year. He is a head of a household. Find the tax. Use the tax table on page 166. (Pages 166–167) $3081

45. A computer operator had a taxable income of $29,450 last year. Find his state income tax. Use the Tax Rate Schedule on page 170. (Pages 170–171) $2683.00

46. Agnes Rothschild's deductions last year were: taxes – $1990; medical expenses – $1120; miscellaneous – $489. Estimate her total deductions. (Pages 172–173) b

a. $4000 **b.** $3600
c. $3000 **d.** $2500

47. Estimate the tax. (Pages 172–173) c

$2510 + 6% of $1000

a. $\$2000 + (\frac{1}{25} \times 1000)$

b. $\$3000 + (\frac{1}{25} \times 1000)$

c. $\$2500 + (\frac{1}{20} \times 1000)$

d. $\$2500 + (\frac{1}{25} \times 1000)$

Chapter Test

The Teacher's Resource Book contains two forms of each chapter test.

Perform the indicated operation.

1. $8.30 × 29 $240.70
2. $6.53 × 38 $248.14
3. $6.00 × 40 $240.00
4. $4.15 × 92 $381.80
5. $47 + $20 + $906 + $3000 $3973
6. $7420.66 + $724.00 + $803.04 $8947.70
7. $20,900 − $508 $20,392
8. $5516.00 − $2196.00 $3320.00
9. $1942 − $1620.19 $321.81

Write a decimal for each per cent.

10. 4% 0.04
11. 17% 0.17
12. 23% 0.23
13. 2.3% 0.023
14. 7.1% 0.071
15. 5.7% 0.057

Find each answer.

16. 8% of 77 6.16
17. 24% of 80 19.2
18. 3.9% of 720 28.08
19. 5.2% of 86 4.472

For Exercises 20–21, use this table to find the federal tax.

Wages		Exemptions		
At Least	Less Than	0	1	2
$150	$160	$22.60	$18.60	$15.00
$160	$170	$24.70	$20.70	$16.80
$170	$180	$26.80	$22.80	$18.80
$180	$190	$32.40	$29.10	$25.00

	Weekly Gross Pay	Number of Exemptions	Federal Tax
20.	$177	2	? $18.80
21.	$165	1	? $20.70

22. Ralph earned $19,040 in wages last year. He also earned $1212 in interest and $3500 from a part time job. Find his adjusted gross income. $23,752
23. The tax on income over $19,000 in a certain state is as follows:

    $600 plus 4% of excess over $19,000

    Find Ginny's state tax on a taxable income of $20,000. $640
24. A flight attendant's deductions last year were: medical expenses – $970; taxes – $2100. Estimate the total deductions. c

    a. $2900 b. $3500

    c. $3100 d. $3200
25. Find the amount of refund.

Federal tax withheld	$ 2,782
Tax owed	$ 2,516
Refund	? $266

Additional Practice

You may wish to use all or some of these exercises, depending on how well students performed on the formal chapter test.

Skills

Multiply. (Pages 8–9)

1. $7.40 × 31 **$229.40**
2. $2.86 × 78 **$223.08**
3. $4.50 × 20 **$90.00**
4. $1.41 × 106 **$149.46**

Add. (Pages 2–5)

5. $801 + $48 + $29 + $4260 + $647 **$5785**
6. $8194.79 + $286.50 + $44.41 **$8525.70**

Subtract. (Pages 2–5)

7. $15,600 − $702 **$14,898**
8. $4322.00 − $401.00 **$3921.00**
9. $1885 − $1709.24 **$175.76**

Find each answer. (Pages 94–95)

10. 2% of 86 **1.72**
11. 42% of 110 **46.2**
12. 4.6% of 801 **36.846**
13. 3.9% of 40 **1.56**

Applications

14. A carpenter earns $178 per week and claims one exemption. Find his federal income tax. Use the table on page 158. (Pages 158–159) **$22.80**

15. A caterer works 30 hours a week at $4.80 per hour. He claims two exemptions. Find his federal income tax. Use the table on page 158. (Pages 158–159) **$12.70**

16. Ted Grissing earned $23,400 in salary last year. He also earned $8020 in rental income and $2500 in interest. Find his adjusted gross income. (Pages 160–161) **$33,920**

17. Ellen Whitcomb and her husband, Ralfe are filing a joint return. Their deductions total $5468. Decide whether they should itemize deductions. See the table on page 160. (Pages 160–161) **Itemize**

18. On William's Form 1040A the amount of tax withheld, $3194 is less than his tax, $4116. Estimate the balance due. (Pages 172–173) **b**
    a. $1100 b. $900
    c. $1200 d. $800

19. Find the tax. (Pages 170–171)
    $675 plus 4.3% of $1390 **$734.77**

20. Alexander Segienko's income last year was $29,468. His deductions total $4,575. He claims three exemptions. Find his taxable income. (Pages 166–167) **$21,893**

21. Lisa's income last year as a hotel manager was $23,500. Find her city income tax. Use the table on page 171. (Pages 170–171) **$615**

CHECK OUT TIME 1 P.M.

REVIEW OF RELATED SKILLS FOR CHAPTER 9

We suggest that some or all of this page be reviewed before proceeding with the chapter.

Add or subtract as indicated. (Pages 4–5)

1. $428.35 + 64.28 + 381.56$ 874.19
2. $963.34 + 25.87 + 125.96$ 1115.17
3. $355.72 + 89 + 195.07$ 639.79
4. $625.08 + 363.75 + 136$ 1124.83
5. $487.10 + 73.62 + 408$ 968.72
6. $253.56 + 191.03 + 87$ 531.59
7. $56 + 387.04 + 925.36 + 1275.50$ 2643.90
8. $72 + 529.73 + 65.97 + 1102.89$ 1770.59
9. $82.36 + 103.47 + 220 + 1393.08$ 1798.91
10. $95.77 + 224.65 + 308 + 63.84$ 692.26

11. $625.50 - 25.50$ 600.00
12. $381.74 - 81.74$ 300.00
13. $278.36 - 78.36$ 200.00
14. $925.42 - 25.42$ 900.00
15. $350 - 125.50$ 224.50
16. $285 - 130.60$ 154.40
17. $368 - 129.75$ 238.25
18. $504 - 287.08$ 216.92
19. $400 - 150.65$ 249.35
20. $500 - 125.80$ 374.20
21. $300 - 29.84$ 270.16
22. $600 - 104.48$ 495.52
23. $1400 - 175.89$ 1224.11
24. $1000 - 650.55$ 349.45
25. $2000 - 746.75$ 1253.25
26. $3000 - 429.54$ 2570.46

Write a decimal for each per cent. (Pages 90–91)

27. 17% 0.17
28. 15% 0.15
29. 13% 0.13
30. 12% 0.12
31. 20% 0.2
32. 16% 0.16
33. 2.5% 0.025
34. 4.3% 0.043
35. 6.8% 0.068
36. 5.5% 0.055
37. 3.5% 0.035
38. 2.9% 0.029
39. $5\frac{1}{4}\%$ 0.0525
40. $4\frac{1}{2}\%$ 0.045
41. $6\frac{3}{4}\%$ 0.0675
42. $5\frac{1}{2}\%$ 0.055
43. $3\frac{1}{2}\%$ 0.035
44. $2\frac{3}{4}\%$ 0.0275

Multiply. (Pages 8–9, 56–57)

45. 1500×0.15 225.00
46. 1600×0.17 272.00
47. 2340×0.20 468.00
48. 1700×0.18 306.00
49. 2200×0.04 88.00
50. 1950×0.05 97.50
51. 1630×0.03 48.90
52. 1820×0.04 72.80
53. 1400×0.045 63.00
54. 1600×0.035 56.00
55. 2500×0.025 62.50
56. 1300×0.055 71.50
57. 1700×0.0425 72.25
58. 1800×0.0575 103.50
59. 2400×0.0625 150.00
60. 3200×0.0725 232.00
61. 5000×1.3401 6700.50
62. 6000×1.3382 8029.20
63. 7000×1.2293 8605.10
64. 9000×1.4461 13,014.90
65. $54.20 \times \frac{1}{4}$ 13.55
66. $96.30 \times \frac{1}{3}$ 32.10
67. $84.82 \times \frac{1}{2}$ 42.41
68. $48.66 \times \frac{1}{6}$ 8.11
69. $36.18 \times \frac{1}{3}$ 12.06
70. $25.40 \times \frac{1}{5}$ 5.08
71. $96.24 \times \frac{1}{12}$ 8.02
72. $57.60 \times \frac{1}{8}$ 7.20
73. $75.42 \times \frac{1}{2}$ 37.71
74. $49.64 \times \frac{1}{4}$ 12.41
75. $43.20 \times \frac{1}{6}$ 7.20
76. $73.92 \times \frac{1}{12}$ 6.16

Round to the nearest hundredth. (Pages 16–17)

77. 21.045 21.05
78. 36.362 36.36
79. 72.982 72.98
80. 56.079 56.08
81. 43.562 43.56
82. 55.776 55.78
83. 47.324 47.32
84. 59.083 59.08
85. 86.941 86.94
86. 94.087 94.09
87. 195.637 195.64
88. 203.448 203.45
89. 731.0946 731.09
90. 328.6472 328.65
91. 406.3481 406.35

Divide. (Pages 14–15)

92. $10 \div 4$ 2.5
93. $18 \div 4$ 4.5
94. $17 \div 4$ 4.25
95. $12 \div 4$ 3
96. $19 \div 4$ 4.75
97. $9 \div 4$ 2.25
98. $15 \div 4$ 3.75
99. $21 \div 4$ 5.25
100. $11 \div 4$ 2.75
101. $16 \div 4$ 4

CHAPTER

9 BANKING

CAREER APPLICATIONS

Loan Officer
Cashier

CONSUMER SKILLS/APPLICATIONS

9-1 Deposit Slips
9-2 Interest
9-3 Compound Interest
9-4 Check Stubs and Check Registers
9-5 Writing Checks
9-6 Reconciling a Bank Statement
Rounding and Estimation

9-1 Deposit Slips

See the Teacher's Manual for the objectives.

Lynn and Tom Hernandez use a checking account to pay bills because it is safer and more convenient. To put money into a checking account, they make out a deposit slip.

EXAMPLE 1 Tom deposits his weekly paycheck for $421.90. He also deposits a second check for $125.00. He wishes to receive $75.00 back in cash. Use this information to show Tom's deposit slip.

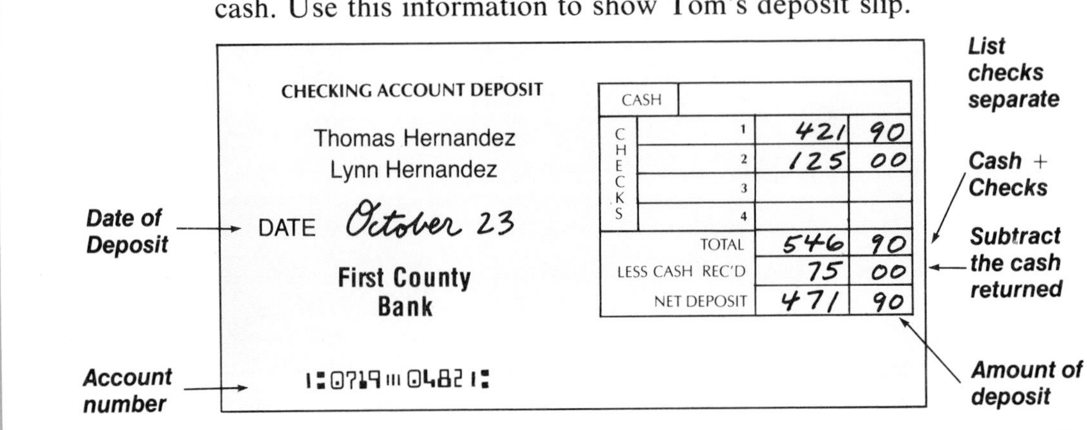

CHECKING ACCOUNT DEPOSIT

Thomas Hernandez
Lynn Hernandez

DATE October 23

First County Bank

⑆0719⑈04821⑆

CASH			
CHECKS	1	421	90
	2	125	00
	3		
	4		
	TOTAL	546	90
	LESS CASH REC'D	75	00
	NET DEPOSIT	471	90

The following week, Lynn Hernandez deposits part of her earnings into her savings account.

EXAMPLE 2 Lynn's weekly pay amounts to $424.60. She deposits $250.00 of this into her savings account. Show the deposit slip for this transaction.

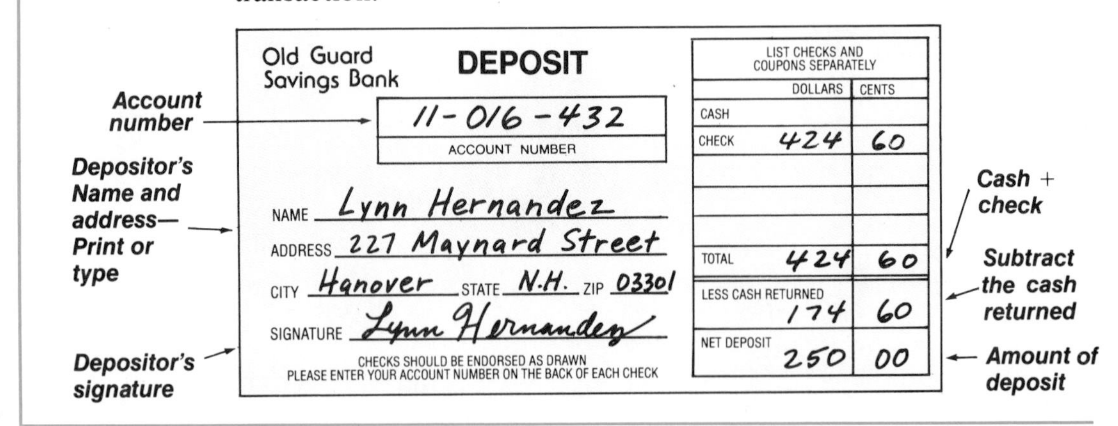

Old Guard Savings Bank DEPOSIT

11-016-432
ACCOUNT NUMBER

NAME Lynn Hernandez
ADDRESS 227 Maynard Street
CITY Hanover STATE N.H. ZIP 03301
SIGNATURE Lynn Hernandez

CHECKS SHOULD BE ENDORSED AS DRAWN
PLEASE ENTER YOUR ACCOUNT NUMBER ON THE BACK OF EACH CHECK

LIST CHECKS AND COUPONS SEPARATELY	DOLLARS	CENTS
CASH		
CHECK	424	60
TOTAL	424	60
LESS CASH RETURNED	174	60
NET DEPOSIT	250	00

REVIEW OF RELATED SKILLS

You may wish to use these exercises before teaching the lesson.

Add or subtract as indicated. (Pages 4–5)

1. 330.48 + 25 + 114.09 469.57
2. 450 + 23.46 + 108.10 581.56
3. 225.50 + 38.90 + 109 373.40
4. 381.28 + 13.47 + 98 492.75
5. 64.40 + 296 + 48.50 + 204.65 613.55
6. 25 + 304.15 + 75.20 + 925.78 1330.13
7. 325.75 − 25.75 300.00
8. 481.09 − 25.09 456.00
9. 473 − 36.40 436.60
10. 395 − 156.80 238.20

EXERCISES

For Exercises 1–3, find the TOTAL *and the* NET DEPOSIT. (Example 1)

1. TOTAL: 406.00 NET DEPOSIT: 406.00

	Dollars	Cents
CASH		
CHECKS 1	21	35
List 2	346	15
Each 3	38	50
Check 4		
TOTAL	?	
▶ Less Cash Rec'd.	0	
NET DEPOSIT	?	

2. TOTAL: 249.38 NET DEPOSIT: 168.18

	Dollars	Cents
CASH		
CHECKS 1	41	25
List 2	208	13
Each 3		
Check 4		
TOTAL	?	
▶ Less Cash Rec'd.	81	20
NET DEPOSIT	?	

3. TOTAL: 532.44 NET DEPOSIT: 507.44

	Dollars	Cents
CASH		
CHECKS 1	51	15
List 2	481	29
Each 3		
Check 4		
TOTAL	?	
▶ Less Cash Rec'd.	25	00
NET DEPOSIT	?	

For Exercises 4–6, correct any errors in the deposit slips shown.

4. TOTAL: 448.69 NET DEPOSIT: 448.69

	Dollars	Cents
CASH	25	19
CHECKS 1	423	50
List 2		
Each 3		
Check 4		
TOTAL	448	59
▶ Less Cash Rec'd.	0	
NET DEPOSIT	448	59

5. TOTAL: 337.95 NET DEPOSIT: 287.45

	Dollars	Cents
CASH		
CHECKS 1	320	14
List 2	17	81
Each 3		
Check 4		
TOTAL	338	95
▶ Less Cash Rec'd.	50	00
NET DEPOSIT	288	95

6. NET DEPOSIT: 473.83

	Dollars	Cents
CASH	33	63
CHECKS 1	415	04
List 2	25	16
Each 3		
Check 4		
TOTAL	473	83
▶ Less Cash Rec'd.	0	
NET DEPOSIT	472	83

7. Helen Shea has a pay check for $254.30 and a gift check for $25.49. She wants to receive $50.00 in cash and deposit the rest in her checking account. Find the net deposit. $229.79

8. George Leonard wants to deposit a check for $434.80 and a check for $55.18 in his savings account. He wants to receive $40.00 back in cash. Find the net deposit. $449.98

9. Peter Kim deposits the following in his checking account: 2 ten-dollar bills, 3 five-dollar bills, 7 one-dollar bills, and $42.50 in checks. What is the net deposit? $84.50

10. Louisa Perez deposits the following in her checking account: a pay check for $210.45, a refund check for $47.53, and $43.98 in cash. Find the net deposit. $301.96

9-2 Interest

See the Teacher's Manual for the objectives.

Ralph Martin has $1500 in his savings account. He is saving to buy a new car.

Money deposited in a savings account earns **interest.** The amount deposited is called the **principal.** **Simple interest** is interest paid on the principal only.

$i = p \times r \times t$ ◀ *i = interest; p = principal; r = rate; t = time in years*

EXAMPLE Ralph's savings account pays a yearly interest rate of $5\frac{3}{4}\%$. How much simple interest would a principal of $1500 earn at the end of 3 months?

Solution: $i = p \times r \times t$ ◀ ***p = $1500; r = $5\frac{3}{4}\%$ = 0.0575; t = 3 months = $\frac{1}{4}$ year***

$i = \$1500 \times 0.0575 \times \frac{1}{4}$

$i = \$86.25 \times \frac{1}{4}$

$i = \$21.5625$, or **$21.56** ◀ ***Rounded to the nearest cent***

After completing Example 1, you may wish to have students do some or all of Exercises 1-10.

Banks often pay interest at the end of a quarter (every 3 months or $\frac{1}{4}$ year). Both the original deposit and the interest earned are left on deposit during the next quarter and earn interest. This is **compound interest paid quarterly.**

TABLE

Quarter	*Interest (to nearest cent)* $i = p \times r \times t$	*New Balance*
First	$1500 $\times$ 0.0575 $\times \frac{1}{4}$ = $21.56	$1500 + $21.56 = $1521.56
Second	$1521.56 $\times$ 0.0575 $\times \frac{1}{4}$ = $21.87	$1521.56 + $21.87 = $1543.43
Third	$1543.43 $\times$ 0.0575 $\times \frac{1}{4}$ = $22.19	$1543.43 + $22.19 = $1565.62
Fourth	$1565.62 $\times$ 0.0575 $\times \frac{1}{4}$ = $22.51	$1565.62 + $22.51 = **$1588.13**

Thus, a principal of $1500 left on deposit for one year at $5\frac{3}{4}\%$ compounded quarterly has earned $88.13 in interest.

$1588.13 − $1500.00 = $88.13

REVIEW OF RELATED SKILLS

You may wish to use these exercises before teaching the lesson.

Write a decimal for each per cent. (Pages 90–91)

1. 4% 0.04 2. 6% 0.06 3. $5\frac{1}{2}$% 0.055 4. $4\frac{3}{4}$% 0.0475 5. $5\frac{1}{4}$% 0.0525 6. $4\frac{1}{2}$% 0.045

Multiply. (Pages 8–9, 56–57)

7. $1400 × 0.055 $77.00 8. $1200 × 0.045 $54.00 9. $1500 × 0.0525 $78.75 10. $2400 × 0.0675 $162.00

11. $36.40 × $\frac{1}{4}$ $9.10 12. $29.50 × $\frac{1}{2}$ $14.75 13. $56.35 × $\frac{1}{5}$ $11.27 14. $48.66 × $\frac{1}{6}$ $8.11

Round to the nearest hundredth. (Pages 16–17)

15. 14.678 14.68 16. 25.423 25.42 17. 346.4772 346.48 18. 288.0421 288.04 19. 597.9571 597.96

Add. (Pages 4–5)

20. 1600 + 14.85 1614.85 21. 3.30 + 46 49.30 22. 564 + 25.43 589.43 23. 1400 + 21.36 1421.36

EXERCISES

For Exercises 1–6, find the simple interest. (Example)

	Principal	Rate	Time	
1.	$500	10%	6 months	$25.00
2.	$1000	15%	4 months	$50.00
3.	$1800	16%	3 months	$72.00
4.	$2400	20%	6 months	$240.00
5.	$11,400	8%	3 months	$228.00
6.	$15,630	12%	4 months	$625.20

7. Mike has $600 in an account that pays a yearly interest rate of 8%. How much simple interest will the account earn in 6 months? $24.00

8. Tamara has $1200 in an account that pays a yearly interest rate of 6%. How much simple interest will the account earn in 3 months? $18.00

9. Wilma's investment account pays a yearly interest rate of 15%. She has $840 in the account. Find the simple interest after 4 months. $42.00

10. Raoul's investment account pays a yearly interest rate of 16%. He has $960 in the account. Find the simple interest after 9 months. $115.20

For Exercises 11–14, complete the table to find the yearly interest on $3000 at 5% compounded quarterly. (Table)

	Quarter	Interest	New Balance
11.	First	? $37.50	? $3037.50
12.	Second	? $37.97	? $3075.47
13.	Third	? $38.44	? $3113.91
14.	Fourth	? $38.92	? $3152.83

Yearly Interest: $152.83

For Exercises 15–18, complete the table to find the yearly interest on $3200 at 6% compounded quarterly. (Table)

	Quarter	Interest	New Balance
15.	First	? $48.00	? $3248.00
16.	Second	? $48.72	? $3296.72
17.	Third	? $49.45	? $3346.17
18.	Fourth	? $50.19	? $3396.36

Yearly Interest: $196.17

9-3 Compound Interest

See the Teacher's Manual for the objectives.

Carol Soong's bank pays 6% interest compounded quarterly.

Compound interest is computed on the principal plus the interest previously earned. You can use a table to compute compound interest.

The table shows how much a principal of $1.00 amounts to for different rates and interest periods.

Total Interest Periods	Interest Rate Per Period									
	1.5%	2%	2.5%	3%	3.5%	4%	5%	6%	7%	8%
1	1.0150	1.0200	1.0250	1.0300	1.0350	1.0400	1.0500	1.0600	1.0700	1.0800
2	1.0302	1.0404	1.0506	1.0609	1.0712	1.0816	1.1025	1.1236	1.1449	1.1664
3	1.0457	1.0612	1.0769	1.0927	1.1087	1.1248	1.1576	1.1910	1.2250	1.2597
4	1.0614	1.0824	1.1038	1.1255	1.1475	1.1699	1.2155	1.2625	1.3108	1.3605
5	1.0773	1.1041	1.1314	1.1593	1.1877	1.2167	1.2763	1.3382	1.4026	1.4693
6	1.0934	1.1262	1.1597	1.1941	1.2293	1.2653	1.3401	1.4186	1.5007	1.5869
7	1.1098	1.1487	1.1887	1.2299	1.2723	1.3159	1.4071	1.5036	1.6058	1.7138
8	1.1265	1.1717	1.2184	1.2668	1.3168	1.3686	1.4775	1.5938	1.7182	1.8059
9	1.1434	1.1951	1.2489	1.3048	1.3629	1.4233	1.5513	1.6895	1.8385	1.9990
10	1.1605	1.2190	1.2801	1.3439	1.4106	1.4802	1.6289	1.7908	1.9672	2.1589

EXAMPLE The Rockside Savings Bank pays 6% interest compounded quarterly on regular savings accounts. Carol Soong has $4000 in one of these accounts. What will be the new balance (amount) at the end of two years?

Solution:

1. Find the quarterly rate: $6\% \div 4 =$ **1.5%**
2. Find the number of quarters (total interest periods).
   2 years $= 2 \times 4 =$ **8 quarters**
3. Use the table to find how much $1.00 will amount to at 1.5% for 8 quarters: **$1.1265**
4. Find the new balance. Multiply $1.1265 and $4000.
   $1.1265 × $4000 = **$4506.00** ◀ ***New balance***

To find the total interest earned in the two years, subtract the previous balance from the new balance.

$4506.00 − $4000.00 = $506.00 ◀ ***Interest Earned***

REVIEW OF RELATED SKILLS

You may wish to use these exercises before teaching the lesson.

Divide. (Pages 14–15)

1. $16 \div 4$ 4
2. $14 \div 4$ 3.5
3. $15 \div 4$ 3.75
4. $5 \div 4$ 1.25
5. $7 \div 4$ 1.75

Multiply. (Pages 8–9)

6. 5000×1.0614 5307
7. 7000×1.3401 9380.7
8. 8000×1.605 12,840
9. 6000×1.298 7788
10. $15{,}000 \times 1.0934$ 16,401
11. $12{,}000 \times 1.3728$ 16,473.6
12. $13{,}000 \times 1.4186$ 18,441.8
13. 9000×1.046 9414

Subtract. (Pages 4–5)

14. $5564.25 - 5000$ 564.25
15. $6427 - 6000$ 427
16. $13{,}548.22 - 12{,}000$ 1548.22
17. $8350 - 8000$ 350

EXERCISES

For Exercises 1–6, complete the table. The interest is compounded quarterly.

	Present Balance	Annual Rate	Quarterly Rate	Time	Number of Quarters	New Balance
1.	$600	6%	? 1.5%	6 months	? 2	? $618.12
2.	$1000	8%	? 2%	$1\frac{1}{2}$ years	? 6	? $1126.20
3.	$1500	14%	? 3.5%	1 year	? 4	? $1721.25
4.	$3800	12%	? 3%	2 years	? 8	? $4813.84
5.	$4400	16%	? 4%	$2\frac{1}{2}$ years	? 10	? $6512.88
6.	$10,000	10%	? 2.5%	9 months	? 3	? $10,769.00

7. Monica has $1500 in an investment account. The account pays 10% interest compounded quarterly. Find the new balance after one year. $1655.70

8. First Federal pays 8% interest compounded quarterly in its time deposit accounts. Fred deposits $800. Find the new balance after $1\frac{1}{2}$ years. $900.96

9. Juan has $900 in a savings account. The account pays 6% interest compounded quarterly. Find the new balance after 18 months. $984.06

10. A bank offers 16% interest compounded quarterly. Find the amount of interest on $2000 after 1 year. $339.80

11. A contractor has $3000 in an account that pays 14% interest compounded quarterly. Find the interest after $2\frac{1}{2}$ years. $1231.80

LOAN OFFICER

Career lessons are optional.
This lesson applies the skills of using a formula and using exponents.

Tina Hernandez is a **loan officer** in a bank. She knows that there are several ways to compute compound interest.

1. Use a computer.
2. Use a compound interest table (see page 184).
3. Use the compound interest formula.

The compound interest formula tells the amount, *A*, in a savings account when the principal, *P*, is left in the account for *n* years at a rate of interest, *r*.

$$A = P(1 + r)^n \longleftarrow \textit{Exponent}$$

The letter *n* in the formula is an **exponent.** It tells how many times you multiply a number by itself. For example,

3^2 means 3×3, or 9.

3^3 means $3 \times 3 \times 3$, or 27.

EXAMPLE Three years ago, Linda put $600 in a savings account. The account earns 5% interest compounded annually. What is the amount in the account now?

Use paper and pencil or use a calculator.

Solution: $A = P(1 + r)^n$ ◀ ***P* = $600; *r* = 5% = 0.05; *n* = 3**

$A = 600(1 + 0.05)^3$

$A = 600(1.05)^3$ ◀ ***1 + 0.05 = 1.05***

$A = 600 \times 1.05 \times 1.05 \times 1.05$

 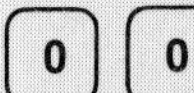 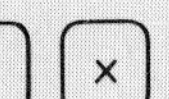 

6 0 0 × 1 . 0 5 × → 630.

1 . 0 5 × 1 . 0 5 = → 694.575

The amount after 3 years is **$694.58.** ◀ ***Rounded to the nearest cent***

EXERCISES Note that Exercises 1-35 are non-verbal.

Evaluate.

1. $3^2 = 3 \times 3 =$? 9
2. 6^2 36
3. 9^2 81
4. 11^2 121
5. 12^2 144
6. $4^3 = 4 \times 4 \times 4 =$? 64
7. 7^3 343
8. 5^3 125
9. 3^3 27
10. 0^3 0
11. $2^4 = 2 \times 2 \times 2 \times 2 =$? 16
12. 3^4 81
13. 5^4 625
14. 1^4 1
15. 10^4 10,000
16. $3^5 = 3 \times 3 \times 3 \times 3 \times 3 =$? 243
17. 4^5 1024
18. 2^5 32
19. 1^5 1
20. 5^5 3125
21. $(1.05)^2$ 1.1025
22. $(1.07)^3$ 1.225043
23. $(1.08)^2$ 1.1664
24. $(1.12)^4$ 1.573519
25. $(1.075)^2$ 1.155625

For Exercises 26–35, use the information to find the amount in each account after the given number of years. The interest is compounded annually.

	Principal	Rate	Number of Years
26.	$ 500	6%	2 $561.80
27.	$ 850	7%	3 $1041.29
28.	$1000	12%	4 $1573.52
29.	$ 900	10%	3 $1197.90
30.	$ 825	9%	4 $1164.55
31.	$ 5,000	7%	2 $5724.50
32.	$10,000	8%	2 $11,664
33.	$ 2,500	10%	2 $3025
34.	$ 3,800	12%	3 $5338.73
35.	$ 6,215	15%	4 $10,870.07

36. Four years ago, Priscilla put $1000 in a savings account. The account earns 6% interest compounded annually. What is the amount in the account now? $1262.48

37. Two years ago, Paul deposited $800 in a savings account. The account earns 8% interest compounded annually. Find the amount in Paul's account now. $933.12

38. Mary Stewart deposited $5000 in an account that earns 7% interest compounded annually. She plans to leave the money on deposit for 3 years. How much money will be in the account then? $6125.22

39. The Daltons deposited $10,000 in a savings account that earns 8% interest compounded annually. Four years later, they decided to close out the account. How much money was in the account? $13,604.89

40. Barbara Gomez bought a $5000 certificate of deposit that pays 12% interest compounded annually. The certificate is to be held for 3 years. How much will Barbara receive then? $7024.64

41. David Borg bought a $1000 savings certificate that pays 15% interest compounded annually. How much will the certificate be worth after 2 years? $1322.50

9-4 Check Stubs and Check Registers

See the Teacher's Manual for the objectives.

Lila Chin knows that a check stub or a check register is used to keep a record of deposits made and checks written. The balance is the amount of money in the account. There are two basic steps to follow when paying out money from a checking account.

1. **Fill in the check stub or check register.**
2. **Make out the check.**

EXAMPLE 1 Lila has $293.16 (Balance Forward) in her checking account. On April 5, she wrote check number 56 for $19.75. She also deposited $65.00 into the account. Complete the check stub.

Solution:

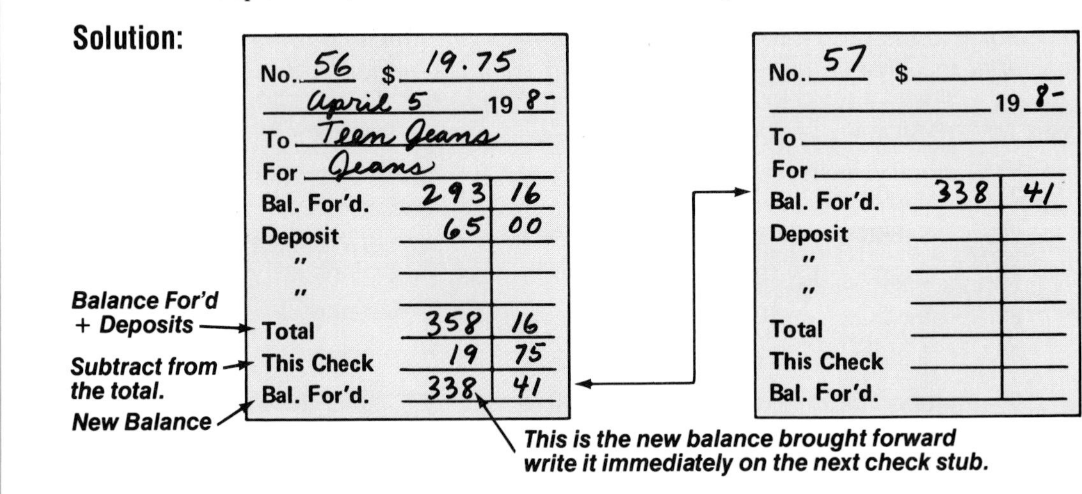

After completing Example 1, you may wish to have students do some or all of Exercises 1-10.

EXAMPLE 2 On October 1, Jaime had a balance of $320.18 in his checking account. On October 3, he wrote check number 127 for $221.00. The check was made out to Clearview Estates Corporation for rent. On October 9, Jaime deposited $135.00 into the account. Complete the check register.

Solution:

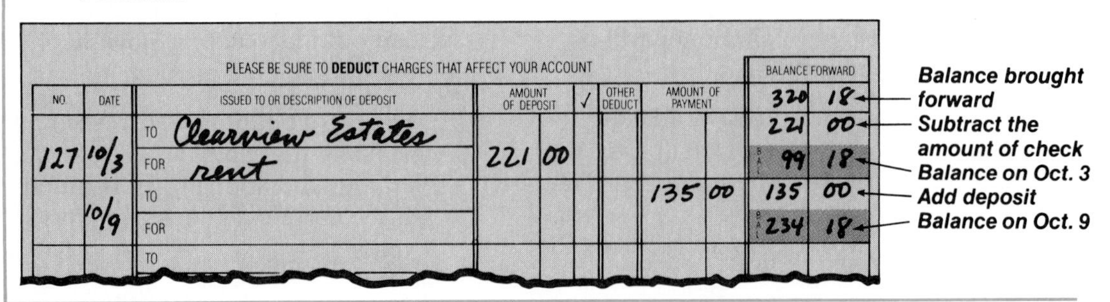

REVIEW OF RELATED SKILLS You may wish to use these exercises before teaching the lesson.

Add or subtract as indicated. (Pages 4–5)

1. 342.17 + 28.05 370.22	**2.** 146.42 + 324.50 470.92	**3.** 488.69 + 55.62 544.31
4. 28.34 + 365.92 + 56.75 451.01	**5.** 13.97 + 246.83 + 104.81 365.61	**6.** 242.81 + 327.53 + 98.70 669.04

7. 289.85 − 14.54 275.31 **8.** 364.75 − 230 134.75 **9.** 384 − 12.98 371.02 **10.** 250 − 13.44 236.56

EXERCISES

For Exercises 1–6, correct any errors in the following check stubs. (Example 1)

Total: 176.94; Bal. For'd.: 157.65 See below. Bal. For'd.: 133.27

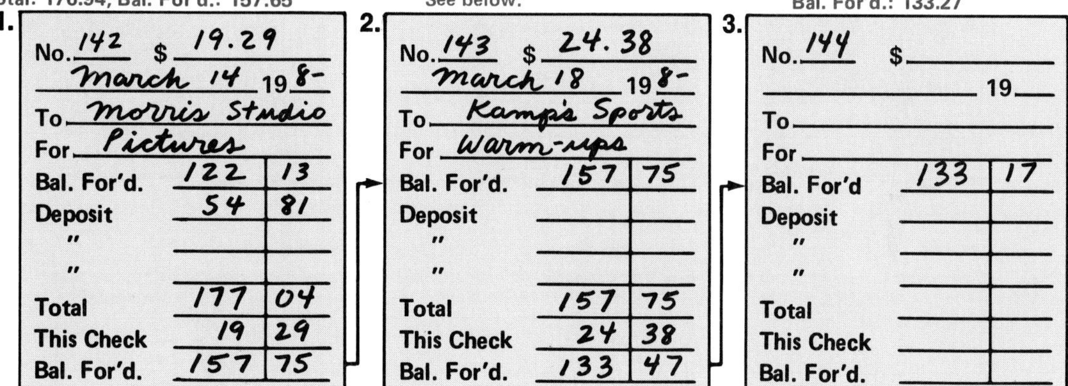

1.

No. 142	$ 19.29	
March 14 198-		
To Morris Studio		
For Pictures		
Bal. For'd.	122	13
Deposit	54	81
"		
"		
Total	177	04
This Check	19	29
Bal. For'd.	157	75

2.

No. 143	$ 24.38	
March 18 198-		
To Kamp's Sports		
For Warm-ups		
Bal. For'd.	157	75
Deposit		
"		
"		
Total	157	75
This Check	24	38
Bal. For'd.	133	47

3.

No. 144	$	
19		
To		
For		
Bal. For'd	133	17
Deposit		
"		
"		
Total		
This Check		
Bal. For'd.		

4.

No. 258	$ 230.00	
July 25 198-		
To Pat Mangan		
For Rent		
Bal. For'd.	485	21
Deposit	15	00
"		
"		
Total	485	21
This Check	230	00
Bal. For'd.	255	21

5.

No. 259	$ 36.48	
July 29 198-		
To District Cable		
For Cable T.V.		
Bal. For'd.	255	00
Deposit		
"		
"		
Total	255	00
This Check	36	48
Bal. For'd.	229	62

6.

No. 260	$ 17.98	
August 1 198-		
To Central Electric		
For Electricity		
Bal. For'd.	229	62
Deposit	24	00
"		
"		
Total	255	62
This Check	17	98
Bal. For'd.	237	64

Total: 500.21 Bal. For'd.: 270.21 See below. Bal. For'd.: 233.73; Total: 257.73; Bal. For'd.: 239.75

For Exercises 7–10, copy the check stub shown in Example 1. Use the information given to complete the stub.

7. On October 14, Janette had a balance of $129.13 in her checking account. She made a deposit of $36.25. She also wrote check number 354 for $12.38 to Smith Hardware for tools. Bal. For'd. is $153.00

8. On December 3, Tim had a balance of $103.74 in his checking account. He wrote check number 528 for $49.79 to Klein Shoes for a pair of boots. He also deposited a check for $180. Bal. For'd. is $233.95.

2. Bal. For'd.: 157.65; Total: 157.65 Bal. For'd.: 133.27

5. Bal. For'd.: 270.21; Total: 270.21; Bal. For'd.: 233.73

9. On February 19, Wilma had a balance of $247.15 in her checking account. She deposited $364.21 and wrote check number 281 for $380.00 to Belmont Commons for rent. Bal. For'd. is $231.36.

10. On June 28, Stephan had a balance of $156.47 in his checking account. He deposited checks for $25.60 and $38.75. He also wrote check number 460 for $110.15 to Acme Auto for repairs. Bal. For'd. is $110.67.

For Exercises 11–12, find the balance in each check register. (Example 2)

11.

PLEASE BE SURE TO **DEDUCT** CHARGES THAT AFFECT YOUR ACCOUNT — BALANCE FORWARD

NO.	DATE	ISSUED TO OR DESCRIPTION OF DEPOSIT	AMOUNT OF PAYMENT	✓	OTHER DEDUCT	AMOUNT OF DEPOSIT	BALANCE FORWARD
							208 17
228	4/18	TO Harmon's Music	12 38				12 38
		FOR Sheet music					BAL 195 79
	4/21	TO				241 25	241 25
		FOR					BAL ?
		TO					

437.04

12.

PLEASE BE SURE TO **DEDUCT** CHARGES THAT AFFECT YOUR ACCOUNT — BALANCE FORWARD

NO.	DATE	ISSUED TO OR DESCRIPTION OF DEPOSIT	AMOUNT OF PAYMENT	✓	OTHER DEDUCT	AMOUNT OF DEPOSIT	BALANCE FORWARD
							321 14
136	9/13	TO Lily's Boutique	49 95				49 95
		FOR dress					BAL 271 19
137	9/15	TO Teal's Books	12 98				12 98
		FOR book					BAL 258 21
	9/15	TO				134 25	134 25
		FOR					BAL ?
138	9/17	TO Grant Homes	240 00				240 00
		FOR rent					BAL ?

392.46

152.46

Correct any errors in this check register.

13.

PLEASE BE SURE TO **DEDUCT** CHARGES THAT AFFECT YOUR ACCOUNT — BALANCE FORWARD

NO.	DATE	ISSUED TO OR DESCRIPTION OF DEPOSIT	AMOUNT OF PAYMENT	✓	OTHER DEDUCT	AMOUNT OF DEPOSIT	BALANCE FORWARD
							196 27
	3/12	TO				228 13	228 13
		FOR					BAL 424 30
204	3/13	TO Maria du Pont	300 00				300 00
		FOR Rent					BAL 124 30
205	3/13	TO American Telephone	23 18				23 18
		FOR Telephone					BAL 101 02
	3/19	TO				228 13	228 13
		FOR					BAL 329 15

424.40

124.40

101.22

329.35

9-5 Writing Checks

See the Teacher's Manual for the objectives.

Meghan DiCarlo is buying a gift at Colson's Department Store. She will pay for the gift by writing a check. A check directs the bank to deduct money from her checking account to pay the bill. Meghan's account must contain as much money as the amount of the check so that the account will not be **overdrawn.**

EXAMPLE The cost of the gift was $47.59. Show how Meghan wrote the check.

Solution:

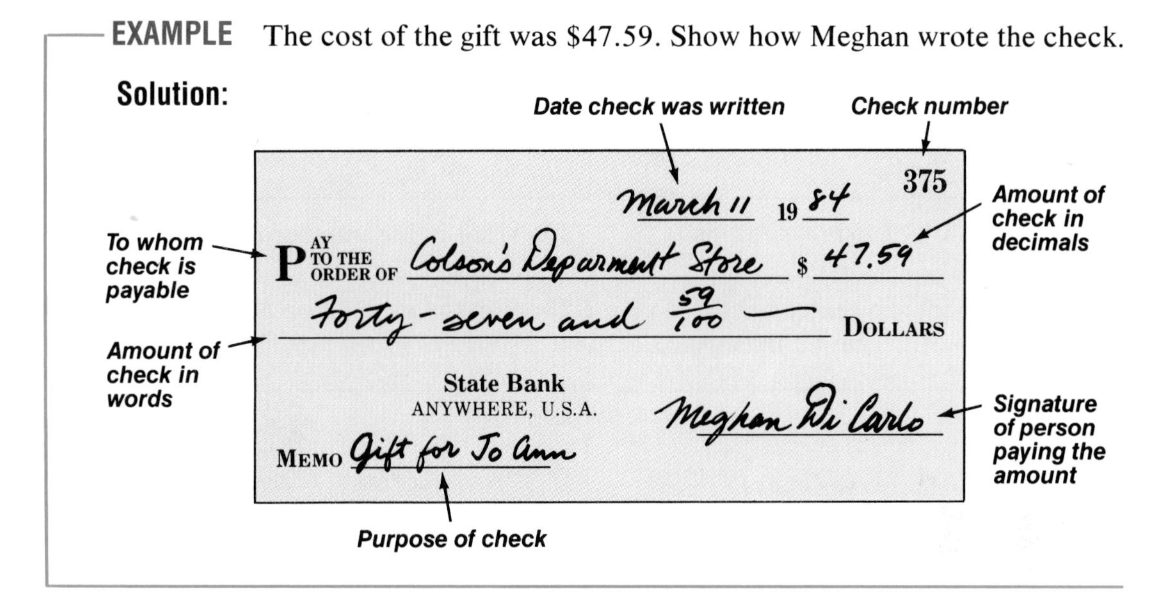

When Meghan receives a check, she knows that she can **endorse** (sign) it in three ways.

Meghan Di Carlo	For deposit only Meghan Di Carlo	Pay to the order of Gregory Di Carlo Meghan Di Carlo
To cash a check, Meghan endorses it on the reverse side after she arrives at the bank.	This check can be deposited only in Meghan's checking or savings account.	This check is signed over to Meghan's brother. Both Meghan and her brother must endorse the check.

EXERCISES

8. Three hundred fifteen and 95/100 9. Two hundred one and 18/100
15. One thousand five hundred and 00/100

For Exercises 1–15, write the amounts in words as they would appear on a check.

1. Three and 47/100 2. Eight and 19/100 3. Thirty-four and 21/100. 4. Fifty-six and 99/100 5. Seventy-five and 00/100

1. $3.47 **2.** $8.19 **3.** $34.21 **4.** $56.99 **5.** $75.00

6. Sixty-three and 00/100 7. One hundred twenty-one and 14/100 8. & 9. See above. 10. Three hundred two and 29/100

6. $63.00 **7.** $121.14 **8.** $315.95 **9.** $201.18 **10.** $302.29

11. Six hundred fifty-five and 00/100 13. One thousand two hundred fourteen and 75/100 15. See above.

11. $655.00 **12.** $781.00 **13.** $1214.75 **14.** $1315.81 **15.** $1500.00

12. Seven hundred eighty-one and 00/100 14. One thousand three hundred fifteen and 81/100

For Exercises 16–23 use the checks to answer the questions.

JOHN LAVIN 476
Feb. 15 19 83
PAY TO THE ORDER OF Harsick Home Center $ 15.67
Fifteen sixty-seven — DOLLARS
Union National
ANYWHERE, U.S.A.
John Lavin
MEMO Curtain rods

SARAH BYRNE 328
May 21 19 83
PAY TO THE ORDER OF Pet Park $
Forty-three and 50/100 — DOLLARS
Federal Savings
ANYWHERE, U.S.A.
Sarah Byrne
MEMO Boarding dog

16. When did John Lavin write this check? February 15, 1983

17. Is the amount written correctly in words? If not, write it correctly. No. Fifteen and 67/100

18. What is the number of Sarah's check? 328

19. What is missing on Sarah's check? The amount, written as a decimal

RAOUL LOPES 275
19
PAY TO THE ORDER OF Central Furniture $ 140.25
One hundred forty and 25/100 DOLLARS
State Bank
ANYWHERE, U.S.A.
Raoul Lopes
MEMO New chair

ALICE LU 196
Oct. 25 19 83
PAY TO THE ORDER OF Buckley's Flowers $ 29.95
Twenty-nine and 95/100 DOLLARS
County Savings
ANYWHERE, U.S.A.
MEMO Present

20. What is missing on Raoul's check? The date

21. What is the purpose of Raoul's check? Payment for a new chair

22. What is missing on Alice's check? Her signature

23. To whom is Alice Lu's check payable? Buckley's Flowers

For Exercises 24–25, use the endorsements shown below.

a. For deposit only
Leo Ryan

b. Pay to the order of
Lola Jarvis
Leo Ryan

c. For deposit only
Juan Ramos

24. Which check is signed over to another person? b

25. Which check can be deposited only in Leo Ryan's account? a

9-6 Reconciling a Bank Statement

See the Teacher's Manual for the objectives.

JoAnn Griffin received her checking account statement below and canceled checks from the bank for April. **Canceled checks** are checks that the bank has paid. **Outstanding checks** and deposits are those listed on JoAnn's check register that did not reach the bank in time to be recorded on the bank statement.

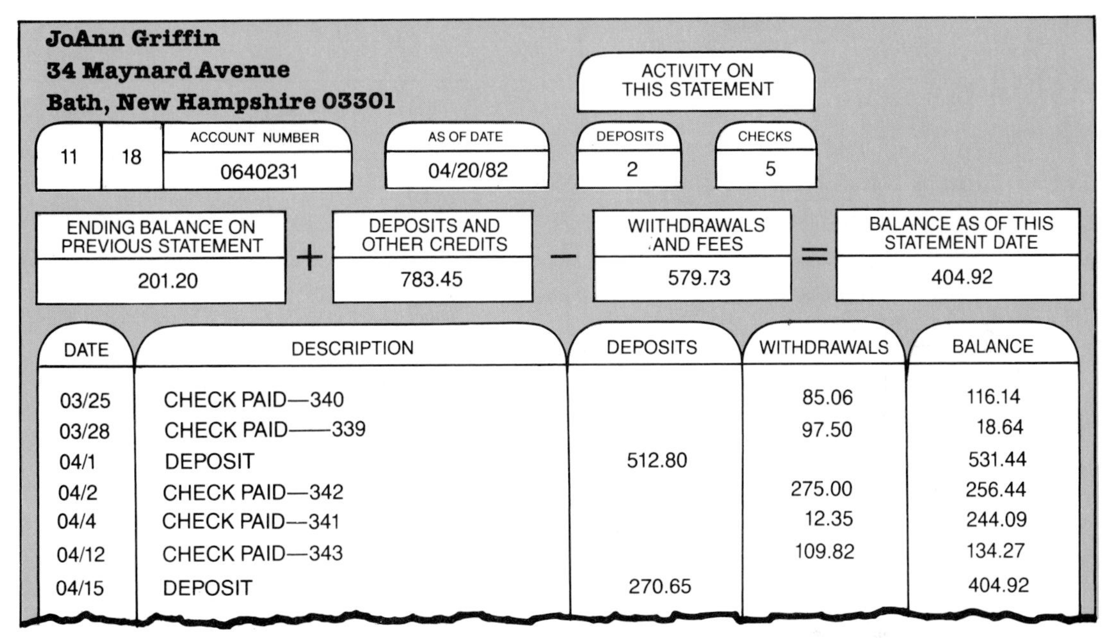

JoAnn Griffin
34 Maynard Avenue
Bath, New Hampshire 03301

ACTIVITY ON THIS STATEMENT

		ACCOUNT NUMBER	AS OF DATE	DEPOSITS	CHECKS
11	18	0640231	04/20/82	2	5

ENDING BALANCE ON PREVIOUS STATEMENT	+	DEPOSITS AND OTHER CREDITS	−	WIITHDRAWALS AND FEES	=	BALANCE AS OF THIS STATEMENT DATE
201.20		783.45		579.73		404.92

DATE	DESCRIPTION	DEPOSITS	WITHDRAWALS	BALANCE
03/25	CHECK PAID—340		85.06	116.14
03/28	CHECK PAID——339		97.50	18.64
04/1	DEPOSIT	512.80		531.44
04/2	CHECK PAID—342		275.00	256.44
04/4	CHECK PAID—341		12.35	244.09
04/12	CHECK PAID—343		109.82	134.27
04/15	DEPOSIT	270.65		404.92

EXAMPLE The balance on JoAnn's check register is \$313.70. In comparing each canceled check and deposit slip with her check register and with the bank statement, she found these outstanding checks and deposits.

Check #342: \$111.62 Check #344: \$62.10 Deposit: \$82.50

Show how she **reconciled** the bank statement and her check register (showed that they agree).

Solution: JoAnn used the form on the reverse side of the bank statement.

(A) CLOSING BALANCE SHOWN ON THIS STATEMENT	404	92	← *Balance on the bank statement*
(B) ADD DEPOSITS MADE AFTER LAST ENTRY	82	50	
(C) TOTAL (A plus B)	487	42	*111.62 + 62.10*
(D) SUBTRACT TOTAL OUTSTANDING CHECKS	173	72	
(E) (C minus D) YOUR CHECK BOOK BALANCE	313	70	← *This is the amount on JoAnn's check register. The bank statement and JoAnn's records agree.*

REVIEW OF RELATED SKILLS

You may wish to use these exercises before teaching the lesson.

Add or subtract as indicated. (Pages 4–5)

1. 264.09 + 121.17 385.26 **2.** 38.46 + 125.04 163.50 **3.** 563.56 + 238.19 801.75

4. 474 + 58.49 + 105.73 638.22 **5.** 632 + 123.96 + 98.89 854.85 **6.** 281.07 + 115.55 + 67 463.62

7. 381.96 − 264.24 117.72 **8.** 472.87 − 356.23 116.64 **9.** 248.63 − 157.95 90.68 **10.** 364.09 − 128.73 235.36

11. 248.12 − 177.53 70.59 **12.** 678 − 134.09 543.91 **13.** 246 − 198.18 47.82 **14.** 753 − 374.65 378.35

EXERCISES

For Exercises 1–5, reconcile the check register balance with the bank statement balance by completing the table.

	1.	2.	3.	4.	5.
Check Register Balance Ⓚ	204.21	125.17	329.58	263.05	119.27
Bank Statement Balance Ⓐ	336.14	138.42	286.39	293.10	137.42
Outstanding Deposits Ⓑ	20.00	35.50	150.00	0.00	50.00
A + B, or Ⓒ	? 356.14	? 173.92	? 436.39	? 293.10	? 187.42
Outstanding Checks Ⓓ	151.93	48.75	106.81	30.05	68.15
C − D, or Ⓔ	? 204.21	? 125.17	? 329.58	? 263.05	? 119.27
Does E = K?	? Yes	? Yes	? Yes	? Yes	? Yes

For Exercises 6–11, use the information in the bank statement below.

ENDING BALANCE ON PREVIOUS STATEMENTS	+	DEPOSITS AND OTHER CREDITS	−	WITHDRAWALS AND FEES	=	BALANCE AS OF THE STATEMENT DATE
142.55		880.95		429.93		593.57

DATE	DESCRIPTION	DEPOSITS	WITHDRAWALS	BALANCE
04/25	CHECK PAID—251		46.50	96.05
04/29	CHECK PAID—249		12.98	83.07
05/1	DEPOSIT	321.40		404.47
05/1	CHECK PAID—250		300.00	104.47
05/3	CHECK PAID—252		24.85	79.62
05/5	CHECK PAID—254		45.60	34.02
05/12	DEPOSIT	238.15		272.17
05/15	DEPOSIT	321.40		593.57

6. What is the date of check 251? 4/25

7. What was the balance on 4/29? $83.07

8. What was the amount of check number 249? $12.98

9. What was the amount of the deposit of 5/12? $238.15

10. What was the total amount of deposits? $880.95

11. What was the total amount of withdrawals? $429.93

For Exercises 12–15, copy the reconciliation form shown on page 193. In each exercise, reconcile the bank statement and the check register. 13. A: $124.60 B: $0.00 C: $124.60 D: $65.70 E: $58.90

12. The balance on Wally Foster's bank statement is $93.75. He has an outstanding deposit of $25.00. The balance in his check register is $118.75. A: $93.75 B: $25.00 C: $118.75 D: $0.00 E: $118.75

13. The balance on Lia Moletti's bank statement is $124.60. She has two outstanding checks: one for $26.75, and one for $38.95. The balance in her check register is $58.90.

14. The balance in Suzanne Lyn's check register is $258.94. She has an outstanding check for $43.75 and one for $49.95. She also has an outstanding deposit for $30.00. The balance on her bank statement is $322.64. A: $322.64 B: $30.00 C: $352.64 D: $93.70 E: $258.94

15. The balance in Bill Matsumi's check register is $156.21. He has an outstanding check for $14.95 and one for $102.13. He also has an outstanding deposit for $59.50. The balance on his bank statement is $213.79. A: $213.79 B: $59.50 C: $273.29 D: $117.08 E: $156.21

16. Reconcile the check register and the bank statement below. Use a copy of the reconciliation form shown on page 193.
A: $138.17 B: $100.00 C: $238.17 D: $25.69 E: $212.48

PLEASE BE SURE TO DEDUCT CHARGES THAT AFFECT YOUR ACCOUNT — BALANCE FORWARD

NO	DATE	ISSUED TO OR DESCRIPTION OF DEPOSIT	AMOUNT OF PAYMENT	✓	AMOUNT OF DEPOSIT	BALANCE
						125.15
120	9/16	Hilbert's Grocery food	24.50	✓		24.50 100.65
	9/21			✓	100.00	100.00 200.65
121	9/22	Mimi's Boutique dress	42.50	✓		42.50 158.15
122	9/23	State Electric electricity	19.98	✓		19.98 138.17
123	9/25	Union Telephone phone	25.69			25.69 112.48
	9/28				100.00	100.00 212.48

DATE	DESCRIPTION	DEPOSITS	WITHDRAWALS	BALANCE
09/18	CHECK PAID-120		24.50	100.65
09/21	DEPOSIT	100.00		200.65
09/25	CHECK PAID-122		19.98	180.67
09/26	CHECK PAID-121		42.50	138.17

CASHIER

Career lessons are optional.
This lesson applies the skills of addition and subtraction of decimals.

Lauren Smythe works as a **cashier** at her neighborhood supermarket. The cash register computes the change. Then Lauren uses this rule to count out the change.

Use as few bills and as few coins as possible.

EXERCISES

Choose the best way to make change. Choose a, b, or c.

1.

(a.) Four $1–bills, 3 quarters, one nickel, and 3 pennies

b. Four $1–bills, 8 dimes, 3 pennies

c. Nineteen quarters, one nickel, 3 pennies

2.

a. Eight quarters, 3 dimes, 1 nickel

b. Nine quarters, 1 dime

(c.) Two $1–bills, 1 quarter, 1 dime

3.

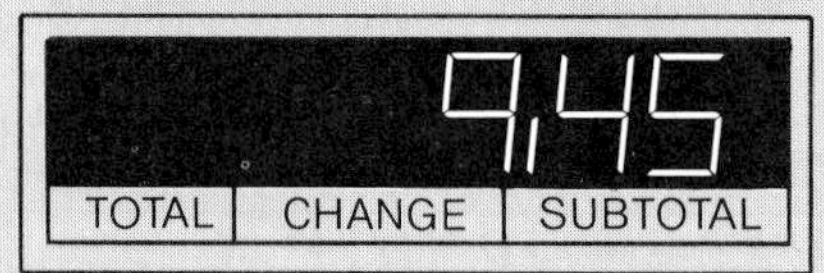

(a.) One $5–bill, four $1–bills, 1 quarter, 2 dimes

b. Nine $1–bills, 4 dimes, 1 nickel

c. One $5–bill, 17 quarters, 2 dimes

4.

a. Five dimes, 2 pennies

(b.) Two quarters, 2 pennies

c. Ten nickels, 2 pennies

For Exercises 5–8, make a chart like the one shown below. Write the number of bills and coins in the boxes to show the best way to make change. The first one is done for you. Note that Exercises 5–12 are non-verbal.

	Change Due	Change: Number of						
		$10–bills	$5–bills	$1–bills	Quarters	Dimes	Nickels	Pennies
5.	$ 2.79	None	None	2	3	None	None	4
6.	$ 1.51	? 0	? 0	? 1	? 2	? 0	? 0	? 1
7.	$14.26	? 1	? 0	? 4	? 1	? 0	? 0	? 1
8.	$ 3.77	? 0	? 0	? 3	? 3	? 0	? 0	? 2

For Exercises 9–12, make a chart like the one below. First, find the change due. Then write the number of bills and coins in the boxes to show the best way to make change.

	Amount of Sale	Money Received	Change Due	Change: Number of						
				$10-bills	$5-bills	$1-bills	Quarters	Dimes	Nickels	Pennies
9.	$ 4.55	$10	$5.45 ?	? 0	? 1	? 0	? 1	? 2	? 0	? 0
10.	$ 9.81	$20	$10.19 ?	? 1	? 0	? 0	? 0	? 1	? 1	? 4
11.	$24.63	$40	$15.37 ?	? 1	? 1	? 0	? 1	? 1	? 0	? 2
12.	$18.19	$20	$1.81 ?	? 0	? 0	? 1	? 3	? 0	? 1	? 1

For Exercises 13–20: **a.** *Find the change due.*
b. *Give the best way to make change.*

13. John's total bill for groceries was $5.69. He gave the clerk a $10–bill. a. $4.31 b. 4 $1-bills, 1 quarter, 1 nickel, 1 penny

14. Maria's total bill for fruit and vegetables was $6.95. She gave the clerk a $10–bill. a. $3.05 b. 3 $1-bills, 1 nickel

15. Joann's total bill for meat was $11.40. She gave the cashier a $20–bill. a. $8.60 b. 1 $5-bill, 3 $1-bills, 2 quarters, 1 dime

16. Jorge's bill for frozen vegetables was $5.62. He gave the cashier a $20–bill. a. $14.38 b. 1 $10-bill, 4 $1-bills, 1 quarter, 1 dime, 3 pennies

17. Sam bought a record for $6.98 and a book for $12.00. The sales tax was $0.84. He gave the cashier two $10–bills. a. $0.18 b. 1 dime, 1 nickel, 3 pennies

18. Linda's bill at a flower shop lists $5.39 for a plant and $1.88 for potting soil. The sales tax is $0.29. She gave the clerk a $50–bill. a. $42.44 b. 2 $20-bills, 2 $1-bills, 1 quarter, 1 dime, 1 nickel, 4 pennies

19. At a department store sale, Julia bought slacks for $14.98, a blouse for $16.00, and a pair of shoes for $35.90. The tax amounted to $3.34. She gave the clerk two $50–bills. a. $29.78 b. 1 $20-bill, 1 $5-bill, 4 $1-bills, 3 quarters, 3 pennies

20. At the neighborhood grocery, Lucy bought a head of lettuce for $0.59, a bag of potatoes for $1.05, and strawberries for $0.99. She gave the grocer a $5–bill. a. $2.37 b. 2 $1-bills, 1 quarter, 1 dime, 2 pennies

Rounding and Estimation

Consumers use rounding and estimation to solve problems related to banking.

EXERCISES See the Teacher's Manual for the objectives.

Skills

Choose the best estimate. Choose a, b, or c.

1. $201.25 + 14.98$ b **a.** $200 + 14$ **b.** $200 + 15$ **c.** $210 + 15$

2. $1121.14 + 28.99$ c **a.** $1120 + 20$ **b.** $1110 + 20$ **c.** $1120 + 30$

3. $218.95 - 11.21$ a **a.** $220 - 10$ **b.** $210 - 10$ **c.** $220 - 20$

4. $102.10 + 22.18 - 9.9$ c **a.** $110 + 30 - 10$ **b.** $100 + 30 - 10$ **c.** $100 + 20 - 10$

5. $88.80 + 11.12 - 4.75$ b **a.** $80 + 10 - 5$ **b.** $90 + 10 - 5$ **c.** $80 + 20 - 10$

6. $619.75 - 12.2 - 28.5$ a **a.** $620 - 10 - 30$ **b.** $600 - 10 - 20$ **c.** $600 - 20 - 30$

7. $91.20 - 11.09 - 5.10$ c **a.** $90 - 20 - 10$ **b.** $90 - 20 - 5$ **c.** $90 - 10 - 5$

8. $1008 \times 4\frac{3}{4}\% \times \frac{1}{2}$ a **a.** $1000 \times \frac{1}{20} \times \frac{1}{2}$ **b.** $1100 \times \frac{1}{20} \times \frac{1}{2}$ **c.** $1000 \times \frac{1}{10} \times \frac{1}{2}$

9. $99.60 \times 9\frac{1}{2}\% \times \frac{1}{4}$ c **a.** $100 \times \frac{1}{8} \times \frac{1}{4}$ **b.** $90 \times \frac{1}{5} \times \frac{1}{4}$ **c.** $100 \times \frac{1}{10} \times \frac{1}{4}$

Choose the best estimate. Choose a, b, c, or d.

10. $319.80 + 21.60$ b **a.** 320 **b.** 340 **c.** 350 **d.** 330

11. $427.78 - 48.90$ a **a.** 380 **b.** 390 **c.** 400 **d.** 370

12. $98.85 + 12.16 - 19.50$ c **a.** 70 **b.** 80 **c.** 90 **d.** 100

13. $212.14 - 19.95 - 11.02$ b **a.** 190 **b.** 180 **c.** 170 **d.** 160

14. $2004 \times 9\frac{3}{4}\% \times \frac{1}{2}$ c **a.** 80 **b.** 90 **c.** 100 **d.** 110

Applications

15. Wanda deposits checks for \$298.30, \$29.76, and \$12.15. Estimate the total deposit. b

a. \$290 + \$30 + \$13
b. \$300 + \$30 + \$10
c. \$290 + \$20 + \$15
d. \$300 + \$20 + \$10

16. Irwin deposits checks for \$158.75 and \$11.05. He wants to receive \$30 back. Estimate the net deposit. a

a. \$160 + \$10 − \$30
b. \$150 + \$10 − \$30
c. \$160 + \$20 − \$30
d. \$170 + \$20 − \$30

17. On March 12, Pierre had a check register balance of $199.69. He wrote checks for $9.95 and $10.15. Estimate the new balance. c

a. $190 − $20 − $10
b. $190 − $10 − $10
c. $200 − $10 − $10
d. $200 − $20 − $20

18. On May 30, Louise had $201.30 in her checking account. She deposited $19.95 and wrote a check for $28.80. Estimate the new balance. b

a. $210 + $20 − $20
b. $200 + $20 − $30
c. $210 + $10 − $20
d. $200 + $20 − $20

19. Juanita has $403 in an account that pays a yearly interest rate of 10%. Estimate how much simple interest the account will earn in 6 months. c

a. $\$410 \times \frac{1}{10} \times \frac{1}{2}$
b. $\$400 \times \frac{1}{8} \times 6$
c. $\$400 \times \frac{1}{10} \times \frac{1}{2}$
d. $\$410 \times \frac{1}{8} \times \frac{1}{2}$

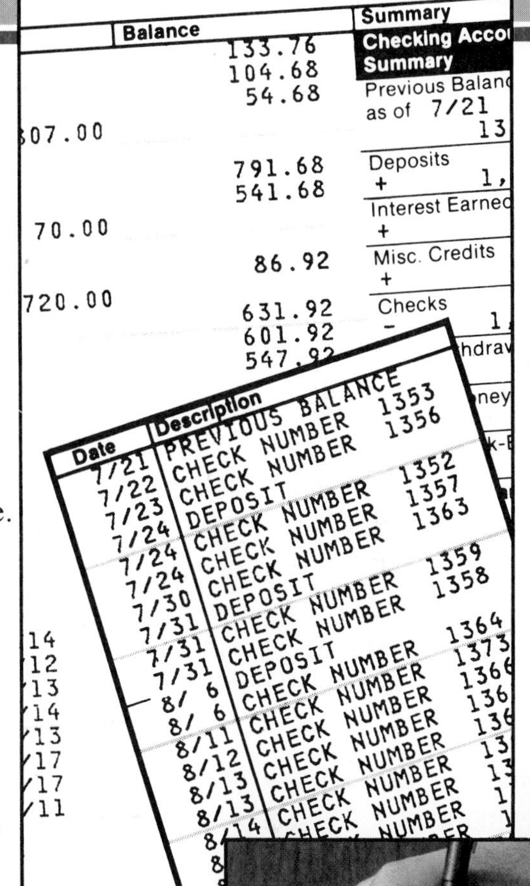

20. Dominic deposits checks for $261.12 and $19.80. He wants to receive $40 back in cash. Estimate the net deposit he makes. a

a. $240
b. $210
c. $250
d. $230

21. On June 1, Lorelle had $347.60 in her checking account. She deposited $21.32 and wrote a check for $49.50. Estimate the new balance. b

a. $300
b. $320
c. $310
d. $330

22. Michiko has $1010 in an account that pays $10\frac{1}{2}\%$ yearly interest. Estimate the simple interest the account will earn in 3 months. a

a. $25
b. $100
c. $50
d. $75

Chapter Review

These exercises review the vocabulary, skills and applications presented in the chapter, as a preparation for the chapter test.

Part 1: VOCABULARY

For Exercises 1–4, choose from the box at the right the word(s) that completes each statement.

principal
canceled
deposit slip
endorse
outstanding

1. To put money into a checking account, a person makes out a __?__. (Pages 180–181) deposit slip
2. Before you deposit a check you must __?__ it. (Pages 191–192) endorse
3. Checks and deposits not listed on your bank statement are called __?__. (Pages 193–195) outstanding
4. Checks that the bank has paid are called __?__ checks. (Pages 193–195) canceled

Part 2: SKILLS

Add or subtract as indicated. (Pages 4–5)

5. $562.04 + 72.98 + 1373.40$ 2008.42
6. $253.78 + 1415.06 + 21.75$ 1690.59
7. $78 + 983.64 + 1347 + 642.07$ 3050.71
8. $645 + 78.49 + 1023.71 + 896.54$ 2643.74
9. $475.60 - 75.60$ 400.00
10. $723.80 - 23.80$ 700.00
11. $573 - 186.54$ 386.46
12. $442 - 205.50$ 236.50

Write a decimal for each per cent. (Pages 90–91)

13. 18% 0.18
14. 15% 0.15
15. 8% 0.08
16. 5% 0.05
17. $4\frac{1}{2}\%$ 0.045
18. $6\frac{3}{4}\%$ 0.0675

Multiply. (Pages 8–9, 56–57)

19. 1100×0.14 154
20. 2400×0.17 408
21. 1500×0.065 97.5
22. 1700×1.2295 2090.15
23. $64.80 \times \frac{1}{4}$ 16.20
24. $29.10 \times \frac{1}{3}$ 9.70
25. $45.30 \times \frac{1}{6}$ 7.55
26. $63.72 \times \frac{1}{12}$ 5.31

Round to the nearest hundredth. (Pages 16–17)

27. 63.462 63.46
28. 75.048 75.05
29. 122.3681 122.37
30. 234.4928 234.49
31. 148.1347 148.13

Part 3: APPLICATIONS

32. Find the TOTAL and the NET DEPOSIT. (Pages 180–181)

	Dollars	Cents
CASH		
CHECKS 1	44	50
List 2	321	60
Each 3		
Check 4		
TOTAL	?	
Less Cash Rec'd.	50	00
NET DEPOSIT	?	

TOTAL: 366.10 NET DEPOSIT: 316.10

33. Ryan Kelly deposited three checks in his checking account. The amounts of the checks were \$47.98, \$52.10, and \$109.75. Estimate the TOTAL. (Pages 198–199) b

a. \$200 b. \$210
c. \$220 d. \$190

For Exercises 34–35, copy the check stub shown on page 188. Use the information given to complete the stub. (Pages 188–190)

34. On September 5, Louise had a balance of $204.16 in her checking account. She deposited $42.50 and wrote check number 285 for $14.95 to Royale Clothes for a dress.
Bal. For'd. is $231.71.

35. On June 7, Tom had a balance of $68.82 in his checking account. He deposited $168.00 and wrote check number 127 for $23.16 to City Electric. Bal. For'd. is $213.66.

For Exercises 36–39, use the information on this check. (Pages 191–192)

JUNE ALCOTT 156

Sept. 24 19 8-

PAY TO THE ORDER OF Wilmott's Paper $ 14.64

Fourteen and 64/100 ——— DOLLARS

State Bank
ANYWHERE, U.S.A.

June Alcott

MEMO Stationery

36. To whom is the check payable? Wilmott's Paper

37. What is the number of the check? 156

38. What is the amount of the check? $14.64

39. What is the purpose of the check? Purchase of stationery

For Exercises 40–41, copy the reconciliation form shown on page 193. Use the information in each exercise to reconcile the bank statement and the check register. (Pages 193–195)

40. The balance on Juan's bank statement is $104.80. He has an outstanding deposit of $24.00 and an outstanding check for $19.50. The balance in his check register is $109.30. A: $104.80 B: $24.00 C: $128.80 D: $19.50 E: $109.30

41. Molly has outstanding checks for $14.65, $64.28, and $19.89, and an outstanding deposit for $56.00. The balance on her bank statement is $203.56. Her check register balance is $160.74. A: $203.56 B: $56.00 C: $259.56 D: $98.82 E: $160.74

For Exercises 42–43, find the simple interest. (Pages 182–183)

	Principal	*Rate*	*Time*	
42.	$600	6%	6 months	$18
43.	$800	8%	3 months	$16

44. Delia Sanchez has $1975 in an account that pays 9% yearly interest. Estimate the simple interest after 6 months. (Pages 198–199) c

a. $250 **b.** $200
c. $100 **d.** $150

For Exercises 45–46, use the table on page 184. (Pages 184–185)

45. Kent has $1800 in an account that pays 14% interest compounded quarterly. Find the new balance after 6 months. $1928.16

46. Julia has $740 in an account that pays 6% interest compounded quarterly. Find the interest after $2\frac{1}{2}$ years. $118.77

Banking at an automated teller.

Chapter Test

The Teacher's Resource Book contains two forms of each chapter test.

Perform the indicated operation.

1. $14.86 + 204 + 116.95$ 335.81

2. $371.46 - 71.46$ 300.00

3. 1400×0.15 210

4. $96.21 \times \frac{1}{3}$ 32.07

Write a decimal for each per cent.

5. 16% 0.16

6. $5\frac{1}{2}\%$ 0.055

Round to the nearest hundredth.

7. 72.058 72.06

8. 21.031 21.03

Find the TOTAL and the NET DEPOSIT
TOTAL: 59.80 NET DEPOSIT: 44.80

9.

	Dollars	Cents
CASH		
CHECKS 1	25	60
List 2	34	20
Each 3		
Check 4		
TOTAL	?	
▶ Less Cash Rec'd.	15	00
NET DEPOSIT	?	

Find the TOTAL and the BALANCE FORWARD. Total: 235.16 Bal. For'd.: 219.08

10.

No. 142 $ 16.08
May 20 198-
To Groceria
For Food

Bal. For'd.	175	16
Deposit	60	00
"		
"		
Total	?	
This Check	16	08
Bal. For'd.	?	

For Exercises 11–15, use the information on this check.

11. What is missing on the check? The signature

12. To whom is the check payable? Cole's Furniture

13. What is the purpose of the check? Purchase of bookcase

14. What is the amount of the check? $104.85

15. What is the number of the check? 72

TIM OLAF 72
Oct. 16 198-
PAY TO THE ORDER OF Cole's Furniture $ 104.85
One hundred four and 85/100 DOLLARS
Federal Savings
ANYWHERE, U.S.A.
MEMO Book Case

Find the simple interest.

	Principal	Rate	Time	
16.	$500	6%	6 months	$15
17.	$1000	15%	4 months	$50
18.	$2000	12%	9 months	$180

19. Marla has $1200 in an account that earns 10% interest compounded quarterly. Use the table on page 184 to find the interest after 9 months. $92.28

20. Kevin Shikado has $2095 in an account that pays $9\frac{1}{2}\%$ yearly interest. Estimate the simple interest after 4 months. c

a. $60 **b.** $80

c. $70 **d.** $90

Additional Practice

You may wish to use all or some of these exercises, depending on how well students performed on the formal chapter test.

Skills

Add or subtract as indicated. (Pages 4–5)

1. 64.81 + 105 + 19.98 + 3.50 **193.29** **2.** 325.60 − 25.60 **300.00** **3.** 400 − 98.75 **301.25**

Write a decimal for each per cent. (Pages 90–91)

4. 14% **0.14** **5.** 25% **0.25** **6.** 4% **0.04** **7.** 8% **0.08** **8.** $3\frac{1}{4}\%$ **0.0325** **9.** $9\frac{1}{2}\%$ **0.095**

Multiply. (Pages 8–9, 56–57)

10. 2200 × 0.045 **99** **11.** 1400 × 1.3384 **1873.76** **12.** $27.24 \times \frac{1}{4}$ **6.81** **13.** $62.76 \times \frac{1}{3}$ **20.92**

Round to the nearest hundredth. (Pages 16–17)

14. 2.463 **2.46** **15.** 5.789 **5.79** **16.** 16.432 **16.43** **17.** 25.961 **25.96** **18.** 38.0488 **38.05**

Applications

19. Correct any errors in this deposit slip. (Pages 180–181)
Net Deposit: 287.95

		Dollars	Cents
CASH			
CHECKS	1	320	14
List	2	17	81
Each	3		
Check	4		
	TOTAL	337	95
▶ Less Cash Rec'd.		50	00
NET DEPOSIT		227	95

20. Find the TOTAL and BALANCE FORWARD. (Pages 188–190)
Total: 100.16 Bal. For'd.: 91.18

No. 235 $ 8.98
November 10 19 8-
To Drake's Pharmacy
For medicine

Bal. For'd.	74	16
Deposit	26	00
"		
"		
Total	?	
This Check	8	98
Bal. For'd.	?	

21. The balance on Keith's bank statement is \$125.63. He has an outstanding check for \$5.89 and an outstanding deposit for \$63.00. The balance in his check register is \$182.74. Reconcile the bank statement and Keith's check register. (Copy the reconciliation form on page 193.) (Pages 193–195) **A: \$125.63 B: \$63.00 C: \$188.63 D: \$5.89 E: \$182.74**

22. Lola has \$2000 in an investment account that pays 16% interest compounded quarterly. Find the interest after $2\frac{1}{2}$ years. Use the table on page 184. (Pages 184–185) **\$960.40**

23. Jasper McCabe is writing a deposit slip. His checks total \$429.50 and he wants \$50 back in cash. Estimate the NET DEPOSIT. (Pages 198–199) **c**

a. \$400 **b.** \$420 **c.** \$380 **d.** \$360

Cumulative Review: Chapters 7–9

Choose the correct answer. Choose a, b, c, or d.

1. Add: $16.95 + 127.38 + 6.84$ a

a. 151.17 **b.** 980.88
c. 161.19 **d.** 212.73

2. Subtract: $275.81 - 80$ d

a. 267.81 **b.** 275.01
c. 95.81 **d.** 195.81

3. Multiply: $7.50 × 35 b

a. $26.25 **b.** $262.50
c. $214.29 **d.** $21.43

4. Multiply: $64.98 \times \frac{4}{9}$ b

a. 29.88 **b.** 28.88
c. 31.29 **d.** 24.64

5. Round 687.375 to the nearest hundredth. c

a. 700.00 **b.** 687.4
c. 687.38 **d.** 687.37

6. Write a decimal for $6\frac{1}{2}\%$. b

a. 6.75 **b.** 0.065 **c.** 6.5 **d.** 6.05

7. Write a fraction for $37\frac{1}{2}\%$. d

a. $\frac{1}{12}$ **b.** $\frac{1}{8}$ **c.** $\frac{3}{5}$ **d.** $\frac{3}{8}$

8. Find 8% of $27.50. c

a. $22.00 **b.** $0.22
c. $2.20 **d.** $3.44

9. Multiply: b

$12 × $3\frac{1}{2}$

a. $54 **b.** $42
c. $50 **d.** $36

10. Multiply: $18,600 × 0.0705 a

a. $1311.30 **b.** $1301.30
c. $2411.40 **d.** $1031.40

11. Theresa earns $8.50 per hour for a 35-hour work week. Find the weekly income. d

a. $321.50 **b.** $305.40
c. $287.50 **d.** $297.50

12. Bill earns $6.80 per hour for a 40–hour work week. He gets time and a half for overtime. Find his income for a 45–hour week. a

a. $323.00 **b.** $357.00
c. $279.50 **d.** $459.00

13. Emily is paid an 18% commission on all appliance sales. What is her commission on $2700? b

a. $4860.00
b. $486.00
c. $48.60
d. $436.00

14. Elizabeth earns a weekly salary of $165 plus a 10% commission on sales. Find her total income for a week when her total sales were $2800. c

a. $345 **b.** $225
c. $445 **d.** $280

15. Kyoki's gross pay last week was $364.98. Her net pay was $258.63. Find the todal deductions. c

a. $206.45 **b.** $200.80
c. $106.35 **d.** $108.42

16. Anthony's gross pay last week was $298.55. His total deductions were $102.26. Estimate the net pay. b

a. $100 **b.** $200
c. $150 **d.** $250

17. Jules earned $39,500 one year. The Social Security tax that year was 6.70%. The maximum amount taxed was $36,000. Find his total F.I.C.A. tax. c

a. $2646.50 **b.** $5058.50
c. $2412.00 **d.** $264.65

18. Cheryll earned $16,275 one year. She won a $500 prize and received $127 in interest. Find the adjusted gross income. d

a. $16,648 **b.** $16,442
c. $15,648 **d.** $16,902

19. Jason's adjusted gross income is $21,350. He claims one exemption and has these deductions.

medical–$750; contributions–$220
interest–$1313; taxes–$2100

Find the taxable income. d

a. $23,633 **b.** $19,067
c. $21,327 **d.** $15,967

20. Find the tax. a

$1280 plus 12% of $500

a. $1340 **b.** $3620
c. $1060 **d.** $3560

21. Juanita had $2917 withheld from her pay for federal income tax. She owes only $2309. Estimate the refund. b

a. $500 **b.** $600
c. $400 **d.** $700

22. Find the balance forward. c

No. 144 $ 43.87
May 30 198-
To Miller's Paints
For Paint

Bal. For'd.	129	53
Deposit	50	00
"		
"		
Total	179	53
This Check	43	87
Bal. For'd.	?	

a. $125.56
b. $129.88
c. $135.66
d. $142.46

23. Jerome's investment account pays a yearly interest rate of 15%. He has $960 in the account. Find the simple interest after 4 months. a

a. $48 **b.** $50 **c.** $40 **d.** $38

24. Louise earned $21,400 last year. She received $309 in interest and a bonus of $297. Estimate her adjusted gross income. a

a. $22,000 **b.** $23,000
c. $22,500 **d.** $21,500

25. Bill earns a 21% commission on all sales. Estimate the commission on $399. c

a. $60 **b.** $70 **c.** $80 **d.** $100

REVIEW OF RELATED SKILLS FOR CHAPTER 10

We suggest that some or all of this page be reviewed before proceeding with the chapter.

Add. (Pages 2–5)

1.	**2.**	**3.**	**4.**	**5.**
486	551	8610	6010.00	8705.50
921	25	942	987.56	803.80
+803	+205	+ 100	+ 183.40	+ 190.00
2210	781	9652	7180.96	9699.30

6. \$979.00 + \$141.50 \$1120.50 **7.** \$9240.00 + \$216.85 \$9456.85 **8.** \$6580.00 + \$193.55 \$6773.55

9. \$5285.00 + \$94.40 \$5379.40 **10.** \$7450.00 + \$162.43 \$7612.43 **11.** \$8400.00 + \$307.46 \$8707.46

12. \$6432.00 + \$87.60 \$6519.60 **13.** \$8541.00 + \$79.54 \$8620.54 **14.** \$6700.00 + \$278.19 \$6978.19

Write a decimal for each per cent. (Pages 90–91)

15. 1% 0.01 **16.** 6% 0.06 **17.** 10% 0.1 **18.** 4.5% 0.045 **19.** 8.7% 0.087 **20.** $3\frac{1}{2}$% 0.035

21. 17% 0.17 **22.** 23% 0.23 **23.** 67% 0.67 **24.** 94% 0.94 **25.** 102% 1.02 **26.** 130% 1.3

27. 225% 2.25 **28.** 314% 3.14 **29.** 6.2% 0.062 **30.** 5.7% 0.057 **31.** 75% 0.75 **32.** 82% 0.82

Find the answer. (Pages 94–95)

33. 5% of 6850 342.5 **34.** 4% of 7510 300.4 **35.** 8% of 6600 528 **36.** 6% of 8300 498

37. 80% of 7850 6280 **38.** 70% of 8610 6027 **39.** 75% of 6200 4650 **40.** 77% of 6000 4620

41. 25% of 1600 400 **42.** 50% of 2420 1210 **43.** 10% of 9000 900 **44.** 20% of 5000 1000

Multiply. (Pages 6–9)

45.	**46.**	**47.**	**48.**	**49.**	**50.**
98	81	67	99	43	187
×24	×50	×41	×12	×26	×69
2352	4050	2747	1188	1118	12,903

51.	**52.**	**53.**	**54.**	**55.**	**56.**
420	841	204	778	129	1812
× 2.6	× 1.7	×3.14	×2.26	×5.04	×2.60
1092.0	1429.7	640.56	1758.28	650.16	4711.20

57. 88 × 22 1936 **58.** 7 × 86 602 **59.** 64 × 46 2944 **60.** 128 × 43 5504

61. 260 × 4.7 1222.0 **62.** 542 × 2.2 1192.4 **63.** 745 × 0.23 171.35 **64.** 208 × 3.64 757.12

65. 308 × 1.2 369.6 **66.** 407 × 3.4 1383.8 **67.** 221 × 0.54 119.34 **68.** 387 × 0.62 239.94

Subtract. (Pages 2–5)

69.	**70.**	**71.**	**72.**	**73.**	**74.**
98	43	84	72	183	402
−27	−32	−49	−24	− 71	− 88
71	11	35	48	112	314

75.	**76.**	**77.**	**78.**	**79.**	**80.**
7.6	9.9	82.6	76.50	12.50	41.80
−4.5	−3.2	−41.3	− 8.88	− 6.01	−40.07
3.1	6.7	41.3	67.62	6.49	1.73

81. 407 − 82 325 **82.** 1200 − 830 370 **83.** 8950 − 604 8346

84. \$810.40 − \$200 \$610.40 **85.** \$461.23 − \$50 \$411.23 **86.** \$5976.00 − \$782.50 \$5193.50

87. \$350.70 − \$14.95 \$335.75 **88.** \$522.46 − \$23.59 \$498.87 **89.** \$3124.00 − \$633.75 \$2490.25

CHAPTER

10 BUYING A CAR

CONSUMER SKILLS/APPLICATIONS

10-1 Sticker Price
10-2 Making a Deal
10-3 Financing a Car
10-4 Liability Insurance
10-5 Collision/Comprehensive Insurance
Rounding and Estimation

CAREER APPLICATIONS

Used Car Dealer
Radiator Technician

10-1 Sticker Price

See the Teacher's Manual for the objectives.

The **sticker price** of a new car is the sum of the **base price,** the cost of the **optional equipment,** and the **destination charge** (delivery charges).

EXAMPLE 1 Christina Foxe is buying a new car. A portion of the sticker for the car is shown below. What is the sticker price?

VOYAGER VG 200	BASE PRICE: $6850	
C/C	OPTIONS DESCRIPTION	LIST PRICE
F 20	Air conditioning	647.50
H 38	Automatic transmission	585.50
G 19	Glass (tinted)	75.00
M 83	Radio, AM/FM	153.00
	DESTINATION CHARGE	205.60

Solution:

Base price:	$6850.00
Options: $647.50 + $585.00 + $75.00 + $153.00 =	1460.50
Destination charge:	205.60
Sticker price:	**$8516.10**

After completing Example 1, you may wish to have students do some or all of Exercises 1-8.

Many states have a sales tax on certain purchases. Thus, to find the total cost of the car, you must first answer the question:

What is the amount of sales tax?

This is the **hidden question** in the problem. Then you can find the cost.

EXAMPLE 2 The state in which Christina lives has a sales tax of 6%. Find the total cost of the car in Example 1.

Solution: [1] Find the amount of sales tax.

6% of $8516.10 = $8516.10 × 0.06

= $510.97 ◀ *Rounded to the nearest cent*

[2] Find the total cost.

$8516.10 + $510.97 = **$9027.07** ◀ *Sticker Price* + *Sales Tax* = *Total Cost*

REVIEW OF RELATED SKILLS You may wish to use these exercises before teaching the lesson.

Add. (Pages 2–5)

1. \$8090 + \$700 + \$502 \$9292
2. \$7069 + \$204 + \$806 \$8079
3. \$4696 + \$518 + \$697 \$5911
4. \$9023.00 + \$631.61 \$9654.61
5. \$6810.00 + \$272.40 \$7082.40
6. \$7469.00 + 526.57 \$7995.57

Write a decimal for each per cent. (Pages 90–91)

7. 8% 0.08
8. 4% 0.04
9. 9% 0.09
10. 53% 0.53
11. $6\frac{1}{2}$% 0.065
12. 4.8% 0.048

Find each answer. (Pages 94–95)

13. 8% of 7500 600
14. 5% of 6800 340
15. 3% of 9400 282
16. 4% of 8196 327.84

EXERCISES

In Exercises 1–6, find the sticker price for each car. (Example 1)

	Base Price	Total Options	Destination Charge	
1.	\$7120	\$2890	\$225.80	\$10,235.80
2.	\$6500	\$1448	\$ 93.20	\$8041.20
3.	\$6200	\$1540	\$108.75	\$7848.75
4.	\$8927	\$1891.75	\$ 65.20	\$10,883.95
5.	\$7025	\$2361.20	\$253.80	\$9640.00
6.	\$6725	\$ 981.50	\$171.75	\$7878.25

7. The base price of a certain car is \$8400. The total cost of the options is \$927 and the destination charge is \$125. Find the sticker price. \$9452.00

8. The base price of a certain car is \$9650. The total cost of the options is \$1807.45 and the destination charge is \$189.25. What is the sticker price? \$11,646.70

Find the total cost of each car. (Example 2)

	Sticker Price	Tax Rate	Sales Tax	Total Cost
9.	\$10,000	7%	? \$700.00	? \$10,700.00
10.	\$ 8,320	4%	? \$332.80	? \$8652.80
11.	\$ 7,500	5%	? \$375.00	? \$7875.00
12.	\$ 9,200	8%	? \$736.00	? \$9936.00
13.	\$12,400	6%	? \$744.00	? \$13,144.00
14.	\$15,620	9%	? \$1405.80	? \$17,025.80

15. Hector plans to buy a car with a basic price of \$8250. The cost of the options that he wants is \$2236.25. The destination charge is \$289.60. The tax rate in his state is 5%.
    a. Find the sticker price. \$10,775.85
    b. Find the total cost. \$11,314.64

16. The sticker price of a certain car is \$12,832. The tax rate is 6%. Find the total cost. \$13,601.92

10-2 Making a Deal See the Teacher's Manual for the objectives.

Eliot Whitecloud is buying a new car. He plans to offer the automobile dealer an amount higher than the dealer's cost but lower than the sticker price.

EXAMPLE The car that Eliot wishes to buy has a base price of \$6815.00, optional equipment which totals \$1592.20, and a destination charge of \$183.00. From a consumer magazine, Eliot learns that the dealer's cost is 80% of the base price and 75% of the options.
Find the dealer's cost.

Solution: [1] Find 80% of the base price.

80% of \$6815 = \$6815 × 0.80
= **\$5452.00**

[2] Find 75% of the cost of the options.

75% of \$1592.20 = \$1592.20 × 0.75
= **\$1194.15**

[3] Add the answers in steps 1 and 2 to the destination charge.

\$5452.00 + \$1194.15 + \$183.00 = **\$6829.15** ◀ *Dealer's cost*

Thus, Eliot knows that he must make an offer higher than \$6829.15. This offer will also be lower than \$8590.20, the sticker price.

\$6815.00 + \$1592.20 + \$183.00 = **\$8590.20** ◀ *Base Price* + *Total Options* + *Destination Charge*

REVIEW OF RELATED SKILLS You may wish to use these exercises before teaching the lesson.

Add. (Pages 4–5)

1. \$8364.00 + \$1583.10 + \$179.00 \$10,126.10
2. \$6898.00 + \$1241.90 + \$170.00 \$8309.90

Write a decimal for each per cent. (Pages 90–91)

3. 95% 0.95
4. 60% 0.6
5. 85% 0.85
6. 76% 0.76
7. 84% 0.84
8. 77.3% 0.773

Find each answer. (Pages 94–95)

9. 80% of \$7215 \$5772.00
10. 75% of \$8715 \$6536.25
11. 77% of \$10,000 \$7700.00
12. 85% of \$12,420 \$10,557.00

EXERCISES

For Exercises 1–6, find the dealer's cost.

	Base Price	Per Cent of Base Price	Options Price	Per Cent of Options Price	Destination Charges	Estimated Dealer's Cost
1.	$7,986.00	80%	$ 984.00	75%	$170.00	? $7296.80
2.	$8,972.00	80%	$1246.00	75%	$184.00	? $8296.10
3.	$10,050.00	90%	$1500.00	80%	$190.00	? $10,435.00
4.	$9,400.00	75%	$1000.00	77%	$180.00	? $8000.00

5. Base price: $8000
Options: $888.00
Destination Charge: $186.00
Dealer pays: 80% of base price
and 70% of options price **$7207.60**

6. Base price: $12,500
Options: $1850
Destination Charge: $220
Dealer pays: 90% of base price
and 75% of options price **$12,857.50**

7. Hank Milton learned that a certain automobile dealer pays 90% of the base price for his cars and 70% of the cost of the options. Hank is interested in a car that has a base price of $10,000. The option prices add up to $1200 and destination charges are $168. Find the dealer's cost. **$10,008.00**

8. Maria Lepescu plans to buy a car that has a base price of $9500. The options she wants cost $900.00. The dealer pays 80% of the base price and 78% of the options. Destination charges are $170. Find the dealer's cost. **$8472.00**

More Challenging Problems

A dealer wants to sell the cars described in Exercises 9–11. The dealer wants to make a $300 profit on each car. The destination charge for each car is $180. Find the lowest price that the dealer will accept for each car.

9. Base price: $8000
Options: $800
Dealer pays: 85% of base price
and 75% of options price **$7880**

10. Base price: $8500
Options: $1100
Dealer pays: 80% of base price
and 70% of options price **$8050**

11. Base price: $9600
Options: $1200
Dealer pays: 80% of base price
75% of options price **$9060**

10-3 Financing a Car

See the Teacher's Manual for the objectives.

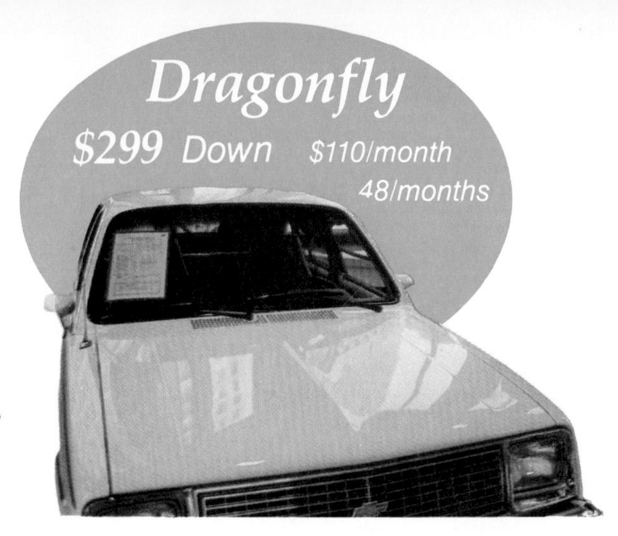

When shopping about for a new car, John Chu noticed newspaper advertisements such as the one at the right. He used this information to compare the total costs of several different cars. To find the total cost, first answer the question:

What is the total of monthly payments?

This is the **hidden question** in the problem. Then find the total cost.

EXAMPLE 1 Find the total cost of the car in the advertisement above.

Solution: [1] Find the total of monthly payments.

Monthly Payment	×	Number of Monthly Payments	=	Total of Monthly Payments
$110	×	**48**	=	**$5280**

[2]

Total of Monthly Payments	+	Down Payment	=	Total Cost
$5280	+	$299	=	**$5579**

After completing Example 1, you may wish to have students do some or all of Exercises 1-8.

When you finance a car, you first make a **down payment** on the car. A finance charge is added to the unpaid balance. The **finance charge** is the interest you pay for borrowing. You then make monthly payments on the unpaid balance. To find the finance charge, first answer this **hidden question:**

What is the total cost?

Then you can find the finance charge.

EXAMPLE 2 Find the finance charge for the car in the advertisement at the right.

SARATOGA '85
$7200 Cash or
$1200 Down and
$7704 over 36 months

Solution: [1] First find the total cost.

$7704 + $1200 = **$8904**

[2]

Total Cost	−	Cash Price	=	Finance Charge
$8904	−	$7200	=	**$1704**

REVIEW OF RELATED SKILLS

You may wish to use these exercises before teaching the lesson.

Multiply. (Pages 6–7)

1. $88 × 60 $5280
2. $192 × 36 $6912
3. $213 × 48 $10,224
4. $140 × 36 $5040
5. $256 × 24 $6144

Add or subtract. (Pages 2–3)

6. $2000 + $8000 $10,000
7. $1490 + $6800 $8290
8. $8446 + $1585 $10,031
9. $9056 + $843 $9899
10. $10,140 − $6400 $3740
11. $9360 − $8135 $1225
12. $12,422 − $10,079 $2343
13. $10,844 − $9235 $1609

EXERCISES

Find the total of monthly payments for the car in each advertisement. (Example 1, step 1)

1. $10,260

SEQUOIA '84
$1050 Down
$285/month
36 months

2. $7980

'85 CHEETAH
$2500 Down
$133/month
60 months

3. $9888

VENORA '83
$800 Down
$206/month
48 months

Find the total cost for the car in each advertisement. (Example 1)

4. $12,720

STARHAWK '86
$1200 Down
$240/month
48 months

5. $8546

'82 SUNCAT
$950 Down
$211/month
36 months

6. $9400

BRAVO '84
$1000 Down
$140/month
60 months

7. Janet Smythe put $800 down on her new car. She is paying $190 per month for 48 months. Find the total cost of the car. $9920

8. Paul Suzuki just bought a car. He put $900 down and will make monthly payments of $289 for the next 36 months. Find the total cost. $11,304

Find the finance charge for the car in each advertisement. (Example 2)

9. $2008

1986 SPORT
$8500 Cash or
$1400 Down and
$9108 over 36 months

10. $3700

INTREPID '82
$12,500 Cash or
$4500 Down and
$11,700 over 60 months

11. $2996

SCORPIO '85
$9460 Cash or
$3000 Down and
$9456 over 48 months

12. The cash price for a new Thor sedan is $9200. Randi White wants to finance the car by paying $2100 down and $9108 in monthly payments. Find the finance charge. $2008

13. Ken Lundquist plans to buy a 1985 Tempo which sells for $8900. He plans to finance the car by paying $400 down and $11,088 in monthly payments. Find the finance charge. $2588

USED CAR DEALER

Career lessons are optional. This lesson combines the skills of reading a table, finding a per cent of a number, and addition and subtraction of decimals.

By reading a used car guide, Martin Jones, a **used car dealer,** obtains information on average retail prices (selling prices) of various models of cars purchased from dealers the previous month. Prices are based on the number of miles driven and on the age of the car.

Compact Car A	*Average Retail Price*	*High Mileage — Subtract from Retail Price*			*Low Mileage — Add to Retail Price*		
		55,001–60,000	60,001–65,000	65,001–70,000	20,001–25,000	25,001–30,000	30,001–35,000
1 yr old	$4540	$400	$450	$525	$ 25	$ 0	$ 0
2 yr old	3765	300	350	400	250	175	125
3 yr old	3275	100	200	250	350	300	250
4 yr old	2590	25	75	150	450	400	350
Standard Car B							
1 yr old	$5465	$575	$625	$725	$325	$250	$200
2 yr old	4514	375	450	525	425	375	325
3 yr old	3650	250	325	375	600	550	500
4 yr old	3135	125	200	250	725	650	600

The table above shows the average retail prices of two models of used cars and the amount to be subtracted or added because of high or low mileage (mileage allowance). Consumers can use such information to determine how much they should expect to pay for a used car.

EXAMPLE Frank wants to buy a used car. He is considering a 2–year–old standard car which has been driven 64,000 miles and a 3–year–old compact car which has been driven 32,000 miles. If the sales tax in Frank's state is 6%, how much can he expect to save by buying the compact car?

Solution: Use the table to find the average retail price and the amount to be added or subtracted for mileage.

	Standard Car (2 years old)	**Compact Car (3 years old)**
Average retail price:	$4514.00	$3275.00
Mileage allowance:	− 450.00	+ 250.00
Total:	$4064.00	$3525.00
Tax:	+ 243.84	+ 211.50
Total + Tax:	**$4307.84**	**$3736.50**

Amount saved: $4307.84 − $3736.50 = **$571.34**

EXERCISES Note that Exercises 1–16 are non-verbal.

For Exercises 1–8, find the cost, including tax, for each used compact car. Use the table on page 214.

	Age of Car	Number of Miles Driven	Sales Tax	
1.	3 yr	22,000	5%	$3806.25
2.	2 yr	63,000	8%	$3688.20
3.	1 yr	26,000	7%	$4857.80
4.	4 yr	30,000	6%	$3169.40
5.	4 yr	65,798	8%	$2635.20
6.	3 yr	60,043	7%	$3290.25
7.	1 yr	20,006	5%	$4793.25
8.	2 yr	57,800	6%	$3672.90

For Exercises 9–16, find the cost, including tax, for each used standard car. Use the table on page 214.

	Age of Car	Number of Miles Driven	Sales Tax	
9.	2 yr	30,500	8%	$5226.12
10.	4 yr	68,000	6%	$3058.10
11.	1 yr	25,000	5%	$6079.50
12.	3 yr	66,000	7%	$3504.25
13.	1 yr	20,105	7%	$6195.30
14.	4 yr	34,998	8%	$4033.80
15.	2 yr	60,057	6%	$4307.84
16.	3 yr	55,032	5%	$3570

For Exercises 17–20, determine which car costs more. The sales tax is 6%.

17. A 2–year–old compact car that has been driven 55,500 miles or a 2–year–old standard car that has been driven 30,000 miles. standard

18. A 4–year–old standard car that has been driven 25,800 miles or a 3–year–old compact car that has been driven 62,500 miles. standard

19. A 3–year–old standard car that has been driven 34,099 miles or a 1–year–old compact car that has been driven 34,099 miles. compact

20. A 2–year–old compact car that has been driven 63,000 miles or a 2–year–old standard car that has been driven 60,000 miles. standard

21. Francis wants to buy a used car. He is considering a 1–year–old standard car that has been driven 56,000 miles and a 2–year–old compact car that has been driven 31,000 miles. The sales tax in Francis's state is 5%. How much will he save by buying the compact car? $1050

10-4 Liability Insurance

See the Teacher's Manual for the objectives.

Many states require that car owners carry **liability insurance.** Liability insurance has two parts.

1. **Bodily injury liability** protects the owner from financial loss if others are injured by the car.
2. **Property damage liability** protects the owner from financial loss if the car damages someone's property.

LIMITS OF LIABILITY

Bodily Injury		*Property Damage*
Each Person	*Each Occurrence*	*Each Occurrence*
$100,000	$300,000	$25,000

In insurance tables, bodily injury liability is often described as

Pays up to $100,000 to any one person injured. ▶ **100/300** ◀ *Pays up to $300,000 to two or more persons injured*

Insurance companies use tables to compute yearly premiums for drivers. The **yearly premium** is the amount you pay each year for insurance.

TABLE

Liability Insurance: Drivers 17 Years Old or Less	
With Driver Training	*Without Driver Training*
Basic rate: Male $280, Female $120	**Basic rate:** Male $310, Female $160
Rates include coverage for property damage up to $50,000.	
Coverage	**Yearly Premiums**
50/100	Basic rate × 2.09
100/300	Basic rate × 2.26
300/500	Basic rate × 2.56

EXAMPLE Maryellen Hanaka is 17. Use the sample rates in the table on page 216 to compute the following.

a. The yearly premium for 100/300 liability coverage without driver training.

b. The yearly premium for the same coverage with driver training.

c. The difference in the two premiums.

Solutions: First find the rate in the table for 100/300 coverage

100/300 Basic rate × 2.26

a. Without driver training: $160 × 2.26 = **$361.60** ◀ *Premium without driver training*

b. With driver training: $120 × 2.26 = **$271.20** ◀ *Premium with driver training*

c. Find the difference: $361.60 − $271.20 = **$90.40**

REVIEW OF RELATED SKILLS

You may wish to use these exercises before teaching the lesson.

Multiply. (Pages 8–9)

1. $280 × 2.09 $585.20 **2.** $310 × 2.56 $793.60 **3.** $160 × 2.26 $361.60 **4.** $120 × 2.56 $307.20

Subtract. (Pages 4–5)

5. $412.73 − $290.83 $121.90 **6.** $802.97 − $578.40 $224.57 **7.** $793.60 − $716.80 $76.80

EXERCISES

In Exercises 1–6, use the table on page 216 to compute the yearly premium.

	Coverage	Driver Training?	Male/Female	
1.	100/300	Yes	Male	$632.80
2.	100/300	No	Male	$700.60
3.	300/500	Yes	Female	$307.20
4.	300/500	No	Female	$409.60
5.	50/100	Yes	Female	$250.80
6.	50/100	Yes	Male	$585.20

7. Find the difference in the premiums paid in Exercises 1 and 2. $67.80

8. Find the difference in the premiums paid in Exercises 3 and 4. $102.40

9. Duane Epstein is 16. Use the table on page 216 to compute the difference between his yearly premium for 50/100 liability without driver training and his yearly premium for the same coverage with driver training. $62.70

10. Ralph and Diana Coote are 17–year old twins. They have both taken a driver's education course. Use the table on page 216 to compute the difference between their premiums for 300/500 liability coverage. $409.60

10-5 Collision/Comprehensive Insurance

See the Teacher's Manual for the objectives.

Collision insurance will help to pay for repairs on your car if it is involved in an accident. A **deductible of $100** means that you pay for the first $100 of damage or loss. The insurance company pays the rest.

EXAMPLE 1 Tim Murphy was involved in an accident in which he was at fault. The repair bill for the car was $342.75. How much will the insurance company pay for each collision coverage in the table?

Solutions:

Collision Insurance	*Amount Tim Pays*	*Amount Insurance Pays*
a. $50 deductible	$50	$342.75 − $50 = **$292.75**
b. $100 deductible	$100	$342.75 − $100 = **$242.75**

After completing Example 1, you may wish to have students do some or all of Exercises 1-6.

Comprehensive car insurance protects the owner from losses due to theft, fire, vandalism, and so on.

To calculate the premium for collision and comprehensive insurance, insurance companies assign a car to a certain class.

Yearly Premiums for Collision and Comprehensive Insurance

		Collision premium for		*Comprehensive premium for*	
Car	*Driver*	*$50 ded*	*$100 ded*	*No ded*	*$50 ded*
Class B	Teen female	$115	$85	$22	$10
	Teen male	$220	$160	$45	$20
	Married over 25	$60	$45	$20	$9
Class C	Teen female	$130	$95	$27	$13
	Teen male	$250	$185	$60	$26
	Married over 25	$65	$53	$26	$11

EXAMPLE 2 Calculate the premium for each of the following.

a. Collision insurance with a $100 deductible.

b. Comprehensive insurance with a $50 deductible.

c. Total collision and comprehensive insurance

Solution:
a. In the table, find the collision premium for a teen male with a $100 deductible. ⟶ $160
b. In the table, find the comprehensive premium for a teen male with a $50 deductible. ⟶ $ 20
c. Add the two premiums. ⟶ **$180**

REVIEW OF RELATED SKILLS

You may wish to use these exercises before teaching the lesson.

Add or subtract. (Pages 2–3, 4–5)

1. $416.83 − $100 $316.83
2. $329.50 − $50 $279.50
3. $809.10 − $100 $709.10
4. $98.12 − $50 $48.12
5. $220 + $9 $229
6. $170 + $15 $185
7. $185 + $10 $195
8. $250 + $60 $310

EXERCISES

How much will an insurance company pay for each accident? (Example 1)

	Amount of Repair Bill	Amount of Deductible	Insurance Pays
1.	$470	$50	? $420
2.	$107	$100	? $7

	Amount of Repair Bill	Amount of Deductible	Insurance Pays
3.	$83.94	$50	? $33.94
4.	$702.80	$100	? $602.80

5. George O'Connor accidently backed his car into a stone wall. The repair bill was $286.63. The collision policy has a $100 deductible. How much will the insurance company pay? $186.63
6. Marge Eckel's car was in an accident in which she was at fault. The repair bill was $87.42. The collision policy has a $50 deductible. How much will the insurance company pay? $37.42

Use the table on page 218 to compute the yearly premiums for collision and comprehensive insurance. (Example 2)

	Driver	Vehicle Class	Deductibles
7.	Teen female	C	Collision: $50 $130 Comprehensive: none $27
8.	Teen male	B	Collision: $50 $220 Comprehensive: $50 $20

	Driver	Vehicle Class	Deductibles
9.	Married over 25	B	Collision: $100 $45 Comprehensive: none $20
10.	Teen male	C	Collision: $50 $250 Comprehensive: $50 $26

11. Mrs. Doone is 30. Her car is in Class C. Compute her yearly premium for collision insurance with a $100 deductible and comprehensive with no deductible. $79
12. Rafael Diaz is 18. His car is in Class B. Compute his yearly premium for collision and comprehensive insurance. The deductible on each is $50. $240

RADIATOR TECHNICIAN

Career lessons are optional. This lesson applies the skills of reading a table and finding a per cent of a number.

Bob Tweedy's work as a **radiator technician** requires that he calculate the amount of coolant needed in the radiator of a car. This table shows how adding coolant to the water in a radiator raises the boiling point of the water (212°F).

Boiling Points with Coolant

Per Cent of Coolant	Boiling Point
50%	265°F
60%	270°F
70%	275°F

EXAMPLE A car radiator holds 15 quarts. How many quarts of coolant must be added to raise the boiling point to 270°F?

Solution: [1] Find 270°F in the table. Read the entry at the left.

60% ◀ ***The water must contain 60% coolant.***

[2] Find 60% of 15.

60% of 15 = 0.60 × 15

= **9**

Amount of coolant needed: **9 quarts.**

EXERCISES Note that Exercises 1--12 are non-verbal.

For Exercises 1–4, find the number of quarts of coolant needed to raise the boiling point of the water in a car radiator to 265°F.

1. 10 quarts 5 **2.** 14 quarts 7 **3.** 18 quarts 9 **4.** 20 quarts 10

For Exercises 5–8, find the number of quarts of coolant needed to raise the boiling point of the water in a car radiator to 270°F.

5. 12 quarts 7.2 **6.** 16 quarts 9.6 **7.** 13 quarts 7.8 **8.** 19 quarts 11.4

For Exercises 9–12, find the number of quarts of coolant needed to raise the boiling point of the water in a car radiator to 275°F.

9. 14 quarts 9.8 **10.** 15 quarts 10.5 **11.** 18 quarts 12.6 **12.** 20 quarts 14

13. A car radiator has a capacity of 10 quarts. How many quarts of coolant are needed to give it a boiling point of 275°F? 7

14. A car radiator has a capacity of 15 quarts. How many quarts of coolant are needed to give it a boiling point of 265°F? 7.5

15. A 20–quart radiator contains 14 quarts of coolant and 6 quarts of water. What is the boiling point? 275° F

CAUTION COMBUSTIBLE MIXTURE

Temperatures are shown in degrees Fahrenheit

Cooling System Capacity Quarts	QUARTS OF COOLANT REQUIRED							
	3	4	5	6				
8	−7	−34°						
9	0	−21						
10	4	−12	−34°					
11	8	−6	−23					
12	10	0	−15	−34°				
13		3	−9	−25				
14		6	−5	−17	−34°			
15		8	0	−12	−26			
16		10	2	−7	−19	−34°		
17			5	−4	−14	−27		
18			7	0	−10	−21	−34°	
19			9	2	−7	−16	−28	
20			10	4	−3	−12	−22	−34°

16. A 15–quart radiator contains 9 quarts of coolant and 6 quarts of water. What is the boiling point? 270° F

17. One–half of the water in a car radiator is replaced with coolant. What is the boiling point? 265° F

18. Three–fifths of the water in a car radiator is replaced with coolant. What is the boiling point of the mixture? 270° F

19. A radiator contains 60% coolant. The amount of coolant is increased 10%. By how many degrees is the boiling point increased? 5°

20. A radiator contains 50% coolant. The amount of coolant is increased 20%. By how many degrees is the boiling point increased? 10°

21. Suppose that a car radiator contains 80% coolant. What would you expect the boiling point of the mixture to be? 280° F

22. Suppose that a car radiator contains 40% coolant. What would you expect the boiling point to be? 260° F

23. Suppose that a car radiator contains no coolant. What is the boiling point? 212° F

Rounding and Estimation

Consumers use rounding and estimation to solve problems related to buying a car.

EXERCISES See the Teacher's Manual for the objectives.

Skills

Choose the best estimate. Choose a, b, or c.

1. $7421 + 188$ b — **a.** $7420 + 180$ **b.** $7420 + 190$ **c.** $7430 + 190$
2. $8397 + 118$ a — **a.** $8400 + 100$ **b.** $8300 + 100$ **c.** $8400 + 200$
3. 111.05×48 a — **a.** 110×50 **b.** 110×40 **c.** 120×50
4. $5\frac{1}{2}\% \times 8025$ a — **a.** $\frac{1}{20} \times 8000$ **b.** $\frac{1}{20} \times 9000$ **c.** $\frac{1}{10} \times 9000$
5. $4\frac{3}{4}\%$ of 8995 b — **a.** $\frac{1}{10} \times 9000$ **b.** $\frac{1}{20} \times 9000$ **c.** $\frac{1}{8} \times 9000$
6. $601.16 - 399.88$ a — **a.** $600 - 400$ **b.** $700 - 400$ **c.** $600 - 300$
7. $221.07 + 32.97$ b — **a.** $210 + 30$ **b.** $220 + 30$ **c.** $230 + 40$

Choose the best estimate. Choose a, b, c, or d.

8. $8603 + 221$ d — **a.** 8700 **b.** 8600 **c.** 8900 **d.** 8800
9. $9489 + 112$ a — **a.** 9600 **b.** 9500 **c.** 9700 **d.** 9900
10. 132.04×48 b — **a.** 6000 **b.** 6500 **c.** 7000 **d.** 7500
11. $9\frac{1}{2}\%$ of 9012 c — **a.** 1000 **b.** 1100 **c.** 900 **d.** 800
12. $10\frac{1}{2}\%$ of 7975 a — **a.** 800 **b.** 700 **c.** 1000 **d.** 900
13. $729.30 - 411.25$ a — **a.** 300 **b.** 400 **c.** 200 **d.** 500
14. $302.70 + 29.95$ b — **a.** 320 **b.** 330 **c.** 340 **d.** 350

Applications

15. The base price of an Onyx is \$7500. The total cost of the options is \$904.20 and the destination charge is \$196.75. Estimate the sticker price. b
    a. \$7500 + \$1000 + \$200
    b. \$7500 + \$900 + \$200
    c. \$7500 + \$800 + \$100
    d. \$8000 + \$1000 + \$200

16. June can purchase a certain car by making 48 monthly payments of \$151.20. Estimate the total of the monthly payments. c
    a. \$160 × 40
    b. \$150 × 40
    c. \$150 × 50
    d. \$160 × 50

Additional Practice

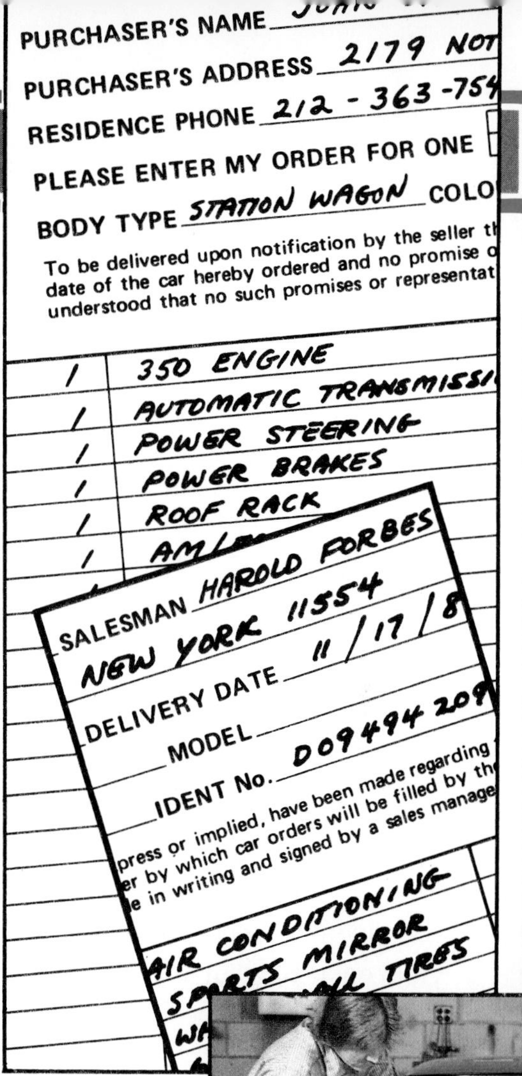

17. Patrick pays a premium of $698 for his liability insurance. Sue, who is the same age as Patrick, pays $361. Estimate the difference in their premiums. b

    a. $690 − $360 b. $700 − $360
    c. $700 − $350 d. $690 − $340

18. In a certain automobile insurance policy, the premium for liability insurance without driver training is $404.25. The premium with driver training is $342.16. Estimate the difference. a

    a. $400 − $340 b. $400 − $350
    c. $400 − $330 d. $450 − $350

19. The base price of a certain car is $8341. The total cost of options is $862.40 and the destination charge is $178.95. Estimate the sticker price. a

    a. $9400 b. $9500
    c. $9300 d. $9600

20. Larry can purchase a certain car by making 48 monthly payments of $133.16. Estimate the total of the monthly payments. c

    a. $6000
    b. $7000
    c. $6500
    d. $7500

21. On a certain automobile insurance policy, the premium for liability insurance without driver training is $397.85. The premium with it is $328.98. Estimate the difference. a

    a. $70
    b. $60
    c. $80
    d. $90

22. The collision insurance premium for a certain car is $181.25. The comprehensive insurance premium is $28.98. Estimate the total premium. b

    a. $200
    b. $210
    c. $220
    d. $230

Chapter Review

These exercises review the vocabulary, skills and applications presented in the chapter, as a preparation for the chapter test.

Part 1: VOCABULARY

For Exercises 1–5, choose from the box at the right the word(s) that complete(s) each statement.

base price finance charge property damage down payment premium collision bodily injury

1. The deposit that you make when you buy a car is the __?__. (Pages 212–213) down payment
2. The interest you pay for borrowing the unpaid balance to pay for a car is the __?__. (Pages 212–213) finance charge
3. The owner of a car is insured against financial loss because of injury to others by __?__ liability insurance. (Pages 216–217) bodily injury
4. The owner of a car is insured against financial loss because of damage to property by __?__ liability insurance. (Pages 216–217) property damage
5. The repairs on a car that has been in an accident will be partly paid for by __?__ insurance. (Pages 218–219) collision

Part 2: SKILLS

Add or subtract. (Pages 2–5)

6. \$119 + \$11 \$130 **7.** \$165 + \$13 \$178 **8.** \$190 + \$10 \$200 **9.** \$270 + \$40 \$310

10. \$7840 + \$203 + \$600 \$8643 **11.** \$9010 + \$312 + \$100 \$9422

12. \$10,060.00 + \$927.40 + \$180.00 \$11,167.40 **13.** \$7960.00 + \$1324.85 + \$160.00 \$9444.85

14. \$278.49 − \$150 \$128.49 **15.** \$741.10 − \$100 \$641.10 **16.** \$413.80 − \$250 \$163.80

17. \$130.84 − \$88.70 \$42.14 **18.** \$501.20 − \$238.76 \$262.44 **19.** \$902.12 − \$61.11 \$841.01

Multiply. (Pages 6–9)

20. \$72 × 60 \$4320 **21.** \$200 × 48 \$9600 **22.** \$156 × 36 \$5616 **23.** \$148 × 72 \$10,656

24. \$402 × 1.98 \$795.96 **25.** \$250 × 2.09 \$522.50 **26.** \$324 × 2.56 \$829.44 **27.** \$130 × 2.26 \$293.80

Write a decimal for each per cent. (Pages 90–91)

28. 3% 0.03 **29.** 5% 0.05 **30.** 7% 0.07 **31.** 6% 0.06 **32.** $8\frac{1}{2}$% 0.085 **33.** 2.3% 0.023

34. 70% 0.7 **35.** 40% 0.4 **36.** 55% 0.55 **37.** 86% 0.86 **38.** 23% 0.23 **39.** 41.2% 0.412

Find each answer. (Pages 94–95)

40. 5% of 1600 80 **41.** 7% of 8300 581 **42.** 3% of 4305 129.15 **43.** 9% of 7007 630.63

44. 90% of 6800 6120 **45.** 85% of 4200 3570 **46.** 67% of 9000 6030 **47.** 87% of 8000 6960

Add or subtract. (Pages 2–3)

48. \$3500 + \$9600 − \$8150 \$4950 **49.** \$1200 + \$7050 − \$6800 \$1450

Part 3: APPLICATIONS

For Exercises 50–53, find the total cost of each car. (Pages 208–209)

	Sticker Price	Tax Rate	Sales Tax	Total Cost
50.	$8000	6%	? $480	? $8480
51.	$9600	8%	? $768	? $10,368
52.	$11,500	5%	? $575	? $12,075
53.	$7400	7%	? $518	? $7918

54. A certain car dealer pays 80% of the base price of each car he sells and 75% of the cost of the optional equipment. The base price of one of his cars is $11,000 and the options are $1500. The destination charge is $180. Find the dealer's cost. (Pages 210–211) $10,105

55. Susan will make monthly payments of $225 for 48 months on a new car. Find the total of monthly payments. (Pages 212–213) $10,800

56. Milo plans to buy a car. He can pay $8000 cash or else pay $3600 down and $6302 over 48 months. Find the finance charge. (Pages 212–213) $1902

For Exercises 57 and 58, use the table below.

Drivers 17 Years Old or Less with Driver Training		
	Male	Female
Basic rate:	$295	$140
Rates include coverage for property damage up to $50,000.		
Coverage	**Yearly Premiums**	
100/300	Basic rate × 2.26	
300/500	Basic rate × 2.56	

57. What is the yearly premium for a 16-year old girl who has 300/500 liability coverage? (Pages 216–217) $358.40

58. What is the yearly premium for a 17-year old boy who has 100/300 liability coverage? (Pages 216–217) $666.70

59. The collision premium for a certain policy is $175. The comprehensive premium is $22. Estimate the total premium. (Pages 222–223) b

a. $190
b. $200
c. $210
d. $220

Chapter Test

The Teacher's Resource Book contains two forms of each chapter test.

Add.

1. \$6900 + \$805 + \$400 \$8105

2. \$8965.00 + \$1144.95 + \$180.00 \$10,289.95

Subtract.

3. \$486 − \$50 \$436

4. \$239 − \$100 \$139

5. \$87.42 − \$52.18 \$35.24

6. \$780.40 − \$116.50 \$663.90

Multiply.

7. \$81 × 36 \$2916

8. \$158 × 48 \$7584

9. \$145 × 2.32 \$336.40

10. \$380 × 2.84 \$1079.20

Find each answer.

11. 4% of 2300 92

12. 7% of 7600 532

13. 75% of 9455 7091.25

14. 83% of 11,000 9130

15. Alexander bought a car with a base price of \$6520. The total cost of the options was \$1572 and the destination charge was \$325. Find the sticker price. \$8417

16. Each monthly payment on Marguerite's car amounts to \$187. She makes 48 payments. Find the total of monthly payments. \$8976

17. Roberta intends to buy a car that has a base price of \$8700. The options she wants cost \$957. The dealer pays 80% of the base price and 75% of the options price. Destination charges are \$175. Find the dealer's cost. \$7852.75

18. The cash price of a new sedan is \$9350. Paul can finance it by making a down payment of \$2250 and monthly payments that total \$9206. Find the finance charge. \$2106

19. On a certain automobile insurance policy, the premium for liability insurance <u>without</u> driver training is \$394.80. The premium <u>with</u> driver training is \$321.60. Estimate the difference in the two premiums. d

a. \$100 **b.** \$60 **c.** \$80 **d.** \$70

20. Kurt drove his car into a parked car to avoid hitting a dog. His bill for repairs was \$173.86. The deductible on his insurance is \$100. How much will the insurance company pay? \$73.86

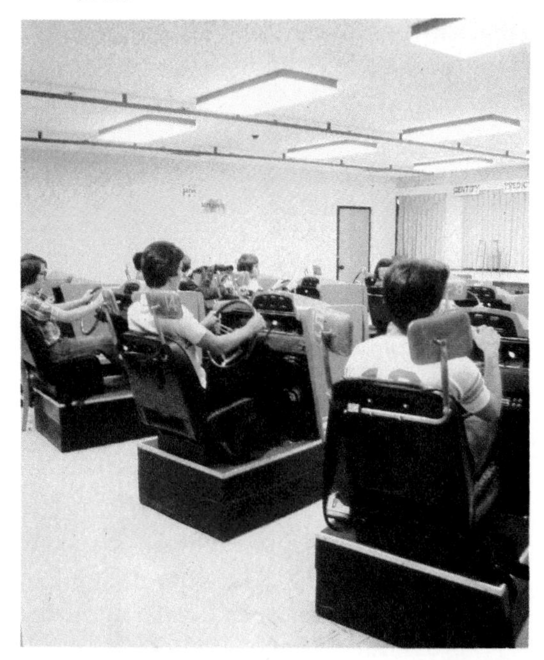

Additional Practice

You may wish to use all or some of these exercises, depending on how well students performed on the formal chapter test.

Skills

Add or subtract. (Pages 2–5)

1. 974 + 250 1224
2. 860.07 + 114.80 974.87
3. 762 − 150 612
4. 902.07 − 29.21 872.86

Multiply. (Pages 6–9)

5. 87 × 42 3654
6. 152 × 83 12,616
7. 212 × 4.26 903.12
8. 500 × 1.95 975

Write a decimal for each per cent. (Pages 90–91)

9. 2% 0.02
10. 8% 0.08
11. 11% 0.11
12. 60% 0.6
13. 90% 0.9
14. 98% 0.98

Applications

15. Della bought a new car. The base price was $7890, and the total cost of the options was $1042. The destination charge was $95. Find the sticker price. (Pages 208–209) $9027

16. A car dealer pays 80% of the base price for one car and 75% of the price of the options. The car has a $9600 base price and options which cost $1260. The destinations charge is $183. Find the dealer's cost. (Pages 210–211) $8808

17. An automobile showroom had the following ad. Find the total cost. (Pages 212–213) $11,940

THE 1983 CONDOR
$900 Down
$230/month
48 months

18. Find the finance charge for the car advertised below. (Pages 212–213) $2000

ASTEROID '86!
$7400 Cash or
$3300 down and
$6100 over 48 months

19. Alice Davis pays a premium of $300 for her liability automobile insurance. Greg Taylor, who is the same age as Alice, pays $690. Estimate the difference in their premiums. (Pages 222–223) b

    a. $300 b. $400
    c. $90 d. $1000

20. Barney's car was in an accident. The repair bill was $378.49. The deductible was $50. Estimate the amount that the insurance company will pay. c (Pages 222–223)

    a. $300 b. $350
    c. $330 d. $340

REVIEW OF RELATED SKILLS FOR CHAPTER 11

We suggest that some or all of this page be reviewed before proceeding with the chapter.

Add. (Pages 4–5)

1. \$17.96 + \$23.45 + \$82.80 + \$1.67 \$125.88
2. \$98.40 + \$13.62 + \$12.90 + \$12.70 \$137.62
3. \$41.68 + \$2.52 + \$99.06 + \$41.28 \$184.54
4. \$71.90 + \$13.26 + \$80.04 + \$44.20 \$209.40
5. \$2500 + \$800 + \$51.80 + \$23.75 \$3375.55
6. \$1750 + \$420 + \$905 + \$12.28 \$3087.28

Write a decimal for each per cent. (Pages 90–91)

7. 2% 0.02 **8.** 4% 0.04 **9.** 7% 0.07 **10.** 11% 0.11 **11.** 14% 0.14 **12.** 17% 0.17

Divide. Round each answer to the nearest hundredth. (Pages 16–17)

13. \$230 ÷ 12,000 \$.02 **14.** \$170 ÷ 9000 \$.02 **15.** \$200 ÷ 16,000 \$.01 **16.** \$700 ÷ 22,000 \$.03

Find each answer. (Pages 94–95)

17. 8% of \$790 \$63.20 **18.** 3% of \$485 \$14.55 **19.** 6% of \$82.70 \$4.96 **20.** 9% of \$43.90 \$3.95
21. 28% of \$8200 \$2296 **22.** 60% of \$8600 \$5160 **23.** 34% of \$2900 \$986 **24.** 47% of \$5100 \$2397

Add. (Pages 2–3)

25. 17 + 28 + 10 + 12 67 **26.** 12 + 15 + 14 + 14 55 **27.** 17 + 12 + 14 + 13 56

Multiply. (Pages 6–7)

28. 17,000 × 4 68,000 **29.** 26,000 × 8 208,000 **30.** 16,000 × 2 32,000 **31.** 31,800 × 3 95,400

Round to the nearest hundredth. (Pages 16–17)

32. 0.031 0.03 **33.** 0.064 0.06 **34.** 0.0791 0.08 **35.** 0.08338 0.08 **36.** 0.06159 0.06

Divide. Round each answer to the nearest hundredth. (Pages 16–17)

37. \$2700 ÷ 54,000 \$.05 **38.** \$4607 ÷ 50,000 \$.09 **39.** \$3940 ÷ 82,000 \$.05
40. \$5680 ÷ 72,000 \$.08 **41.** \$3565 ÷ 62,000 \$.06 **42.** \$2803 ÷ 41,000 \$.07

Round to the nearest whole number. (Pages 16–17)

43. 42.71 43 **44.** 16.01 16 **45.** 81.92 82 **46.** 46.23 46 **47.** 47.91 48 **48.** 64.51 65

Multiply. (Pages 8–9)

49. 0.071 × 35,000 2485 **50.** 0.084 × 26,000 2184 **51.** 0.068 × 27,000 1836

Divide. Round each answer to the nearest thousandth. (Pages 16–17)

52. \$7484.75 ÷ 16,000 \$.468 **53.** \$4267.50 ÷ 29,000 \$.147 **54.** \$8844.60 ÷ 21,000 \$.421
55. \$4856.60 ÷ 13,000 \$.374 **56.** \$6556.70 ÷ 21,000 \$.312 **57.** \$7268.90 ÷ 24,000 \$.303
58. \$5428.20 ÷ 14,000 \$.388 **59.** \$7364.80 ÷ 18,000 \$.409 **60.** \$3863.70 ÷ 12,000 \$.322

CHAPTER

11 OWNING A CAR

CONSUMER SKILLS/APPLICATIONS

11-1 Maintenance Costs
11-2 Depreciation
11-3 Gasoline Costs
11-4 Yearly Driving Costs
Rounding and Estimation

CAREER APPLICATIONS

Auto Mechanic
Police Officer

11-1 Maintenance Costs

See the Teacher's Manual for the objectives.

Greg's car is $1\frac{1}{2}$ years old. He knows that he saves money by having his car checked regularly at a reliable dealer to keep it in good running condition. The costs of upkeep and repair for a car are called **maintenance costs.**

GREAT RIDGE AUTO CENTER
Wheel Alignment & Balancing
Brakes Checked & Installed
42 Jerome Street 442-6995

EXAMPLE 1 Compute the total cost for these repairs. The sales tax rate in Greg's state is 4%. (This total cost does not include labor.)

Wheel alignment: \$14.75 Air filter: \$5.93

Shock absorbers: \$32.50 Other parts: \$48.75

Solution: 1 Find the total cost for parts.

\$14.75 + \$32.50 + \$5.93 + \$48.75 = **\$101.93**

2 Find the sales tax.

4% of \$101.93 = \$101.93 × 0.04 = **\$4.08** ◀ *Rounded to the nearest cent*

3 Find the total cost.

\$101.93 + \$4.08 = **\$106.01** ◀ *Total cost, not including labor*

After completing Example 1, you may wish to have students do some or all of Exercises 1-6.

The following table shows estimated maintenance costs for a car over 6 years.

Year	1	2	3	4	5	6
Maintenance Costs	\$100	\$150	\$300	\$340	\$490	\$500

EXAMPLE 2 Laura's car is 3 years old. She drives her car 7000 miles per year. Estimate her maintenance cost per mile for next year.

Solution: **Estimated costs** ÷ **Number of miles** = **Cost per mile**

\$340 ÷ 7000 = \$ 0.05 ◀ *7000)340.000 = 0.048*

= **5¢ per mile** (nearest cent)

REVIEW OF RELATED SKILLS

You may wish to use these exercises before teaching the lesson.

Add. (Pages 4–5)

1. \$16.83 + \$19.95 + \$64.70 + \$2.85 \$104.33

2. \$65.70 + \$18.95 + \$14.50 + \$21.75 \$120.90

3. \$10.50 + \$5.98 + \$14.89 + \$19.60 \$50.97

4. \$17.89 + \$23.45 + \$6.48 + \$12.50 \$60.32

Write a decimal for each per cent. (Pages 90–91)

5. 4% 0.04 **6.** 6% 0.06 **7.** 5% 0.05 **8.** 8% 0.08 **9.** 10% 0.1 **10.** 15% 0.15

Divide. Round each answer to the nearest hundredth. (Pages 16–17)

11. $150 ÷ 10,000 $0.02 **12.** $490 ÷ 8000 $0.06 **13.** $300 ÷ 15,000 $0.02 **14.** $500 ÷ 21,000 $0.02

Find each answer. (Pages 94–95)

15. 4% of $640 $25.60 **16.** 5% of $305 $15.25 **17.** 7% of $25.60 $1.79 **18.** 6% of $50.10 $3.01

EXERCISES

For Exercises 1–6, find the total cost for the repairs. For Exercises 1–4, the sales tax rate is 5%. (Example 1)

	Oil Change	Air Filter	Wheel Alignment	Shock Absorbers	Engine Tune-up	Other Parts	Amount of Tax	Total Cost
1.	$6.50	$4.95	$12.98	—	$43.50	$50.65	? $5.93	? $124.51
2.	$7.75	—	$11.75	$38.00	—	$36.50	? $4.70	? $98.70
3.	—	$5.25	$12.50	—	$38.95	$40.00	? $4.84	? $101.54
4.	—	$4.50	—	$42.25	—	$21.50	? $3.41	? $71.66

5. Sam paid $28.95 to have a muffler installed and $12.98 for a brake adjustment. Other parts cost $38.50. Find the total cost when the sales tax is 4%. $83.65

6. Maura paid $42.75 for an engine tune-up and $12.50 for a new oil filter and an oil change. Other parts cost $27.60. Find the total cost when the sales tax is 7%. $88.65

For Exercises 7–16, find the estimated maintenance cost per mile or per kilometer for the following year. Use the table on page 230. (Example 2)

	Age of Car (Years)	(cost per mile) Miles Per Year
7.	2	15,000 2¢
8.	1	8,000 2¢
9.	5	14,000 4¢

	Age of Car (Years)	(cost per kilometer) Kilometers Per Year
10.	5	20,000 3¢
11.	4	18,000 3¢
12.	3	12,000 3¢

13. Wanda's car is 4 years old. She drives her car 13,000 kilometers per year. 4¢ per kilometer

14. Jeremy's car is 3 years old. He drives his car 14,000 kilometers per year. 2¢ per kilometer

15. Casey's car is 2 years old. He drives his car 9000 miles per year. 3¢ per mile

16. Joan's car is 5 years old. She drives her car 12,000 miles per year. 4¢ per mile

11-2 Depreciation

See the Teacher's Manual for the objectives.

The table at the right shows the per cent of depreciation of a new car for each of 6 years. **Depreciation** is the decrease in value of a car because of its age and condition.

End of Year	1	2	3	4	5	6
Depreciation	20%	12%	11%	11%	10%	10%

EXAMPLE 1 Lisa Turog paid $6700 for a new car. Find the total depreciation after 4 years.

Solution: [1] Find the total depreciation in per cent after 4 years.

$20\% + 12\% + 11\% + 11\% = \mathbf{54\%}$

[2] Find the total depreciation.

$54\% \text{ of } \$6700 = \$6700 \times 0.54$

$= \mathbf{\$3618}$ ◀ *Depreciation after 4 years*

After completing Example 1, you may wish to have students do some or all of Exercises 1-16.

Depreciation is often computed in cents per kilometer or per mile.

EXAMPLE 2 Lisa drives her car about 24,000 kilometers per year. Use the answer to Example 1 to compute the amount of depreciation per kilometer for the 4 years.

Solution: [1] Find the number of kilometers driven over 4 years.

$24{,}000 \times 4 = \mathbf{96{,}000}$

[2] Divide the amount of depreciation by the number of kilometers.

$\$3618 \div 96{,}000 = \$0.037$ ◀ *Round to the nearest cent.*

$= \$0.04$ or **4¢ per kilometer**

REVIEW OF RELATED SKILLS

You may wish to use these exercises before teaching the lesson.

Add. (Pages 2–3)

1. $19 + 25 + 14 + 11$ 69
2. $13 + 16 + 10 + 10$ 49
3. $15 + 13 + 12 + 10$ 50

Find each answer. (Pages 94–95)

4. 35% of $6400 $2240
5. 32% of $2400 $768
6. 43% of $3100 $1333
7. 54% of $3500 $1890

Multiply. (Pages 6–7)

8. $18{,}000 \times 3$ 54,000
9. $21{,}000 \times 5$ 105,000
10. $19{,}000 \times 4$ 76,000
11. $23{,}800 \times 2$ 47,600

Round to the nearest hundredth. (Pages 16–17)

12. 0.047 0.05 **13.** 0.032 0.03 **14.** 0.0563 0.06 **15.** 0.0439 0.04 **16.** 0.0748 0.07

Divide. Round each answer to the nearest hundredth. (Pages 16–17)

17. \$4200 ÷ 48,000 \$.09 **18.** \$3716 ÷ 60,000 \$.06 **19.** \$2850 ÷ 36,000 \$.08

EXERCISES

For Exercises 1–16, find the total depreciation after the given number of years. Use the table on page 232. (Example 1)

	Price of New Car	Years		Price of New Car	Years		Price of New Car	Years
1.	\$7500	2 \$2400	**5.**	\$7100	5 \$4544	**9.**	\$6900	2 \$2208
2.	\$8600	4 \$4644	**6.**	\$8400	1 \$1680	**10.**	\$5800	4 \$3132
3.	\$6800	1 \$1360	**7.**	\$9600	3 \$4128	**11.**	\$6300	6 \$4662
4.	\$7400	3 \$3182	**8.**	\$7800	6 \$5772	**12.**	\$7200	5 \$4608

13. Robin's car cost \$8600 when it was new. It is now 3 years old. \$3698

14. Paul paid \$7500 for his car when he bought it. It is now 2 years old. \$2400

15. Bill's car is now 5 years old. When it was new, it cost \$5800. \$3712

16. Alice's car is now 4 years old. When it was new, it cost \$6600. \$3564

For Exercises 17–24, find the amount of depreciation per kilometer or per mile. (Example 2)

	Kilometers Per Year	Number of Years	Total Depreciation	(per kilometer)
17.	18,000	4	\$3800	5¢
18.	16,000	2	\$2700	8¢
19.	20,000	1	\$1800	9¢
20.	22,000	5	\$4200	4¢

	Miles Per Year	Number of Years	Total Depreciation	(per mile)
21.	19,000	6	\$5100	4¢
22.	14,000	3	\$3400	8¢
23.	12,000	4	\$4100	9¢
24.	18,000	2	\$2800	8¢

More Challenging Problems

For Exercises 25–26, find the following:
a. total depreciation
b. depreciation per kilometer or per mile

25. Wilhelm drives his car 20,000 kilometers per year. The car is 3 years old and cost \$6800 when it was new. \$2924; 5¢ per kilometer

26. Sheila's car is 4 years old. It cost \$7200 when it was new. She drives it 14,000 miles per year. \$3888; 7¢ per mile

AUTO MECHANIC

Career lessons are optional.
This lesson applies the skills of using a formula and using exponents.

Automobile mechanics must be able to work with both metric and customary measures, because many measurements relating to cars are given in both systems.

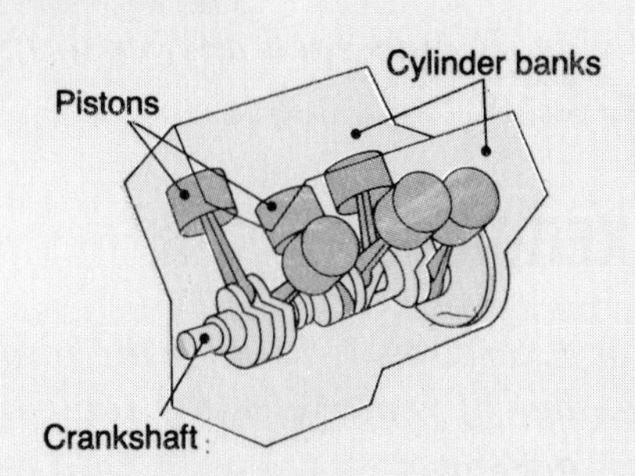

Here are some important terms that auto mechanics must be familiar with.

IMPORTANT TERMS

Displacement: total volume of an engine's cylinders
Bore: diameter of an engine cylinder
Stroke: the distance a piston moves

Larry Lovisa, a mechanic, knows how to compute the displacement of an engine by using the following formula.

$$D = \pi \times \left(\frac{b}{2}\right)^2 \times s \times n$$

***D* = displacement in cubic cm or cubic in**
***b* = bore in cm or in**
***s* = stroke in cm or in**
***n* = number of cylinders**

Recall the following:

$\left(\frac{b}{2}\right)^2$ means $\frac{b}{2} \times \frac{b}{2}$ ***The raised "2" is an exponent.***

EXAMPLE Larry wants to find the displacement of an engine with a bore of 7 cm and a stroke of 7.3 cm. The engine has 4 cylinders. Round the answer to the nearest cubic centimeter.

Solution: Use paper and pencil or use a calculator.

$$D = \pi \times \frac{b}{2} \times \frac{b}{2} \times s \times n$$

π = 3.14; b = 7; s = 7.3; n = 4

$$D = 3.14 \times \frac{7}{2} \times \frac{7}{2} \times 7.3 \times 4$$

3 . 1 4 × 7 ÷ 2 × — 10.99

7 ÷ 2 × 7 . 3 × 4 = — 1123.178

The displacement is about **1123 cubic centimeters.**

EXERCISES Note that Exercises 1–8 are non-verbal.

For Exercises 1–8, use $D = \pi \times \left(\frac{b}{2}\right)^2 \times s \times n$ *to find the displacement of each engine. Round each answer to the nearest cubic centimeter or cubic inch.*

	Bore	Stroke	Number of Cylinders
1.	8.5 cm	8.6 cm	4 1951 cm^3
2.	8.55 cm	6.9 cm	4 1584 cm^3
3.	8.4 cm	8.44 cm	4 1870 cm^3
4.	9.0 cm	5.89 cm	4 1498 cm^3

	Bore	Stroke	Number of Cylinders
5.	3.75 in	3.9 in	6 258 in^3
6.	3.15 in	3.35 in	6 157 in^3
7.	4 in	3 in	8 301 in^3
8.	3.5 in	3.38 in	8 260 in^3

For Exercises 9–16, round each answer to the nearest cubic centimeter or cubic inch.

9. Find the displacement of a 4–cylinder engine with a bore of 8.8 cm and a stroke of 9.2 cm. 2237 cm^3

10. Find the displacement of an 8–cylinder engine that has a bore of 3.5 in and a stroke of 2.8 in. 215 in^3

11. A certain six–cylinder sedan has a bore of 3.5 inches and a stroke of 3 inches. Find the displacement of the engine. 173 in^3

12. A 8–cylinder sedan has a 9.2 centimeter bore and a 7.3 centimeter stroke. Find the displacement. 3880 cm^3

13. One luxury sedan has a bore of 3.25 inches and a stroke of 3.6 inches. It has a six–cylinder engine. Find the engine's displacement. 179 in^3

14. Find the displacement of a four–cylinder engine that has a bore of 9.6 cm and a stroke of 7.94 cm. 2298 cm^3

15. Find the displacement of an 8–cylinder engine that has a bore of 3.74 in and a stroke of 3.48 in. 306 in^3

16. An 8–cylinder station wagon has a bore of 9.93 centimeters and a stroke of 8.41 centimeters. Find the engine's displacement. 5208 cm^3

11-3 Gasoline Costs

See the Teacher's Manual for the objectives.

Julio is trying to decide which of two intermediate cars to buy. He knows that the <u>fuel economy</u> of the car will affect gasoline costs. The **fuel economy** of a car refers to how many miles it can travel on one gallon of gasoline.

EXAMPLE 1 A certain intermediate car travels 495 miles on 19.5 gallons of of gasoline. A second intermediate car travels 420 miles on 15 gallons of gasoline. Which car has the greater fuel economy?

Solution: **Number of Miles ÷ Number of Gallons = Fuel Economy**

Fuel Economy (first car): 495 ÷ 19.5 = 25.38 ◀ *Round down to nearest gallon*

= **25 miles per gallon.**

Fuel Economy (second car): 420 ÷ 15 = **28 miles per gallon.**

Since 28 > 25, the **second car** has the greater fuel economy.

After completing Example 1, you may wish to have students do some or all of Exercises 1-13.

Businesses that use cars for travel often calculate car expenses in terms of cost per mile or cost per kilometer.

EXAMPLE 2 Karl Whitmore, a book salesperson, drives his car 64,000 kilometers per year. The yearly cost for gasoline is $3072. Find his yearly cost per kilometer.

Solution: **Total Yearly Cost for Gasoline ÷ Total Kilometers Driven = Cost per Kilometer**

$3072 ÷ 64,000 = $0.048 ◀ *Round to the nearest cent.*

= **5¢ per kilometer**

REVIEW OF RELATED SKILLS

You may wish to use these exercises before teaching the lesson.

Round to the nearest whole number. (Pages 16–17)

1. 21.36 21 **2.** 19.04 19 **3.** 25.73 26 **4.** 18.92 19 **5.** 26.08 26 **6.** 31.51 32

Divide. Round each answer to the nearest whole number. (Pages 16–17)

7. 306 ÷ 16.1 19 **8.** 470 ÷ 23.8 20 **9.** 530 ÷ 12.9 41 **10.** 444 ÷ 18.5 24

Round to the nearest hundredth. (Pages 16–17)

11. 0.043 0.04 **12.** 0.059 0.06 **13.** 0.064 0.06 **14.** 0.078 0.08 **15.** 0.0473 0.05 **16.** 0.0539 0.05

Divide. Round each answer to the nearest hundredth. (Pages 16–17)

17. $2450 ÷ 48,000 $0.05

18. $2800 ÷ 36,000 $0.08

19. $3000 ÷ 55,000 $0.05

20. $3600 ÷ 66,000 $0.05

EXERCISES

For Exercises 1–9, determine the fuel economy. (Example 1)

	Miles	Gallons of Fuel	(miles per gallon)
1.	270	10	27
2.	344	13.2	26
3.	451	16.1	28

	Miles	Gallons of Fuel	(miles per gallon)
4.	400	11.1	36
5.	260	12.9	20
6.	297	10.6	28

	Kilometers	Liters of Fuel	(kilometers per liter)
7.	496	47.6	10
8.	565	48.4	12
9.	888	68.8	13

For Exercises 10–13, determine which car has the greater fuel economy. (Example 1)

10. One compact car travels 513 miles on 12.5 gallons of gasoline. Another compact car travels 480 miles on 13.2 gallons of gasoline. First car

11. One intermediate car travels 335 miles on 15.8 gallons of gasoline. Another car travels 328 miles on 16.4 gallons of gasoline. First car

12. One luxury car travels 506 kilometers on 75.9 liters of fuel. Another luxury car travels 516 kilometers on 71.8 liters of fuel. Second car

13. One sports car travels 388 kilometers on 52.6 liters of fuel. Another sports car travels 460 kilometers on 58.1 liters of fuel. Second car

For Exercises 14–27, find the yearly gasoline cost per kilometer or per mile. (Example 2)

	Yearly Fuel Cost	Kilometers Per Year	(cost per kilometer)
14.	$1104	24,000	5¢
15.	$1064	28,000	4¢
16.	$2700	36,000	8¢
17.	$2240	40,000	6¢
18.	$1332	18,000	7¢
19.	$1280	20,000	6¢

	Yearly Fuel Cost	Miles Per Year	(cost per mile)
20.	$ 780	10,000	8¢
21.	$ 780	12,000	7¢
22.	$1176	14,000	8¢
23.	$1314	18,000	7¢
24.	$1005	15,000	7¢
25.	$1014	13,000	8¢

26. Jeanne Keily, a taxi driver, travels 50,000 kilometers per year. The yearly cost for gasoline is $3400. 7¢ per kilometer

27. Bob Hines, a fire inspector, drives 25,000 miles per year. The yearly cost for gasoline is $1800. 7¢ per mile

11-4 Yearly Driving Costs

See the Teacher's Manual for the objectives.

Martha read a news report that gave the average cost of driving a compact car 15,000 miles per year as 25.1¢ per mile. Martha decided to compute the average yearly cost per mile for her compact car.

To find the cost per mile, you must know the:

1. Fixed costs
2. Variable costs
3. Other costs

EXAMPLE Martha drives her car 25,000 miles per year. She listed the fixed costs and the variable costs for operating her car over the previous year. Compute each of the following:

a. Total fixed costs
b. Total variable costs
c. Total driving cost per year
d. Cost per mile

Solutions:

		YEARLY TOTALS	
a.	**FIXED COSTS**		
	1. Depreciation	$2100	
	2. Insurance	$ 700	
	3. License, registration, taxes	$ 250	
	4. Finance charges	$ 875	
	5. **TOTAL FIXED COSTS**	$3925	*Line 1 + line 2 + Line 3 + line 4*
b.	**VARIABLE COSTS**		
	6. Gas and oil per mile	$ 0.076	
	7. Number of miles driven	25,000	
	8. Cost per year	$1900	*Line 6 × Line 7*
	9. Maintenance	$ 325	
	10. Tires (average yearly cost)	$ 12.50	
	11. **TOTAL VARIABLE COSTS**	$2237.50	*Line 8 + Line 9 + Line 10*
	12. **OTHER COSTS** (car wash, tolls, parking fees, etc.)	$ 300	
c.	13. **TOTAL YEARLY DRIVING COSTS**	$6462.50	*Line 5 + Line 11 + Line 12*
d.	14. **COST PER MILE**	$0.2585	*Line 13 ÷ Line 7*

Thus, the cost per mile is **25.9¢**. *Rounded to the nearest tenth of a cent*

REVIEW OF RELATED SKILLS

You may wish to use these exercises before teaching the lesson.

Perform the indicated operation. (Pages 4–5, 8–9)

1. $3200 + $700 + $49.50 + $16.25 $3695.75
2. $1300 + $360 + $875 + $14.95 $2549.95
3. 0.084 × 24,000 2016
4. 0.092 × 18,000 1656
5. 0.072 × 25,000 1800
6. 0.069 × 28,000 1932

Divide. Round each answer to the nearest thousandth. (Pages 16–17)

7. $5321.50 ÷ 18,000 $.296
8. $3465.75 ÷ 24,000 $.144
9. $6498.40 ÷ 27,000 $.241

EXERCISES

For Exercises 1–4, find the cost per mile to the nearest tenth of a cent.

	Total Fixed Costs	Total Variable Costs	Other Costs	Total Mileage	Total Yearly Driving Costs	Cost Per Mile
1.	$3416	$1825	$450	20,000	$5691 ?	? 28.5¢
2.	$4650	$1975	$320.50	18,000	$6945.50 ?	? 38.6¢
3.	$3829	$2120.50	$218.75	21,000	$6168.25 ?	? 29.4¢
4.	$3118	$1865.70	$455.60	24,000	$5439.30 ?	? 22.7¢

For Exercises 5–7, find the missing amounts.

		5. Yearly Totals	6. Yearly Totals	7. Yearly Totals
a.	**FIXED COSTS**			
	1. Depreciation	$1800	$2400	$2000
	2. Insurance	$ 650	$ 780	$ 760
	3. License, registration, taxes	$ 200	$ 210	$ 240
	4. Finance charge	$ 760	$ 815	$ 850
	5. **TOTAL FIXED COSTS**	$3410 ?	$4205 ?	$3850 ?
b.	**VARIABLE COSTS**			
	6. Gas and oil per mile	$0.072	$0.078	$0.086
	7. Number of miles driven	25,000	18,000	15,000
	8. Cost per year	$1800 ?	$1404 ?	$1290 ?
	9. Maintenance	$ 415	$ 350	$ 298
	10. Tires	$14.70	$12.50	$10.75
	11. **TOTAL VARIABLE COSTS**	$2229.70 ?	$1766.50 ?	$1598.75 ?
	12. **OTHER COSTS**	$350	$400	$200
c.	13. **TOTAL DRIVING COSTS**	$5989.70 ?	$6371.50 ?	$5648.75 ?
d.	14. **COST PER MILE**	24.0¢ ?	35.4¢ ?	37.7¢ ?

POLICE OFFICER

Career lessons are optional.
This lesson combines the skills of using a formula, reading a table, and multiplication of decimals.

Police officers have training in driving safety and in handling emergencies. They learn that a car's speed and the conditions of the road affect a driver's ability to stop quickly.

Reaction distance is the distance a car travels during the time it takes a driver to brake the car. You can use the following formula to estimate reaction distance.

$d = 1.1 \times r$ ◀ ***d = reaction distance in feet***
r = speed in mi/hr

EXAMPLE 1 Dan Schneider is driving at 50 miles per hour on a dry asphalt road. Estimate the reaction distance.

Solution: $d = 1.1 \times r$ ◀ ***r = 50***

$d = 1.1 \times 50 = 55$ The reaction distance is **55 feet.**

Braking distance is the distance traveled by a car after the driver brakes and until the car stops completely. You can use the following formula to estimate braking distance.

$b = \frac{r \times r}{30 \times F}$ ◀ ***b = braking distance in feet***
F = driving surface factor

Type of Surface	*Driving Surface Factor Dry Road*	*Wet Road*
Asphalt	0.85	0.65
Concrete	0.90	0.60
Gravel	0.65	0.65
Packed Snow	0.45	0.45

EXAMPLE 2 Use the table at the right above to estimate Dan's braking distance from Example 1 to the nearest foot.

Solution: Use pencil and paper or use a calculator.

$b = \frac{r \times r}{30 \times F}$ ◀ ***r = 50; F = 0.85 from the table***

1 First compute the denominator. Store the value in memory.

3 0 × . 8 5 = M+

2 Compute the numerator. Then divide it by the denominator.

5 0 × 5 0 = ÷ MR =

M 98.039216

The braking distance is about **98 feet.**

EXERCISES

For Exercises 1–5, estimate the reaction distance for each period. (Example 1)

1. 35 mi/hr 38.5 ft **2.** 40 mi/hr 44 ft **3.** 55 mi/hr 60.5 ft **4.** 48 mi/hr 52.8 ft **5.** 26 mi/hr 28.6 ft

Use the formula $b = \frac{r \times r}{30 \times F}$ *to complete the tables. Round each answer to the nearest foot.* (Example 2)

	Rate r	Driving Surface Factor F	Braking Distance b
6.	50 mi/hr	0.65	? 128
7.	55 mi/hr	0.45	? 224
8.	45 mi/hr	0.85	? 79
9.	35 mi/hr	0.65	? 63
10.	30 mi/hr	0.90	? 33

	Rate r	Driving Surface Factor F	Braking Distance b
11.	25 mi/hr	0.60	? 35
12.	37 mi/hr	0.85	? 54
13.	43 mi/hr	0.90	? 68
14.	55 mi/hr	0.85	? 119
15.	40 mi/hr	0.65	? 82

In Exercises 16–23, use the table on page 240. Round each answer to the nearest foot.

16. Darlene is driving at 25 miles per hour on a snow-packed road. Estimate the reaction distance. 28 feet

17. Doug is driving at 30 miles per hour on a wet concrete road. Estimate the reaction distance. 33 feet

18. Estimate Darlene's braking distance from Exercise 16. 46 feet

19. Estimate Doug's braking distance from Exercise 17. 50 feet

20. Abe is driving at 45 miles per hour on a dry asphalt road. Ann is driving at 40 miles per hour over the same road. What is the difference in their reaction distances? 5.5 feet

21. What is the difference in the braking distances in Exercise 20? 16 feet

22. Elaine is driving at 40 miles per hour on a dry concrete road. Earl is driving at 40 miles per hour on a wet concrete road. What is the difference in reaction distances? 0 feet

23. What is the difference in the braking distances in Exercise 23? 30 feet

Rounding and Estimation

Consumers use rounding and estimation to solve problems related to owning a car.

EXERCISES See the Teacher's Manual for the objectives.

Skills

Choose the best estimate. Choose a, b, or c.

	a.	b.	c.
1. 37.98 + 11.15 c	**a.** 38 + 12	**b.** 37 + 11	**c.** 38 + 11
2. 109.65 + 41.22 a	**a.** 110 + 40	**b.** 100 + 40	**c.** 110 + 50
3. $5\frac{1}{2}$% of 61.30 c	**a.** $\frac{1}{10} \times 60$	**b.** $\frac{1}{5} \times 60$	**c.** $\frac{1}{20} \times 60$
4. 32% of 8113 b	**a.** $\frac{1}{3} \times 8200$	**b.** $\frac{1}{3} \times 8100$	**c.** $\frac{1}{4} \times 8100$
5. 439 ÷ 11.1 c	**a.** 440 ÷ 20	**b.** 430 ÷ 20	**c.** 440 ÷ 10
6. 15,015 × 0.071 b	**a.** 16,000 × 0.08	**b.** 15,000 × 0.07	**c.** 15,000 × 0.08
7. 23,985 × 0.082 a	**a.** 24,000 × 0.08	**b.** 23,000 × 0.08	**c.** 24,000 × 0.09

Choose the best estimate. Choose a, b, c, or d.

	a.	b.	c.	d.
8. 43.05 + 10.65 b	**a.** 51	**b.** 54	**c.** 56	**d.** 58
9. 212.33 + 37.89 c	**a.** 230	**b.** 240	**c.** 250	**d.** 260
10. $4\frac{3}{4}$% of 81.20 b	**a.** 2	**b.** 4	**c.** 6	**d.** 8
11. 34% of 7189 b	**a.** 2300	**b.** 2400	**c.** 2500	**d.** 2600
12. 392 ÷ 13.2 a	**a.** 30	**b.** 32	**c.** 34	**d.** 36
13. 478 ÷ 11.9 d	**a.** 38	**b.** 44	**c.** 36	**d.** 40
14. 13,850 × 0.061 d	**a.** 880	**b.** 820	**c.** 920	**d.** 840

Applications

15. Joel paid $24.65 to have a muffler installed in his car and $10.15 for an oil change. The labor charge was $29.80. Estimate the total cost before sales tax. b

a. $24 + $10 + $29
b. $25 + $10 + $30
c. $25 + $12 + $25
d. $24 + $11 + $29

16. Maria took her car for a maintenance check. The cost for parts and labor was $59.95. The sales tax rate is $4\frac{1}{2}$%. Estimate the amount of sales tax. d

a. $60 × $\frac{1}{5}$
b. $60 × $\frac{1}{8}$
c. $60 × $\frac{1}{10}$
d. $60 × $\frac{1}{20}$

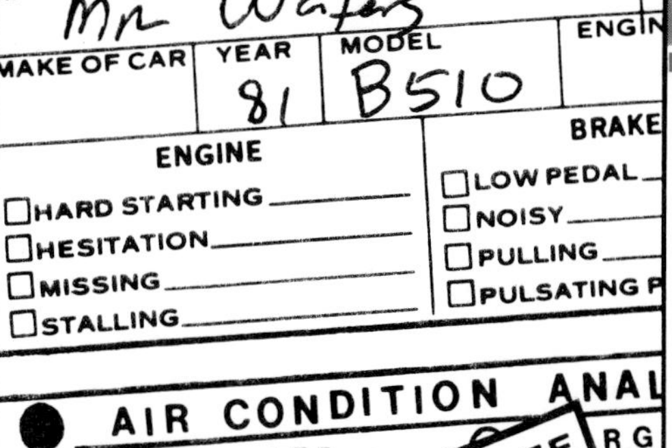

PRECISION AUTO TUNE-UP CEN
6000 MILE OR 120 DAY
GUARANTEE

NAME Mr Waters

MAKE OF CAR	YEAR	MODEL	ENGIN
	81	B510	

ENGINE	BRAKE
HARD STARTING	LOW PEDAL
HESITATION	NOISY
MISSING	PULLING
STALLING	PULSATING P

17. Roberta's car cost $8398 when it was new. Two years later, the value of the car has depreciated by 34%. Estimate the amount of depreciation. c

a. $\$8300 \times \frac{1}{3}$ b. $\$8200 \times \frac{1}{3}$
c. $\$8400 \times \frac{1}{3}$ d. $\$8100 \times \frac{1}{3}$

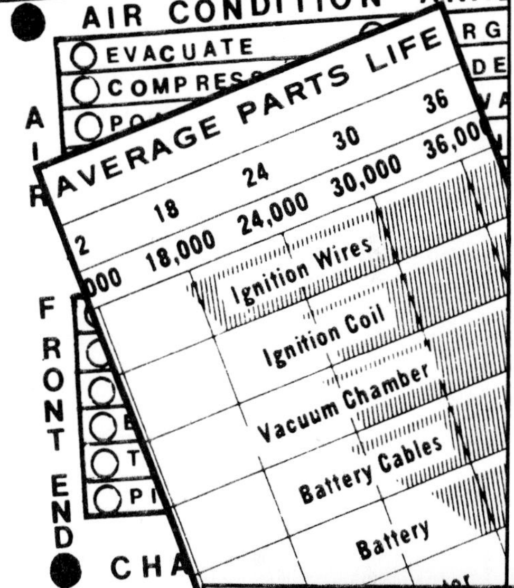

18. A certain compact car travels 259 miles on 12.8 gallons of gasoline. Estimate the fuel economy. c

a. 250 ÷ 12 b. 250 ÷ 13
c. 260 ÷ 13 d. 260 ÷ 12

19. Pedro paid $10.98 for a wheel alignment for his car and $39.95 for shock absorbers. The labor charge was $41.20. Estimate the cost before sales tax. d

a. $80 b. $100 c. $70 d. $90

20. Dot took her car for a maintenance check. The cost for parts and labor was $58.50. The sales tax rate is $4\frac{3}{4}$%. Estimate the sales tax. c

a. $5 b. $6 c. $3 d. $1

21. Judy's car cost $9025 when it was new. Two years later, the value of the car has depreciated by 33%. Estimate the amount of depreciation. b

a. $3100
b. $3000
c. $2900
d. $2500

22. A certain intermediate car travels 798 kilometers on 80.2 liters of gasoline. Estimate the fuel economy of the car in kilometers per liter. b

a. 8
b. 10
c. 12
d. 14

23. Ali drove his car 14,990 miles last year. The cost for gas and oil per mile is $0.099. Estimate the cost for last year. b

a. $1400
b. $1500
c. $1300
d. $1200

Chapter Review

These exercises review the vocabulary, skills and applications presented in the chapter, as a preparation for the chapter test.

Part 1: VOCABULARY

For Exercises 1–5, choose from the box at the right the word(s) that complete(s) each statement.

cost per kilometer
depreciation
variable costs
fuel economy
maintenance costs
fixed costs

1. The costs of upkeep and repair for a car are called __?__. (Pages 230–231) maintenance costs
2. The decrease in value of a car because of its age and condition is called __?__. (Pages 232–233) depreciation
3. The __?__ of a car refers to how many miles it can travel on one gallon of gasoline. (Pages 236–237) fuel economy
4. Insurance and taxes are costs that are __?__. (Pages 238–239) fixed costs
5. Gas and tires are costs that are __?__. (Pages 238–239) variable costs

Part 2: SKILLS

Add. (Pages 2–5)

6. $21+18+15+11$ 65 **7.** $17+11+11+10$ 49 **8.** $18+13+19+9$ 59

9. $15.23 + $30.50 $45.73 **10.** $78.60 + $42.20 + $18.91 $139.71 **11.** $72.94 + $87.11 + $5.28 $165.33

12. $1900 + $350 $2250 **13.** $1450 + $875 + $9.45 $2334.45 **14.** $2200 + $570 + $42.10 $2812.10

Write a decimal for each per cent. (Pages 90–91)

15. 5% 0.05 **16.** 3% 0.03 **17.** 9% 0.09 **18.** 16% 0.16 **19.** 11% 0.11 **20.** 24% 0.24

Find each answer. (Pages 94–95)

21. 7% of $810 $56.70 **22.** 2% of $58.20 $1.16 **23.** 5% of $1600 $80.00 **24.** 43% of $6200 $2666.00

25. 52% of $78.25 $40.69 **26.** 70% of $360 $252.00 **27.** 36% of $1780 $640.80 **28.** 58% of $2600 $1508.00

Multiply. (Pages 6–9)

29. $18{,}000 \times 6$ 108,000 **30.** $42{,}500 \times 3$ 127,500 **31.** $24{,}000 \times 5$ 120,000 **32.** $31{,}000 \times 2$ 62,000

33. $0.065 \times 38{,}000$ 2470 **34.** $0.081 \times 27{,}500$ 2227.5 **35.** $0.072 \times 29{,}000$ 2088 **36.** $0.093 \times 44{,}000$ 4092

Round to the nearest hundredth. (Pages 16–17)

37. 0.059 0.06 **38.** 0.027 0.03 **39.** 0.0418 0.04 **40.** 0.0611 0.06 **41.** 0.0189 0.02

Divide. Round each answer to the nearest hundredth. (Pages 16–17)

42. $3400 \div 58{,}000$ 0.06 **43.** $5408 \div 72{,}000$ 0.08 **44.** $7726 \div 24{,}000$ 0.32 **45.** $5505 \div 32{,}000$ 0.17

46. $6472 \div 39{,}000$ 0.17 **47.** $7317 \div 45{,}000$ 0.16 **48.** $5880 \div 62{,}000$ 0.09 **49.** $4955 \div 56{,}000$ 0.09

Round to the nearest whole number. (Pages 16–17)

50. 87.26 87 **51.** 31.09 31 **52.** 17.42 17 **53.** 48.80 49 **54.** 61.19 61 **55.** 20.31 20

Part 3: APPLICATIONS

For Exercises 56–59, the sales tax rate is 6%. Find the amount of tax and the total cost for repairs. (Pages 230–231)

	Oil Change	Air Filter	Wheel Alignment	Shock Absorbers	Engine Tune-up	Other Parts	Amount of Tax	Total Cost
56.	$7.50	$5.15	$10.50	$42.00	—	$44.50	$6.58 ?	$116.23 ?
57.	—	$5.80	$12.75	$37.55	$40.00	$51.00	$8.83 ?	$155.93 ?
58.	$8.00	$4.80	—	—	$38.95	$28.50	$4.82 ?	$85.07 ?
59.	$6.90	—	$13.05	$44.50	$35.00	$34.50	$8.04 ?	$141.99 ?

60. Phyllis's car is now 5 years old. When it was new, it cost $7800. Find the car's total depreciation. Use the table on page 232. (Pages 232–233) $4992

61. Nigel paid $8800 for his car when he bought it 6 years ago. Find the car's total depreciation. Use the table on page 232. (Pages 232–233) $6512

For Exercises 62–69, find the amount of depreciation per kilometer or per mile. (Pages 232–233)

	Kilometers Per Year	Number of Years	Total Depreciation	(per kilometer)
62.	22,000	3	$3400	5¢
63.	17,000	5	$4000	5¢
64.	21,000	2	$2200	5¢
65.	15,000	6	$4600	5¢

	Miles Per Year	Number of Years	Total Depreciation	(per mile)
66.	12,000	4	$4200	9¢
67.	8,000	3	$3800	16¢
68.	10,000	3	$3600	12¢
69.	11,000	5	$5500	10¢

For Exercises 70–71, determine which car has the greater fuel economy. (Pages 236–237)

70. One intermediate car travels 260 miles on 14.4 gallons of gasoline. Another car travels 346 miles on 15.1 gallons of gasoline. second car

71. One compact car travels 500 kilometers on 45.6 liters of fuel. Another compact car travels 460 kilometers on 34.9 liters of fuel. second car

72. One year Max found that the fixed costs of owning his car were as follows: depreciation: $1700; insurance: $630; fees and taxes: $210; finance charge: $786. Estimate the total fixed costs. (Pages 242–243) b

 a. $3000 **b.** $3300 **c.** $3400 **d.** $4000

73. Melanie kept a record of the major variable costs of operating her car for one year. They were as follows: gas and oil: $1850; maintenance: $320; tires: $18. Estimate the total variable costs. (Pages 242–243) a

 a. $2200 **b.** $2000 **c.** $1900 **d.** $2500

Chapter Test

The Teacher's Resource Book contains two forms of each chapter test.

Add.

1. 25 + 19 + 14 + 12 70 **2.** \$14.87 + \$61.82 + \$7.41 \$84.10 **3.** \$84.84 + \$61.91 + \$48.23 \$194.98

Write a decimal for each per cent.

4. 7% 0.07 **5.** 3% 0.03 **6.** 13% 0.13 **7.** 18% 0.18 **8.** 28% 0.28 **9.** 47% 0.47

Multiply.

10. 17,000 × 7 119,000 **11.** 0.079 × 41,000 3239 **12.** 0.048 × 24,500 1176

Divide. Round each answer to the nearest hundredth.

13. \$2900 ÷ 65,000 \$0.04 **14.** 4307 ÷ 84,000 0.05 **15.** 8706 ÷ 31,000 0.28

16. Dan Bliss received the following bill for repairs to his car. He lives in a state that has no sales tax.

Acme Garage	
Wheel alignment	\$12.90
Oil change	8.00
Engine tune-up	43.00
Labor	27.20
TOTAL	?

Estimate the total repair bill. d

a. \$110 **b.** \$100

c. \$80 **d.** \$90

17. Alice LaRoche paid \$9200 for her new car. After the first year, it depreciated 20%. At the end of the second year the car depreciated another 12%. Find the car's total depreciation in two years. \$2944

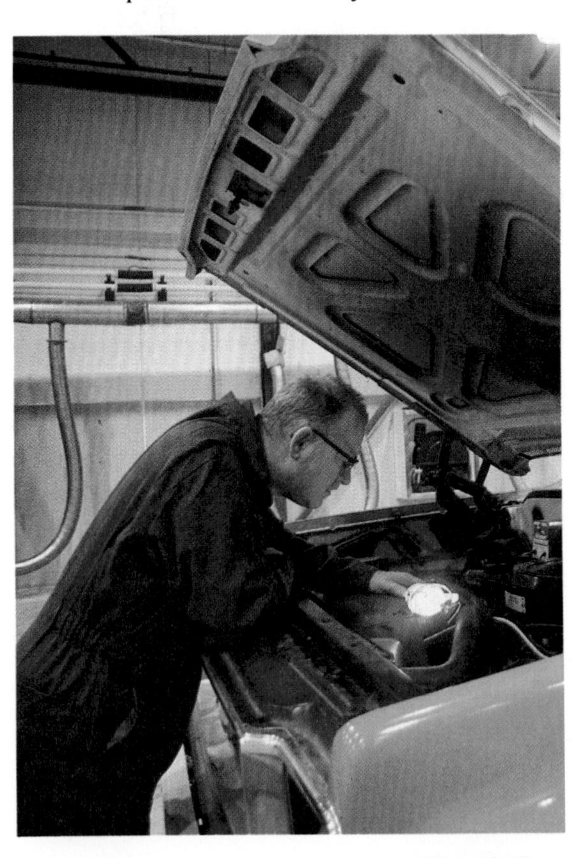

For Exercises 18–19, determine the fuel economy for each car.

18. Car A travels 178 miles on 19.8 gallons of gasoline. 9 miles per gallon

19. Car B travels 302 kilometers on 25.1 liters of gasoline. 12 kilometers per liter

20. Albert found that the fixed costs of owning his car were as follows: depreciation: \$1875, insurance: \$720; fees and taxes: \$289. Find the total fixed costs. \$2884

Additional Practice

You may wish to use all or some of these exercises, depending on how well students performed on the formal chapter test.

Skills

Perform the indicated operation. (Pages 2–5, 6–9)

1. 18 + 16 + 12 + 11 57 **2.** \$69.66 + \$43.10 + \$20.19 \$132.95 **3.** \$90.12 + \$71.14 + \$11.24 \$172.50

4. 24,000 × 4 96,000 **5.** 54,500 × 3 163,500 **6.** 0.051 × 41,000 2091 **7.** 0.092 × 25,500 2346

Find each answer. (Pages 94–95)

8. 8% of \$790 \$63.20 **9.** 3% of \$42.58 \$1.28 **10.** 4% of \$1750 \$70.00 **11.** 51% of \$7600 \$3876.00

Divide. Round each answer to the nearest hundredth. (Pages 16–17)

12. 5300 ÷ 82,000 0.06 **13.** 2300 ÷ 49,000 0.05 **14.** 6054 ÷ 31,000 0.20

Applications

15. Deirdre had her car repaired. The repair costs were as follows: oil change: \$5.40; air filter: \$3.80; engine tune-up: \$37.40; other parts: \$22.20. The sales tax rate was 5%. Find the total repair cost. (Pages 230–231) \$72.24

16. Pablo's car is 5 years old. He drives his car 9500 miles per year. Find the estimated maintenance cost per mile for next year. Use the table on page 230. (Pages 230–231). 5¢ per mile

17. Bob's new car cost \$8800. After 6 years, the car depreciated 52%. Estimate the car's depreciation. (Pages 242–243) c

a. \$9000 × 0.60 **b.** \$8000 × 0.60

c. \$9000 × 0.50 **d.** \$8000 × 0.50

18. Hisako drove her car about 15,000 kilometers per year. After 5 years the depreciation on the car was \$5248. Find the amount of depreciation per kilometer. (Pages 232–233) 7¢ per kilometer

19. One sports car travels 420 kilometers on 52.5 liters of fuel. Another sports car travels 360 kilometers on 51.4 liters of fuel. Which car has the greater fuel economy? (Pages 236–237) First car

20. Victor, a regional sales manager, travels 50,000 kilometers per year. The yearly cost of his fuel is \$2400. Find the yearly fuel cost per kilometer. (Pages 236–237) 5¢ per kilometer

For Exercises 21–24, complete the table. (Pages 238–239)

	Fixed Costs	Variable Costs	Other Costs	Total Driving Costs	Number of Miles	Cost per Mile
21.	\$3250	\$2600	\$450	\$6300 ?	24,000	? 26.3¢
22.	\$2900	\$ 900	\$350	\$4150 ?	8,000	? 51.9¢
23.	\$3400	\$1500	\$200	\$5100 ?	12,000	? 42.5¢
24.	\$2750	\$1700	\$500	\$4950 ?	17,000	? 29.1¢

REVIEW OF RELATED SKILLS FOR CHAPTER 12

We suggest that some or all of this page be reviewed before proceeding with the chapter.

Multiply. (Pages 8–9)

1. $18.00 × 6 $108.00 **2.** $51.40 × 4 $205.60 **3.** $43.80 × 7 $306.60 **4.** $87.40 × 5 $437.00

5. $43.50 × 8 $348.00 **6.** $88.80 × 5 $444.00 **7.** $22.83 × 3 $68.49 **8.** $47.90 × 9 $431.10

9. 190 × $0.21 $39.90 **10.** 240 × $0.75 $180.00 **11.** 683 × $0.30 $204.90 **12.** 780 × $0.48 $374.40

13. 693 × $0.40 $277.20 **14.** 705 × $0.50 $352.50 **15.** 1050 × $0.35 $367.50 **16.** 1150 × $0.28 $322.00

17. 80 × $1.54 $123.20 **18.** 64 × $1.50 $96.00 **19.** 70 × $1.72 $120.40 **20.** 92 × $1.38 $126.96

Add. (Pages 2–5)

21. $180.40 + $82.50 + $67.15 $330.05 **22.** $183.12 + $120.16 + $80.01 $383.29

23. $197.80 + $110.00 + $41.12 $348.92 **24.** $87.05 + $86.12 + $38.77 $211.94

25. $144.05 + $97.00 + $49.54 $290.59 **26.** $207.50 + $190.04 + $102.83 $500.37

27. $186.40 + $144.14 + $80.00 $410.54 **28.** $177.54 + $96.44 + $58.07 $332.05

29. 15¢ + 10¢ + 5¢ 30¢ **30.** 20¢ + 10¢ + 5¢ 35¢ **31.** 40¢ + 25¢ + 15¢ 80¢

32. 60¢ + 10¢ + 10¢ 80¢ **33.** 40¢ + 25¢ + 25¢ 90¢ **34.** 45¢ + 15¢ + 15¢ 75¢

35. 70¢ + 15¢ + 10¢ 95¢ **36.** 80¢ + 10¢ + 5¢ 95¢ **37.** 40¢ + 20¢ + 10¢ 70¢

Multiply. (Pages 6–9)

38. 30 × $0.60 $18.00 **39.** 34 × $0.65 $22.10 **40.** 70 × $0.80 $56.00 **41.** 15 × $0.50 $7.50

42. 20 × $0.65 $13.00 **43.** 35 × $0.85 $29.75 **44.** 60 × $0.45 $27.00 **45.** 30 × $0.55 $16.50

46. 15 × $0.90 $13.50 **47.** 25 × $0.95 $23.75 **48.** 18 × $1.10 $19.80 **49.** 24 × $1.25 $30.00

50. 5 × $1.40 $7.00 **51.** 27 × $1.00 $27.00 **52.** 28 × $1.15 $32.20 **53.** 30 × $1.90 $57.00

54. 22 × 2 × $0.50 $20.00 **55.** 10 × 2 × $0.60 $12.00 **56.** 24 × 2 × $0.85 $40.80

57. 20 × 2 × $0.45 $18.00 **58.** 25 × 2 × $0.80 $40.00 **59.** 26 × 2 × $0.90 $46.80

60. 24 × 2 × $1.00 $48.00 **61.** 26 × 2 × $1.20 $62.40 **62.** 20 × 2 × $1.45 $58.00

63. $190 × 4 $760 **64.** $315 × 2 $630 **65.** $440 × 3 $1320 **66.** $615 × 4 $2460

67. $160 × 3 $480 **68.** $199 × 3 $597 **69.** $216 × 4 $864 **70.** $340 × 2 $680

71. $176.50 × 2 $353.00 **72.** $183.40 × 4 $733.60 **73.** $304.70 × 3 $914.10 **74.** $512.60 × 2 $1025.20

75. $447.23 × 2 $894.46 **76.** $339.18 × 3 $1017.54 **77.** $607.98 × 4 $2431.92 **78.** $1017.12 × 2 $2034.24

79. $600 × 0.04 $24.00 **80.** $400 × 0.05 $20.00 **81.** $200 × 0.07 $14.00 **82.** $500 × 0.06 $30.00

83. $750 × 0.03 $22.50 **84.** $840 × 0.02 $16.80 **85.** $450 × 0.06 $27.00 **86.** $370 × 0.03 $11.10

87. $405.50 × 0.02 $8.11 **88.** $510.75 × 0.04 $20.43 **89.** $416.40 × 0.05 $20.82

90. $410.11 × 0.08 $32.81 **91.** $506.00 × 0.045 $22.77 **92.** $416.20 × 0.035 $14.57

CHAPTER

12 OTHER WAYS TO TRAVEL

CONSUMER SKILLS/APPLICATIONS

CAREER APPLICATIONS

12-1 Renting a Car

See the Teacher's Manual for the objectives.

Susan wants to visit her grandfather, who lives in another state. She decides to rent a car for the trip. Usually, to rent a car, you must be <u>at least</u> 25 years old <u>or</u> have a major credit card in your name.

EXAMPLE Susan rented a car for 3 days and drove it 810 miles. The base fee was \$41.25 per day plus 24¢ for each mile driven. The car used 27 gallons of gasoline for which Susan paid \$1.51 per gallon. Find the total cost for rental and gasoline.

Solution:

1. Find the total base rental fee for 3 days.
   $\$41.25 \times 3 = \$123.75$
2. Find the rental cost for mileage.
   $810 \times \$0.24 = \$194.40$
3. Find the cost of gasoline.
   $27 \times \$1.51 = \$40.77$
4. Find the total cost for rental and gasoline.
   $\$123.75 + \$194.40 + \$40.77 =$ **\$358.92**

REVIEW OF RELATED SKILLS

You may wish to use these exercises before teaching the lesson.

Multiply. (Pages 8–9)

1. $17.00 × 5 $85.00 **2.** $23.50 × 3 $70.50 **3.** $38.20 × 8 $305.60 **4.** $46.10 × 4 $184.40

5. 170 × $0.19 $32.30 **6.** 650 × $0.25 $162.50 **7.** 725 × $0.29 $210.25 **8.** 1022 × $0.24 $245.28

9. 50 × $1.46 $73.00 **10.** 28 × $1.60 $44.80 **11.** 72 × $1.66 $119.52 **12.** 84 × $1.55 $130.20

Add. (Pages 4–5)

13. $160.20 + $78.30 + $52.10 $290.60

14. $140.15 + $193.75 + $35.05 $368.95

15. $165.18 + $112.46 + $88.52 $366.16

16. $92.66 + $144.80 + $76.59 $314.05

17. $135.67 + $88.40 + $59.09 $283.16

18. $112.35 + $105.98 + $65.56 $283.89

19. $155.03 + $102.44 + $90.50 $347.97

20. $171.80 + $120.36 + $68.89 $361.05

EXERCISES

For Exercises 1–10, find the total cost. Use \$38.95 as the base fee per day, 33¢ as the cost per mile, and \$1.65 as the cost per gallon of gasoline.

	Number of Days	Miles Driven	Gasoline Used	
1.	4	320	15 gallons	$286.15
2.	2	815	26 gallons	$389.75
3.	7	1020	35 gallons	$667.00
4.	5	748	23 gallons	$479.54
5.	3	316	10 gallons	$237.63

	Number of Days	Miles Driven	Gasoline Used	
6.	6	644	21 gallons	$480.87
7.	10	1502	54 gallons	$974.26
8.	9	558	24 gallons	$574.29
9.	4	906	31 gallons	$505.93
10.	8	1752	59 gallons	$987.11

11. Denise rented a car and drove it 642 miles for 4 days. The base fee was \$49.95 per day with no mileage charge. Denise used 28 gallons of gasoline and paid \$1.62 per gallon. Find the total cost. $245.16

12. Paul rented a car for one week and drove it 1208 miles. The base fee was \$32.95 per day plus 19¢ per mile. The car used 42 gallons of gasoline for which Paul paid \$1.70 per gallon. Find the total cost for rental and gasoline. $531.57

13. Stan rented a car for 6 days and drove it 536 miles. The base rate was \$27.95 per day plus 30¢ per mile. The company offers a weekly rate of \$159 plus 30¢ per mile. How much would Stan have saved on rental costs if he had used the weekly rate? $8.70

14. Luisa rented a car for 7 days. She drove a total of 459 miles. The base fee was \$34.50 per day plus 26¢ per mile. The rental company also offers a weekly rate of \$199 plus 26¢ per mile. How much would she have saved if she had used the weekly rate? $42.50

15. Minoru rented a car for 6 days and drove it 958 miles. The base fee was \$38.50 per day plus 28¢ per mile. He paid \$1.55 per gallon for the 56 gallons of gasoline he used. Find the total cost. $586.04

16. Sandra drove her rented car 426 miles over 2 days. The base rate was \$32.35 per day plus 25¢ per mile. She paid \$1.58 per gallon for the 21 gallons of gasoline used. Find the total cost for rental and gasoline. $204.38

CAR LEASING AGENT

Career lessons are optional. This lesson combines the skill of reading a table with the skills of adding and multiplying decimals.

In his work as a **car leasing agent,** Steve Bond computes the costs of a lease for customers who need the use of a car for a period of time. The customer signs a leasing contract agreeing to pay a certain amount per month. Sometimes the lease also requires a down payment. In addition, the customer must pay the costs of gasoline.

TETRO LEASING
$168.58 per month
for 36 months
$1500 DOWN

EXAMPLE Claire Murphy leased the car in the advertisement. During that time, she used 4788 liters of gasoline at an average cost of $0.36 per liter. Find her total costs.

Solution:

Down payment:		$1500.00
Total monthly payments:	$168.58 × 36 =	6068.88
Gasoline costs:	4788 × 0.36 =	+ 1723.68
Total costs:		**$9292.56**

EXERCISES Note that Exercises 1-6 are non-verbal.

For Exercises 1–6, find the total costs. Use the advertisement at the right. No down payment is required.

	Car Leased	*Length of Lease*	*Gasoline Costs*	
1.	Turtle	7 months	2345 L at $0.58/L	$3173.10
2.	Drift	11 months	90 gal at $1.52/gal	$3095.80
3.	Snail	5 months	1650 L at $0.35/L	$1772.50
4.	Wingo	10 months	850 gal at $1.54/gal	$3849
5.	Snail	8 months	2640 L at $0.34/L	$2649.60
6.	Drift	4 months	336 gal at $1.56/gal	$1700.16

SHORT TERM LEASE
NO DOWN PAYMENT

	4-6 mos.	6-9 mos.	9-12 mos.
Snail	$239	$219	$204
Turtle	$279	$259	$244
Wingo	$289	$269	$254
Drift	$294	$274	$269

Use this advertisement for Exercises 7–8. Find the total cost.

7. Arnold Gomez leased an Eluder for 48 months. During that time, he used 3840 gallons of gasoline at an average cost of $1.55 per gallon. $12,184

8. Milan Yee leased a Wagonwheel for 48 months. She used 15,840 liters of gasoline at an average cost of $0.36 per liter. $17,706.40

WE LEASE NEW CARS ALL MAKES

Car	Monthly Payment
Eluder $1000 DOWN	$109
Speedwing $1500 DOWN	$146
Wagonwheel $2500 DOWN	$198

Use this advertisement for Exercises 9–10. Find the total costs.

9. The Polar Bear was leased by an engineering consultant who used 13,500 liters of gasoline at an average cost of $0.40 per liter. $13,860

10. The Deerfoot was leased by a real estate developer who used 3240 gallons of gasoline at an average cost of $1.58 per gallon. $17,539.20

Deerfoot	$345	PER MO.
Elk	$254	PER MO.
Polar Bear	$235	PER MO.

36-MONTH LEASES
NO DOWN PAYMENTS

Use the advertisement at the right for Exercises 11–13. Remember: At the end of the lease, the renter owns the car.

11. How much more will it cost to own the Sparrow than the Bluejay? $768

12. How much more will it cost to own the Pluto than the Whistler? $11,616

13. Karl Albert is planning to lease a car for his business. Find how much more it would cost him per year to lease the Pluto rather than the Whistler. $2904

MAIN STREET LEASING
NO DOWN PAYMENT
48-MONTH LEASE
THEN YOU OWN THE CAR!

SPARROW	$286.82/MO.
WHISTLER	$362.82/MO.
PLUTO	$604.82/MO.
BLUEJAY	$270.82/MO.

Leases Galore charges an additional amount for any number of miles over 60,000. Use this advertisement for Exercises 14–15.

14. Mary Lee Stokes leased a car from Leases Galore. Gasoline costs for 4 years amounted to $4030. She traveled 65,000 miles. Find the total cost. $18,154

15. Tony Arico traveled 75,000 miles in the car he leased. His car gets an average of 30 miles per gallon of gasoline. He pays $1.56 per gallon. Find the total cost over the 4 years. $18,624

LEASES GALORE
48-Month leases
No down payment
$288
per month

Mileage allowance-
60,000 miles

6¢ per mile for
additional mileage

12-2 Commuting to Work

See the Teacher's Manual for the objectives.

Rosa commutes (travels) to and from work each day by bus. Since the bus fare can be paid in coins only, she has to be certain that she has enough change for the bus fare each week.

EXAMPLE 1 Rosa puts three quarters, a dime and a nickel in the coin box of the bus twice each day. How much is her monthly bus fare in a month of 21 working days?

Solution: [1] Find the fare for 1 trip.

3 quarters + 1 dime + 1 nickel = 75¢ + 10¢ + 5¢ = 90¢

[2] Find the number of trips in 21 days.

$21 \times 2 = 42$

[3] Find the fare for 21 days.

42 × \$0.90 = **\$37.80**

After completing Example 1, you may wish to have students do some or all of Exercises 1-10.

Many people use more than one form of transportation.

EXAMPLE 2 Francis uses a commuter train and the subway to commute to work each day. His monthly train ticket costs \$64.50. A one-way subway fare is 85¢. Find his total commuting costs for a month of 21 working days.

Solution: [1] Find the subway fare for 21 days.

\$0.85 × 2 × 21 = \$35.70 ◀ ***Fare for one day: \$0.85 × 2***

[2] Find the total monthly cost.

\$64.50 + \$35.70 = **\$100.20**

REVIEW OF RELATED SKILLS

You may wish to use these exercises before teaching the lesson.

Write each answer as a dollar amount. (Pages 4–5, 8–9)

1. 45¢ + 25¢ + 20¢ \$0.90
2. 75¢ + 30¢ + 15¢ \$1.20
3. 50¢ + 40¢ + 5¢ \$0.95
4. \$29.50 + \$58.00 \$87.50
5. \$52.75 + \$45.15 \$97.90
6. \$90.00 + \$43.65 + \$18.35 \$152.00
7. 40 × \$0.80 \$32.00
8. 24 × \$0.95 \$22.80
9. 20 × \$0.85 \$17.00
10. 22 × \$1.20 \$26.40
11. 23 × 2 × \$0.75 \$34.50
12. 26 × 2 × \$1.40 \$72.80
13. 20 × 2 × \$1.00 \$40.00
14. 22 × 2 × \$0.95 \$41.80

EXERCISES

For Exercises 1–8, find the monthly fare for each commuter. Assume that each commuter makes one round-trip each day. (Example 1)

	Commuter	One-Way Fare	Working Days in Month	
1.	Cindy	$0.90	23	$41.40
2.	Mei	$1.10	21	$46.20
3.	Ramon	$0.85	24	$40.80
4.	Tanya	$1.30	20	$52.00
5.	Sergio	$0.95	22	$41.80
6.	Missy	$1.05	23	$48.30
7.	Tom	$1.25	21	$52.50
8.	Pierre	$0.80	23	$36.80

9. Lou puts four quarters and two dimes in the coin box of a bus twice each day. One month, he made the round trip to work 22 times. Find his total commuting costs that month. $52.80

10. Karen puts two quarters and four nickels in the coin box of a bus twice each day. How much are her total costs for commuting in a month of 20 working days? $28.00

For Exercises 11–18, find the total commuting costs. (Example 2)

	Monthly Train Fare	One-Way Subway Fare	Working Days in Month	
11.	$ 90.50	$0.80	22	$125.70
12.	$103.00	$1.10	21	$149.20
13.	$ 72.45	$0.90	23	$113.85
14.	$ 66.50	$0.90	20	$102.50
15.	$81.25	$0.95	24	$126.85
16.	$75.30	$1.05	20	$117.30
17.	$90.05	$1.00	22	$134.05
18.	$112.55	$0.85	23	$151.65

19. Betty buys a monthly commuter train ticket for $90.60. She also pays a one-way fare of $0.80 on a city bus. Find her total commuting costs for a month of 22 working days. $125.80

20. Julio uses a commuter bus and the subway to get to work. His monthly bus ticket costs $73.00 and a one-way subway fare is $0.95. Find his cost of commuting for 21 days. $112.90

12-3 Comparing Costs of Travel

See the Teacher's Manual for the objectives.

Jaime Herrara is planning a vacation for himself, his wife, and their two children, ages 5 and 15. He made a table to compare the costs of travel by plane, train, and bus.

ONE-WAY COSTS PER PERSON

	Plane	Train	Bus
Adult	\$215 (Coach)	\$180	\$165
	\$108 (Night Fare)	--	--
Children (Ages 2–11)	25% off adult fare	$\frac{2}{3}$ adult fare	$\frac{1}{2}$ adult fare
Meals/Snacks	None	\$20.00	\$20.00
Number of Miles	928	1325	1284
Time	2.6 hours	28.8 hours	30.1 hours

EXAMPLE Find the round–trip cost if the Herraras travel by plane (coach). Include a 4% tax on the plane fare.

Solution:

1. Find the cost of three adult round–trip fares.
   $\$215 \times 2 = \$430 \longrightarrow \$430 \times 3 = \mathbf{\$1290}$

2. A child's fare is 25% off the adult fare.
   $\$430 \times 0.25 = \$107.50 \longrightarrow \$430 - \$107.50 = \mathbf{\$322.50}$

3. Include a 4% tax on the plane fare.

$$\begin{array}{r} \$129.00 \\ +\ 322.50 \\ \hline \$1612.50 \end{array} \text{ Plane fare} \longrightarrow \begin{array}{r} \$1612.50 \\ \times\ \ 0.04 \\ \hline \$64.5000 \end{array} \text{ Tax} \longrightarrow \begin{array}{r} \$1612.50 \\ +\ \ 64.50 \\ \hline \mathbf{\$1677.00} \end{array} \text{ Round–trip cost}$$

REVIEW OF RELATED SKILLS

You may wish to use these exercises before teaching the lesson.

Multiply. (Pages 6–9)

1. \$165 × 3 \$495 **2.** \$215 × 4 \$860 **3.** \$120 × 2 \$240 **4.** \$87.50 × 4 \$350.00

5. \$520 × 0.05 \$26.00 **6.** \$755 × 0.03 \$22.65 **7.** \$180 × 0.06 \$10.80 **8.** \$324 × 0.04 \$12.96

Add. (Pages 2–5)

9. \$580 + \$29 \$609 **10.** \$735 + \$29.40 \$764.40 **11.** \$615.35 + \$9.00 \$624.35 **12.** \$542.80 + \$20.25 \$563.05

13. \$640 + \$34 \$674 **14.** \$524 + \$32.50 \$556.50 **15.** \$746.29 + \$7.32 \$753.61 **16.** \$656.54 + \$23.16 \$679.70

EXERCISES

For Exercises 1–8, use the table on page 256 to find the cost of a round-trip ticket. Include a 4% sales tax on each fare.

	Means of Travel	Number of Passengers	
1.	Train	2 adults	$748.80
2.	Plane (coach)	2 adults 2 children, 7 and 14	$1677.00
3.	Bus	1 adult 2 children, 5 and 9	$686.40
4.	Plane (night)	2 adults	$449.28
5.	Bus	2 adults	$686.40
6.	Train	2 adults 2 children, 5 and 15	$1372.80
7.	Plane (coach)	2 adults 2 children, 5 and 9	$1565.20
8.	Train	1 adult 3 children, 6, 8, and 14	$1248.00

For Exercises 9–18, use the table on page 256.

9. Find the round-trip travel costs for the Herrara family if they decide to travel by train. Include a 5% tax on the train fare. $1546.00
10. Find the difference between the travel costs the Herraras would pay if they traveled by train instead of airplane. $211.00
11. Find the round-trip travel costs for the Herrara family if they decide to travel by bus. Include a 5% tax on the bus fare. $1372.75
12. Find the difference between the travel costs the Herraras would pay if they traveled by bus instead of airplane. $384.25
13. Find the difference between the time a round trip takes on the train and on the airplane. 52.4 hours
14. Find the difference between the time a one-way trip takes on the airplane and on the bus. 27.5 hours
15. Find the difference between the distance traveled during a one-way trip by the bus and the airplane. 356 miles
16. Find the difference between the one-way fare for a 6-year old child on the bus and on the train. $37.50
17. Find the difference between the round-trip fare for an 8-year old child on the airplane (coach fare) and on the train. $82.50
18. Find the difference between the adult one-way coach fare and the adult one-way night fare on the airplane. $107.00

FLIGHT ATTENDANT

Career lessons are optional. This lesson applies the skill of subtracting units of time to find elapsed travel time.

As part of her work as a **flight attendant,** Lydia March computes the length of time needed for a flight. Time zones are involved in calculating the number of hours and minutes for longer flights.

New York

Chicago

Denver

Los Angeles

The map below shows four standard time zones.

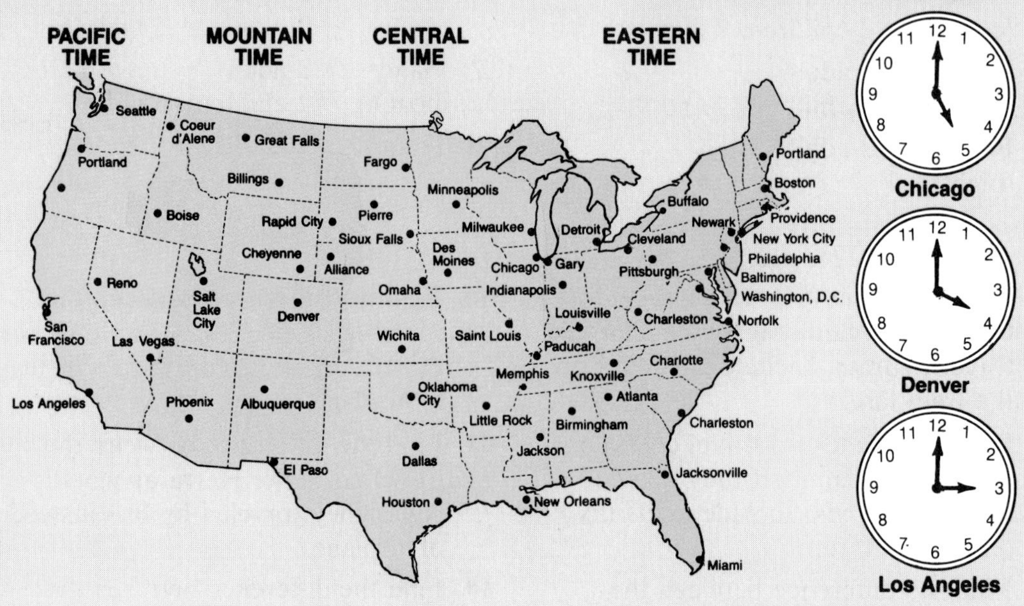

RULE

Going from east to west, subtract one hour for each zone. Going from west to east, add one hour for each zone.

EXAMPLE A plane leaves Los Angeles at 10:45 A.M. Pacific time and arrives in Boston at 6:30 P.M. Eastern time. How long did the trip take?

Solution:

1 Find the number of time zones traveled.

PT MT CT ET

1 2 3 ◀ *3 zones*

2 Write the hour of departure as Eastern time.

10:45 A.M. + 3 hours: **1:45 P.M.** Eastern time

3 Subtract the departure time from the arrival time.

$$\begin{array}{r} 6{:}30 \text{ P.M.} \\ -1{:}45 \text{ P.M.} \\ \hline \end{array} \longrightarrow \begin{array}{r} 5{:}90 \text{ P.M.} \\ -1{:}45 \text{ P.M.} \\ \hline 4{:}45, \end{array}$$

or **4 hours 45 minutes**

◀ *6 hr 30 min = 5 hr + 60 min + 30 min*

EXERCISES Note that Exercises 1-10 are non-verbal.

List the time zones through which you would travel for each flight.

1. From New York City to El Paso Eastern, Central, Mountain
2. From Las Vegas to Atlanta Pacific, Mountain, Central, Eastern
3. From Dallas to Norfolk Central, Eastern
4. From Chicago to Seattle Central, Mountain, Pacific

Give the Central time for each of the following.

5. 6:00 A.M. Mountain time 7:00 A.M.
6. 4:00 P.M. Eastern time 3:00 P.M.
7. 9:00 P.M. Pacific time 11:00 P.M.
8. 12:00 A.M. Pacific time 2:00 A.M.
9. 12:00 A.M. Eastern time 11:00 P.M.
10. 11:00 P.M. Pacific time 1:00 A.M.

In Exercises 11–14, find the length of time for each flight.

11. Left at 8:00 A.M. Pacific time 2 hours
Arrived at 12:00 P.M. Central time
12. Left at 4:30 P.M. Eastern time
Arrived at 8:30 P.M. Pacific time 7 hours
13. Left at 1:15 P.M. Central time 2 hr 15 min
Arrived at 4:30 P.M. Eastern time
14. Left at 9:20 A.M. Eastern time
Arrived at 10:15 A.M. Pacific time 3 hr 55 min
15. Dolores left Boston at 8:00 P.M. (Eastern time) and arrived in Houston at 10:30 P.M. (Central time) How long did the trip take? 3 hr 30 min
16. Mark left Boise at 9:45 A.M. (Mountain time) and arrived in Buffalo at 2:00 P.M. (Eastern time). How long did the trip to Buffalo take? 2 hr 15 min
17. Rob Brill left Denver by plane at 9:15 A.M. (Mountain time) and landed in Newark at 2:45 P.M. (Eastern time). How long did the flight take? 3 hr 30 min
18. Rita Ritz left Norfolk, Virginia by plane at 8:00 A.M. (Eastern time) and arrived in Phoenix at 11:20 A.M. (Mountain time) How long did the trip take? 5 hr 20 min
19. Melissa's flight left Miami at 6:00 P.M. (Eastern time). Michael's flight left San Francisco at 4:00 P.M. (Pacific time). Whose flight left earlier? How much earlier? Melissa's; 1 hour
20. Helen's flight left Billings, Montana, at 8:30 A.M. (Mountain time), and arrived in Norfolk, Virginia 5 hours later. At what time did she arrive? 3:30 P.M.
21. Phillip flew out of Minneapolis at 9:45 P.M. (Central time) and arrived in Portland, Oregon $2\frac{1}{2}$ hours later. When did he arrive? 10:15 P.M.

Rounding and Estimation

Consumers use rounding and estimation to solve problems related to traveling.

EXERCISES See the Teacher's Manual for the objectives.

Skills

Choose the best estimate. Choose a, b, or c.

1. 809×0.31 c — **a.** 800×0.30 **b.** 810×0.40 **c.** 810×0.30

2. $134.09 + 25.88$ a — **a.** $130 + 30$ **b.** $140 + 30$ **c.** $130 + 20$

3. 22.88×4 b — **a.** 22×4 **b.** 23×4 **c.** 20×4

4. 49.91×4.2 b — **a.** 40×4 **b.** 50×4 **c.** 50×5

5. 26% of 802 a — **a.** $\frac{1}{4} \times 800$ **b.** $\frac{1}{5} \times 800$ **c.** $\frac{1}{4} \times 900$

6. 21% of 398 b — **a.** $\frac{1}{4} \times 400$ **b.** $\frac{1}{5} \times 400$ **c.** $\frac{1}{5} \times 300$

7. $378.95 - 267.50$ c — **a.** $370 - 270$ **b.** $380 - 260$ **c.** $380 - 270$

Choose the best estimate. Choose a, b, c, or d.

8. 598×0.19 d — **a.** 100 **b.** 140 **c.** 130 **d.** 120

9. $162.13 + 26.98$ a — **a.** 190 **b.** 180 **c.** 200 **d.** 170

10. $131.04 + 47.50$ b — **a.** 190 **b.** 180 **c.** 200 **d.** 170

11. 61.08×4 a — **a.** 240 **b.** 230 **c.** 280 **d.** 260

12. 38.69×4.1 c — **a.** 170 **b.** 150 **c.** 160 **d.** 140

13. 21% of 497 c — **a.** 120 **b.** 110 **c.** 100 **d.** 90

14. 24% of 805 d — **a.** 170 **b.** 220 **c.** 180 **d.** 200

Applications

15. Lewis Januez rented a car and drove it 902 kilometers. The rental cost per kilometer is $0.21. Estimate the total driving charge. a

a. 900 × $0.20
b. 910 × $0.30
c. 900 × $0.30
d. 910 × $0.40

16. Maria Ortega rented a car and paid $121.60 for the rental fee, $188.40 for the mileage, and $31.25 for gasoline. Estimate the total cost. c

a. $120 + $190 + $40
b. $130 + $190 + $40
c. $120 + $190 + $30
d. $120 + $180 + $30

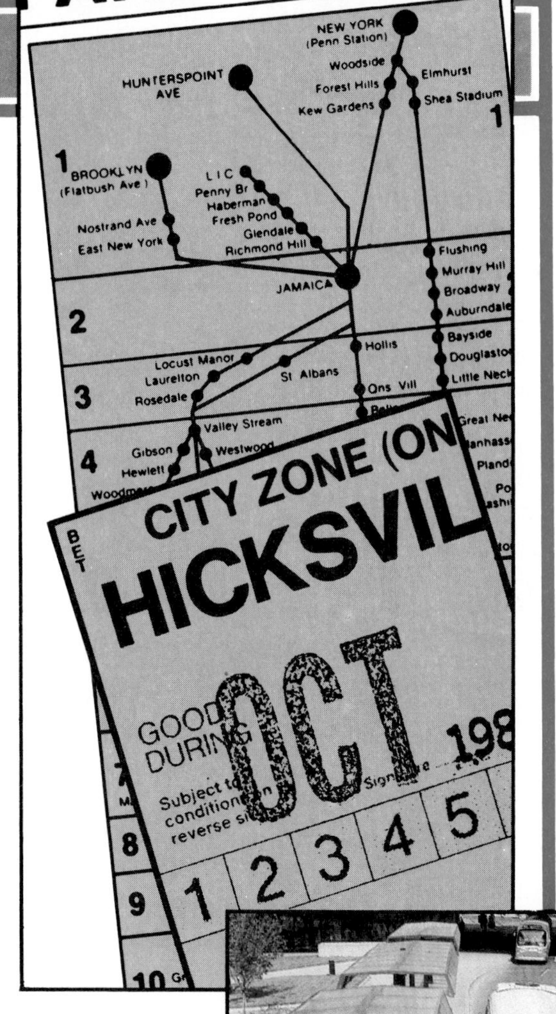

17. Frank buys 4 weekly commuter train tickets per month. Each ticket costs $19.70. Estimate his monthly commuting costs. b

a. $\$10 \times 4$ b. $\$20 \times 4$
c. $\$25 \times 4$ d. $\$15 \times 4$

18. The children's fare on a certain airline is 26% off the adult fare. The adult round–trip fare is $396. Estimate the discount for children. c

a. $\$390 \times \frac{1}{4}$ b. $\$400 \times \frac{1}{24}$
c. $\$400 \times \frac{1}{4}$ d. $\$390 \times \frac{1}{24}$

19. Saundra Tillis rented a car and drove it 396 kilometers. The rental cost per kilometer is $0.21. Estimate the total driving charge. b

a. $70 b. $80 c. $90 d. $100

20. Kim Kyoto rented a car and paid $201.25 for the rental fee, $29.75 for the mileage, and $11.05 for gasoline. Estimate the total cost. c

a. $250 b. $260 c. $240 d. $220

21. The children's fare on a certain train is 26% off the adult fare. The adult fare is $162.50. Estimate the discount for children. a

a. $40
b. $50
c. $30
d. $60

22. Diana took a trip by bus. Her fare cost $168.95 one way. If she had gone by train, her fare would have been $179.50. Estimate the difference. c

a. $3
b. $5
c. $10
d. $12

Chapter Review

These exercises review the vocabulary, skills, and applications presented in the chapter, as a preparation for the chapter test.

Part 1: VOCABULARY

For Exercises 1–4, choose from the box at the right the word(s) or number(s) that complete(s) each statement.

base fee
commuting
25
coach fare
round trip
21

1. To rent a car, you must be at least __?__ years old or have a credit card in your own name. (Pages 250–251) 25
2. A rental car agency charges $29.50 per day plus 28¢ for each mile driven. The $29.50 is called the __?__. (Pages 250–251) base fee
3. Traveling to and from work each day by bus or train is called __?__. (Pages 254–255) commuting
4. When you travel to a place and then return, you are making a __?__. (Pages 254–255) round trip

Part 2: SKILLS

Multiply. (Pages 8–9)

5. $22.00 × 8 $176.00
6. $52.40 × 5 $262.00
7. $34.80 × 3 $104.40
8. $88.20 × 7 $617.40
9. 210 × $0.19 $39.90
10. 310 × $0.85 $263.50
11. 90 × $2.10 $189.00
12. 65 × $1.60 $104.00

Add. (Pages 4–5)

13. $148.40 + $83.90 + $27.50 $259.80
14. $154.40 + $61.20 + $46.70 $262.30
15. $83.16 + $42.97 $126.13
16. $68.41 + $20.31 $88.72
17. $191.40 + $52.73 $244.13

Add. If the sum is a dollar or more, write your answer in dollars. (Pages 2–3)

18. 20¢ + 15¢ + 5¢ 40¢
19. 35¢ + 20¢ + 10¢ 65¢
20. 50¢ + 80¢ + 15¢ $1.45

Multiply. (Pages 6–9)

21. 40 × $0.75 $30.00
22. 30 × $0.90 $27.00
23. 25 × $1.50 $37.50
24. 60 × $2.40 $144.00
25. $320 × 3 $960
26. $425 × 4 $1700
27. $600 × 0.05 $30
28. $725 × 0.06 $43.50

Part 3: APPLICATIONS

For Exercises 29–34, find the total cost for car rental and gasoline. Use $27.50 as the base fee per day, 28¢ as the cost per mile, and $1.42 as the cost per gallon of gasoline. (Pages 250–251)

	Number of Days	Miles Driven	Gasoline Used	
29.	3	512	26 gallons	$262.78
30.	5	824	38 gallons	$422.18
31.	14	1972	90 gallons	$1064.96
32.	2	409	20 gallons	$197.92
33.	7	950	60 gallons	$543.70
34.	6	1100	48 gallons	$541.16

35. Floyd rented a car for 4 days and drove it 760 miles. The base fee was $30.50 per day plus 21¢ per mile. The car used 34 gallons of gasoline. Floyd paid $1.50 per gallon. Find the total cost for rental and gasoline. (Pages 250–251) $332.60

36. Rachel rented a car and drove it 950 miles for 6 days. The base fee was $25.30 per day plus 18¢ per mile. The car used 50 gallons of gasoline. She paid $1.58 per gallon. Find the total cost for rental and gasoline. (Pages 250–251) $401.80

37. Carla puts three quarters and one nickel in the coin box of a bus twice a day. One month, she made the round trip 19 times. Find her total bus fare. (Pages 254–255) $30.40

38. Ben puts five quarters, one dime, and a nickel in the coin box of a bus twice each day. How much is his monthly bus fare in a month of 18 working days? (Pages 254–255) $50.40

39. Tim travels to work by bus. The one-way fare is $0.95. Estimate the bus fare in a month of 22 working days. (Pages 260–261) c

a. $0.90 × 2 × 20

b. $0.90 × 2 × 25

c. $1.00 × 2 × 20

d. $1.00 × 2 × 25

40. Astrid uses both a commuter train and a bus to get to work. Her monthly commuter train ticket costs $75.50. The one-way bus fare is $0.90. Find the total commuting costs for a month of 20 working days. (Pages 254–255) $111.50

For Exercises 41–45, use the table on page 256 to find the cost of the round-trip tickets. Include a 5% tax on the plane, train, or bus fare. (Pages 256–257)

	Means of Travel	Number of Passengers
41.	Plane	2 adults (coach) $903.00
42.	Bus	1 adult 1 child, age 7 $519.75

	Means of Travel	Number of Passengers
43.	Train	2 adults, 1 child, age 9 $1008.00
44.	Plane (coach)	1 adult 3 children, ages 3, 9, 12 $1580.25

45. The Appletons have two children, ages 10 and 11. Find the round-trip travel costs for the Appleton family, traveling by bus. (Pages 256–257)

$1199.50

46. The child's fare on a certain airline is 87% of the adult fare. The adult fare is $207. Estimate the child's fare. (Pages 260–261) d

a. $200 × 0.80 **b.** $300 × 0.90

c. $210 × 0.80 **d.** $210 × 0.90

Chapter Test

The Teacher's Resource Book contains two forms of each chapter test.

Multiply.

1. \$27.00 × 7 \$189.00 **2.** \$61.80 × 9 \$556.20 **3.** 380 × \$0.74 \$281.20 **4.** 215 × \$2.30 \$494.50

5. \$370 × 6 \$2220 **6.** \$525 × 4 \$2100 **7.** \$600 × 0.06 \$36.00 **8.** \$870 × 0.05 \$43.50

Add.

9. \$217.90 + \$61.80 + \$18.40 \$298.10 **10.** \$504.70 + \$94.02 + \$71.86 \$670.58

Add. If the sum is a dollar or more, write your answer in dollars.

11. 35¢ + 20¢ + 10¢ 65¢ **12.** 60¢ + 35¢ + 25¢ \$1.20 **13.** 50¢ + 40¢ + 15¢ \$1.05

For Exercises 14–17, find the total cost for car rental and gasoline. Use \$35.60 as the base fee per day, 30¢ as the cost per mile, and \$1.60 as the cost per gallon of gasoline.

	Number of Days	Miles Driven	Gasoline Used	
14.	5	716	37	\$452.00
15.	2	402	18	\$220.60
16.	6	946	50	\$577.40
17.	10	1240	62	\$827.20

18. Vera travels to work each day by suburban bus. The one-way fare is \$1.90. Estimate the monthly fare in a month of 21 working days. b

a. \$1.50 × 2 × 20

b. \$2.00 × 2 × 20

c. \$1.50 × 2 × 25

d. \$2.00 × 2 × 25

19. Miguel uses both a commuter train and the subway to get to work. His monthly commuter ticket costs \$66.80. The one-way subway fare is \$0.80. Find his total commuting cost for a month of 22 working days. \$102.00

20. Mr. and Mrs. Kahn and their 7-year old child took a round-trip flight to visit relatives. The adult one-way fare was \$280. The child's fare was 80% of the adult fare. There was a 5% tax on the plane fare. Find the round-trip travel costs. \$1646.40

Additional Practice

You may wish to use all or some of these exercises, depending on how well students performed on the formal chapter test.

Skills

Multiply. (Pages 6–9)

1. $34.00 × 5 $170.00
2. $97.50 × 3 $292.50
3. 565 × $0.55 $310.75
4. 140 × $4.10 $574.00
5. $620 × 5 $3100
6. $310 × 3 $930
7. $400 × 0.09 $36.00
8. $920 × 0.04 $36.80

Add. (Pages 4–5)

9. $442.30 + $174.00 + $20.20 $636.50
10. $817.20 + $112.88 + $81.65 $1011.73

Add. If the sum is a dollar or more, write your answer in dollars. (Pages 2–3)

11. 40¢ + 40¢ + 10¢ 90¢
12. 50¢ + 40¢ + 30¢ $1.20
13. 75¢ + 20¢ + 20¢ $1.15

Applications

14. Ralph Bok rented a car and drove it 896 miles. The rental cost was 32¢ per mile. Estimate the mileage charge. (Pages 260–261) b

    a. 890 × $0.30 b. 900 × $0.30
    c. 890 × $0.40 d. 900 × $0.40

15. Sonya Romanov rented a car for 8 days and drove it 1590 miles. The base fee was $26.50 per day plus 29¢ per mile. The car used 70 gallons of gasoline for which Sonya paid $1.45 per gallon. Find the total cost. (Pages 250–251) $774.60

16. Beatrice puts three quarters and two nickels in the coin box of a bus twice a day. One month she made the round trip to work 24 times. Find her total bus fare for that month. (Pages 254–255) $40.80

17. Benedict buys a monthly commuter train ticket for $72.00. He also uses an in-town bus that has a one-way fare of $1.10. Find his total commuting costs for a month of 17 working days. (Pages 254–255) $109.40

For Exercises 18–22, use the table on page 256 to find the cost of the round-trip tickets. Include a 4% sales tax. (Pages 256–257)

	Means of Travel	Number of Passengers
18.	Bus	1 adult 1 child, age 15 $686.40
19.	Plane	1 adult (night fare) $224.64

	Means of Travel	Number of Passengers
20.	Train	1 adult $374.40
21.	Bus	2 adults 1 child, age 10 $858.00

22. The Nerudas have three children, aged 5, 7, and 12. Find the round-trip travel costs for the Neruda family, traveling by plane (coach). (Pages 256–257). $2012.40

23. The train offers a special child's fare of 69% of the regular fare of $238. Estimate the child's fare. (Pages 260–261) c

    a. $120 b. $150 c. $168 d. $144

The Teacher's Resource Book also contains a cumulative review for Chapters 10-12.

Cumulative Review: Chapters 10–12

Choose the correct answer. Choose a, b, c, or d.

1. Add: \$2975 + \$713.29 + \$859.33 a

a. \$4547.62 **b.** \$160,237
c. \$3547.52 **d.** \$4757.52

2. Subtract: \$763.20 − \$475.81 b

a. \$212.10 **b.** \$287.39
c. \$312.61 **d.** \$1239.01

3. Multiply: 24 × \$1.35 d

a. \$324 **b.** \$3.24
c. \$30.24 **d.** \$32.40

4. Multiply: 395 × 2.15 d

a. 610 **b.** 8492.5
c. 183.72 **d.** 849.25

5. Round 0.07639 to the nearest hundredth. a

a. 0.08 **b.** 0.07
c. 0.076 **d.** 0.075

6. Divide. Round the answer to the nearest hundredth. b

5226 ÷ 10,000

a. 0.523 **b.** 0.52
c. 0.05 **d.** 0.052

7. Write a decimal for 87.2% b

a. 0.0872 **b.** 0.872
c. 8720.0 **d.** 8.72

8. Find 8% of \$9500. c

a. \$9508 **b.** \$10,268
c. \$760 **d.** \$76

9. Find 36% of \$2800. c

a. \$1000 **b.** \$1080
c. \$1008 **d.** \$100.80

10. Find the value of three quarters, one dime and one nickel. a

a. \$0.90 **b.** \$0.75
c. \$0.95 **d.** \$0.85

11. The base price of Ray's new car was \$7315. The options cost \$2175 and the destination charge was \$215. Find the sticker price. c

a. \$9695 **b.** \$11,640
c. \$9705 **d.** \$9375

12. The sticker price for a certain car is \$11,950. The tax rate is 7%. Find the total cost. c

a. \$836.50 **b.** \$11,957.00
c. \$12,786.50 **d.** \$11,950.07

13. Find the total cost of the car below. a

SKYBIRD '85
\$1500 Down
\$230 per month for 48 months

a. \$12,540
b. \$9540
c. \$11,040
d. \$83,040

14. The cash price for a certain car is \$9350. Michelle can buy it by paying \$2300 down and \$9100 in monthly payments. Find the finance charge. b

a. \$250 **b.** \$2050
c. \$2550 **d.** \$2500

15. Kevin's repair bill after an accident was $398.50. His deductible was $100. How much will the insurance company pay? c

a. $198.50 b. $398.50
c. $298.50 d. $498.50

16. Jill paid $26.15 for a tune-up for her new car. She also paid $6.00 for a wheel alignment and $27.30 for other parts. Find the total cost when the sales tax is 8%. b

a. $59.45 b. $64.21
c. $4.76 d. $62.02

17. Harold paid $8750 for his car. It has depreciated 43% over the last three years. Find the amount of depreciation. d

a. $4987.50 b. $11,287.50
c. $3937.50 d. $3762.50

18. A certain car is driven 62,000 kilometers per year. The yearly gasoline cost is $3085. Find the cost per kilometer. c

a. $20.10
b. $0.04
c. $0.05
d. $21.00

19. Regina listed the following yearly expenses for her car.

Fixed costs: $3520
Variable costs: $1980
Other costs: $350

Find the total yearly costs. c

a. $5500 b. $5750
c. $5850 d. $5400

20. Bart drove a rented car 740 miles in 4 days. The base fee was $51.90 per day with no mileage charge. He paid $1.70 per gallon for 33 gallons of gasoline. Find the total cost. d

a. $207.60 b. $56.10
c. $108.00 d. $263.70

21. Miguel commutes to and from work each day by train and bus. His monthly train ticket costs $75.70. A one-way bus ride is 60¢. Find his total commuting costs for a month with 20 working days. a

a. $99.70 b. $87.70
c. $76.30 d. $76.90

22. Lori puts two quarters, a dime, and a nickel into the coin box of a bus twice a day. Find the total cost for 22 days. b

a. $14.30 b. $28.60
c. $33.00 d. $16.50

23. On a certain airline, the children's fare is $\frac{1}{2}$ the adult fare. Find the fare for two adults and a child when the adult fare is $230. c

a. $475 b. $690
c. $575 d. $500

24. A certain plane fare is $402.43. The train fare for the same trip is $361.29. Estimate the difference. d

a. $10 b. $20
c. $30 d. $40

25. Ramon rented a car and drove 502 kilometers. The cost per kilometer is $0.19. Estimate the total cost. d

a. $70 b. $80 c. $90 d. $100

REVIEW OF RELATED SKILLS FOR CHAPTER 13

We suggest that some or all of this page be reviewed before proceeding with the chapter.

Round to the nearest tenth. (Pages 16–17)

1. 4.87 4.9 **2.** 2.98 3.0 **3.** 9.47 9.5 **4.** 5.01 5.0 **5.** 49.06 49.1 **6.** 83.22 83.2

7. 13.09 13.1 **8.** 47.44 47.4 **9.** 66.12 66.1 **10.** 17.98 18.0 **11.** 138.20 138.2 **12.** 166.74 166.7

Divide. Round each quotient to the nearest tenth. (Pages 16–17)

13. 157 ÷ 3 52.3 **14.** 47 ÷ 2 23.5 **15.** 53 ÷ 14 3.8 **16.** 61 ÷ 16 3.8 **17.** 64 ÷ 13 4.9

18. 87 ÷ 12 7.3 **19.** 55 ÷ 16 3.4 **20.** 138 ÷ 15 9.2 **21.** 186 ÷ 700 0.3 **22.** 406 ÷ 300 1.4

Add. (Pages 4–5)

23. $6.07 + $0.54 + $0.71 $7.32 **24.** $0.81 + $0.91 + $1.55 $3.27 **25.** $0.44 + $0.70 + $0.95 $2.09

26. $0.45 + $0.87 + $1.43 $2.75 **27.** $2.18 + $8.17 + $0.16 $10.51 **28.** $0.71 + $2.98 + $1.99 $5.68

29. $4.16 + $1.09 + $0.58 $5.83 **30.** $5.00 + $2.91 + $0.04 $7.95 **31.** $4.60 + $2.60 + $0.15 $7.35

Subtract. (Pages 4–5)

32. $2.87 − $0.41 $2.46 **33.** $5.07 − $1.02 $4.05 **34.** $1.61 − $0.40 $1.21 **35.** $2.79 − $1.58 $1.21

36. $1.91 − $1.64 $0.27 **37.** $4.83 − $2.67 $2.16 **38.** $3.27 − $0.17 $3.10 **39.** $2.88 − $1.29 $1.59

40. $4.24 − $1.98 $2.26 **41.** $5.07 − $4.19 $0.88 **42.** $3.26 − $1.87 $1.39 **43.** $4.17 − $4.08 $0.09

Multiply. (Pages 8–9)

44. $0.25 × 2 $0.50 **45.** $0.40 × 2 $0.80 **46.** $0.85 × 2 $1.70 **47.** $0.97 × 2 $1.94 **48.** $0.74 × 2 $1.48

49. $1.08 × 2 $2.16 **50.** $1.15 × 2 $2.30 **51.** $1.24 × 2 $2.48 **52.** $2.01 × 2 $4.02 **53.** $1.81 × 2 $3.62

Round each amount to the nearest cent. (Pages 16–17)

54. $0.5077 $0.51 **55.** $0.8136 $0.81 **56.** $0.4175 $0.42 **57.** $0.2194 $0.22 **58.** $0.8449 $0.84

59. $1.8062 $1.81 **60.** $2.0765 $2.08 **61.** $5.5555 $5.56 **62.** $7.1918 $7.19 **63.** $4.0051 $4.01

Write a fraction for each mixed number. (Pages 56–57)

64. $4\frac{1}{2}$ $\frac{9}{2}$ **65.** $3\frac{1}{2}$ $\frac{7}{2}$ **66.** $6\frac{1}{4}$ $\frac{25}{4}$ **67.** $5\frac{1}{5}$ $\frac{26}{5}$ **68.** $9\frac{1}{6}$ $\frac{55}{6}$ **69.** $7\frac{1}{3}$ $\frac{22}{3}$

70. $2\frac{1}{4}$ $\frac{9}{4}$ **71.** $8\frac{2}{3}$ $\frac{26}{3}$ **72.** $7\frac{1}{5}$ $\frac{36}{5}$ **73.** $11\frac{1}{4}$ $\frac{45}{4}$ **74.** $6\frac{1}{7}$ $\frac{43}{7}$ **75.** $2\frac{1}{9}$ $\frac{19}{9}$

Divide. Round each amount to the nearest cent. (Pages 58–59, 16–17)

76. $\$4.68 \div 1\frac{1}{2}$ $\$3.12$ **77.** $\$8.34 \div 2\frac{1}{2}$ $\$3.34$ **78.** $\$6.36 \div 4\frac{1}{4}$ $\$1.50$ **79.** $\$9.20 \div 6\frac{1}{4}$ $\$1.47$

80. $\$4.13 \div 2\frac{1}{3}$ $\$1.77$ **81.** $\$7.80 \div 1\frac{1}{3}$ $\$5.85$ **82.** $\$8.50 \div 1\frac{1}{5}$ $\$7.08$ **83.** $\$4.44 \div 1\frac{1}{6}$ $\$3.81$

84. $\$1.17 \div 1\frac{1}{4}$ $\$0.94$ **85.** $\$3.04 \div 3\frac{1}{7}$ $\$0.97$ **86.** $\$4.02 \div 2\frac{2}{3}$ $\$1.51$ **87.** $\$3.14 \div 1\frac{1}{9}$ $\$2.83$

88. $\$1.19 \div 1\frac{1}{5}$ $\$0.99$ **89.** $\$2.34 \div 2\frac{1}{2}$ $\$0.94$ **90.** $\$5.60 \div 2\frac{3}{4}$ $\$2.04$ **91.** $\$4.40 \div 3\frac{1}{2}$ $\$1.26$

CHAPTER

13 FOOD COSTS

CONSUMER SKILLS / APPLICATIONS

13-1 Comparing Costs: Unit Price
13-2 Saving Money: No-Name Brands
13-3 Saving Money: Coupons
13-4 Cost Per Serving
Rounding and Estimation

CAREER APPLICATIONS

Accounting Clerk
Waiter / Waitress

13-1 Comparing Costs: Unit Price

See the Teacher's Manual for the objectives.

Gina bought the Fine Farms brand of potatoes because the unit price was less than that of the Blue Fields brand.

FINE FARMS POTATOES
UNIT PRICE $0.18 per kilogram
ITEM PRICE $0.90 5 kilograms

Unit price is the cost per gram, per pound, per liter, and so on.

Unit Price = Cost of Item ÷ Number of Units

EXAMPLE A 16-ounce container of cottage cheese costs $0.96. A 24-ounce container is selling for $1.38. Which is the better buy?

Cottage Cheese
Regular or Low Fat
16 oz. cont. 96¢

COTTAGE CHEESE
24-oz. cont. $1 38

Solution: [1] Find the unit price of the 16-ounce container. Write $0.96 as 96¢.

Unit price = 96 ÷ 16 ◀ $16\overline{)96}$ = 6

Unit price: **6¢ per ounce**

[2] Find the unit price of the 24-ounce container. Write $1.38 as 138¢.

Unit Price: 138 ÷ 24 ◀ $24\overline{)138.00}$ = 5.75, or 5.8

5.8¢ per ounce

[3] Compare the unit prices.

Since the **24-ounce container** has the lower unit price, it is the better buy.

When using unit price to determine the better buy, be sure that the quality of the products compared is the same.

REVIEW OF RELATED SKILLS

You may wish to use these exercises before teaching the lesson.

Round to the nearest tenth. (Pages 16–17)

1. 3.46 3.5 **2.** 4.52 4.5 **3.** 6.97 7.0 **4.** 4.98 5.0 **5.** 23.55 23.6 **6.** 42.78 42.8
7. 46.92 46.9 **8.** 32.13 32.1 **9.** 57.31 57.3 **10.** 18.99 19.0 **11.** 156.41 156.4 **12.** 237.61 237.6

Divide. Round each quotient to the nearest tenth. (Pages 16–17)

13. 149 ÷ 2 74.5 **14.** 59 ÷ 3 19.7 **15.** 41 ÷ 15 2.7 **16.** 59 ÷ 12 4.9 **17.** 49 ÷ 16 3.1
18. 71 ÷ 24 3.0 **19.** 65 ÷ 18 3.6 **20.** 129 ÷ 15 8.6 **21.** 119 ÷ 500 0.2 **22.** 129 ÷ 200 0.6

EXERCISES

For Exercises 1–12, find the unit price. Round each answer to the nearest tenth of a cent.

	Item	Quantity	Price		Item	Quantity	Price
1.	Celery seed	45 g	$1.35 3¢/g	**7.**	Canned beans	16 oz	40¢ 2.5¢/oz
2.	Ground mustard	50 g	$1.05 2.1¢/g	**8.**	Orange drink	2 L	$1.19 59.5¢/L
3.	Pickling spice	30 g	93¢ 3.1¢/g	**9.**	Vanilla extract	118 mL	$2.49 2.1¢/mL
4.	Allspice	50 g	$1.75 3.5¢/g	**10.**	Oranges	10	99¢ 9.9¢ each
5.	Mayonnaise	8 oz	66¢ 8.3¢/oz	**11.**	Cucumbers	4	$1.00 25¢ each
6.	Juice	12 fl oz	45¢ 3.8¢/fl oz	**12.**	Canned peaches	8 oz	42¢ 5.3¢/oz

13. A 500–gram box of oatmeal costs 90¢. Find the unit price. 0.2¢ per gram

14. A 5–ounce jar of mustard costs 39¢. Find the unit price. 7.8¢ per ounce

15. A 16–ounce can of whole kernel corn costs 46¢. Find the unit price. 2.9¢ per ounce

16. A 1.5–kilogram can of kidney beans costs 99¢. Find the unit price. 66¢ per kilogram

For Exercises 17–27, find the better buy.

	Item	Smaller Size	Larger Size		Item	Smaller Size	Larger Size
17.	Soup (Larger)	305 g/79¢	539 g/$1.09	**21.**	Vinegar (Larger)	473 mL/43¢	946 mL/75¢
18.	Flour (Larger)	2 lb/59¢	5 lb/$1.08	**22.**	Juice (Larger)	40 fl oz/$1.15	64 fl oz/$1.75
19.	Cereal (Larger)	226 g/$1.19	510 g/$2.15	**23.**	Pear (Larger)	4/$1.00	5/$1.10
20.	Orange (Smaller)	6/55¢	10/99¢	**24.**	Tuna (Smaller)	$6\frac{1}{2}$ oz/88¢	12 oz/$1.65

25. Cottage Cheese Larger

26. Vanilla Extract Larger

27. Vegetable Oil Larger

28. A 16–ounce can of peaches costs 70¢. A 24–ounce can costs $1.00. Which is the better buy? The 24-ounce can

29. A 360–milliliter bottle of maple syrup costs $1.15. A 720–milliliter bottle costs $1.79. Which is the better buy? The 720-milliliter bottle

30. A bag of four grapefruits costs $1.09. A bag of six grapefruits costs $1.65. Which is the better buy? The bag of four

13-2 Saving Money: No-Name Brands

See the Teacher's Manual for the objectives.

The supermarket in Sam Fong's neighborhood offers **no-name** (or **generic**) **products.** These items are usually less expensive than brand-name products.

EVERGREEN SUPERMARKET		
NO-NAME BRANDS		
Paper towels	100-roll	69¢
Sliced Carrots	1 lb. can	39¢
Corn Oil	16 oz.	$1.17

EXAMPLE Sam bought the 3 no-name items advertised at the right above. Julie Temple bought the 3 similar items advertised at the right. Find the difference in their total costs.

TOP-NOTCH MARKET		
Tolan's Corn Oil	16 oz.	$1.53
O'Hare Carrots	1 lb	60¢
Heartland Towels	100-roll	98¢

Solution: [1] Find Sam's total cost.

$0.69 + $0.39 + $1.17 = **$2.25**

[2] Find Julie's total cost.

$1.53 + $0.60 + $0.98 = **$3.11**

[3] Find the difference in the total costs.

$3.11 − $2.25 = **$0.86** ◀ ***Julie paid 86¢ more than Sam.***

REVIEW OF RELATED SKILLS

You may wish to use these exercises before teaching the lesson.

Add or subtract. (Pages 4–5)

1. $2.04 + $0.45 + $0.69 $3.18
2. $0.75 + $0.89 + $1.15 $2.79
3. $0.55 + $0.75 + $0.85 $2.15
4. $0.95 + $0.54 + $1.12 $2.61
5. $1.15 + $2.06 + $0.77 $3.98
6. $0.85 + $3.04 + $1.09 $4.98
7. $1.15 − $0.29 $0.86
8. $3.28 − $1.05 $2.23
9. $1.57 − $0.88 $0.69
10. $4.55 − $1.20 $3.35
11. $1.45 − $0.66 $0.79
12. $2.25 − $1.09 $1.16
13. $4.05 − $0.53 $3.52
14. $1.16 − $1.08 $0.08

EXERCISES

For Exercises 1–12, find the difference between the brand-name price and the no-name price.

Item	Brand-Name Price	No-Name Price
1. Sugar	$1.79	$1.15 $0.64
2. Instant coffee	$3.99	$2.48 $1.51

Item	Brand-Name Price	No-Name Price
3. Juice	$1.19	$0.64 $0.55
4. Crackers	$0.95	$0.49 $0.46

	Item	Brand-Name Price	No-Name Price	
5.	Shortening	$1.85	$1.06	$0.79
6.	Rice	$2.99	$2.45	$0.54
7.	Canned corn	$0.85	$0.59	$0.26
8.	Catsup	$1.05	$0.79	$0.26

	Item	Brand-Name Price	No-Name Price	
9.	Corn oil	$1.85	$1.17	$0.68
10.	Soda water	$0.75	$0.61	$0.14
11.	Milk powder	$3.49	$2.80	$0.69
12.	Sardines	$1.09	$0.55	$0.54

For Exercises 13–17, refer to the advertisements below.

13. Find the difference in cost between the brand-name dish detergent and the generic brand detergent. $0.45

14. Find the difference in cost between the brand-name asparagus and the no-name asparagus. $0.38

15. Find the difference in cost between the brand-name almonds and the generic almonds. $0.93

16. Find the total difference in cost between the brand-name napkins and macaroni and the no-name napkins and macaroni. $0.51

17. Find the total difference in cost between the brand-name navy beans and jam and the generic navy beans and jam. $0.67

18. Price-Right Market is selling brand name tomato paste at $0.39 and pudding mix at $0.45. No-name products of the same size are priced at $0.24 and $0.39. Louisa decided to buy the no-name products. How much did she save? $0.21

19. Eric bought generic laundry detergent at $1.09 and window cleaner at $0.69. He saw brand–name laundry detergent and window cleaner of the same size advertised at $1.69 and $0.98. Find the total difference between the cost of the brand-name and generic products. $0.89

CORNER MARKET'S LOW PRICES
BRAND NAME PRODUCTS

PQ Paper Napkins	150	85¢
Lark Strawberry Jam	12 oz	$1.19
Big Valley Asparagus	16 oz	$1.03
O'Riley Macaroni	16 oz	89¢
Timber Navy Beans	15 oz	75¢
Pluto's Salted Almonds	500 g	$2.50
Handy Dish Detergent	30 oz	$1.60

A-TO-Z SUPERMARKET HAS NO-NAME PRODUCTS!

Navy Beans	15 oz	52¢
Macaroni	16 oz	66¢
Strawberry Jam	12 oz	75¢
Paper Napkins	150	57¢
Almonds	500 g	$1.57
Dish Detergent	32 oz	$1.15
Asparagus	16 oz	65¢

ACCOUNTING CLERK

Career lessons are optional. This lesson combines the skills of reading a table and addition of decimals.

Businesses must keep accurate records of their **operating costs** or **overhead.** One of Harry Winkler's responsibilities as **accounting clerk** for the Timely Food, Inc. is to prepare a monthly statement of the operating costs.

Each account on the monthly statement is **coded** with a number. This makes it easier to "feed" the information to a computer.

ACCOUNT	*CODE*
Wages—Salary	101
Wages—Hourly	102
B and L Gas	201
Acme Repairs	202
Ajax Tires	205
Star Insurance	301
Blue Dot Oil	401
T. G. Electric	402
Telephone	403
First Bank	404
J. K. Office Supplies	501
Taxes	601

MONTHLY STATEMENTS

Timely Food, Incorporated

Period Beginning *Mar. 1*
Ending *Mar. 31*

Code	Amount	Accumulated Total	Date
301	$425.05	$425.05	March 1, 1982
205	865.05	1290.10	March 3, 1982
101	6295.50		March 4, 1982
102	4250.75	11,836.35	March 9, 1982
202	725.45		March 11, 1982
403	250.20	12,812.00	March 15, 1982
201	865.50	13,677.50	March 18, 1982
501	85.90		March 20, 1982
401	475.95	14,239.35	March 21, 1982
404	365.60		March 23, 1982
402	176.25	14,781.20	March 27, 1982
601	865.10		March 29, 1982
	TOTAL		March 31, 1982

After recording a code and its amount, Harry adds this amount to the previous accumulated total to find the **accumulated total** for that date.

EXAMPLE 1 Find the accumulated total through March 4.

Solution: Add the amount for code 101 to the previous accumulated total.

$1290.10 ← ***Previous Accumulated Total: March 3***
+ 6295.50 ← ***101 Amount***
$7585.60 ← ***Accumulated Total: March 4***

EXAMPLE 2 Find the total amount paid to the following accounts.
B and L Gas, Blue Dot Oil, T. G. Electric

Solution:

1 Find the code for each account

B and L Gas: **201** Blue Dot Oil: **401** T. G. Electric: **402**

2 Write the amounts for each code.

201: **$865.50** 401: **$475.95** 402: **$176.25**

3 Add. $865.50 + $475.95 + $176.25 = **$1517.70**

EXERCISES

Find the accumulated total through the following dates. (Example 1)

1. March 11, 1982 $12,561.80
2. March 20, 1982 $13,763.40
3. March 23, 1982 $14,604.95
4. March 29, 1982 $15,646.30
5. Find the total overhead in March. $15,646.30

Find the total amount paid to the following accounts. (Example 2)

6. Ajax Tires, Blue Dot Oil, Acme Repairs
7. Wages – Salary, Wages – Hourly, Taxes

6. $2066.45 7. $11,411.35 8. $7846 9. $11,696.75 10. $12,017.55 11. $12,393.50 12. $12,664.25 13. $13,529.35 14. $13,529.35

Complete the monthly statement below. (Example 1)

MONTHLY STATEMENTS

Timely Food, Incorporated

Period Beginning APRIL 1
Ending APRIL 30

Code	Amount	1 Accumulated Total	2 Date
301	$450.50	$450.50	APRIL 5, 1982
101	7395.50	8	APRIL 8, 1982
102	3850.75	9	APRIL 9, 1982
403	320.80	10	APRIL 14, 1982
404	375.95	11	APRIL 20, 1982
401	270.75	12	APRIL 23, 1982
601	865.10	13	APRIL 26, 1982
	TOTAL	14	APRIL 30, 1982

Find the total amount paid to the following accounts in April. (Example 2)

15. Wages – Salary, Blue Dot Oil, Telephone $7987.05
16. Taxes, Wages – Hourly, First Bank $5091.80

13-3 Saving Money: Coupons

See the Teacher's Manual for the objectives.

Elaine Brady saves money on food costs by clipping **discount coupons** from advertisements. Some stores offer **double value coupons** or specify a fixed time when they will double the savings on all coupons.

EXAMPLE Elaine uses the three coupons shown below at a store offering double savings on all coupons. How much did she pay for the items?

REGULAR PRICE 65¢
SAVE 15¢
SPAGHETTI
ENRICHED!
PRICE $1.09
SAVE 20¢
WITH THIS COUPON
PEANUT BUTTER
YUMMY YOGURT
20¢ OFF
REGULAR 49¢

Solution: [1] Find the total regular price.

$\$0.49 + \$0.65 + \$1.09 = \mathbf{\$2.23}$

[2] Find the total coupon savings.

$(\$0.20 + \$0.15 + \$0.20) \times 2 = \$0.55 \times 2$ ◀ ***Double the savings.***

$= \mathbf{\$1.10}$

[3] Find the amount she paid.

$\$2.23 - \$1.10 = \mathbf{\$1.13}$ ◀ ***Regular Price − Coupon Savings = Amount Paid***

Elaine paid **$1.13** for the items.

REVIEW OF RELATED SKILLS

You may wish to use these exercises before teaching the lesson.

Add. (Pages 4–5)

1. $0.55 + $1.15 + $0.60 $2.30
2. $1.12 + $0.72 + $0.48 $2.32
3. $0.55 + $1.16 + $0.77 $2.48
4. $0.59 + $0.79 + $0.94 $2.32
5. $1.16 + $0.88 + $0.58 $2.62
6. $1.12 + $1.56 + $1.95 $4.63

Multiply. (Pages 8–9)

7. $0.35 × 2 $0.70
8. $0.63 × 2 $1.26
9. $1.04 × 2 $2.08
10. $0.98 × 2 $1.96
11. $1.17 × 2 $2.34

Subtract. (Pages 4–5)

12. $1.12 − $0.35 $0.77
13. $1.35 − $0.42 $0.93
14. $3.56 − $1.15 $2.41
15. $5.14 − $0.89 $4.25

EXERCISES

For Exercises 1–12, first double the coupon savings. Then find the actual price.

	Item	Regular Price	Coupon Savings	
1.	Bread	$0.75	$0.15	$0.45
2.	Corn syrup	$1.09	$0.20	$0.69
3.	Pie filling	$0.89	$0.10	$0.69
4.	Detergent	$1.49	$0.16	$1.17
5.	Pet food	$0.55	$0.08	$0.39
6.	Cream cheese	$0.99	$0.15	$0.69

	Item	Regular Price	Coupon Savings	
7.	Frankfurters	$1.20	$0.25	$0.70
8.	Macaroni	$0.65	$0.12	$0.41
9.	Sugar	$2.20	$0.35	$1.50
10.	Eggs	$0.99	$0.10	$0.79
11.	Sliced cheese	$1.29	$0.17	$0.95
12.	Vinegar	$0.85	$0.20	$0.45

For Exercises 13–20, refer to the coupons at the right.

13. Find the price Stuart paid for the paper plates and pineapple juice when he used discount coupons. $2.65
14. Mary Ann used the discount coupons at a store offering double coupon savings. She bought paper plates and juice. Find the price she paid for the items. $2.10
15. Find the difference between the price Stuart paid and the price Mary Ann paid. $0.55
16. Dominic used discount coupons to buy pancake mix and tomato paste. Find the price he paid for the items. $1.52
17. Gina bought tomato paste and pancake mix at a store offering double savings on discount coupons. Find the price she paid for the items. $1.24
18. Find the difference between the price Dominic paid and the price Gina paid for the same products. $0.28
19. Sal used coupons to buy juice, rice, and tomato paste at a store offering double savings. Find the price he paid for the items. $3.41
20. Miyo bought rice, paper plates, and pancake mix with coupons at a store offering double savings. Find the price she paid. $4.23

13-4 Cost per Serving

See the Teacher's Manual for the objectives.

Anita saves money on food costs by not wasting food. She uses this table to compute the number of pounds of meat to buy.

Meat	Servings Per Pound	Meat	Servings Per Pound	Meat	Servings Per Pound
Beef		**Lamb**		**Pork-Cured**	
Sirloin Steak	$2\frac{1}{2}$	Chops	3	Picnic ham	2
Porterhouse	2	Leg of lamb	3	Ham (cooked)	$3\frac{1}{2}$
Rib roast	$2\frac{1}{2}$	**Pork-Fresh**		**Poultry**	
Ground beef	4	Chops	4	Broiler	$1\frac{1}{2}$
Frankfurters	4	Roast	$2\frac{1}{2}$	Legs, thighs	3
Stew meat	5	Spare ribs	$1\frac{1}{3}$	Breasts	4

EXAMPLE 1 How many pounds of each of these meats should Anita buy for 6 servings?

a. Lamb chops **b.** Ground beef **c.** Spare ribs

Solutions: **Servings Needed ÷ Servings per Pound = Number of Pounds**

a. Lamb chops: $6 \div 3 = \mathbf{2}$ **pounds**

b. Ground beef: $6 \div 4 = \mathbf{1\frac{1}{2}}$ **pounds**

c. Spare ribs: $6 \div 1\frac{1}{3} = 6 \div \frac{4}{3}$

$= 6 \times \frac{3}{4} = \mathbf{4\frac{1}{2}}$ **pounds** ◀ $\frac{\overset{3}{\cancel{6}}}{1} \times \frac{3}{\underset{2}{\cancel{4}}} = \frac{9}{2}$, *or* $4\frac{1}{2}$

After completing Example 1, you may wish to have students do some or all of Exercises 1-8.

EXAMPLE 2 Which is the less expensive meat for Anita to serve?

Spare ribs: \$1.39 per pound Leg of lamb: \$1.79 per pound

Solution: [1] Use the table to find the number of servings per pound.

Spare ribs: $1\frac{1}{3}$ Leg of lamb: 3

[2] **Cost per Pound ÷ Servings per Pound = Cost Per Serving**

Spare ribs: $\$1.39 \div 1\frac{1}{3} = \$1.39 \div \frac{4}{3}$

$= 1.39 \times \frac{3}{4} = \$1.04$ ◀ *Rounded to the nearest cent*

Leg of lamb: $\$1.79 \div 3 = \$0.60$ ◀ *Rounded to the nearest cent*

[3] Compare the costs. The **leg of lamb** is less expensive.

REVIEW OF RELATED SKILLS

You may wish to use these exercises before teaching the lesson.

Write a fraction for each mixed number. (Pages 56–57)

1. $1\frac{1}{2}$ $\frac{3}{2}$ **2.** $3\frac{1}{3}$ $\frac{10}{3}$ **3.** $1\frac{2}{3}$ $\frac{5}{3}$ **4.** $4\frac{1}{5}$ $\frac{21}{5}$ **5.** $2\frac{1}{4}$ $\frac{9}{4}$ **6.** $3\frac{1}{8}$ $\frac{25}{8}$

Divide. (Pages 58–59)

7. $9 \div 1\frac{1}{4}$ $7\frac{1}{5}$ **8.** $8 \div 2\frac{1}{2}$ $3\frac{1}{5}$ **9.** $10 \div 3\frac{1}{2}$ $2\frac{6}{7}$ **10.** $7 \div 1\frac{1}{3}$ $5\frac{1}{4}$ **11.** $6 \div 2\frac{1}{4}$ $2\frac{2}{3}$

Divide. Round each answer to the nearest cent. (Pages 58–59, 16–17)

12. $\$2.39 \div 1\frac{1}{2}$ $1.59 **13.** $\$1.69 \div 1\frac{1}{3}$ $1.27 **14.** $\$3.29 \div 2\frac{1}{2}$ $1.32 **15.** $\$1.19 \div 1\frac{1}{4}$ $0.95

EXERCISES

For Exercises 1–8, use the table on page 278 to find the number of pounds of each kind of meat needed. (Example 1)

Meat	Number of Servings	Pounds
1. Pork chops	12	? 3
2. Stew meat	10	? 2
3. Cooked ham	7	? 2

Meat	Number of Servings	Pounds
4. Porterhouse	5	? $2\frac{1}{2}$
5. Roast pork	10	? 4
6. Lamb chops	7	? $2\frac{1}{3}$

7. Dan wants to buy enough sirloin steak to make ten servings. How many pounds should he buy? 4 pounds

8. How many pounds of ground beef should Helen buy to make 9 servings for dinner? $2\frac{1}{4}$ pounds

In Exercises 9–14, round each answer to the nearest cent. Use the table on page 278. (Example 2)

Meat	Price Per Pound	Cost Per Serving
9. Sirloin Steak	$2.69	? $1.08
10. Pork: Picnic	$0.79	? $0.40
11. Lamb Chops	$2.29	? $0.76
12. Broiler	$0.59	? $0.39
13. Stew Meat	$2.49	? $0.50
14. Ground Beef	$1.69	? $0.42

15. Chicken breasts are advertised at $1.99 per pound, and pork roast is also advertised at $1.99 per pound. Which meat costs less per serving? Chicken breasts

16. At one store, sirloin steak costs $2.99 per pound and a rib roast costs $2.79 per pound. Which meat is less expensive per serving? Rib roast

WAITER/WAITRESS

Career lessons are optional. This lesson applies the skills of finding a percent of a number, addition of decimals, and using a formula.

Waiting on tables requires a knowledge of adding with dollar amounts, and especially a knowledge of per cent. To find the total of a bill, you must also answer the question:

What is the tax?

This is the **hidden question** in the problem. Then you can find the total bill.

HUDSON'S RESTAURANT
13th STREET AT MAPLE AVE.
TEL: 005-3211

2 chicken dinners	$10.50
1 lamb chops	7.50
1 mineral water	.75
1 orange juice	.60
3 ice cream	3.45
TAX	
TOTAL	

EXAMPLE 1 Tom Marini, a waiter, is computing the total of the bill at the right. Find the total if the meal tax is 5%.

Solution: Use paper and pencil or use a calculator.

1 Find the total cost of the meal.

1 0 . 5 + 7 . 5 + . 7 5

+ . 6 + 3 . 4 5 = 22.8

2 What is the tax? ◀ ***This is the hidden question.***

2 2 . 8 × 5 % 1.14

3 Add the total meal cost and the tax.

2 2 . 8 + 1 . 1 4 = 23.94

In restaurants, a general rule is that the tip is 15% of the total cost of the food.

EXAMPLE 2 Compute the tip that Tom should receive from the bill in Example 1. Round your answer to the nearest ten cents.

Solutions:

Method 1

Total Cost of Meal × **15%** = **Tip**

$22.80 × 0.15 = $3.42

The tip is about **$3.40.**

Method 2

Since 15% = 3 × 5%, multiply the amount of the tax by 3.

$1.14 × 3 = $3.42

EXERCISES Note that Exercises 1-7 are non-verbal.

Find the total cost for each meal. The tax is 8%. (Example 1)

1. $11.88

HARRY'S BURGERAMA
MAIN STREET AT 10th AVE.
TEL: 342-0896

2 cheeseburgers	$5.90
1 bacon burger	3.15
1 milk	.75
2 orange juice	1.20
TAX	
TOTAL	

2. $34.29

MAGGIE'S
12th AVE. AT CLAY STREET
TEL: 872-3706

3 chicken dinners	$16.50
1 veal chop dinner	8.25
4 apple juice	2.40
4 ice cream	4.60
TAX	
TOTAL	

For Exercises 3–7, the total cost of a meal is given. Compute the tip. Round each answer to the nearest ten cents. (Example 2)

3. $25.80 $3.90 **4.** $9.05 $1.40 **5.** $35.60 $5.30 **6.** $8.75 $1.30 **7.** $17.40 $2.60

8. Doris had lunch at the Assembly Room. The cost of the meal amounted to $4.80. The tax was 5%. Find the total cost, including a 15% tip. $5.76

9. Nick has breakfast at the City Diner. The cost of the meal amounted to $3.60. What was the total cost if the tax was 7% and he left a 15% tip? $4.39

10. Melanie's dinner check amounted to $17.50. The sales tax was 8%. Melanie left a 20% tip. How much did she spend in all? $22.40

11. There were 250 people at a business banquet. The meal cost $15.95 per person. The tax is 6%. What is the total cost, including a 20% tip? $5024.25

12. The bill for Randy's dinner at the Cow Corral had a total meal cost of $11.75. Randy left a tip of $1.75. Was his tip over or under 15%? under

Rounding and Estimation

Consumers use rounding and estimation to solve problems related to food costs.

EXERCISES See the Teacher's Manual for the objectives.

Skills

Choose the best estimate. Choose a, b, or c.

		a.	b.	c.
1. $92 \div 9$	b	**a.** $100 \div 9$	**b.** $90 \div 9$	**c.** $110 \div 9$
2. $69 \div 5$	a	**a.** $70 \div 5$	**b.** $60 \div 5$	**c.** $70 \div 10$
3. $13.02 - 11.98$	a	**a.** $13 - 12$	**b.** $20 - 10$	**c.** $14 - 11$
4. $12.11 - 0.97$	c	**a.** $13 - 1$	**b.** $10 - 1$	**c.** $12 - 1$
5. $0.69 + 1.11$	c	**a.** $0 + 1$	**b.** $1 + 2$	**c.** $1 + 1$
6. $3.21 + 4.78$	a	**a.** $3 + 5$	**b.** $3 + 4$	**c.** $4 + 5$
7. $3.59 \div 4$	c	**a.** $8 \div 4$	**b.** $3 \div 4$	**c.** $4 \div 4$

Choose the best estimate. Choose a, b, c, or d.

		a.	b.	c.	d.
8. $59 \div 6$	c	**a.** 8	**b.** 9	**c.** 10	**d.** 11
9. $51 \div 7$	a	**a.** 7	**b.** 8	**c.** 9	**d.** 10
10. $15.87 - 13.04$	b	**a.** 2	**b.** 3	**c.** 4	**d.** 5
11. $21.14 - 18.98$	c	**a.** 5	**b.** 4	**c.** 2	**d.** 3
12. $0.83 + 4.19$	a	**a.** 5	**b.** 4	**c.** 6	**d.** 7
13. $6.39 + 1.32$	d	**a.** 10	**b.** 9	**c.** 6	**d.** 7
14. $34.89 \div 7$	c	**a.** 7	**b.** 4	**c.** 5	**d.** 8

Applications

15. A 5-ounce jar of mayonnaise costs 49¢. Estimate the unit price. b

a. 40¢ ÷ 5 **b.** 50¢ ÷ 5
c. 40¢ ÷ 10 **d.** 50¢ ÷ 10

16. A 5-pound bag of flour costs \$1.49. Estimate the unit price. d

a. \$1.45 ÷ 5 **b.** \$1.45 ÷ 10
c. \$1.50 ÷ 10 **d.** \$1.50 ÷ 5

17. Brand-name corn costs 79¢. No-name corn costs 51¢. Estimate the difference in cost. a

a. 80¢ − 50¢ **b.** 75¢ − 50¢
c. 75¢ − 55¢ **d.** 80¢ + 50¢

18. Brand-name tuna fish costs \$1.22. No-name tuna costs 89¢. Estimate the difference in cost. b

a. \$1.00 − \$0.80 **b.** \$1.25 − \$0.90
c. \$0.85 + \$1.25 **d.** \$1.30 − \$0.90

19. Tamara bought no-name items for $1.39, $0.63, and $0.88. Estimate the total cost. a

a. $1.40 + $0.60 + $0.90

b. $1.30 + $0.60 + $0.80

c. $1.40 + $0.70 + $0.90

d. $1.30 + $0.70 + $0.80

20. Michael had coupons totaling $0.49 before he doubled their value. He used them to save money on food that cost $4.98. Estimate the amount Michael paid. b

a. $4 − $1 **b.** $5 − $1

c. $4 − $0.80 **d.** $5 − $0.80

21. Brand-name honey costs $1.79. No-name honey costs $1.31. Estimate the difference in cost. c

a. $3.00 **b.** 45¢ **c.** 50¢ **d.** $1.50

22. Irene bought three no-name items for $2.12. Ben bought three similar brand-name items for $2.98. Estimate the difference. d

a. $1.50 **b.** 25¢ **c.** 50¢ **d.** $1.00

23. Conrad bought no-name items for $2.19, $2.75, $1.29, and $3.02. Estimate the total cost of the items that Conrad bought. c

a. $6.00
b. $8.00
c. $9.00
d. $10.00

24. Lola had coupons totaling $0.51 before she doubled their value. She bought food that cost $5.19. Estimate how much she spent. b

a. $3.00
b. $4.00
c. $3.50
d. $4.50

25. A pound of lamb chops serves three people. Lamb chops cost $2.39 per pound. Estimate the cost per serving for lamb chops. a

a. $0.80
b. $0.90
c. $0.70
d. $1.00

Chapter Review

These exercises review the vocabulary, skills and applications presented in the chapter, as a preparation for the chapter test.

Part 1: VOCABULARY

For Exercises 1–5, choose from the box at the right the word(s) that complete(s) each statement.

coupons
unit price
brand-name
quality
no-name
servings per pound

1. The cost of an item per gram, per pound, or per liter is called the __?__. (Pages 270–271) unit price
2. When using unit price to determine the better buy, be sure that the __?__ of the products compared is the same. (Pages 270–271) quality
3. Products that are sold without any brand name are called __?__ products. (Pages 272–273) no-name
4. Shoppers can save money on food costs by using discount __?__ found in advertisements. (Pages 276–277) coupons
5. A shopper can find the amount of meat needed for a meal by knowing the number of servings needed and the number of of __?__. (Pages 278–279) servings per pound

Part 2: SKILLS

Divide. Round each quotient to the nearest tenth. (Pages 16–17)

6. 191 ÷ 3 63.7 **7.** 81 ÷ 14 5.8 **8.** 77 ÷ 17 4.5 **9.** 512 ÷ 200 2.6 **10.** 197 ÷ 800 0.2

Add. (Pages 4–5)

11. \$5.10 + \$0.74 + \$1.20 \$7.04 **12.** \$0.58 + \$0.90 + \$0.87 \$2.35 **13.** \$3.16 + \$0.21 + \$0.86 \$4.23

14. \$3.14 + \$0.79 + \$8.02 \$11.95 **15.** \$3.44 + \$5.09 + \$4.08 \$12.61 **16.** \$6.26 + \$0.19 + \$7.41 \$13.86

Subtract. (Pages 4–5)

17. \$3.12 − \$0.87 \$2.25 **18.** \$1.78 − \$0.30 \$1.48 **19.** \$5.61 − \$0.19 \$5.42 **20.** \$3.10 − \$3.07 \$0.03

21. \$5.02 − \$4.91 \$0.11 **22.** \$4.71 − \$1.94 \$2.77 **23.** \$6.01 − \$5.82 \$0.19 **24.** \$4.01 − \$3.50 \$0.51

Multiply. (Pages 8–9)

25. \$0.35 × 2 \$0.70 **26.** \$0.50 × 2 \$1.00 **27.** \$0.80 × 2 \$1.60 **28.** \$0.92 × 2 \$1.84 **29.** \$1.15 × 2 \$2.30

Round each amount to the nearest cent. (Pages 16–17)

30. \$0.6010 \$0.60 **31.** \$0.3298 \$0.33 **32.** \$0.4289 \$0.43 **33.** \$0.5016 \$0.50 **34.** \$0.3105 \$0.31

35. \$1.0411 \$1.04 **36.** \$3.1896 \$3.19 **37.** \$9.1113 \$9.11 **38.** \$6.1791 \$6.18 **39.** \$3.2125 \$3.21

Divide. Round each amount to the nearest cent. (Pages 58–59, 16–17)

40. \$8.50 ÷ $2\frac{1}{2}$ \$3.40 **41.** \$6.12 ÷ $1\frac{1}{2}$ \$4.08 **42.** \$14.07 ÷ $2\frac{1}{3}$ \$6.03 **43.** \$8.22 ÷ $1\frac{1}{5}$ \$6.85

44. \$7.01 ÷ $1\frac{1}{4}$ \$5.61 **45.** \$9.85 ÷ $2\frac{2}{3}$ \$3.69 **46.** \$2.10 ÷ $1\frac{1}{6}$ \$1.80 **47.** \$1.21 ÷ $1\frac{1}{3}$ \$0.91

Part 3: APPLICATIONS

For Exercises 48–53, find the unit price. Round each answer to the nearest tenth of a cent. (Pages 270–271)

	Item	Quantity	Price	
48.	Lima beans	2 lb	69¢	34.5¢/lb
49.	Potatoes	10 lb	85¢	8.5¢/lb
50.	Cereal	205 g	50¢	0.2¢/g

	Item	Quantity	Price	
51.	Cottage cheese	12 ounces	48¢	4¢/oz
52.	Tuna	6 ounces	80¢	13.3¢/oz
53.	Syrup	500 mL	$1.30	0.3¢/mL

54. A 300–mL bottle of vinegar costs 28¢. An 880–mL bottle costs 70¢. Which is the better buy? (Pages 270–271) The 880-mL bottle

55. A 1–pound bag of flour costs 38¢. A 5–pound bag costs $1.60. Which is the better buy? (Pages 270–271) The 5-pound bag

56. Randolph saw a can of tuna selling for $1.25 and a package of macaroni selling for 93¢. In the same supermarket, no–name products of the same size were 79¢ and 74¢. How much did Randolph save by buying the no-name products? (Pages 272–273) $0.65

For Exercises 57–58, refer to the advertisements at the right. (Pages 276–277)

57. Denise bought a dozen eggs and cream cheese using discount coupons. Find the price that she paid for both items. $1.79

58. Brent used discount coupons at a store that offered double coupon savings. He bought bread and sliced cheese. Find the price that he paid for the items. $1.11

25¢ savings on Mrs. Barton's cream cheese with this coupon. **Regular price $1.10.**

15¢ saving on purchase of 1 dozen eggs. **Regular price $1.09**

Sliced Cheese **Regular price $1.17. Save: 23¢**

Pearson's Bread 1 loaf: **Regular price** 80¢ **Save: 20¢**

For Exercises 59–62, use the table on page 278. Find the number of pounds of each kind of meat needed. (Pages 278–279)

	Meat	Number of Servings	Pounds	
59.	Sirloin steak	2	?	$\frac{4}{5}$
60.	Lamb chops	4	?	$1\frac{1}{3}$

	Meat	Number of Servings	Pounds	
61.	Pork chops	6	?	$1\frac{1}{2}$
62.	Ground beef	3	?	$\frac{3}{4}$

63. A pound of beef serves 4 people. It costs $1.99 per pound. Estimate the cost per serving. (Page 283)

a. 50¢ **b.** 30¢ **c.** 60¢ **d.** 40¢

64. A pound of meat serves 5 people. It costs $2.49 per pound. Estimate the cost per serving. (Page 283)

a. 50¢ **b.** 60¢ **c.** 40¢ **d.** 70¢

Chapter Test

The Teacher's Resource Book contains two forms of each chapter test.

Add or subtract.

1. \$8.70 + \$1.12 + \$0.50 \$10.32
2. \$9.42 + \$0.86 + \$2.07 \$12.35
3. \$4.87 + \$1.17 + \$0.43 \$6.47
4. \$6.25 − \$5.84 \$0.41
5. \$3.87 − \$2.88 \$0.99
6. \$12.17 − \$11.06 \$1.11

Multiply.

7. \$0.75 × 2 \$1.50
8. \$0.96 × 2 \$1.92
9. \$1.25 × 2 \$2.50
10. \$1.37 × 2 \$2.74

Divide. Round each amount to the nearest cent.

11. \$9.66 ÷ $2\frac{1}{3}$ \$4.14
12. \$4.75 ÷ $1\frac{1}{4}$ \$3.80
13. \$7.33 ÷ $2\frac{1}{2}$ \$2.93
14. \$6.11 ÷ $1\frac{1}{2}$ \$4.07

15. A 16-ounce jar of mayonnaise costs \$1.26. Find the unit price. Round your answer to the nearest tenth of a cent. 7.9¢ per ounce

16. A 50-gram jar of mustard costs \$1.09. A 100-gram jar costs \$2.09. Which is the better buy? The 100-gram jar

For Exercises 17–20, find the difference between the brand-name price and the no-name price.

	Item	Brand-Name Price	No-Name Price	
17.	Asparagus	\$1.12	75¢	\$0.37
18.	Almonds	\$2.65	\$1.63	\$1.02

	Item	Brand-Name Price	No-Name Price	
19.	Jam	\$1.09	69¢	\$0.40
20.	Detergent	\$1.50	90¢	\$0.60

21. The regular prices for sugar, bread, and eggs are \$1.80, \$0.70, and \$0.89. Dan Potter bought these items using three discount coupons, each was worth 20¢. Find the price paid for the three items. \$2.79

22. Joan Traxler had discount coupons worth \$0.31. On a double-value discount day at her supermarket, Joan used the coupons on food that usually cost \$7.08. Estimate the amount that Joan paid. c

a. \$8 − \$0.60
b. \$7 − \$0.30
c. \$7 − \$0.60
d. \$7 + \$0.30

23. One pound of lamb chops will serve 3 people. How many pounds are needed to serve 9 people? 3 pounds

24. A pound of cooked ham will serve $3\frac{1}{2}$ people. How many pounds are needed to serve 14 people? 4 pounds

25. A pound of chicken breasts will serve 4 people. A pound of chicken breasts costs 79¢. Find the cost per serving. 20¢

Additional Practice

You may wish to use all or some of these exercises, depending on how well students performed on the formal chapter test.

Skills

Add or subtract. (Pages 4–5)

1. $9.10 + $2.11 + $0.60 $11.81
2. $4.03 + $6.01 + $1.10 $11.14
3. $3.97 + $2.24 + $0.86 $7.07
4. $8.76 − $8.04 $0.72
5. $4.07 − $3.12 $0.95
6. $14.09 − $12.92 $1.17

Multiply. (Pages 8–9)

7. $0.80 × 2 $1.60
8. $0.99 × 2 $1.98
9. $1.46 × 2 $2.92
10. $1.87 × 2 $3.74

Divide. Round each amount to the nearest cent. (Pages 58–59)

11. $8.75 ÷ $2\frac{1}{2}$ $3.50
12. $3.12 ÷ $1\frac{1}{2}$ $2.08
13. $6.01 ÷ $1\frac{1}{4}$ $4.81
14. $5.92 ÷ $2\frac{2}{3}$ $2.22

Applications

15. A 12-ounce container of juice costs 49¢. Estimate the unit price. b (Pages 282–283)

    a. 5¢ b. 4¢ c. 3¢ d. 6¢

16. A bag of 10 oranges costs 85¢. A bag of 15 oranges costs $1.30. Which bag of oranges is the better buy? (Pages 270–271)
    The bag of 10 oranges

For Exercises 17–20, find the difference between the brand–name price and the no–name price. (Pages 272–273)

	Item	Brand-Name Price	No-Name Price	
17.	Seltzer water	$0.65	$0.35	$0.30
18.	Pudding mix	$0.50	$0.37	$0.13

	Item	Brand-Name Price	No-Name Price	
19.	Rice	$2.84	$2.35	$0.49
20.	Crackers	$1.07	$0.85	$0.22

21. The regular prices for frankfurters and a box of macaroni are $1.35 and $0.85. Phil Yang bought these two items using two discount coupons worth 15¢ and 25¢. Find the price that he paid for both items. (Pages 276–277) $1.80

22. On double–value coupon day at her supermarket, Polly used coupons worth 14¢ and 30¢ to buy pet food and napkins, regularly priced at $0.80 and $0.90. Find the price that Polly paid for these items. (Pages 276–277) $0.82

For Exercises 23–26, use the table on page 278 to find the number of pounds of meat or the cost per serving. (Pages 278–279)

	Meat	Number of Servings	Pounds	
23.	Pork chops	8	?	2
24.	Broiler	6	?	4

	Meat	Price Per Pound	Cost Per Serving	
25.	Stew meat	$2.60	?	$0.52
26.	Broiler	$0.69	?	$0.46

REVIEW OF RELATED SKILLS FOR CHAPTER 14

We suggest that some or all of this page be reviewed before proceeding with the chapter.

Multiply. (Pages 56–57)

1. $2165 \times \frac{1}{5}$ $433 **2.** $1470 \times \frac{1}{3}$ $490 **3.** $1790 \times \frac{1}{2}$ $895 **4.** $1836 \times \frac{1}{6}$ $306 **5.** $1920 \times \frac{1}{4}$ $480

6. $1806 \times \frac{2}{7}$ $516 **7.** $2110 \times \frac{3}{5}$ $1266 **8.** $1616 \times \frac{5}{8}$ $1010 **9.** $1701 \times \frac{2}{3}$ $1134 **10.** $1902 \times \frac{3}{4}$ $1426.50

Write a decimal for each per cent. (Pages 90–91)

11. 50% 0.5 **12.** 40% 0.4 **13.** 35% 0.35 **14.** 20% 0.2 **15.** 5% 0.05 **16.** 45% 0.45

17. 38% 0.38 **18.** 7% 0.07 **19.** 33% 0.33 **20.** 16% 0.16 **21.** 49% 0.49 **22.** 87% 0.87

Find each answer. (Pages 94–95)

23. 20% of $90,000 $18,000 **24.** 40% of $60,000 $24,000 **25.** 10% of $75,000 $7500

26. 35% of $98,000 $34,300 **27.** 45% of $110,000 $49,500 **28.** 49% of $65,000 $31,850

Multiply. (Pages 6–9)

29. $704 × 12 × 20 $168,960 **30.** $600 × 12 × 25 $180,000 **31.** $800 × 12 × 15 $144,000

32. $617.40 × 12 × 25 $185,220 **33.** $894.60 × 12 × 30 $322,056 **34.** $916.24 × 12 × 20 $219,897.60

Subtract. (Pages 2–3)

35. $90,000 − $40,000 $50,000 **36.** $60,000 − $20,000 $40,000 **37.** $85,000 − $27,000 $58,000

38. $197,850 − $61,800 $136,050 **39.** $281,500 − $102,000 $179,500 **40.** $225,654 − $92,405 $133,249

Divide. (Pages 12–13)

41. $52,800 ÷ 100 $528.00 **42.** $43,500 ÷ 100 $435.00 **43.** $61,400 ÷ 1000 $61.40

44. $76,000 ÷ 1000 $76.00 **45.** $86,000 ÷ 1000 $86.00 **46.** $108,500 ÷ 1000 $108.50

Multiply. (Pages 8–9)

47. $15.72 × 60 $943.20 **48.** $13.17 × 70 $921.90 **49.** $14.36 × 85 $1220.60 **50.** $11.06 × 67 $741.02

51. $8.70 × 390 $3393.00 **52.** $5.40 × 470 $2538.00 **53.** $7.10 × 492 $3493.20 **54.** $6.23 × 507 $3158.61

Write a fraction for each per cent. (Pages 90–91)

55. 80% $\frac{4}{5}$ **56.** 30% $\frac{3}{10}$ **57.** 15% $\frac{3}{20}$ **58.** 35% $\frac{7}{20}$ **59.** 70% $\frac{7}{10}$ **60.** 90% $\frac{9}{10}$

61. 40% $\frac{2}{5}$ **62.** 60% $\frac{3}{5}$ **63.** 65% $\frac{13}{20}$ **64.** 55% $\frac{11}{20}$ **65.** 33% $\frac{33}{100}$ **66.** 24% $\frac{6}{25}$

Divide. Round each answer to the nearest cent. (Pages 16–17)

67. $384 ÷ 12 $32.00 **68.** $564 ÷ 12 $47.00 **69.** $528 ÷ 12 $44.00 **70.** $612 ÷ 12 $51.00

71. $156 ÷ 12 $13.00 **72.** $194 ÷ 12 $16.17 **73.** $402 ÷ 12 $33.50 **74.** $206 ÷ 12 $17.17

75. $503 ÷ 12 $41.92 **76.** $617 ÷ 12 $51.42 **77.** $670 ÷ 12 $55.83 **78.** $428 ÷ 12 $35.67

CHAPTER

14 HOUSING

CONSUMER SKILLS/APPLICATIONS

14-1 Renting
14-2 Mortgage Loans
14-3 Monthly Mortgage Payments
14-4 Homeowner's Insurance
14-5 Property Taxes
Rounding and Estimation

CAREER APPLICATIONS

Surveyor
Property Manager
Real Estate Agent

14-1 Renting

See the Teacher's Manual for the objectives.

Clare and William Yue are looking for an apartment. They read in a consumer magazine that they should expect to pay between $\frac{1}{4}$ and $\frac{1}{3}$ of their net income for rent.

Sunny, spacious, 5 rooms
Near all shopping and
transportation.
$423.50 per month
Call 759-8032.

EXAMPLE The Yue's combined net income per month is $1675. Can they afford the rent for the apartment in the ad above?

Solution: [1] Find $\frac{1}{4}$ and $\frac{1}{3}$ of their combined monthly income. Round to the nearest cent.

$\frac{1}{4}$ of \$1675 = \$1675 $\times \frac{1}{4}$ = **\$418.75**

$\frac{1}{3}$ of \$1675 = \$1675 $\times \frac{1}{3}$ = **\$558.33**

[2] Compare these amounts with $423.50.

$418.75 $423.50 $558.33 ◀ ***$423.50 is between $418.75 and $558.33***

They **can afford** the rent for the apartment.

REVIEW OF RELATED SKILLS

You may wish to use these exercises before teaching the lesson.

Multiply. (Pages 56–57)

1. \$1854 $\times \frac{1}{6}$ \$309.00
2. \$1928 $\times \frac{1}{2}$ \$964.00
3. \$1460 $\times \frac{1}{5}$ \$292.00
4. \$1530 $\times \frac{1}{3}$ \$510.00
5. \$1620 $\times \frac{1}{8}$ \$202.50
6. \$1794 $\times \frac{2}{3}$ \$1196.00
7. \$2144 $\times \frac{3}{4}$ \$1608.00
8. \$1850 $\times \frac{2}{5}$ \$740.00
9. \$1323 $\times \frac{3}{7}$ \$567.00
10. \$1952 $\times \frac{3}{8}$ \$732.00

EXERCISES

For Exercises 1–5, determine if the proposed rent is between $\frac{1}{4}$ and $\frac{1}{3}$ of the given net income.

	Proposed Rent	Net Income	$\frac{1}{4}$ of Income	$\frac{1}{3}$ of Income	Between $\frac{1}{3}$ and $\frac{1}{4}$?
1.	$460	$1580	? $395.00	? $526.67	? Yes
2.	$525	$1645	? $411.25	? $548.33	? Yes
3.	$850	$1750	? $437.50	? $583.33	? No
4.	$380	$1420	? $355.00	? $473.33	? Yes
5.	$725	$1975	? $493.75	? $658.33	? No

6. The Lafayette family read the ad at the right. Their monthly net income is $2245. Can they afford to rent the apartment? Yes

7. Mr. and Mrs. Kohout read the same ad. Their monthly net income is $2000. Can they afford to rent the apartment? No

NEW LUXURY APARTMENT

1 Bedroom, Living Room with fireplace, Deck, on ski slope. $700 per month.

Call 732-4059

8. Jeanine Calhoun wants to rent a 1-bedroom apartment. Her monthly net income is $1150. Can she afford to rent the apartment in the advertisement at the right? No

50's WEST, 1 BEDROOM $475

Modern Kitchen, High Ceilings, Large Rooms, Closets. Call 865-3872

9. Abraham Stein saw the ad at the right in a local newspaper. He and his wife have a combined monthly net income of $2350. Can they afford to rent this apartment? Yes

WEST WASHINGTON PARK
3 BEDROOMS $650, A BARGAIN!

Kitchen with dishwasher.
24 hr. fully serviced building.

Another consumer agency recommends that rent be between $\frac{1}{4}$ and $\frac{2}{5}$ of net income. Use these guidelines for Exercises 10–13.

Studio Apartment
Buses & Subway at Doorstep $285/mo.
Call 863-9221

Parkside Brownstone.
1 bedroom, high ceilings, wood floors.
$550/mo. Call 787-9634

10. Julia Wong is looking for an apartment near public transportation. Her monthly net income is $905. Can she afford the apartment in the ad above? Yes

11. Juan Martinez and his wife have a combined monthly net income of $1450. Can they afford the brownstone apartment advertised above? Yes

More Challenging Problems

12. The Jansen family is looking for a 3-bedroom apartment. They have a yearly net income of $21,500. They find an apartment for which the rent is $700 per month. Can they afford the rent? Yes

13. Mr. and Mrs. Heath have a combined net yearly income of $34,350. They have found a 6-room apartment that costs $850 per month. Can they afford the rent? Yes

14-2 Mortgage Loans

See the Teacher's Manual for the objectives.

Most people who buy a new home pay part of the purchase price with a **down payment.** Then they obtain a **mortgage loan** from a bank or other lending institution.

PARKHURST
SECTION $80,000
Own your own home for as little as 10% down. Kingsboro Homes. 469-3857
Fillmore Hills $68,000
MODERN LOW TAXES
$12,000 down payment
Modern home in beautiful Fillmore Hills. Includes 3 bedrooms, lovely living room, eat-in kitchen, spacious dining room. Call 778-4431

EXAMPLE 1 The Cox family purchased a house for \$100,000. They made a down payment of 30% of the purchase price and took out a mortgage for the rest.

a. Find the amount of the down payment.

b. Find the amount of the mortgage.

Solutions: **a.** 30% of \$100,000 = \$100,000 × 0.30 ◀ *30% = 0.30*

= **\$30,000**

b. \$100,000 − \$30,000 = **\$70,000** ◀ *Purchase Price − Down Payment = Amount of Mortgage*

After completing Example 1, you may wish to have students do some or all of Exercises 1-12.

Mortgage loans are repaid with interest in equal monthly payments over a specified number of years.

EXAMPLE 2 The Cox family took out a \$70,000 mortgage for 30 years. The monthly payment is \$1054.90. Find the total interest charged.

Solution: [1] Find the total of monthly payments.

\$1054.90 × 12 × 30 = **\$379,764** ◀ *Monthly Payments × 12 months per year × 30 years*

[2] Find the total interest charged.

\$379,764 − \$70,000 = **\$309,764** ◀ *Total of Monthly Payments − Amount of Mortgage = Total Interest*

REVIEW OF RELATED SKILLS

You may wish to use these exercises before teaching the lesson.

Write a decimal for each per cent. (Pages 90–91)

1. 25% 0.25 **2.** 30% 0.3 **3.** 40% 0.4 **4.** 23% 0.23 **5.** 18% 0.18 **6.** 17% 0.17

Find each answer. (Pages 94–95)

7. 25% of \$78,000 \$19,500 **8.** 30% of \$96,000 \$28,800 **9.** 24% of \$84,000 \$20,160 **10.** 18% of \$105,000 \$18,900

Perform the indicated operations. (Pages 8–9, 2–3)

11. \$865 × 12 × 25 \$259,500 **12.** \$950.60 × 12 × 30 \$342,216 **13** \$1074.70 × 12 × 20 \$257,928

14. \$278,450 − \$90,000 \$188,450 **15.** \$189,760 − \$58,500 \$131,260 **16.** \$246,978 − \$89,000 \$157,978

EXERCISES

1. $13,000; $52,000 2. $10,000; $30,000 3. $12,375; $70,125 4. $33,000; $77,000 5. $19,950; $59,850 6. $7650; $22,950 7. $14,850; $84,150 8. $13,740; $54,960 9. $10,000; $40,000

For Exercises 1–12, find the amount of the down payment and the amount of the mortgage. (Example 1)

	Purchase Price	Rate of Down Payment		Purchase Price	Rate of Down Payment		Purchase Price	Rate of Down Payment
1.	$65,000	20%	**4.**	$110,000	30%	**7.**	$99,000	15%
2.	$40,000	25%	**5.**	$79,800	25%	**8.**	$68,700	20%
3.	$82,500	15%	**6.**	$30,600	25%	**9.**	$50,000	20%

10. The Brisbane family bought a house for $99,500. The down payment was 25% of the purchase price. $24,875; $74,625

11. Sue Ellen Latham bought a house for $44,500. The down payment was 30% of the purchase price. $13,350; $31,150

12. Art Wiseman bought a house for $51,300. The down payment was 20% of the purchase price. $10,260; $41,040

For Exercises 13–20, find the total of the monthly payments. (Example 2, step 1)

	Amount of Mortgage	Length of Mortgage (Years)	Monthly Payment		Amount of Mortgage	Length of Mortgage (Years)	Monthly Payment
13.	$80,000	30	$ 948.50 ($341,460)	**17.**	$45,000	35	$ 568.80 ($238,896)
14.	$35,000	25	$ 470.00 ($141,000)	**18.**	$55,000	30	$ 739.75 ($266,310)
15.	$90,000	20	$1185.30 ($284,472)	**19.**	$65,000	20	$ 904.15 ($216,996)
16.	$60,000	35	$ 793.20 ($333,144)	**20.**	$25,000	25	$ 318.50 ($95,550)

21. The Morrison family took out an $85,000 mortgage for 30 years. Their monthly payment is $1143.25. Find the total interest charged. $326,570

22. The Valdez family took out a $32,000 mortgage for 25 years. Their monthly payment is $456.32. Find the total interest charged. $104,896

23. Tim Lee took out a $45,000 mortgage for 25 years. The monthly payment is $604.80. Find the total interest charged. $136,440

SURVEYOR

Career lessons are optional. This lesson combines the skills of using a formula and reading a table.

Surveyors are responsible for accurately measuring and mapping land. Surveyors use equipment such as **transits** to do this. A knowledge of geometry is necessary when surveyors need to find a distance across uneven land or a body of water. One rule from geometry is the **Rule of Pythagoras,** which uses the length of two sides of a right triangle to find the length of the third side.

(Hypotenuse)^2 = (First Leg)^2 + (Second Leg)^2

$$c^2 = a^2 + b^2$$

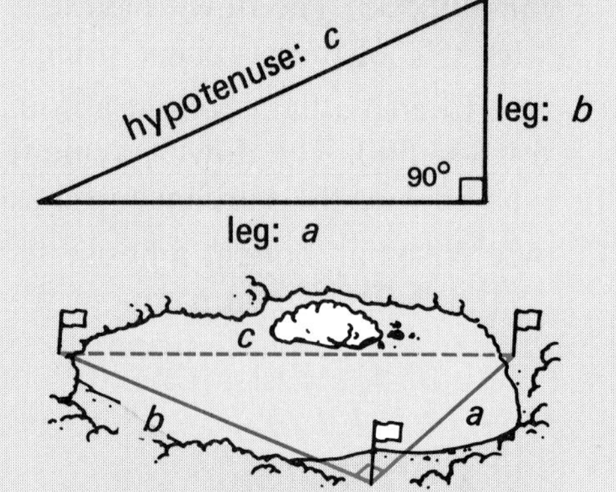

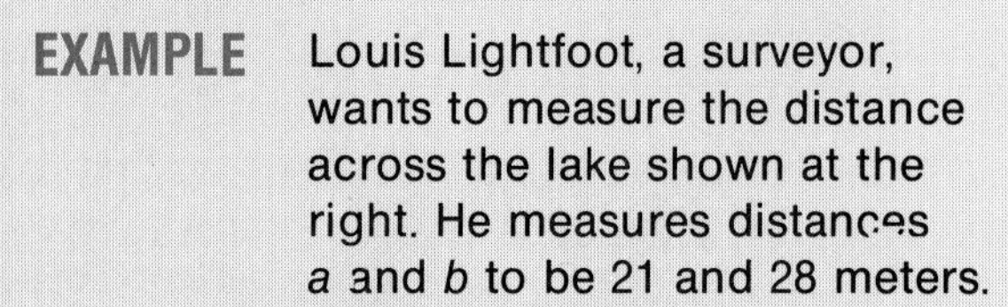

EXAMPLE Louis Lightfoot, a surveyor, wants to measure the distance across the lake shown at the right. He measures distances a and b to be 21 and 28 meters. Find the distance, c, across the lake.

Solution: Use the portion of the Table of Squares and Square Roots shown.

$c^2 = a^2 + b^2$ ◀ ***a* = 21 m, *b* = 28 m**

$c^2 = (21)^2 + (28)^2$

$c^2 = 441 + 784$

$c^2 = 1225$

$c = 35$ ◀ ***From the table***

The distance across the lake is **35 meters.**

Number	Square	Square Root
26	676	5.099
27	729	5.196
28	784	5.292
29	841	5.385
30	900	5.477
31	961	5.568
32	1024	5.657
33	1089	5.745
34	1156	5.831
35	1225	5.916

EXERCISES

For Exercises 1–6, complete the table. Use the portion of the Table of Squares and Square Roots on page 295.

	First Leg (a)	Second Leg (b)	Hypotenuse (c)
1.	10 m	24 m	? 26 m
2.	8 m	6 m	? 10 m
3.	7 m	24 m	? 25 m
4.	9 m	40 m	? 41 m
5.	12 m	35 m	? 37 m
6.	15 m	36 m	? 39 m

For Exercises 7–10, use the table of Squares and Square Roots.

7. Louis wants to measure the distance across the valley shown below. Find the distance, c, across the valley. 17 km

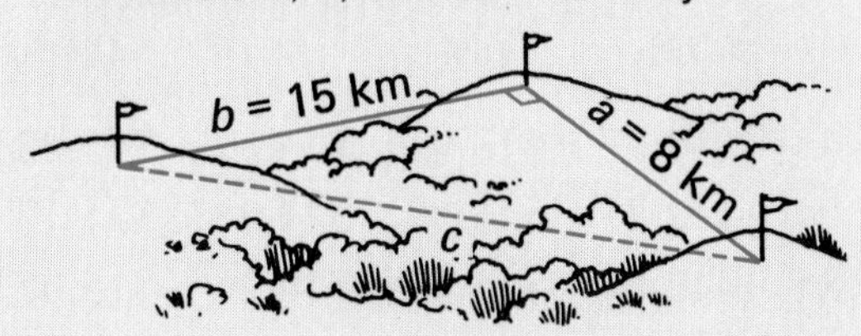

8. A surveyor wants to find the length of a bridge across a lake, as shown below. Find the length of the bridge, c. 35 m

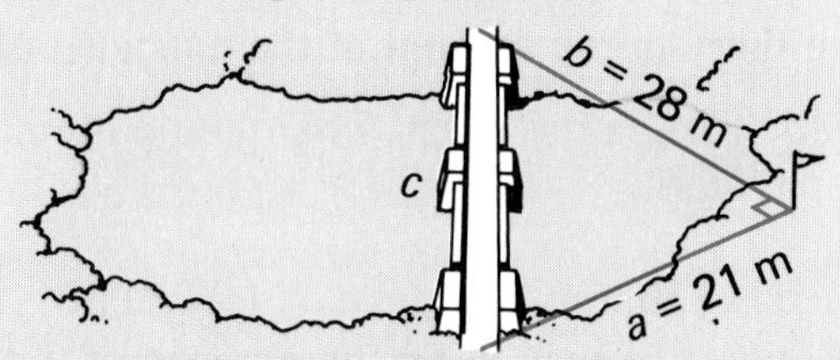

9. Susan Roth, a surveyor, wants to find the distance across a sinkhole, as shown below. Find the distance, c. 45 m

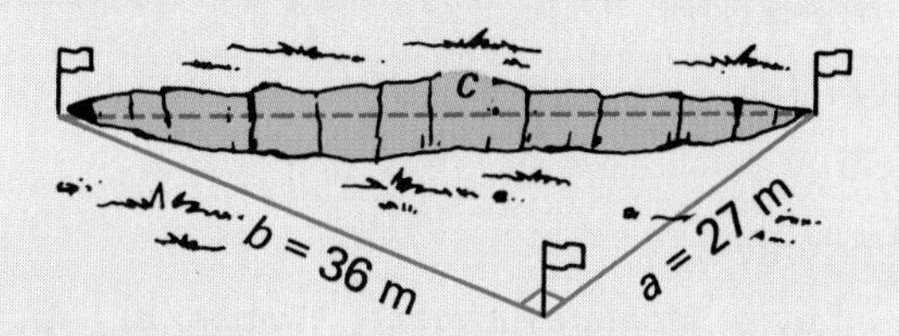

10. Susan wants to find the distance across a pond, as shown below. Find the distance, c, across the pond. 34 m

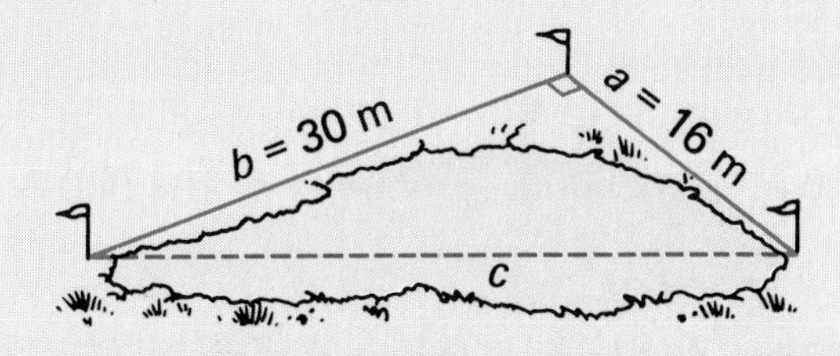

Table of Squares and Square Roots

Number	Square	Square Root
1	1	1.000
2	4	1.414
3	9	1.732
4	16	2.000
5	25	2.236
6	36	2.449
7	49	2.646
8	64	2.828
9	81	3.000
10	100	3.162
11	121	3.317
12	144	3.464
13	169	3.606
14	196	3.742
15	225	3.873
16	256	4.000
17	289	4.123
18	324	4.243
19	361	4.359
20	400	4.472
21	441	4.583
22	484	4.690
23	529	4.796
24	576	4.899
25	625	5.000
26	676	5.099
27	729	5.196
28	784	5.292
29	841	5.385
30	900	5.477
31	961	5.568
32	1024	5.657
33	1089	5.745
34	1156	5.831
35	1225	5.916
36	1296	6.000
37	1369	6.083
38	1444	6.164
39	1521	6.245
40	1600	6.325
41	1681	6.403
42	1764	6.481
43	1849	6.557
44	1936	6.633
45	2025	6.708

14-3 Monthly Mortgage Payments

See the Teacher's Manual for the objectives.

You can use a table such as the one below to find the amount of a monthly mortgage payment. The amounts in the table are for each $1000 of the loan.

MORTGAGE LOAN SCHEDULE
(Monthly Cost per $1000)

Years	13%	14%	15%	16%	17%	18%
20	$11.72	$12.43	$13.17	$13.91	$14.67	$15.43
25	$11.28	$12.04	$12.81	$13.59	$14.38	$15.17
30	$11.06	$11.85	$12.64	$13.45	$14.26	$15.07

To find the amount of the monthly mortgage payment, you must first answer the question:

How many 1000's are there in the amount of the mortgage loan?

This is the hidden question in the problem. Then you can find the monthly mortgage payment.

EXAMPLE The Chu family obtained a $50,000 mortgage at 16%. The mortgage is to be paid over 30 years. Find the amount of the monthly payment.

Solution:

1. Find "30" under Years in the table. Look to the right under 16%. — $13.45 ◀ ***Monthly Payment per $1000***
2. Find the number of 1000's in 50,000.
   50,000 ÷ 1000 = **50**
3. Find the monthly payment.
   $13.45 × 50 = **$672.50** ◀ ***Monthly Payment per $1000*** × ***Number of 1000's*** = ***Monthly Payment***

REVIEW OF RELATED SKILLS

You may wish to use these exercises before teaching the lesson.

Divide. (Pages 12–13)

1. 80,000 ÷ 1000 80 **2.** 90,000 ÷ 1000 90 **3.** 75,000 ÷ 1000 75 **4.** 104,000 ÷ 1000 104

Multiply. (Pages 8–9)

5. $14.38 × 50 $719.00 **6.** $13.50 × 65 $877.50 **7** $12.81 × 85 $1088.85 **8.** $13.71 × 75 $1028.25

EXERCISES

For Exercises 1–15, find the amount of the monthly payment. Use the Table on page 296. (Example)

	Amount of Mortgage	Rate of Mortgage	Length of Mortgage (Years)	
1.	$65,000	18%	30	$ 979.55
2.	$80,000	15%	20	$1053.60
3.	$95,000	14%	25	$1143.80
4.	$70,000	17%	30	$ 998.20
5.	$60,000	17%	25	$ 862.80
6.	$82,000	16%	20	$1140.62
7.	$84,000	15%	30	$1061.76
8.	$94,000	14%	30	$1113.90

9. Daniel obtained a $55,000 mortgage at 16%. The mortgage is to be paid over 25 years. $747.45

10. The Halvis family obtained at $75,000 mortgage at 16%. The mortgage is to be paid over 25 years. $1019.25

11. Elizabeth obtained a $70,000 mortgage at 17%. The mortgage is to be paid over 20 years. $1026.90

12. Ramon took out a 25–year mortgage for $45,000. The interest rate is 15%. $576.45

13. Kay took out a 30–year mortgage for $72,000. The interest rate is 17%. $1026.72

14. The Coe family obtained a 20–year mortgage for $50,000. The interest rate is 18%. $771.50

15. Rena took out a 30–year mortgage for $75,000. The interest rate is 16%. $1008.75

More Challenging Problems

16. Mr. and Mrs. Siempo read this ad in the local paper. They can afford to make monthly payments of $1200. Can they afford this house? Yes

WYCLIFF $115,000
NEW—14% MORTGAGE (30 YEARS)
4 Bedrooms, 3 baths, 2 car garage.
20% down. Call 368-5210

17. The Trabert family is looking for a new house. They can afford to make monthly payments of $1000 per month. Can they afford the house advertised at the right? Yes

HOLDEN $95,000
15% MORTGAGE (25 YEARS)
3 Bedrooms, large living room
30% down. Call 678-9000

career PROPERTY MANAGER

Career lessons are optional. This lesson applies the skill of using formula to solve problems.

The **property manager** of large stores, buildings, and shopping centers must be familiar with using decimals. Carol Sheehan is property manager of Golden Acres Mall, which contains 25,000 square meters of space. She must determine the yearly operating expenses, such as advertising costs, for the entire mall.

EXAMPLE Carol estimates that the cost of advertising for the mall is \$0.30 per square meter. Find the estimated yearly cost for advertising.

Solution: **Cost per Square Meter** × **Number of Square Meters** = **Advertising Cost**

\$0.30 × 25,000 = \$7500

The yearly advertising cost is about **\$7500.**

EXERCISES Note that Exercises 1-8 are non-verbal.

For Exercises 1–8, complete the table.

	Operating Expense	*Estimated Cost per Square Meter*	*Number of Square Meters*	*Estimated Yearly Cost*
1.	Utilities	\$1.50	25,000	? \$37,500
2.	Insurance	\$0.60	25,000	? \$15,000
3.	Public areas	\$0.50	25,000	? \$12,500
4.	Maintenance	\$2.80	25,000	? \$70,000
5.	Administrative	\$1.30	25,000	? \$32,500
6.	Services	\$0.80	25,000	? \$20,000
7.	Parking lot	\$0.70	25,000	? \$17,500
8.	Real estate taxes	\$4.00	25,000	? \$100,000

9. Find the total of the mall's estimated yearly fixed expenses (insurance, administrative, and real estate taxes). \$147,500

10. Find the total of the mall's estimated yearly variable expenses. (HINT: Don't forget to include the advertising cost.) \$165,000

11. The mall has a total rental space of 20,000 square meters. If space in the mall is leased at a rate of \$18 per square meter, how much profit will the owners make? (HINT: **Total Rental Income − Total of Operating Expenses = Profit**) \$47,500

14-4 Homeowner's Insurance

See the Teacher's Manual for the objectives.

When Amanda Mayer applied at her bank for a mortgage, she learned that she must purchase homeowner's insurance to protect herself and the bank from loss. The table at the right shows the kinds of protection and the amount of coverage provided by many homeowner's insurance policies.

Category	Coverage
Home	Full policy
Personal property on premises	50% of policy
Additional structures	10% of policy
Personal property not on premises	50% of policy
Additional living expenses	20% of policy
Personal liability	$25,000

EXAMPLE 1 Amanda's coverage for homeowner's insurance is $70,000. Use the table to find the coverage for each of the following.

a. A garage on the property. **b.** Personal property.

Solutions: **a.** Garage (additional structure on property)

10% of $\$70{,}000 = \$70{,}000 \times \frac{1}{10} = \mathbf{\$7000}$

b. Personal property (furniture, clothing, etc.)

50% of $\$70{,}000 = \$70{,}000 \times \frac{1}{2} = \mathbf{\$35{,}000}$

After completing Example 1, you may wish to have students do some or all of Exercises 1-11.

The amount of the premium depends on the amount of coverage, the material from which the house is constructed, and the quality of the fire protection (fire protection class).

YEARLY PREMIUMS

Amount of Insurance Coverage	Brick/Masonry Veneer				Wood Frame			
	Fire Protection Class				Fire Protection Class			
	1–6	7–8	9	10	1–6	7–8	9	10
40,000	127	136	164	171	136	143	171	181
50,000	146	157	188	197	157	165	197	209
60,000	169	182	219	229	182	191	229	242
70,000	193	208	250	262	208	218	262	277
80,000	222	239	288	301	239	251	301	319
90,000	250	270	325	341	270	283	341	361
100,000	280	302	364	381	302	317	381	404
150,000	425	459	554	581	459	482	581	615

EXAMPLE 2 Amanda's house is a wood-frame construction. It is rated in fire protection class 4. Find the monthly premium for homeowner's coverage of $70,000.

Solution: [1] In the table, find 70,000 under "Amount of Insurance Coverage." Look to the right under "Wood Frame—Fire Protection Class 1–6." **208** ◀ ***Yearly Premium: 208***

[2] Divide the yearly premium by 12. Round to the nearest cent.

$208 ÷ 12 = $17.33 ◀ ***Monthly premium***

REVIEW OF RELATED SKILLS

You may wish to use these exercises before teaching the lesson.

Write a fraction for each per cent. (Pages 90–91)

1. 10% $\frac{1}{10}$ **2.** 50% $\frac{1}{2}$ **3.** 20% $\frac{1}{5}$ **4.** 25% $\frac{1}{4}$ **5.** 40% $\frac{2}{5}$ **6.** 75% $\frac{3}{4}$

Write a decimal for each per cent. (Pages 90–91)

7. 15% 0.15 **8.** 17% 0.17 **9.** 24% 0.24 **10.** 23% 0.23 **11.** 28% 0.28 **12.** 31% 0.31

Find each answer. (Pages 94–95)

13. 20% of $80,000 $16,000 **14.** 50% of $70,000 $35,000 **15.** 10% of $50,000 $5000 **16.** 15% of $60,000 $9000

Divide. Round each answer to the nearest cent. (Pages 16–17)

17. $288 ÷ 12 $24.00 **18.** $302 ÷ 12 $25.17 **19.** $459 ÷ 12 $38.25 **20.** $188 ÷ 12 $15.67 **21.** $425 ÷ 12 $35.42

EXERCISES

For Exercises 1–8, find the amount of coverage for each item. Use the table on page 299. (Example 1)

	Amount Policy	Personal Property on Premises	Additional Structures	Personal Property not on Premises	Additional Living Expenses
1.	$60,000	$30,000 ?	$6000 ?	$30,000 ?	$12,000 ?
2.	$80,000	$40,000 ?	$8000 ?	$40,000 ?	$16,000 ?
3.	$90,000	$45,000 ?	$9000 ?	$45,000 ?	$18,000 ?
4.	$50,000	$25,000 ?	$5000 ?	$25,000 ?	$10,000 ?
5.	$70,000	$35,000 ?	$7000 ?	$35,000 ?	$14,000 ?
6.	$100,000	$50,000 ?	$10,000 ?	$50,000 ?	$20,000 ?
7.	$150,000	$75,000 ?	$15,000 ?	$75,000 ?	$30,000 ?
8.	$40,000	$20,000 ?	$4000 ?	$20,000 ?	$8000 ?

For Exercises 9–11, find the amount of coverage for each item. Use the table on page 299. (Example 1)

9. Wynn's coverage for homeowner's insurance is $80,000. He has a tool shed on his property and a valuable stamp collection. $8000; $40,000

10. Myrna's coverage for homeowner's insurance is $60,000. She owns some valuable jewelry and has a 2-car garage. $30,000; $6000

11. Wanda had $90,000 coverage for homeowner's insurance on her house. The house and the garage were destroyed in a fire. While they were rebuilt, she stayed in a hotel. $90,000; $9000; $18,000

For Exercises 12–22 find the monthly premium. Use the table on page 299. (Example 2)

	Amount of Policy	Type of Construction	Fire Protection Class
12.	$60,000	Brick	5 $14.08
13.	$80,000	Wood-frame	7 $20.92
14.	$100,000	Brick	9 $30.33
15.	$70,000	Wood-frame	4 $17.33
16.	$90,000	Wood-frame	8 $23.58
17.	$150,000	Brick	10 $48.42

18. The Borilli family has coverage of $80,000 for homeowner's insurance. Their home is a brick structure rated in a fire protection class 5. $18.50

19. Lionel's house is a wood-frame construction rated in fire protection class 9. His coverage for homeowner's insurance is $150,000. $48.42

20. The Santos family owns a wood-frame house rated in fire protection class 3. The coverage for homeowner's insurance is $100,000. $25.17

21. The Duffy family has coverage of $100,000 for homeowner's insurance. Their house is a wood-frame construction rated in fire protection class 7. $26.42

22. Joann's house is a brick structure rated in fire protection class 5. Her coverage for homeowner's insurance is $60,000. $14.08

REAL ESTATE AGENT

Career lessons are optional.
This lesson applies the skill of finding a number, given a per cent of it.

Sara Andrews is a **real estate agent.** She is trying to find a buyer for Jack LeBeau's **condominium.**

When you buy a condominium, you are given a deed to your apartment or house. You pay your property taxes directly to the local government and you pay your share of the property's operating expenses.

EXAMPLE Jack LeBeau told Sara that he wishes to receive at least $60,000 for the sale of his condominium. Sara will receive a 5% commission. What is the lowest price for which the condominium should be sold? Round your answer up to the next hundred dollars.

Solution: Let n represent the selling price. Then the commission is represented by

$$5\% \text{ of } n, \text{ or } 0.05 \times n.$$

Also, the amount desired by the owner is represented by

$$(100\% - 5\%), \text{ or } 95\% \text{ of } n.$$

$95\% \text{ of } n = 60{,}000$

$0.95n = 60{,}000$ ◀ ***Divide each side by 0.95.***

$\frac{0.95n}{0.95} = \frac{60{,}000}{0.95}$

$n = 63157.894$

$n = \mathbf{\$63{,}200}$ ◀ ***Rounded up to the next hundred dollars.***

Sara also sells **co–ops.** When you buy a co–op you actually buy shares in the corporation which owns the building. You pay your share of the building's operating expenses, property taxes, and mortgage payments.

EXERCISES

Note that Exercises 1-8 are non-verbal.

For Exercises 1–14, round each answer up to the next hundred dollars.

Find the lowest price for which each condominium or co-op should be sold.

	Amount Desired by Seller	***Rate of Commission***		***Amount Desired by Seller***	***Rate of Commission***
1.	$96,000	6% $102,200	**3.**	$110,000	7% $118,300
2.	$45,000	5% $47,400	**4.**	$ 80,000	6% $85,200

	Amount Desired by Seller	Rate of Commission	
5.	$65,000	7%	$69,900
6.	$50,000	6%	$53,200

	Amount Desired by Seller	Rate of Commission	
7.	$75,000	5%	$79,000
8.	$70,000	6%	$74,500

9. One of Sara's customers wishes to receive at least $70,000 for the sale of her co–op. On this sale, Sara will receive a 4% commission. What is the lowest price for which the co–op should be sold? $73,000

10. Melissa Chang wants to receive at least $85,000 for her co–op. Sara will receive a 6% commission on the sale. What is the lowest price for which the co–op should be listed? $90,500

11. John Rincon wants to receive at least $125,000 for the sale of his condominium. Sara will receive a 5% commission. What is the lowest price Sara should accept for the condominium? $131,600

12. A real estate agency received a 6% commission for selling Ann Tamura's condominium. The commission amounted to $3000. What was the selling price of the condominium? $50,000

13. The Lakeview Real Estate Agency received a commission of $5000 for selling a co–op. The rate of commission was 5%. For how much was the co–op sold? $100,000

Real
Estate
Co-op Apartments
Condominiums
Hours: 9 AM—8 PM

14-5 Property Taxes

See the Teacher's Manual for the objectives.

Homeowners pay yearly city or county property taxes. The amount of the tax depends on two things:

1. The assessed value of the property
2. The tax rate

The **assessed value** is found by multiplying the **market value** (the amount the property would likely sell for) and the rate of assessment.

EXAMPLE 1 The assessed value of the Sneed family's home is 40% of its market value of $98,000. What is the assessed value?

Solution: 40% of $98,000 = $98,000 × 0.40

= **$39,200** ◀ ***Assessed value***

After completing Example 1, you may wish to have students do some or all of Exercises 1-8.

The tax rate is often expressed as an amount per $100 of assessed value.

To find the property tax, you must first answer the question:

How many 100's are there in the amount of assessed value?

This is the **hidden question** in the problem.

EXAMPLE 2 The tax rate for the city where the Sneeds live is $6.60 per $100 of assessed value. Use the assessed value in Example 1 to find the amount of their property tax.

Solution: [1] Find the number of 100's in the assessed value.

39,200 ÷ 100 = **392**

[2] Find the property tax.

$6.60 × 392 = **$2857.20**

REVIEW OF RELATED SKILLS

You may wish to use these exercises before teaching the lesson.

Write a decimal for each per cent. (Pages 90–91)

1. 34% 0.34 **2.** 41% 0.41 **3.** 50% 0.5 **4.** 62% 0.62 **5.** 45% 0.45 **6.** 31% 0.31

Find each answer. (Pages 94–95)

7. 40% of $86,000 $34,400 **8.** 35% of $90,000 $31,500 **9.** 30% of $75,000 $22,500 **10.** 45% of $88,000 $39,600

Divide. (Pages 12–13)

11. 48,600 ÷ 100 486 **12.** 52,400 ÷ 100 524 **13.** 37,500 ÷ 100 375 **14.** 54,300 ÷ 100 543

Multiply. (Pages 8–9)

15. \$7.20 × 462 \$3326.40 **16.** \$5.80 × 395 \$2291.00 **17.** \$8.80 × 454 \$3995.20 **18.** \$7.30 × 563 \$4109.90

EXERCISES

For Exercises 1–8, find the assessed value. (Example 1)

	Market Value	Rate of Assessment	Assessed Value	
1.	\$86,000	40%	?	\$34,400
2.	\$95,000	50%	?	\$47,500
3.	\$75,000	30%	?	\$22,500
4.	\$110,000	45%	?	\$49,500
5.	\$120,000	65%	?	\$78,000
6.	\$150,000	55%	?	\$82,500

7. The assessed value of the Bottone family's home is 45% of its market value of \$85,000. \$38,250

8. The assessed value of the Goldman family's home is 60% of its market value of \$95,000. \$57,000

For Exercises 9–19, find the amount of property tax. (Example 2)

	Assessed Value	Tax Rate (Per \$100)	Property Tax	
9.	\$45,600	\$6.40	?	\$2918.40
10.	\$54,200	\$7.30	?	\$3956.60
11.	\$85,300	\$8.20	?	\$6994.60
12.	\$94,400	\$9.20	?	\$8684.80
13.	\$86,700	\$8.50	?	\$7369.50
14.	\$57,500	\$7.10	?	\$4082.50

15. The Salomon family lives in a city where the property tax rate is \$7.60 per \$100 of assessed value. Their property is assessed at \$49,500. \$3762.00

16. Tom Jacques lives in a city where the property tax rate is \$8.10 per \$100 of assessed value. His property is assessed at \$64,700. \$5240.70

17. Lia Morales has a home assessed at \$56,800. The property tax rate in her city is \$6.90 per \$100 of assessed value. \$3919.20

18. The Leahy family's home is assessed at \$89,500. The property tax rate in their city is \$8.60 per \$100 of assessed value. \$7697.00

19. The Winslow family's home is assessed at \$56,300. The property tax rate is \$7.90 per \$100 of assessed value. \$4447.70

Rounding and Estimation

Consumers use rounding and estimation to solve problems related to housing.

EXERCISES See the Teacher's Manual for the objectives.

Skills

Choose the best estimate. Choose a, b, or c.

	a.	b.	c.
1. 32% of 92,900 a	$\frac{1}{3} \times 93{,}000$	$\frac{1}{4} \times 93{,}000$	$\frac{1}{3} \times 100{,}000$
2. 26% of 119,800 b	$\frac{1}{4} \times 100{,}000$	$\frac{1}{4} \times 120{,}000$	$\frac{1}{3} \times 120{,}000$
3. 62% of 71,400 b	$0.70 \times 80{,}000$	$0.60 \times 70{,}000$	$0.60 \times 80{,}000$
4. 29% of 59,750 c	$0.20 \times 60{,}000$	$0.30 \times 50{,}000$	$0.30 \times 60{,}000$
5. 468.75 + 192.16 b	460 + 190	470 + 190	470 + 200
6. 203.19 + 597.82 a	200 + 600	300 + 600	200 + 500
7. 1504 − 783 c	1500 − 700	1600 − 800	1500 − 800

Choose the best estimate. Choose a, b, c, or d.

	a.	b.	c.	d.
8. 33% of 88,700 b	20,000	30,000	40,000	50,000
9. 24% of 61,200 d	13,000	16,000	14,000	15,000
10. 59% of 49,700 a	30,000	25,000	35,000	40,000
11. 41% of 70,400 c	35,000	31,000	28,000	25,000
12. 369.75 + 221.13 a	590	570	580	600
13. 602.24 + 788.19 c	1200	1300	1400	1500
14. 1621 − 894 a	700	600	800	500

Applications

15. The Lucio family bought a house for $88,900. The down payment was 33% of the price. Estimate the amount of the down payment. c

a. $\frac{1}{3} \times \$80{,}000$

b. $\frac{1}{4} \times \$80{,}000$

c. $\frac{1}{3} \times \$90{,}000$

d. $\frac{1}{4} \times \$90{,}000$

16. The Klein family took out a mortgage for 30 years. The monthly payment is $1018.40. Estimate the total of monthly payments for one year. a

a. $\$1000 \times 12$

b. $\$1100 \times 12$

c. $\$1000 \times 1$

d. $\$1100 \times 1$

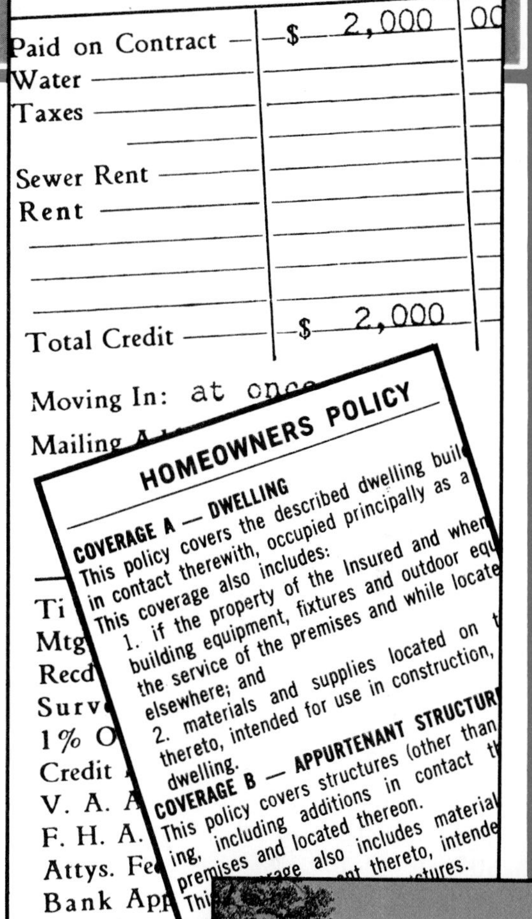

CLOSING STATEMENT
ADJUSTMENTS
Paid on Contract $ 2,000 00
Water
Taxes
Sewer Rent
Rent
Total Credit $ 2,000
Moving In: at once
HOMEOWNERS POLICY
COVERAGE A — DWELLING
This policy covers the described dwelling
in contact therewith, occupied principally as a
This coverage also includes:
1. if the property of the Insured and when
building equipment, fixtures and outdoor
the service of the premises and while located
elsewhere; and
2. materials and supplies located on
thereto, intended for use in construction,
dwelling.
COVERAGE B — APPURTENANT STRUCTURE
This policy covers structures (other than
ing, including additions in contact
premises and located thereon.
Credit
V. A.
F. H. A.
Attys. Fe
Bank App
Total

17. Tim Scott has a $150,000 insurance policy on his home. His yearly premium is $482. Estimate the monthly premium. c

a. $490 ÷ 10 **b.** $490 ÷ 12
c. $480 ÷ 12 **d.** $480 ÷ 10

18. The assessed value of the Cooper family's home is 48% of its market value of $81,500. Estimate the assessed value. c

a. $\frac{1}{2} \times \$90{,}000$ **b.** $\frac{1}{4} \times \$90{,}000$
c. $\frac{1}{2} \times \$80{,}000$ **d.** $\frac{1}{4} \times \$80{,}000$

19. The Framus family bought a house for $120,200. The down payment was 34% of the price. Estimate the down payment. c

a. $50,000 **b.** $60,000
c. $40,000 **d.** $30,000

20. The Wallenski family took out a mortgage for 20 years. The monthly payment is $989.70. Estimate the monthly payment total for one year. b

a. $10,000 **b.** $12,000
c. $1000 **d.** $14,000

21. Lorita Clemens has a $90,000 insurance policy on her home. Her yearly premium is $361. Estimate the monthly premium. b

a. $20
b. $30
c. $10
d. $40

22. Juan Cortez has a $70,000 insurance policy on his home. His yearly premium is $238. Estimate the monthly premium. a

a. $20
b. $30
c. $10
d. $40

23. The assessed value of the Mishima family's home is 51% of its market value of $121,000. Estimate the assessed value. c

a. $50,000
b. $40,000
c. $60,000
d. $70,000

Chapter Review

These exercises review the vocabulary, skills and applications presented in the chapter as a preparation for the chapter test.

Part 1: VOCABULARY

For Exercises 1–5, choose from the box at the right the word(s) that complete(s) each statement.

homeowner's insurance
assessed value
monthly payments
market value
down payment
loan balance

1. Most people pay part of the purchase price of a new home by making a __?__. (Pages 292–293) down payment
2. Mortgage loans are repaid with interest in equal __?__. (Pages 292–293) monthly payments
3. __?__ protects both the homeowner and the bank which holds the mortgage from loss. (Pages 299–300) homeowner's insurance
4. The amount of property tax depends on the tax rate and the __?__ of the property. (Pages 304–305) assessed value
5. The __?__ of a property is the amount it would likely sell for. (Pages 304–305) market value

Part 2: SKILLS

Multiply. (Pages 56–57, 6–9)

6. $\$1563 \times \frac{1}{3}$ \$521
7. $\$1704 \times \frac{1}{6}$ \$284
8. $\$1464 \times \frac{1}{2}$ \$732
9. $\$1227 \times \frac{2}{3}$ \$818
10. $\$1395 \times \frac{3}{5}$ \$837
11. $\$750 \times 12 \times 25$ \$225,000
12. $\$612 \times 12 \times 30$ \$220,320
13. $\$798.24 \times 12 \times 20$ \$191,577.60
14. $\$19.87 \times 75$ \$1490.25
15. $\$14.23 \times 90$ \$1280.70
16. $\$9.20 \times 480$ \$4416.00

Write a decimal for each per cent. (Pages 90–91)

17. 60% 0.6
18. 25% 0.25
19. 4% 0.04
20. 59% 0.59
21. 47% 0.47
22. 91% 0.91

Find each answer. (Pages 94–95)

23. 30% of \$80,000 \$24,000
24. 35% of \$106,000 \$37,100
25. 49% of \$112,000 \$54,880

Subtract. (Pages 2–3)

26. \$85,000 − \$55,000 \$30,000
27. \$216,000 − \$195,000 \$21,000
28. \$196,502 − \$87,505 \$108,997

Divide. Round each answer to the nearest cent. (Pages 16–17)

29. \$180 ÷ 12 \$15.00
30. \$312 ÷ 12 \$26.00
31. \$347 ÷ 12 \$28.92
32. \$409 ÷ 12 \$34.08
33. \$629 ÷ 12 \$52.42

Part 3: APPLICATIONS

For Exercises 34–38, determine if the proposed rent is between $\frac{1}{4}$ and $\frac{1}{3}$ of the given income. (Pages 290–291)

	Proposed Rent	Net Income	$\frac{1}{4}$ of Income	$\frac{1}{3}$ of Income	Between $\frac{1}{4}$ and $\frac{1}{3}$?
34.	\$288	\$1128	\$282 __?__	\$376 __?__	Yes __?__
35.	\$356	\$1392	\$348 __?__	\$464 __?__	Yes __?__

	Proposed Rent	Net Income	$\frac{1}{4}$ of Income	$\frac{1}{3}$ of Income	Between $\frac{1}{4}$ and $\frac{1}{3}$?
36.	$540	$1506	$376.50 ?	$502.00 ?	No ?
37.	$650	$1800	$450.00 ?	$600.00 ?	No ?
38.	$590	$1775	$443.75 ?	$591.67 ?	Yes ?

39. The McGraw family bought a house for $68,000. The down payment was 30% of the purchase price. Find the amount of the down payment and the amount of the mortgage. (Pages 292–293)
$20,400; $47,600

40. Victoria took out a $60,000 mortgage for 25 years. Her monthly payment is $896.40. Find the total interest charged. (Pages 292–293)
$208,920

For Exercises 41–48, find the amount of the monthly payment. Use the table on page 296. (Pages 296–297)

	Amount of Mortgage	Rate of Mortgage	Length of Mortgage (years)	
41.	$55,000	18%	25	$834.35
42.	$40,000	15%	30	$505.60
43.	$90,000	16%	20	$1251.90
44.	$50,000	17%	25	$719.00
45.	$65,000	17%	20	$953.55
46.	$80,000	18%	25	$1213.60
47.	$87,000	16%	30	$1170.15
48.	$72,000	15%	30	$910.08

For Exercises 49–50, use the tables on page 299. (Pages 299–301)

49. Bill's coverage for homeowner's insurance is $100,000. He has a collection of five paintings and a garage. Find the coverage for each. $50,000; $10,000

50. The Daly family has a coverage of $90,000 for homeowner's insurance. Their home is a wood frame structure rated in fire protection class 7. Find the monthly premium.
$23.58

51. The assessed value of the Johnson family's home is 38% of its market value of $110,000. Estimate the assessed value. (Pages 306–307) b

a. $60,000 **b.** $40,000
c. $30,000 **d.** $50,000

52. Lisa Timmons lives in a city where the property tax is $9.12 per $100 of assessed value. Her property is assessed at $70,500. Estimate the property tax. (Pages 306–307) a

a. $\$9 \times 700$ **b.** $\$10 \times 800$
c. $\$9 \times 800$ **d.** $\$10 \times 700$

Chapter Test

The Teacher's Resource Book contains two forms of each chapter test.

Multiply.

1. $\$1832 \times \frac{3}{4}$ $1374 **2.** $\$1662 \times \frac{1}{3}$ $554 **3.** $\$9.73 \times 86$ $836.78 **4.** $\$750 \times 12 \times 25$ $225,000

Write a decimal for each per cent.

5. 80% $0.80 **6.** 15% 0.15 **7.** 12% 0.12 **8.** 34% 0.34 **9.** 79% 0.79

Subtract.

10. $\$97{,}000 - \$45{,}000$ $52,000 **11.** $\$76{,}500 - \$30{,}000$ $46,500 **12.** $\$207{,}000 - \$150{,}000$ $57,000

Divide. Round each answer to the nearest cent.

13. $\$408 \div 12$ $34 **14.** $\$297 \div 12$ $24.75 **15.** $\$580 \div 12$ $48.33

16. Lynne Waters wants to move into a studio apartment that rents for $280. To afford the apartment, the rent should be between $\frac{1}{4}$ and $\frac{1}{3}$ of her monthly salary of $1000. Can she afford the apartment? Yes

17. The Suzuki family took out a $73,000 mortgage for 20 years. Their monthly payment is $971.88. Find the total interest charged. $160,251.20

18. Ted Smith owns a home that is assessed at $62,500. The property tax rate in his city is $5.80 per $100 of assessed value. Find the amount of the property tax. $3625

19. The Winkler family has a homeowner's insurance policy on their home. The yearly premium is $592. Estimate the monthly premium. c

a. $\$500 \div 12$ **b.** $\$500 \div 10$

c. $\$600 \div 12$ **d.** $\$600 \div 10$

20. The Anatro family obtained an $80,000 mortgage at 16%. The mortgage is to be paid over 20 years. Find the amount of the monthly payment. Use the table at the right. $1112.80

MORTGAGE LOAN SCHEDULE
(Monthly Cost per $1000)

Years	14%	15%	16%
20	$12.43	$13.17	$13.91
25	$12.04	$12.81	$13.59
30	$11.85	$12.64	$13.45

Additional Practice

You may wish to use some or all of these exercises depending on how well students performed on the formal chapter test.

Skills

Multiply. (Pages 8–9, 56–57)

1. $\$220 \times \frac{1}{6}$ $36.67
2. $\$8.07 \times 41$ $330.87
3. $\$13.21 \times 68$ $898.28
4. $\$600 \times 12 \times 15$ $108,000

Find each answer. (Pages 94–95)

5. 29% of $70,000 $20,300
6. 30% of $95,000 $28,500
7. 20% of $80,000 $16,000
8. 10% of $84,000 $8400

Divide. (Pages 12–13)

9. $\$67,500 \div 100$ $675
10. $\$66,000 \div 100$ $660
11. $\$86,800 \div 100$ $868
12. $\$94,500 \div 1000$ $94.50

Write a fraction for each per cent. (Pages 90–91)

13. 75% $\frac{3}{4}$
14. 23% $\frac{23}{100}$
15. 40% $\frac{2}{5}$
16. 66% $\frac{33}{50}$
17. 95% $\frac{19}{20}$
18. 28% $\frac{7}{25}$

Applications

19. The Rubinowitz family bought a house for $58,000. The down payment was 20% of the price. Estimate the amount of down payment. (Pages 306–307) a

    a. $\frac{1}{5} \times \$60,000$ b. $\frac{1}{4} \times \$60,000$

    c. $\frac{1}{5} \times \$70,000$ d. $\frac{1}{4} \times \$70,000$

20. The assessed value of the Ramos family's home is 48% of its market value. The market value of their house is $118,000. Estimate the assessed value. (Pages 306–307) b

    a. $\frac{4}{10} \times \$115,000$ b. $\frac{1}{2} \times \$120,000$

    c. $\frac{1}{5} \times \$120,000$ d. $\frac{2}{5} \times \$120,000$

21. Barbara obtained a $45,000 mortgage at 17%. The mortgage is to be paid over 25 years. Find the amount of the monthly payment. Use the table on page 296. $647.10 (Pages 296–297)

22. Trixie took out an $60,000 mortgage at 16%. The mortgage is to be paid over 30 years. Find the amount of the monthly payment. Use the table on page 296. $807 (Pages 296–297)

23. Brian's coverage for homeowner's insurance is $100,000. Find the coverage for Brian's personal property kept at home. Use the table on page 299. (Pages 299–301) $50,000

24. John's brick home is in fire protection class 10. Find the monthly premium for homeowner's insurance of $80,000. Use the table on page 299. (Pages 299–301) $25.08

25. Louise Crowfoot lives in a city where the property tax is $7.30 per $100 of assessed value. Her property is assessed at $55,000. Find the amount of the property tax. (Pages 304–305) $4015

26. Red O'Neill bought a house for $72,000. The down payment was 40% of the purchase price. Find the amount of the down payment and the amount of the mortgage. (Pages 292–293) $28,800; $43,200

REVIEW OF RELATED SKILLS FOR CHAPTER 15

Subtract. (Pages 2–3)

1. 78 − 61 17 **2.** 83 − 58 25 **3.** 65 − 64 1 **4.** 71 − 59 12 **5.** 88 − 67 21

Write a decimal for each per cent. (Pages 90–91)

6. 16% 0.16 **7.** 41% 0.41 **8.** 7% 0.07 **9.** 79% 0.79 **10.** 35% 0.35

11. 19% 0.19 **12.** 32% 0.32 **13.** 94% 0.94 **14.** 2% 0.02 **15.** 21% 0.21

Multiply. (Pages 6–7, 8–9)

16. 6 × 3% 18% **17.** 5 × 3% 15% **18.** 10 × 3% 30% **19.** 8 × 3% 24%

20. $970 × 0.14 $135.80 **21.** $1106 × 0.26 $287.56 **22.** $674 × 0.20 $134.80 **23.** $590 × 0.07 $41.30

24. 14 × 100 1400 **25.** 5 × 100 500 **26.** 59 × 100 5900 **27.** 18 × 100 1800

Multiply. Write your answer as an amount in dollars. (Pages 6–7, 56–57)

28. 6¢ × 40 $2.40 **29.** 24¢ × 20 $4.80 **30.** 4¢ × 50 $2 **31.** 31¢ × 6 $1.86 **32.** 65¢ × 8 $5.20

33. 40¢ × 26 $10.40 **34.** 90¢ × 86 $77.40 **35.** 83¢ × 44 $36.52 **36.** 3½¢ × 70 $2.45 **37.** 2½¢ × 38 $0.95

38. 8¢ × 24 $1.92 **39.** 43¢ × 15 $6.45 **40.** 2½¢ × 50 $1.25 **41.** 30¢ × 365 $109.50 **42.** 9¢ × 72 $6.48

Subtract. (Pages 2–3)

43. 981 − 872 109 **44.** 486 − 408 78 **45.** 837 − 604 233 **46.** 5407 − 4103 1304 **47.** 8219 − 7908 311

Add. (Pages 4–5)

48. 8 + 4.5 12.5 **49.** 7 + 2.5 9.5 **50.** 4.5 + 2 6.5 **51.** 1.5 + 7 8.5 **52.** 3.5 + 1 4.5

53. 4.2 + 3.7 + 4.2 + 3.7 15.8 **54.** 2.9 + 3.4 + 2.9 + 3.4 12.6

55. 6.0 + 3.5 + 6.0 + 3.5 19 **56.** 5.1 + 4.7 + 5.1 + 4.7 19.6

Subtract. Round each answer to the nearest whole number. (Pages 4–5, 16–17)

57. 19 − 5.5 14 **58.** 16 − 4.5 12 **59.** 12 − 3.5 9 **60.** 8 − 1.5 7 **61.** 17 − 2.5 15

Multiply. Round each answer to the nearest tenth. (Pages 8–9, 16–17)

62. 8.7 × 4.4 38.3 **63.** 9.8 × 3.2 31.4 **64.** 8.6 × 5.0 43.0 **65.** 17.4 × 2.4 41.8 **66.** 20.1 × 1.7 34.2

67. 7.9 × 3.6 28.4 **68.** 4.5 × 2.9 13.1 **69.** 10.5 × 4.2 44.1 **70.** 9.6 × 8.3 79.7 **71.** 15.7 × 10.8 169.6

Divide. Round each answer to the nearest whole number. (Pages 12–13, 16–17)

72. 72 ÷ 9 8 **73.** 85 ÷ 9 9 **74.** 71.2 ÷ 9 8 **75.** 58.0 ÷ 9 6 **76.** 87.5 ÷ 9 10

77. 68.3 ÷ 9 8 **78.** 83.6 ÷ 9 9 **79.** 92.0 ÷ 9 10 **80.** 120.6 ÷ 9 13 **81.** 142.8 ÷ 9 16

CHAPTER

15 HOUSING COSTS

CONSUMER SKILLS/APPLICATIONS

15-1 Heating and Cooling Costs
15-2 Cost of Operating Appliances
15-3 Reading Meters
15-4 Wallpapering and Estimation
15-5 Painting and Estimation
Rounding and Estimation

CAREER APPLICATIONS

Utilities Clerk
Drafting Technician

15-1 Heating and Cooling Costs

See the Teacher's Manual for the objectives.

At an exhibit on energy conservation, Donna Williams learned how to reduce heating and cooling costs.

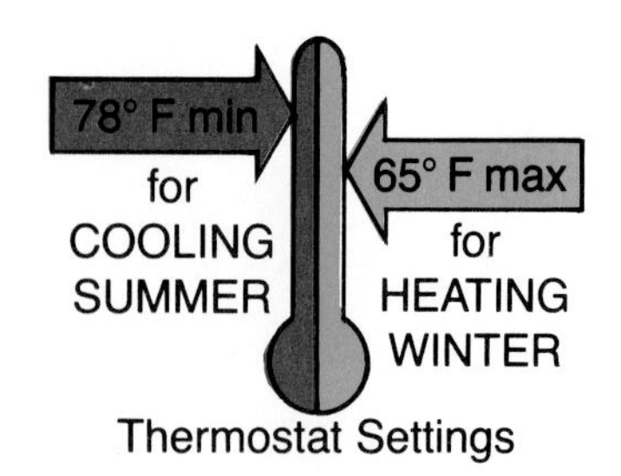

HEATING For each degree Fahrenheit that the thermostat setting is lowered, you can lower heating costs by 3%.

EXAMPLE 1 Last year, the Williams family spent \$1200 to heat their home with the thermostat set at 70°F. How much could they save by setting the thermostat at 65°F?

Solution: [1] Find the per cent of savings.

Change in setting: 70° − 65° = 5° lower

Since 1° lower reduces costs by 3%,

5° lower reduces costs by (5 × 3%) or **15%**.

[2] Find the amount saved. \$1200 × 0.15 = **\$180** ◀ ***Amount saved***

After completing Example 1, you may wish to have students do some or all of Exercises 1-10.

COOLING The recommended setting for air conditioning is 78° Fahrenheit. As the chart shows a setting of 79°F will save 8% of cooling costs.

Thermostat Setting	*Saving(s) or Loss(L)*
80°F	16%(S)
79	8%(S)
78	0
77	8%(L)
76	18%(L)
75	28%(L)
74	39%(L)
73	50%(L)
72	63%(L)

EXAMPLE 2 Last year, the Ramirez family spent \$600 to operate their air conditioner with the thermostat set at 75°F. How much would they save by setting the thermostat at 78°F?

Solution: There would be a 28% saving. ◀ ***From the table***

\$600 × 0.28 = \$168 They would save **\$168.**

REVIEW OF RELATED SKILLS

You may wish to use these exercises before teaching the lesson.

Subtract. (Pages 2–3)

1. 81° − 72° 9° **2.** 69° − 66° 3° **3.** 75° − 69° 6° **4.** 78° − 71° 7° **5.** 73° − 65° 8°

Write a decimal for each per cent. (Pages 90–91)

6. 18% 0.18 **7.** 39% 0.39 **8.** 8% 0.08 **9.** 21% 0.21 **10.** 63% 0.63 **11.** 14% 0.14

Multiply. (Pages 6–7, 8–9)

12. $4 \times 3\%$ 12% **13.** $7 \times 3\%$ 21% **14.** $3 \times 3\%$ 9% **15.** $2 \times 3\%$ 6% **16.** $\$900 \times 0.06$ $54

17. $\$1000 \times 0.12$ $120 **18.** $\$850 \times 0.09$ $76.50 **19.** $\$720 \times 0.18$ $129.60 **20.** $\$550 \times 0.39$ $214.50 **21.** $\$832 \times 0.28$ $232.96

EXERCISES

For Exercises 1–8, find how much each family could save on last year's heating costs. (Example 1)

	Yearly Heating Costs	Last Year's Thermostat Setting	This Year's Thermostat Setting	
1.	$800	68°F	64°F	$96
2.	$1100	69°F	63°F	$198
3.	$720	66°F	64°F	$43.20
4.	$570	70°F	65°F	$85.50
5.	$1020	66°F	61°F	$153
6.	$1285	67°F	64°F	$115.65
7.	$1305	66°F	62°F	$156.60
8.	$1095	70°F	65°F	$164.25

9. Last year, the Shin family spent $1080 on heating their home with the thermostat set at 71°F. How much could they save if they set their thermostat at 65°F this year? $194.40

10. Mr. and Mrs. Lombard spent $945 last year to heat their house. Their thermostat was set at 67°F. If they set their thermostat at 63°F, how much could they save this year? $113.40

For Exercises 11–18, use the table on page 314 to find how much each family could save over last year's air conditioning costs. (Example 2)

	Yearly Cooling Costs	Last Year's Thermostat Setting	This Year's Thermostat Setting	
11.	$750	74°F	78°F	$292.50
12.	$490	78°F	80°F	$78.40
13.	$645	72°F	78°F	$406.35
14.	$585	78°F	79°F	$46.80
15.	$875	76°F	78°F	$157.50
16.	$765	75°F	78°F	$214.20
17.	$900	78°F	80°F	$144
18.	$665	73°F	78°F	$332.50

19. Last year, the Cass family spent $690 on air conditioning costs. Their thermostat was set at 75°F. If they set the thermostat at 78°F this year, how much could they save on cooling costs? $193.20

20. The Anastos family spent $765 on cooling costs last year with the thermostat set at 72°F. How much could they save this year if they set their thermostat at 78°F? $481.95

15-2 Cost of Operating Appliances

See the Teacher's Manual for the objectives.

Electricity is measured in kilowatt–hours. You use 1 **kilowatt–hour** (abbreviated: kwh) of electricity when you use 1 kilowatt (1000 watts) for 1 hour.

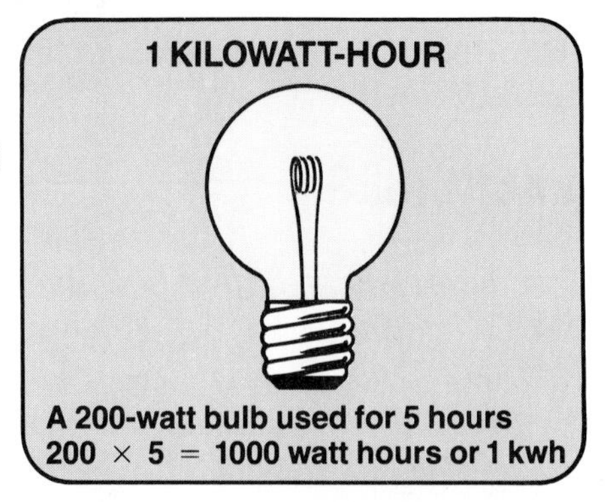

1 KILOWATT-HOUR
A 200-watt bulb used for 5 hours
200 × 5 = 1000 watt hours or 1 kwh

This table lists estimated costs for some appliances. The costs are based on electricity costs of 14¢ per kilowatt–hour.

Appliance	Cost	Appliance	Cost
Refrigerator/Freezer (18 cu ft, frost–free)	30¢ per day	Vacuum Cleaner	9¢ per hour
		Iron	8¢ per hour
Television (color)	5¢ per hour	Coffee Maker	2¢ per pot
Television (black and white)	$3\frac{1}{2}$¢ per hour	Dishwasher	8¢ per load
		Washing Machine	$2\frac{1}{2}$¢ per load
Light Bulb (60 watt)	1¢ per hour	Dryer	43¢ per load

EXAMPLE Find the cost for each appliance.

a. Refrigerator/Freezer: Week **b.** Color Television: 24 Hours **c.** Washing Machine: 10 loads

Solutions:

a. Cost per day: 30¢ ◀ *From the table*

Cost per week: 30¢ × 7 = 210¢, or **$2.10**

b. Cost per hour: 5¢ ◀ *From the table*

Cost for 24 hours: 5¢ × 24 = 120¢, or **$1.20**

c. Cost per load: $2\frac{1}{2}$¢ ◀ *From the table*

Cost for 10 loads: $2\frac{1}{2}$¢ × 10 = **25¢**

REVIEW OF RELATED SKILLS

You may wish to use these exercises before teaching the lesson.

Multiply. Write your answer as an amount in dollars. (Pages 6–7, 56–57)

1. 8¢ × 20 $1.60 **2.** 43¢ × 10 $4.30 **3.** 2¢ × 25 $0.50 **4.** 5¢ × 12 $0.60 **5.** 8¢ × 16 $1.28

6. $3\frac{1}{2}$¢ × 14 $0.49 **7.** $2\frac{1}{2}$¢ × 25 $0.63 **8.** 30¢ × 30 $9 **9.** 9¢ × 10 $0.90 **10.** 2¢ × 35 $0.70

EXERCISES

For Exercises 1–20, use the table on page 316 to find the cost of operating each appliance. When your answer is more than $1.00, write your answer in dollars.

	Appliance	Amount of Use
1.	Color television	10 hours 50¢
2.	Light bulb	1 day 24¢
3.	Iron	12 hours 96¢
4.	Dryer	5 loads $2.15
5.	Coffee maker	30 pots 60¢
6.	Refrigerator/ freezer	5 days $1.50

	Appliance	Amount of Use
7.	Washing machine	25 loads 63¢
8.	Vacuum cleaner	8 hours 72¢
9.	Black-and-white television	11 hours 39¢
10.	Light bulb	48 hours 48¢
11.	Dryer	25 loads $10.75
12.	Dishwasher	40 loads $3.20

13. The Tortola family used their dishwasher for seven loads one week. Find the cost of electricity. 56¢

14. Mr. and Mrs. Jenkins estimated that a 60-watt light bulb worked for 400 hours. Find the cost of electricity. $4

15. George Salazar used his washing machine to do 5 loads of laundry last week. Find the cost of electricity. 13¢

16. Tina Champy watches her color television set an average of 50 hours each week. Find the weekly cost of electricity. $2.50

17. Debby Dinkins used her iron for 7 hours last month. Find the cost of electricity. 56¢

18. Larry O'Hare estimates that he has had his refrigerator/freezer for 40 days. Find the cost of electricity. $12

More Challenging Problems

19. The Santiago family does an average of 15 loads of laundry each month. Find the total monthly cost of electricity for operating the washer <u>and</u> the dryer. $6.83

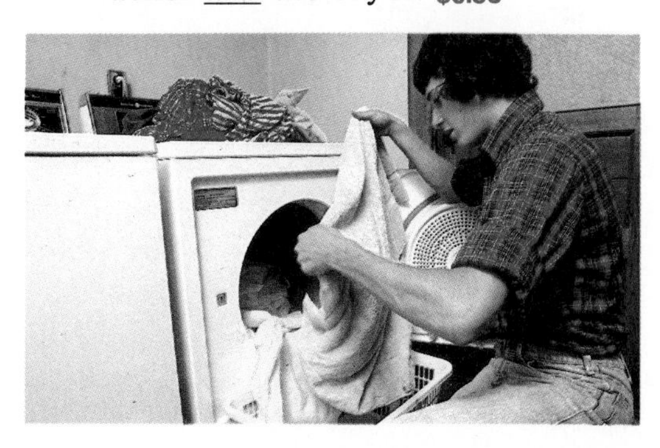

20. A black-and-white television in an appliance store has been running continuously for 45 days. Find the cost of electricity. $37.80

UTILITIES CLERK

Career lessons are optional.

This lesson combines the skill of reading a table with the skills of subtracting whole numbers and multiplying decimals.

Joann Duffy is a **utilities clerk** for the Public Electric and Power Company. One of her duties is to prepare monthly electric bills. The amount of a bill is based on the number of kilowatt-hours (kwh) of electricity used.

Rate Schedule	
First 10 kwh or less	$2.79
Next 90 kwh	0.1259 per kwh
Next 500 kwh	0.1052 per kwh
Over 600 kwh	0.0928 per kwh

PUBLIC ELECTRIC & POWER COMPANY

025-6100

DATE FROM		READING FROM	DATE TO		READING TO	Kwh USED	AMT.
4	30	6982	5	31	7579		

ACCOUNT NUMBER

012 38 45

MILES FUSCO
17 QUEENS ROAD
ST. JOSEPH, MO. 64502

To find the number of kilowatt-hours used, subtract the meter readings.

Present − Previous = kwh used

7579 − 6982 = **597 kwh**

Even though Joann feeds the necessary information for computing each electric bill into a computer, she must be able to compute each bill. She uses the **rate schedule** at the right above.

EXAMPLE Use the rate schedule to compute the cost of 597 kwh to the nearest cent.

Solution:

[1] First 10 kwh: **$2.79**

[2] Next 90 kwh rate: $0.1259 per kwh

$90 \times \$0.1259 = \mathbf{\$11.331}$

[3] Steps [1] and [2] account for 10 + 90 = 100 kwh.

This leaves 497 kwh. ◀ ***597 − 100***

The rate for this is $0.1052 per kwh.

$497 \times \$0.1052 = \mathbf{\$52.2844}$

4 Add with paper and pencil or use a calculator.

2 . 7 9 + 1 1 . 3 3 1

+ 5 2 . 2 8 4 4 = 66.4054

To the nearest cent, the bill is **$66.41.**

EXERCISES Note that Exercises 1-14 are non-verbal.

Find the number of kwh used.

1. Previous: 1286 Present: 2103 817
2. Previous: 892 Present: 1361 469
3. Previous: 1905 Present: 2464 559
4. Previous: 3307 Present: 3678 371
5. Previous: 5983 Present: 6612 629
6. Previous: 7836 Present: 9112 1276

Use the rate schedule on page 318 to compute the cost.

7. 485 kwh $54.62
8. 396 kwh $45.26
9. 514 kwh $57.67
10. 575 kwh $64.09
11. 622 kwh $68.76
12. 708 kwh $76.74
13. 918 kwh $96.23
14. 1255 kwh $127.51

Each year the Arlington family receives a computer printout that shows the number of kwh that they used and the cost. Use paper and pencil or use a calculator for Exercises 15–18.

PERIOD END-DATE	KWH USED	NO. OF DAYS	AVG. DAILY USE	COST FOR PERIOD
10-23-83	1138	59	19.2	137.78
08-25-83	1302	63	20.6	162.19
06-23-83	1278	61	20.9	151.14
04-23-83	1578	59	26.7	178.78
02-23-83	2255	63	35.7	253.01
12-22-82	1790	60	?	202.00
YEAR TOTALS	?	365	.	?

641G

15. Find the total number of kwh used. 9341
16. Find the total cost for the year. $1084.90
17. Find the average monthly cost to the nearest cent. $90.41
18. Find the average daily use to the nearest tenth for the end-date of 12-22-82. (HINT: 1790 ÷ 60 = ?) 29.8 kwh

15-3 Reading Meters

See the Teacher's Manual for the objectives.

Electric bills are based on the number of kilowatt-hours of electricity used. You can read your electric meter to find how much electricity was used from one reading to the next.

Previous Reading **Present Reading**

KILOWATT-HOURS KILOWATT-HOURS

EXAMPLE 1 **a.** What is the reading on the dials above?
b. How many kilowatt-hours were used?

Solution: **a.** Follow these rules to read the dials:

> **1.** Read the dials from left to right.
> **2.** When the hand is between the numbers, read the smaller number.
> **3.** When the hand is between 0 and 9, read 9.

Previous Reading: **5402** Present Reading: **6519**

b. Subtract: $6519 - 5402 = \mathbf{1117}$ ◀ ***1117 kilowatt-hours were used.***

After completing Example 1, you may wish to have students do some or all of Exercises 1-9.

Gas bills are based on the number of cubic feet of gas used. You can also read your gas meter to find how many cubic feet you have used between readings. (Some gas meters have four dials.)

Previous Reading **Present Reading**

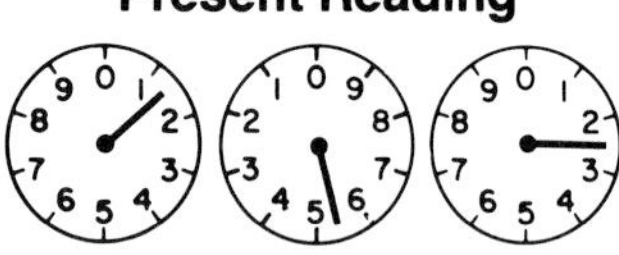

CUBIC FEET CUBIC FEET

EXAMPLE 2 **a.** What is the reading on the dials above?
b. How many cubic feet were used?

Solution: **a.** Follow the same rules you used in Example 1.
Previous Reading: **143** Present Reading: **152**

b. [1] Subtract: $152 - 143 = 9$
This difference, 9, is the number of units of 100 cubic feet used.
[2] Multiply the difference by 100: $9 \times 100 =$ **900 cubic feet**

REVIEW OF RELATED SKILLS

You may wish to use these exercises before teaching the lesson.

Subtract. (Pages 2–3)

1. 7502 − 7342 160 **2.** 4990 − 4515 475 **3.** 7909 − 6892 1017 **4.** 612 − 598 14 **5.** 217 − 149 68

Multiply. (Pages 6–7)

6. 16 × 100 1600 **7.** 7 × 100 700 **8.** 33 × 100 3300 **9.** 19 × 100 1900 **10.** 21 × 100 2100

EXERCISES

For Exercises 1–4, find the meter reading. (Example 1)

1. 7103

2. 3880

3.

6386

4.

6594

For Exercises 5–9, find how many kilowatt-hours were used.

5. Present Reading: 6605
Previous Reading: 6238 367

6. Present Reading: 7991
Previous Reading: 7547 444

7. Present Reading: 3580
Previous Reading: 2261 1319

8. Dawn DeLuca's electric meter now has a reading of 4515. One month ago the meter read 4166. How many kilowatts of electricity were used? 349

9. Steven Yamana's electric meter was read last month at 8840. It now reads 9233. Find how many kilowatts of electricity he used. 393

For Exercises 10–12, read the meters to find how many cubic feet of gas were used. (Example 2)

10. **Previous Reading**

Present Reading

3600

11. **Previous Reading**

Present Reading

13,700

12. **Previous Reading**

Present Reading

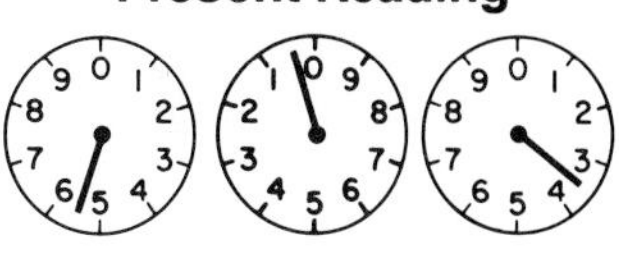

1900

13. Tina Ruiz read her gas meter last week at 857. It now is at 912. How many cubic feet of gas have been used? 5500

14. The gas meter in Bob Spencer's home reads 433. Last month it read 405. How many cubic feet of gas did Bob use? 2800

15-4 Wallpapering and Estimation

See the Teacher's Manual for the objectives.

When Philip Whitecloud decided to paper the walls of his den, he used a table like the one below to find how much he needed.

CEILING HEIGHT	2.4 Meters	2.7 Meters	3 Meters	3.3 Meters	3.6 Meters
Size of Room in Meters	NUMBER OF SINGLE ROLLS				
2.4×3.0	9	10	11	12	13
3.0×3.0	10	11	13	14	15
3.0×4.3	12	14	15	15	16
3.6×3.6	12	14	15	16	18
3.6×4.3	13	15	16	18	18
3.6×4.9	14	16	17	18	18

NOTE: Subtract 1 roll for each door.
Subtract 1 roll for every two windows.

To find the number of rolls needed, you must also answer the question:

What is the allowance for doors and windows?

This is the **hidden question** in the problem. Then you can find the number of rolls.

EXAMPLE A room is 3.5 meters wide and 3.5 meters long. The ceiling is 2.7 meters high. The room has 2 doors and 3 windows. How many single rolls of wallpaper will be needed?

Solution:

1 Round 3.5×3.5 up to the nearest measures in the table. ⟶ **3.6×3.6**

2 Use the table to find the number of rolls. ⟶ **14**

3 Calculate the allowance for doors and windows:

2 doors: 2 rolls
3 windows: 1.5 rolls
Total allowance: **3.5** rolls

From the note in the table

4 Subtract. ⟶ $14 - 3.5 = \mathbf{10.5}$

Number of single rolls needed: **11**

Round up to the next whole number.

REVIEW OF RELATED SKILLS You may wish to use these exercises before teaching the lesson.

Add. (Pages 4–5)

1. $3 + 3.5$ 6.5 **2.** $4 + 2.5$ 6.5 **3.** $5.5 + 1$ 6.5 **4.** $3.5 + 4$ 7.5 **5.** $6 + 1.5$ 7.5

Subtract. Round your answer to the nearest whole number. (Pages 4–5, 16–17)

6. $17 - 4.5$ 13 **7.** $18 - 2.5$ 16 **8.** $13 - 3.5$ 10 **9.** $9 - 4.5$ 5 **10.** $15 - 3.5$ 12

EXERCISES

For Exercises 1–9, use the table on page 322 to find the number of single rolls of wallpaper needed for each room.

	Room	Length	Width	Height	Doors	Windows	
1.	Kitchen	3.0 m	3.0 m	2.7 m	1	2	9
2.	Living room	4.3 m	3.6 m	3.3 m	2	4	14
3.	Bedroom	3.6 m	3.6 m	3.0 m	2	3	12
4.	Dining room	2.9 m	2.9 m	3.6 m	2	5	11
5.	Den	4.2 m	3.6 m	3.3 m	1	4	15
6.	Hall	2.8 m	2.2 m	2.7 m	2	0	8

7. Living Room 15

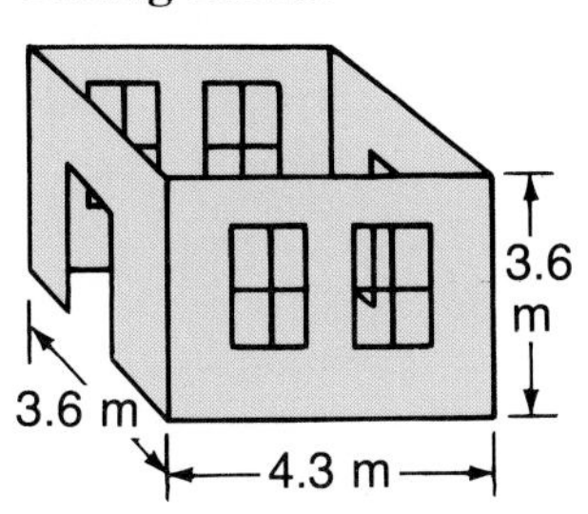

8. Playroom 8

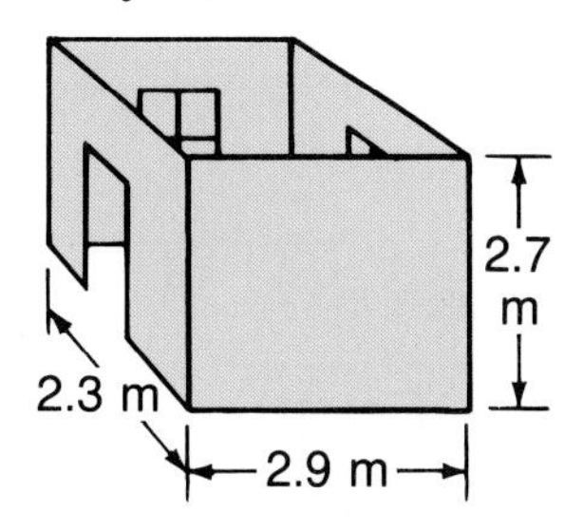

9. Kitchen 14

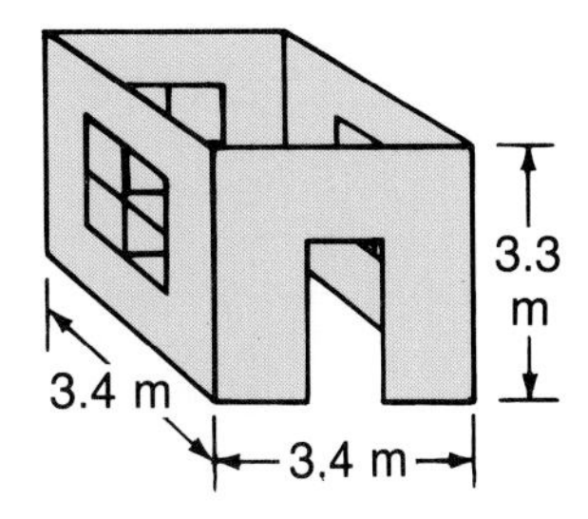

10. Stan Levine plans to wallpaper his bedroom. The room is 3 meters long, 2.4 meters wide, and 3 meters high. There are two windows and a door. How many single rolls of wallpaper should Stan buy? 9

11. Sue Scotto wants to paper the walls of her den. The den is 3.5 meters long, 3.4 meters wide, and 3 meters high. There are four windows and three doors. How many single rolls of wallpaper will Sue need? 10

DRAFTING TECHNICIAN

Career lessons are optional.
This lesson applies the skill of solving proportions.

Drafting technicians must have a knowledge of ratios and proportions in order to prepare scale drawings.

EXAMPLE Jane Ladino, a drafting technician, prepares blueprints for the house shown below. The scale will be:

1 cm represents 1.5 m

Find the blueprint size of the living room.

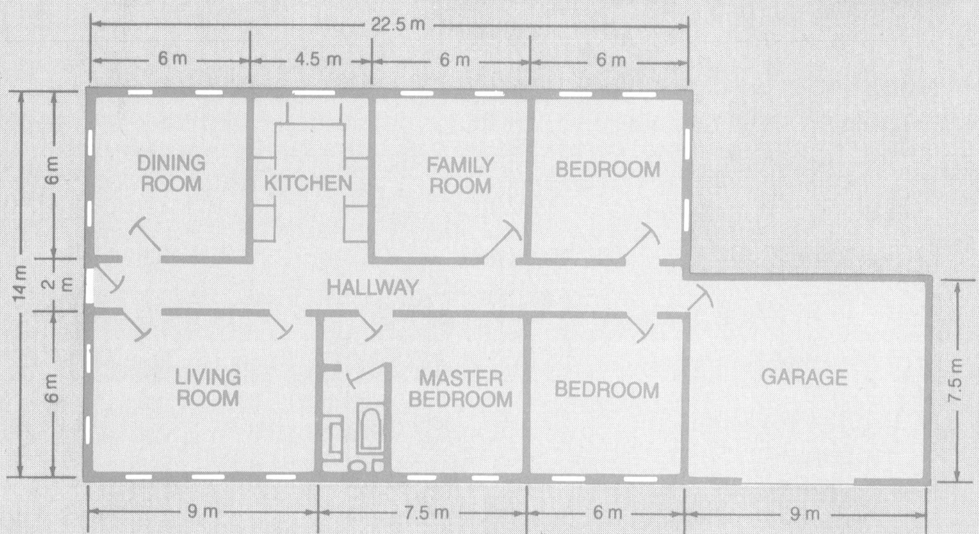

Solution: Use the scale to write proportions.

Blue print size ⟶ 1 cm represents 1.5 m ⟵ ***Real size***

Length

Real size ⟶ / ***Blueprint size*** ⟶ $\frac{1.5}{1} = \frac{9}{n}$ ⟵ ***Real size*** / ***Blueprint size***

$1.5 \times n = 1 \times 9$

$1.5n = 9$

$n = 6$

Width

Real size ⟶ / ***Blueprint size*** ⟶ $\frac{1.5}{1} = \frac{6}{n}$ ⟵ ***Real size*** / ***Blueprint size***

$1.5 \times n = 1 \times 6$

$1.5n = 6$

$n = 4$

The blueprint size of the living room is **6 centimeters** by **4 centimeters.**

EXERCISES Note that Exercises 1-8 are non-verbal.

For Exercises 1–8, find the blueprint size.

	Scale	Real Size
1.	1 cm represents 2 m	6 m 3 cm
2.	1 cm represents 2.5 m	10 m 4 cm
3.	1 cm represents 0.5 m	5 m 10 cm
4.	1 cm represents 1.5 m	3 m 2 cm

	Scale	Real Size
5.	1 cm represents 2.5 m	12.5 m 5 cm
6.	1 cm represents 3 m	10.5 m 3.5 cm
7.	1 cm represents 1.5 m	6.75 m 4.5 cm
8.	1 cm represents 2 m	13.2 m 6.6 cm

For Exercises 9–12, use the floor plan on page 324.

9. Find the blueprint size of the garage. 6 cm by 5 cm

10. Find the blueprint size of the kitchen. 4 cm by 3 cm

11. Find the blueprint size of the master bedroom. 5 cm by 4 cm

12. Find the blueprint size of the dining room. 4 cm by 4 cm

*For Exercises 13–16, refer to the floor plan below. The scale for the blueprint will be: **1 in represents 4 ft.***

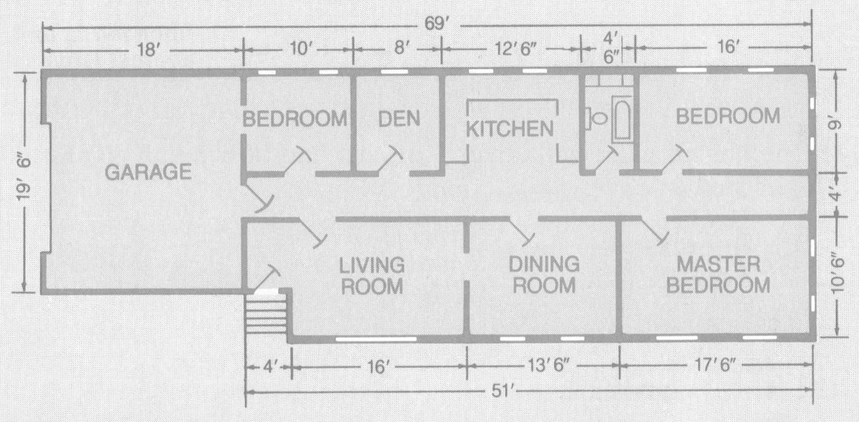

13. Find the blueprint size of the kitchen. $2\frac{1}{4}$ in by $3\frac{1}{8}$ in
(Remember: 6 inches $= \frac{1}{2}$ foot.)

14. Find the blueprint size of the dining room. $3\frac{3}{8}$ in by $2\frac{5}{8}$ in

15. Find the blueprint size of the den. 2 in by $2\frac{1}{4}$ in

16. Find the blueprint size of the master bedroom. $4\frac{3}{8}$ in by $2\frac{5}{8}$ in

15-5 Painting and Estimation

See the Teacher's Manual for the objectives.

Luis is planning to paint his room. Luis finds this information on the paint can.

One liter of paint will cover 9 square meters.

To estimate the amount of paint needed, you must first answer the question:

What is the combined area of the walls and ceiling?

This is the **hidden question** in the problem.

EXAMPLE The room Luis wants to paint is 4.8 meters long and 3.3 meters wide. It is 2.6 meters high. Find the number of liters Luis should buy.

Solution: 1 To find the total area of the walls, multiply the perimeter of the room by the height of the room.

FRONT	SIDE	BACK	SIDE	2.6 m
3.3 m	4.8 m	3.3 m	4.8 m	

Perimeter: 3.3 m + 4.8 m + 3.3 m + 4.8 m = **16.2 m**

Area of walls: 16.2 m × 2.6 m = **42.1 m²** ◀ *Rounded to the nearest tenth*

2 Area of the ceiling: 4.8 m × 3.3 m = **15.8 m²** ◀ *Rounded to the nearest tenth*

3 Total area (walls and ceiling): 42.1 m² + 15.8 m² = 57.9, or **58 m²**

4 One liter of paint will cover 9 m². To find how much paint is needed to cover 58 m², divide 58 by 9.

58 ÷ 9 = 6.44, or **7 liters** ◀ *Round up to the next whole liter.*

REVIEW OF RELATED SKILLS

You may wish to use these exercises before teaching the lesson.

Add. (Pages 4–5)

1. 2.3 + 4.7 + 2.3 + 4.7 14 **2.** 3.3 + 4.5 + 3.3 + 4.5 15.6 **3.** 4.6 + 5.4 + 4.6 + 5.4 20

4. 1.9 + 2.6 + 1.9 + 2.6 9 **5.** 3.6 + 4.0 + 3.6 + 4.0 15.2 **6.** 1.8 + 3.2 + 1.8 + 3.2 10

Multiply. Round each answer to the nearest tenth. (Pages 8–9, 16–17)

7. 15.6 × 3.3 51.5 **8.** 17.4 × 2.9 50.5 **9.** 3.5 × 4.0 14.0 **10.** 4.2 × 3.8 16.0 **11.** 2.9 × 4.4 12.8

Divide. Round each answer to the nearest whole number. (Pages 12–13, 16–17)

12. 54 ÷ 9 6 **13.** 73 ÷ 9 8 **14.** 62.3 ÷ 9 7 **15.** 67.9 ÷ 9 8 **16.** 58.6 ÷ 9 7

EXERCISES

For Exercises 1–4, complete the table to find the number of liters of paint you should buy to paint each room. (NOTE: One liter of paint covers 9 square meters.)

Room	Perimeter	Height	Area of Walls	Area of Ceiling	Area of Walls and Ceiling	Liters of Paint
1. Living room	20.2 m	2.8 m	56.6m² ?	24.9 m²	? 82m²	? 10
2. Den	22.8 m	2.5 m	57m² ?	31.7 m²	? 89m²	? 10
3. Bedroom	27.2 m	2.8 m	76.2m² ?	43.7 m²	? 120m²	? 14
4. Kitchen	12.4 m	2.6 m	32.2m² ?	9.5 m²	? 42m²	? 5

For Exercises 5–7, find the number of liters of paint needed to paint the walls and ceiling of each room. (NOTE: One liter of paint covers 9 square meters.)

5. Kitchen 5

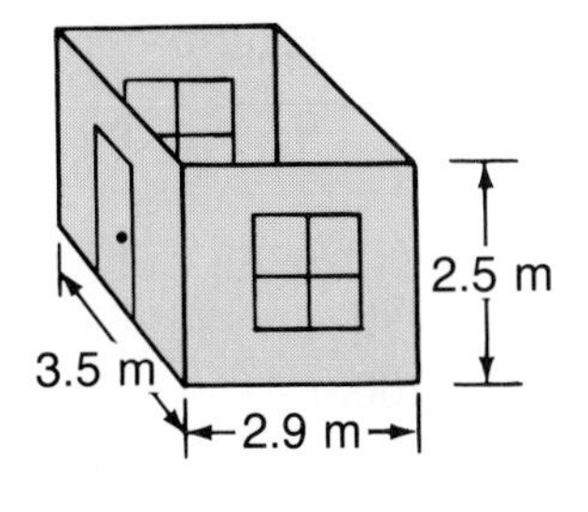

6. Hallway 8

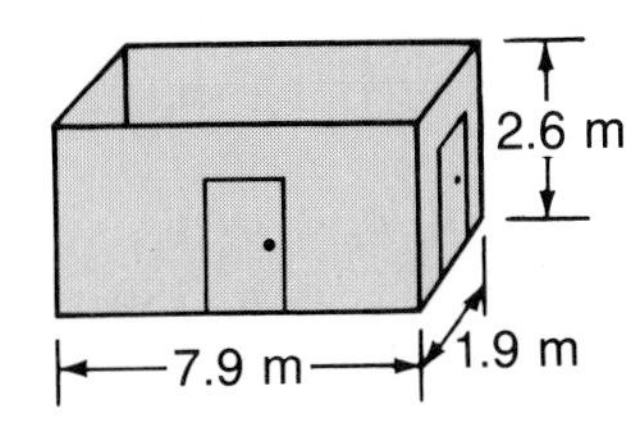

7. Dining Room 8

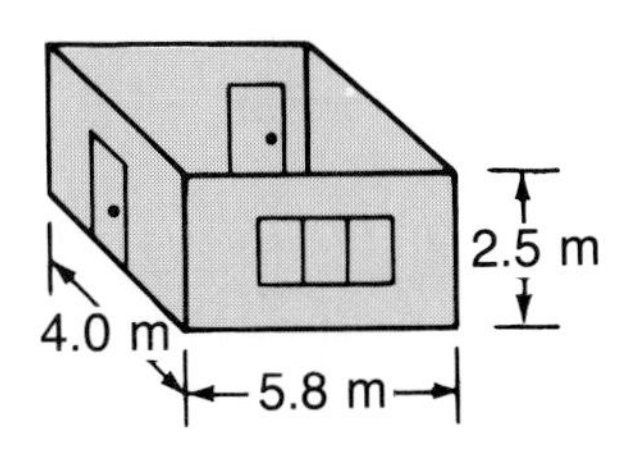

8. The living room in Kitty's apartment is 6 meters long, 4 meters wide, and 2.5 meters high. How many liters of paint should she buy to paint this room? 9

9. The family room in Yoshiro's house is 8.7 meters long and 3.9 meters wide. The walls are 2.8 meters high. How many liters of paint would be needed to paint this room? 12

More Challenging Problems

Sylvia and Lester Tobin buy paint in 4-liter cans. One can covers 50 square meters. Paint for the walls of their apartment costs \$15.25 per can. Paint for the ceilings costs \$10.80 per can. Use this information for Exercises 10–12.

10. The Tobins are painting a room that is 7.5 meters wide and 8.5 meters long. The walls are 2.8 meters high. Find the cost of painting the walls. \$30.50

11. Find the cost of painting the ceiling of the room in Exercise 10. \$21.60

12. Find the total cost of painting the room described in Exercise 10. \$52.10

Rounding and Estimation

Consumers use rounding and estimation to solve problems related to housing costs.

EXERCISES

See the Teacher's Manual for the objectives.

Skills

Choose the best estimate. Choose a, b, or c.

		a.	b.	c.
1. 19% of 604	c	$\frac{1}{5} \times 700$	$\frac{1}{4} \times 600$	$\frac{1}{5} \times 600$
2. 41×9	a	40×9	40×10	50×9
3. $3806 - 3695$	b	$3800 - 3600$	$3800 - 3700$	$3900 - 3600$
4. $671 - 649$	a	$670 - 650$	$680 - 650$	$680 - 640$
5. 4.2×7.1	c	4×8	5×7	4×7
6. 19.7×3.1	c	10×4	10×3	20×3
7. $21.2 \div 7.3$	a	$21 \div 7$	$22 \div 7$	$21 \div 8$

Choose the best estimate. Choose a, b, c, or d.

		a.	b.	c.	d.
8. 21% of 798	a	160	180	140	200
9. 39×11	d	350	450	300	400
10. $4102 - 3995$	b	80	100	120	140
11. $389 - 372$	a	20	10	30	40
12. 5.1×6.9	d	32	33	34	35
13. 20.3×3.8	c	60	70	80	90
14. $44.8 \div 9.1$	c	3	4	5	6

Applications

15. Last year, the Ruiz family spent \$995 on heating their home with the thermostat set at 71°F. They will save 18% of this if they lower the setting to 65°F. Estimate the amount of savings. d

a. $\$900 \times \frac{1}{8}$ **b.** $\$900 \times \frac{1}{10}$

c. $\$1000 \times \frac{1}{10}$ **d.** $\$1000 \times \frac{1}{5}$

16. Tony Marcella watches his color television set an average of 31 hours each week. The cost for electricity is 5¢ per hour. Estimate the weekly cost of electricity for the television. b

a. 40 × 5¢ **b.** 30 × 5¢

c. 40 × 10¢ **d.** 30 × 10¢

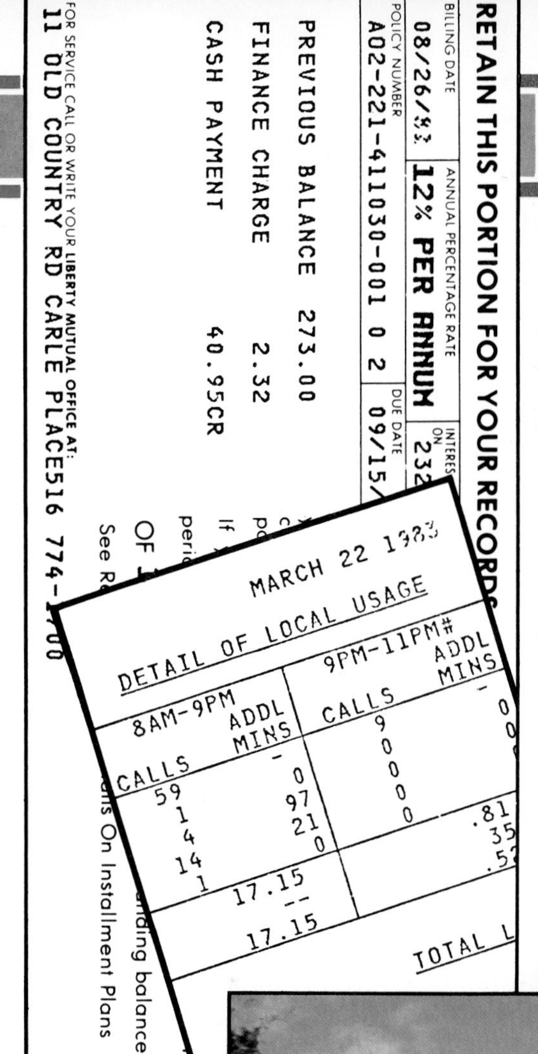

17. Last month, Marina's electric meter read 6104. This month, the reading is 6298. Estimate the number of kilowatt hours used. c

    a. 6200 − 6100 b. 6300 − 6200
    c. 6300 − 6100 d. 6300 − 6000

18. Chaim wants to paint a room that is 5.1 meters long and 3.8 meters wide. Estimate the area of the ceiling in square meters. b

    a. 5×3 b. 5×4
    c. 6×3 d. 6×4

19. Last year the Saunders family spent \$905 on heating their home with the thermostat set at 72°F. They will save 21% of this if they lower the setting to 65°F. Estimate the amount of savings. c

    a. \$160 b. \$220 c. \$180 d. \$210

20. It costs 29¢ per day to run Jorge's refrigerator/freezer. Estimate the cost of electricity for 31 days. a

    a. \$9 b. \$6 c. \$8 d. \$12

21. Last month, Manuel's electric meter read 7987. This month, the reading is 8192. Estimate the number of kilowatt-hours used. c

    a. 300
    b. 100
    c. 200
    d. 400

22. LaVerne wants to paint a room that is 4.9 meters long and 3.2 meters wide. Estimate the area of the ceiling in square meters. b

    a. 12
    b. 15
    c. 20
    d. 24

23. The walls of a storage room are being painted. The room's perimeter is 16.4 meters and it is 2.9 meters high. Estimate the area of the walls. b

    a. 44
    b. 48
    c. 52
    d. 56

Chapter Review

These exercises review the vocabulary, skills and applications presented in the chapter as a preparation for the chapter test.

Part 1: VOCABULARY

For Exercises 1–5, choose from the box at the right the word(s) that complete(s) each statement.

cubic feet
one hour
perimeter
area
previous reading
present reading
kilowatt-hours

1. Electricity is measured in ___?___. kilowatt-hours (Pages 316–317)
2. You use one kilowatt-hour of electricity when you use one kilowatt for ___?___. one hour (Pages 316–317)
3. Your gas bill is based on the number of ___?___ of gas that you use. cubic feet (Pages 320–321)
4. To find the number of cubic feet of gas used, subtract the ___?___ previous reading from the ___?___. present reading (Pages 320–321)
5. To find the amount of paint you need for painting your room, you need to know the combined ___?___ of the wall and ceiling. area (Pages 326–327)

Part 2: SKILLS

Add or subtract. (Pages 2–5)

6. 85 − 67 18
7. 68 − 63 5
8. 81 − 74 7
9. 870 − 705 165
10. 8512 − 7605 907
11. 1109 − 806 303
12. 7 + 3.5 10.5
13. 4 + 4.5 8.5
14. 2.5 + 4 6.5
15. 8.2 + 7.6 15.8

Multiply. (Pages 6–7, 8–9)

16. 21 × 100 2100
17. 63 × 100 6300
18. 9 × 3% 27%
19. $680 × 0.06 $40.80
20. $475 × 0.12 $57

Multiply. Write each answer as an amount in dollars. (Pages 6–7, 56–57)

21. 7¢ × 30 $2.10
22. 18¢ × 15 $2.70
23. 85¢ × 6 $5.10
24. $2\frac{1}{2}$¢ × 42 $1.05
25. $3\frac{1}{2}$¢ × 56 $1.96

Multiply. Round each answer to the nearest tenth. (Pages 8–9, 16–17)

26. 9.2 × 3.8 35.0
27. 3.4 × 3.1 10.5
28. 7.4 × 4.0 29.6
29. 18.2 × 9.1 165.6
30. 26.5 × 2.3 61.0

Divide. Round each answer to the nearest whole number. (Pages 12–13, 16–17)

31. 63 ÷ 9 7
32. 68 ÷ 9 8
33. 82.1 ÷ 9 9
34. 107.6 ÷ 9 12
35. 151.8 ÷ 9 17

Part 3: APPLICATIONS

For Exercises 36–39, find how much each family could save over last year's heating costs. For each degree Fahrenheit that the thermostat is lowered, you can lower heating costs by 3%. (Pages 314–315)

	Yearly Heating Costs	Last Year's Thermostat Setting	This Year's Thermostat Setting	
36.	$780	67°	64°	$70.20
37.	$840	70°	68°	$50.40
38.	$ 900	72°	67°	$135
39.	$1200	71°	68°	$108

For Exercises 40–41, use the table on page 314. (Pages 314–315)

40. Last year, the Dibbs family spent $900 on air conditioning costs. The thermostat was set at 75°. If they set the thermostat at 78° this year, how much can they save? $252

41. The Costa family spent $850 on air conditioning costs last year. The thermostat was set at 72°. If they set the thermostat at 78° this year, how much can they save? $535.50

For Exercises 42–43, use the table on page 316 to find the cost of operating each appliance. Write each answer as an amount in dollars. (Pages 316–317)

42. Dishwasher: 8 loads per week for 52 weeks $33.28

43. Color television: 6 hours a day for 52 weeks $109.20

For Exercises 44–45, find the meter reading. (Pages 320–321)

4843

44.    

45.   

8425

46. Angela's gas meter read 923 last week. The reading this week is 990. How many cubic feet of gas have been used? (Pages 320–321) 6700

For Exercises 47–48, use the table on page 322 to find the number of single rolls of paper needed. (Pages 322–323)

47. Dina Eckel plans to wallpaper her living room. The room is 4 meters long and 2.6 meters wide. The ceiling is 3.3 meters high. There are 2 windows and 1 door. 13

48. Ted Fox intends to paper the walls of his kitchen. The room's height is 3 meters. The kitchen is 2.9 meters wide and 3.4 meters long. There are 4 windows and 2 doors. 11

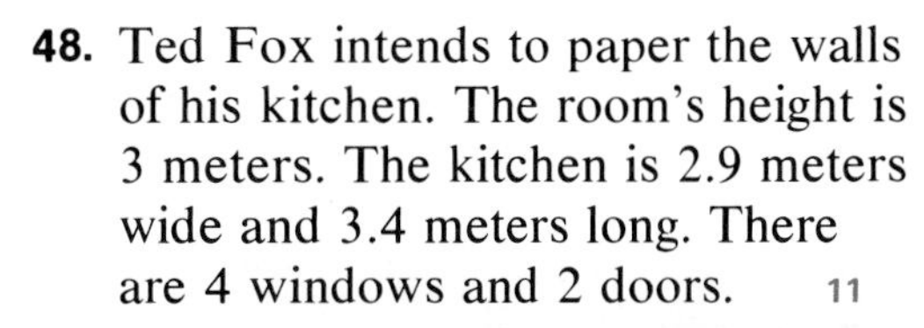

49. Jack plans to paint a room that is 5.9 meters long and 4.1 meters wide. Estimate the area of the ceiling in square meters. a (Pages 328–329)

a. 24 **b.** 20 **c.** 30 **d.** 25

Chapter Test

The Teacher's Resource Book contains two forms of each chapter test.

Add or subtract.

1. $82 - 68$ 14 **2.** $67 - 61$ 6 **3.** $77 - 71$ 6 **4.** $920 - 880$ 40 **5.** $7605 - 7254$ 351

6. $1210 - 970$ 240 **7.** $8 + 2.5$ 10.5 **8.** $5 + 1.5$ 6.5 **9.** $3.5 + 7$ 10.5 **10.** $9.1 + 2.5$ 11.6

Multiply or divide.

11. 32×100 3200 **12.** $8 \times 4\%$ 32% **13.** $\$750 \times 0.05$ \$37.50 **14.** $\$695 \times 0.15$ \$104.25 **15.** $8¢ \times 11$ \$0.88

16. $14¢ \times 6$ \$0.84 **17.** 6.7×3.1 20.77 **18.** 5.1×5.1 26.01 **19.** $81 \div 9$ 9 **20.** $108 \div 9$ 12

21. Mr. and Mrs. Rollins spent \$1100 last year to heat their house. If they had set their thermostat 5 degrees lower, they would have saved 15% of their fuel costs. How much would they have saved? \$165

22. Sam Dudley used his dryer 29 times last summer. The cost per load is 43¢. Estimate the cost of electricity for the dryer. c

a. $40¢ \times 20$ **b.** $50¢ \times 20$

c. $40¢ \times 30$ **d.** $50¢ \times 30$

23. Read the meters to find how many cubic feet of gas were used. 12,300

Previous Reading

Present Reading

24. Virginia Martinez wants to paper the walls of her living room. It is 4.3 meters long, 3.6 meters wide and 3 meters high. There are five windows and two doors. Use the table below to find the number of single rolls needed. 12

SIZE OF ROOM (METERS): 3.6 × 4.3				
Ceiling height (meters)	2.7	3.0	3.3	3.6
Number of Single Rolls	15	16	18	18

NOTE: Subtract 1 roll for each door.
Subtract 1 roll for every two windows.

25. The family room in Fred Rubin's house is 9.4 meters long and 5.1 meters wide. The walls are 3 meters high. One liter of paint will cover 9 square meters. How many liters of paint are needed to paint the four walls and the ceiling? 15

Additional Practice

You may wish to use some or all of these exercises depending on how well students performed on the formal chapter test.

Skills

Add or subtract. (Pages 2–5)

1. 65 − 62 3 **2.** 71 − 68 3 **3.** 79 − 73 6 **4.** 906 − 794 112 **5.** 4012 − 3706 306

6. 2019 − 1107 912 **7.** 5 + 2.5 7.5 **8.** 3 + 3.5 6.5 **9.** 1.5 + 6 7.5 **10.** 9.4 + 3.9 13.3

Write a decimal for each per cent. (Pages 90–91)

11. 7% 0.07 **12.** 14% 0.14 **13.** 43% 0.43 **14.** 3% 0.03 **15.** 98% 0.98

Multiply. Write each answer as an amount in dollars. (Pages 6–7, 56–57)

16. 8¢ × 50 $4 **17.** 22¢ × 30 $6.60 **18.** 70¢ × 3 $2.10 **19.** $2\frac{1}{2}$¢ × 88 $2.20 **20.** $3\frac{1}{2}$¢ × 104 $3.64

Subtract. Round each answer to the nearest whole number. (Pages 4–5, 16–17)

21. 18 − 3.5 15 **22.** 19 − 2.5 17 **23.** 13 − 4.5 9 **24.** 7 − 2.5 5 **25.** 16 − 3.5 13

Multiply. Round each answer to the nearest tenth. (Pages 8–9, 16–17)

26. 4.8 × 2.9 13.9 **27.** 9.1 × 5.6 51.0 **28.** 7.7 × 7.7 59.3 **29.** 3.4 × 4.3 14.6 **30.** 11.8 × 9.7 114.5

Applications

31. The Bell family spent $825 on air conditioning costs last year with the thermostat set at 76°. How much will they save this year if they set the thermostat at 78°? Use the table on page 314. (Pages 314–315) $148.50

32. Mr. and Mrs. Faletta used their black and white television set for 14 hours last month. Find the cost of operating the set. Use the table on page 316. (Pages 316–317) $0.49

33. Yvonne Sebastiani's electric meter was read last month at 7698. It now reads 8105. Estimate the number of kilowatt-hours she used. (Pages 328–329) d

a. 600 **b.** 1000

c. 500 **d.** 400

34. Use the table on page 322 to find the number of single rolls of wallpaper needed for this room. (Pages 322–323) 14

Width: 3.6 m 1 door
Length: 4.2 m 2 windows
Height: 3.0 m

For Exercises 35–36, complete the table to find the number of liters of paint you should buy to paint each room. One liter of paint covers 9 square meters. (Pages 326–327)

Room	Perimeter	Height	Area of Walls	Area of Ceiling	Area of Walls and Ceiling	Liters of Paint
35. Den	23.2 m	2.6 m	? 60.3m²	31.6 m²	? 92m²	? 11
36. Hallway	22.4 m	2.7 m	? 60.5m²	28.6 m²	? 89m²	? 10

The Teacher's Resource Book also contains a cumulative review for Chapters 13-15.

Cumulative Review: Chapters 13–15

Choose the correct answer. Choose a, b, c, or d.

1. Add: $3.01 + 2.97 + 0.46$ c

a. 6.53 **b.** 10.58
c. 6.44 **d.** 10.67

2. Subtract. Round the answer to the nearest whole number. d

$$21 - 5.5$$

a. 3.4 **b.** 15.5 **c.** 34 **d.** 16

3. Multiply: $\$2208 \times \frac{3}{4}$ a

a. \$1656 **b.** \$552
c. \$736 **d.** \$428

4. Divide. Round the answer to the nearest tenth. a

$$75 \div 16$$

a. 4.7 **b.** 0.2 **c.** 3.1 **d.** 4.5

5. Multiply: $\$308 \times 12 \times 20$ d

a. \$6160 **b.** \$71,920
c. \$8280 **d.** \$73,920

6. Write a fraction for $5\frac{7}{8}$. d

a. $40\frac{7}{8}$ **b.** $\frac{40}{8}$ **c.** $\frac{43}{8}$ **d.** $\frac{47}{8}$

7. Multiply: $\$860 \times 0.015$ c

a. \$129 **b.** \$1.29
c. \$12.90 **d.** \$57.33

8. Divide. Round the answer to the nearest cent. b

$$\$2.78 \div 2\frac{1}{3}$$

a. \$6.49 **b.** \$1.19
c. \$0.45 **d.** \$5.11

9. A 12–ounce can of tomato paste costs 53¢. Find the unit price. a

a. 4.4¢ **b.** 22¢
c. 5.2¢ **d.** 23¢

10. Jim bought three no–name items for 59¢, 87¢, and 51¢. Elisa bought three similar brand–name items for 72¢, 95¢, and 68¢. How much did Jim save on the total purchase? b

a. \$1.14 **b.** \$0.38
c. \$0.60 **d.** \$0.76

11. Susan bought a jar of peanuts marked \$2.19 at a store giving double coupon savings. She used the coupon below. How much did she pay? c

a. \$1.79
b. \$2.59
c. \$1.39
d. \$2.99

12. Ground beef gives 4 servings per pound. A pound of ground beef costs \$1.89. What is the cost per serving? a

a. \$0.47 **b.** \$1.93
c. \$7.56 **d.** \$1.85

13. Nancy's net monthly income is \$960. She cannot spend more than $\frac{1}{3}$ of this for rent. What is the most she can spend? d

a. \$2880 **b.** \$480
c. \$360 **d.** \$320

14. The Wallen family bought a new house for \$87,500. The down payment was 30% of the purchase price. Find the down payment. c

a. \$61,250 b. \$29,167
c. \$26,250 d. \$12,500

15. Carlos Esteves took out a \$70,000 mortgage for 30 years. The monthly payments are \$885. Find the total interest. d

a. \$248,500 b. \$318,528
c. \$318,600 d. \$248,600

16. Virginia Fasulo's home is assessed at 45% of its market value of \$92,000. What is its assessed value? b

a. \$50,000 b. \$41,400
c. \$204,444 d. \$44,100

17. The Loock's home is assessed at \$54,500. The property tax rate is \$7.20 per \$100 of assessed value. Find the amount of property tax. a

a. \$3924 b. \$39,240
c. \$39.24 d. \$392.40

18. The assessed value of the Loring family's home is 49% of its market value of \$104,000. Estimate the assessed value. b

a. \$40,000 b. \$52,000
c. \$45,000 d. \$60,000

19. What is the meter reading? a

KILOWATT-HOURS

a. 8562 b. 9672
c. 8672 d. 8572

20. Last year the Sugihara family spent \$1250 for heat. By lowering the thermostat setting 4° they save 12% of this. Find the amount they save. d

a. \$500 b. \$12
c. \$1100 d. \$150

21. Electricity for a dishwasher costs 8¢ per load. Find the cost of washing one load of dishes each day for 2 weeks. c

a. \$1.02 b. \$0.96
c. \$1.12 d. \$0.56

22. The present reading on the O'Hare's electric meter is 8704. The previous reading was 8497. Estimate the kilowatt hours of electricity used. c

a. 400 b. 300 c. 200 d. 100

23. A liter of paint covers 9 square meters. Ken wants to paint the walls of a room that is 5 meters long, 4 meters wide, and 2.5 meters high. How many liters should he buy? b

a. 4 b. 5 c. 6 d. 7

24. How many cubic feet of gas were used? b

Present Reading:	896
Previous Reading:	889

a. 7 b. 700 c. 70 d. 7000

25. Ceiling paint costs \$2.70 per liter. A liter covers 9 square meters. What is the cost of painting a ceiling that measures 4 meters by 4.5 meters? c

a. \$2.70 b. \$8.10
c. \$5.40 d. \$10.10

We suggest that some or all of this page be reviewed before proceeding with the chapter.

REVIEW OF RELATED SKILLS FOR CHAPTER 16

Write a decimal for each per cent. (Pages 90–91)

1. 13% 0.13 **2.** 7% 0.07 **3.** 34% 0.34 **4.** 40% 0.40 **5.** 17% 0.17 **6.** 27% 0.27

7. 1.9% 0.019 **8.** 2.4% 0.024 **9.** 3.7% 0.037 **10.** 2.7% 0.027 **11.** 3.2% 0.032 **12.** 1.8% 0.018

Find each answer. (Pages 94–95)

13. 30% of \$50 \$15 **14.** 20% of \$75 \$15 **15.** 25% of \$80 \$20 **16.** 10% of \$170 \$17

17. 16% of \$60 \$9.60 **18.** 24% of \$40 \$9.60 **19.** 12% of \$160 \$19.20 **20.** 18% of \$200 \$36

21. 10% of \$87.50 \$8.75 **22.** 30% of \$110.00 \$33 **23.** 50% of \$76.42 \$38.21 **24.** 40% of \$121.81 \$48.72

Multiply. (Pages 56–57)

25. $\frac{1}{3} \times \$99$ \$33 **26.** $\frac{1}{2} \times \$160$ \$80 **27.** $\frac{1}{4} \times \$48$ \$12 **28.** $\frac{2}{3} \times \$261$ \$174

29. $\frac{1}{2} \times \$61.74$ \$30.87 **30.** $\frac{1}{4} \times \$106.12$ \$26.53 **31.** $\frac{2}{5} \times \$38.35$ \$15.34 **32.** $\frac{1}{4} \times \$382.72$ \$95.68

Subtract. (Pages 2–5)

33. \$976 − \$801 \$175 **34.** \$154 − \$119 \$35 **35.** \$208 − \$151 \$57 **36.** \$3031 − \$790 \$2241

37. \$1976 − \$704 \$1272 **38.** \$2111 − \$831 \$1280 **39.** \$1770 − \$500 \$1270 **40.** \$1880 − \$942 \$938

41. \$29.98 − \$17.82 \$12.16 **42.** \$41.25 − \$37.62 \$3.63 **43.** \$871.23 − \$50.00 \$821.23

44. \$1824.80 − \$1400 \$424.80 **45.** \$2379.06 − \$1900 \$479.06 **46.** \$3414.72 − \$2300 \$1114.72

Multiply. (Pages 8–9)

47. 6 × \$6.85 \$41.10 **48.** 4 × \$3.99 \$15.96 **49.** 2 × \$7.88 \$15.76 **50.** 3 × \$1.95 \$5.85

51. 8 × \$19.05 \$152.40 **52.** 7 × \$24.99 \$174.93 **53.** 10 × \$50.95 \$509.50 **54.** 2 × \$99.99 \$199.98

55. 12 × \$107.16 \$1285.92 **56.** 15 × \$240.95 \$3614.25 **57.** 24 × \$100.00 \$2400 **58.** 20 × \$174.88 \$3497.60

Add. (Pages 4–5)

59. \$183.50 + \$4.72 + \$18.00 \$206.22 **60.** \$405.21 + \$8.76 + \$41.07 \$455.04

61. \$207.81 + \$7.09 + \$84.09 \$298.99 **62.** \$492.87 + \$2.13 + \$97.79 \$592.79

63. \$11.09 + \$2.77 + \$61.05 + \$6.71 \$81.62 **64.** \$28.33 + \$45.54 + \$5.97 + \$16.71 \$96.55

Multiply. Round each answer to the nearest cent. (Pages 8–9, 16–17)

65. \$26.00 × 0.015 \$0.39 **66.** \$40.25 × 0.015 \$0.60 **67.** \$471.85 × 0.015 \$7.08

68. \$2000 × 0.25 \$500 **69.** \$1496 × 0.20 \$299.20 **70.** \$3074 × 0.30 \$922.20

71. \$5072 × 0.15 \$760.80 **72.** \$80.00 × 24 \$1920 **73.** \$120 × 18 \$2160

74. \$54.00 × 12 \$648 **75.** \$68.73 × 36 \$2474.28 **76.** \$214.20 × 30 \$6426

CHAPTER

16 BUYING GOODS

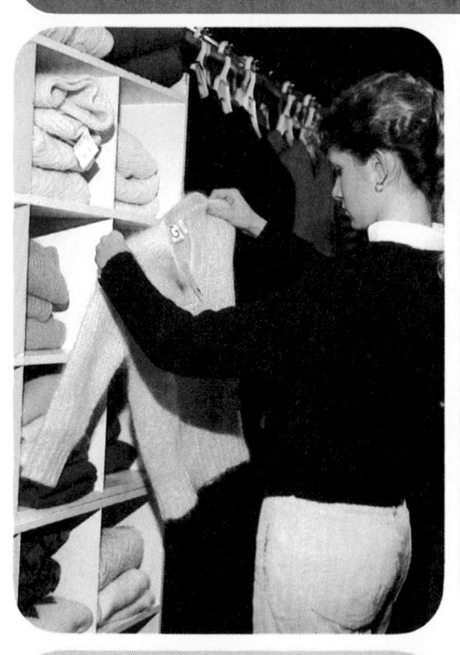

CONSUMER SKILLS/ APPLICATIONS

CAREER APPLICATIONS

See the Teacher's Manual for the objectives.

16-1 Discount

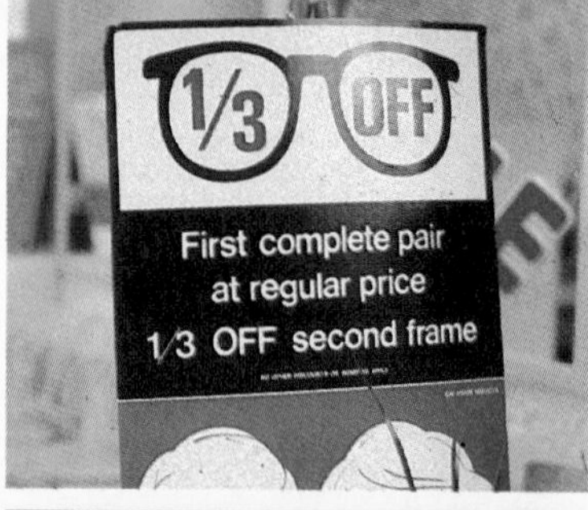

THE CASHIER
WILL TAKE
50% OFF THE
TICKETED PRICE
OF THIS
MERCHANDISE

Sale!
LEATHER
HANDBAGS
beautifully styled
incredibly priced
REG. 25.
13.99

Stores often sell items at sale prices which are lower than their regular price. The **discount** is the amount of money you save by purchasing an item at the sale price.

To find the selling price, you must first answer the question:

What is the amount of discount?

This is the **hidden question** in the problem. Then you can find the selling price.

EXAMPLE 1 The Newfare Custom Shop had a 25%–off sale on summer furniture. Alix Gallagher bought a lawn chair that regularly sells for $59.80. What was the selling price?

Solution:

[1] Amount of discount: 25% of \$59.80 = \$59.80 × 0.25
= **\$14.95**

[2] **Selling Price = Regular Price − Amount of Discount**
= \$59.80 − \$14.95
= **\$44.85** ◀ ***Amount Alix paid***

After completing Example 1, you may wish to have students do some or all of Exercises 1-8.

Sometimes the rate of discount is written as a fraction.

EXAMPLE 2 The RPQ Hardware is advertising a $\frac{1}{3}$–off sale. What is the selling price of a polishing cloth that regularly sells for 96¢?

Solution:

[1] Amount of discount: 96¢ × $\frac{1}{3}$ = **32¢**.

[2] Selling price: 96¢ − 32¢ = **64¢**.

REVIEW OF RELATED SKILLS

You may wish to use these exercises before teaching the lesson.

Write a decimal for each per cent. (Pages 90–91)

1. 14% 0.14 **2.** 15% 0.15 **3.** 20% 0.20 **4.** 30% 0.30 **5.** 5% 0.05 **6.** 8% 0.08

Find each answer. (Pages 94–95)

7. 25% of \$45.60 \$11.40 **8.** 30% of \$18.70 \$5.61 **9.** 18% of \$42.00 \$7.56 **10.** 24% of \$104.50 \$25.08

Multiply. (Pages 56–57)

11. $\frac{1}{4} \times \$51.96$ \$12.99 **12.** $\frac{1}{3} \times \$37.80$ \$12.60 **13.** $\frac{2}{5} \times \$113.75$ \$45.50 **14.** $\frac{1}{2} \times \$123.84$ \$61.92

Subtract. (Pages 2–5)

15. \$132 − \$127 \$5 **16.** \$148 − \$139 \$9 **17.** \$24.99 − \$18.98 \$6.01 **18.** \$32.50 − \$29.98 \$2.52

EXERCISES

For Exercises 1–6, find the amount of discount. (Example 1, step 1)

	Regular Price	Rate of Discount	Amount of Discount
1.	\$64	15%	? \$9.60
2.	\$89	30%	? \$26.70
3.	\$105	25%	? \$26.25

	Regular Price	Rate of Discount	Amount of Discount
4.	\$14.98	10%	? \$1.50
5.	\$29.80	20%	? \$5.96
6.	\$18.50	30%	? \$5.55

7. Jim Barnes bought slacks on sale at 24% off. The regular price was \$27.00. What did Jim pay? \$20.52

8. Marla Dubois bought a sweater on sale at 15% off. The regular price was \$24.60. What did Marla pay? \$20.91

Find the selling price. (Example 2)

	Regular Price	Rate of Discount	Selling Price
9.	\$55.60	$\frac{1}{5}$	? \$44.48
10.	\$48.69	$\frac{1}{3}$	? \$32.46
11.	\$68.72	$\frac{1}{4}$	? \$51.54
12.	\$289.80	$\frac{1}{10}$	? \$260.82
13.	\$168.24	$\frac{1}{2}$	? \$84.12
14.	\$123.75	$\frac{1}{3}$	? \$82.50

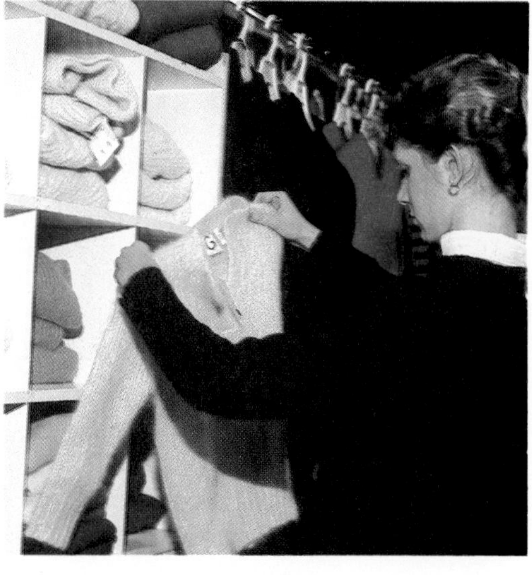

15. Ride–On Bicycle Shop is having a $\frac{1}{4}$–off sale. What is the selling price of a bicycle that regularly sells for \$164.80? \$123.60

16-2 Buying by Mail

See the Teacher's Manual for the objectives.

When you order items from a catalog, you have to pay for the shipping charges. Shipping charges are based on two factors.

1. The total weight of the order.
2. The postal zone to which the order is sent.

The Wilsons used this table to compute shipping charges.

Weight in Pounds	*Shipping Charges*				
	Local	*Zones 1 and 2*	*Zone 3*	*Zone 4*	*Zone 5*
4 lb 1 oz to 5 lb	$1.57	$1.65	$1.82	$2.04	$2.38
5 lb 1 oz to 6 lb	1.64	1.73	1.93	2.19	2.60
6 lb 1 oz to 7 lb	1.70	1.81	2.04	2.35	2.75
7 lb 1 oz to 8 lb	1.77	1.89	2.16	2.50	2.92
8 lb 1 oz to 9 lb	1.83	1.97	2.27	2.61	3.11
9 lb 1 oz to 10 lb	1.90	2.05	2.38	2.73	3.32

EXAMPLE 1 Find the total shipping charge for these items. The Wilsons live in zone 3.

Item	*Shipping Weight Each*	
	lb	*oz*
6 pr socks		3
3 shirts		9
1 pr shoes	2	10

Solution: [1] Find the total weight.

Socks: 3 oz × 6 = 18 oz = 1 lb 2 oz

Shirts: 9 oz × 3 = 27 oz = 1 lb 11 oz

Shoes: +2 lb 10 oz

4 lb 23 oz = **5 lb 7 oz** ◀ *23 oz = 1 lb 7 oz.*

[2] Use the table to find the shipping charges.

	Zone 3
5 lb 1 oz to 6 lb	**1.93**

The shipping charges are **$1.93.**

After completing Example 1, you may wish to have students do some or all of Exercises 1-4.

The Wilsons filled out the following order form.

Catalog Number	How Many	Item	Color Number	Size	Price each	Shipping Wt. each lb	Shipping Wt. each oz	Total Price
137 P481	6 pr	socks	81	$9\frac{1}{2}$	\$1.59		3	?
247 A912	3	shirts	37	M	\$12.53		9	?
540 Q411	1 pr	shoes	42	$10\frac{1}{2}$	\$41.80	2	10	?
					Total for goods			?
					Tax			?
				From Example 1	Shipping Charges			\$1.93
					TOTAL COST			?

EXAMPLE 2 Find the total cost of the order above. There is a 4% sales tax.

Solution: [1] Find the total price for each item and the total for goods.

Socks: \$ 9.54 ◀ *\$1.59 × 6 = \$9.54*
Shirts: 37.59
Shoes: + 41.80
Total for goods: **\$88.93**

[2] Find the sales tax.

4% of \$88.93 = \$88.93 × 0.04
= **\$3.56** ◀ *Rounded to the nearest cent*

[3] **Total Cost = Total for Goods + Sales Tax + Shipping Charges**
= \$88.93 + \$3.56 + \$1.93
= **\$94.42**

REVIEW OF RELATED SKILLS

You may wish to use these exercises before teaching the lesson.

Perform the indicated operations. (Pages 8–9, 4–5)

1. 3 × \$5.95 \$17.85 **2.** 2 × \$4.99 \$9.98 **3.** 6 × \$1.49 \$8.94 **4.** 5 × \$7.98 \$39.90

5. 5 × \$10.99 \$54.95 **6.** 8 × \$21.25 \$170 **7.** 3 × \$114.59 \$343.77 **8.** 2 × \$122.89 \$245.78

9. \$13.49 + \$15.98 + \$2.52 + \$43.80 \$75.79 **10.** \$24.98 + \$15.95 + \$1.97 + \$16.50 \$59.40

11. \$24.99 + \$36.14 + \$15.98 + \$3.22 \$80.33 **12.** \$17.85 + \$28.36 + \$54.70 + \$4.21 \$105.12

EXERCISES

For Exercises 1–4, find the total shipping charge for each group of items. Use postal zone 3 from the table on page 340. (Example 1)

1.

Item	Shipping Wt. Each lb	oz
2 pr slacks	1	2
4 shirts		13
5 ties		2

$2.04

2.

Item	Shipping Wt. Each lb	oz
2 ponchos	3	8
3 aprons		10
1 thermos		12

$2.38

3.

Item	Shipping Wt. Each lb	oz
6 hose		1
1 jacket	2	3
2 pr gloves		8
3 tablecloths	1	3

$2.16

4.

Item	Shipping Wt. Each lb	oz
1 sleeping bag	4	
2 alarm clocks	2	3
2 ties		2
4 sheets		4

$2.38

For Exercises 5–8, find the total cost of each order. The tax rate is 6%. Use the table on page 340 to find the postage for zone 2. (Example 2)

5.

How Many	Name of Item	Price Each	Shipping Wt. Each lb	oz
6 pr	Socks	$0.98		2
3	Leather Belts	$10.50	1	3
2	Sweaters	$13.98		15

$71.07

6.

How Many	Name of Item	Price Each	Shipping Wt. Each lb	oz
4	Pillow Cases	$2.50		2
4	Shirts	$8.00		12
3 pr	Pajamas	$6.50	1	4

$67.08

7.

How Many	Name of Item	Price Each	Shipping Wt. Each lb	oz
2 pr	Jeans	$14.65	2	5
1	Sweat Shirt	$11.99	1	8
2	Sweaters	$35.00	1	4

$119.94

8.

How Many	Name of Item	Price Each	Shipping Wt. Each lb	oz
1	Suede Coat	$99.96	6	2
6 pr	Socks	$0.98		2
2	Shirts	$8.00		12

$131.12

POSTAL CLERK

career

Career lessons are optional. This lesson combines the skill of reading a table with the skills of addition and multiplication of decimals.

As part of her work as a **postal clerk,** Thelma King must calculate the postage on mail. Since postal rates change from time to time, Thelma must keep up-to-date on all changes.

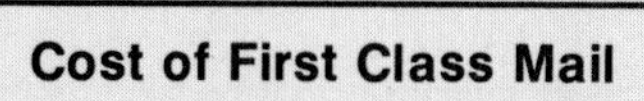

Cost of First Class Mail	
First ounce or fraction of an ounce . .	20¢
Each additional ounce or fraction of an ounce (up to 12 ounces).	17¢

EXAMPLE Find the cost of a letter weighing $2\frac{1}{2}$ ounces.

Solution:
Cost of first ounce: 20¢
Cost of next $1\frac{1}{2}$ ounces $(2\frac{1}{2} - 1 = 1\frac{1}{2})$: +34¢ ◀ *17¢ × 2 = 34¢*
Total Cost: 54¢

EXERCISES

Compute the cost of sending each letter by first class mail.

1. $1\frac{1}{2}$ oz 37¢
2. 3 oz 54¢
3. 8 oz $1.39
4. $2\frac{3}{4}$ oz 54¢
5. $5\frac{1}{8}$ oz $1.05
6. $\frac{1}{2}$ oz 20¢
7. $\frac{1}{8}$ oz 20¢
8. $1\frac{1}{8}$ oz 37¢
9. $11\frac{1}{2}$ oz $2.07
10. $10\frac{2}{3}$ oz 10. $1.90

The rates for second class mail apply to magazines and newspapers. Use the rate table for second class mail shown at the right to find the cost for each weight.

Cost of Second Class Mail	
0 to 1 ounce	19¢
Over 1 to 2 ounces	35¢
Over 2 to 3 ounces	45¢
Over 3 to 4 ounces	55¢
Over 4 to 5 ounces	65¢
Over 5 to 6 ounces	75¢
Over 6 to 7 ounces	85¢
Over 7 to 8 ounces	95¢
Over 8 to 10 ounces	$1.05
Over 10 to 12 ounces	$1.15
Over 12 to 14 ounces	$1.25
Over 14 to 16 ounces	$1.35
Over 16 ounces	$1.45
Plus 10¢ for each additional 2 ounces over 16 ounces	

11. 10 oz $1.05
12. 6 oz 75¢
13. 9 oz $1.05
14. $15\frac{1}{2}$ oz $1.35
15. $3\frac{3}{4}$ oz 55¢
16. $13\frac{5}{8}$ oz $1.25
17. 18 oz: Cost of 16 oz: ? $1.45
    Cost of 2 additional oz: 10¢
    Total: ? $1.55
18. 20 oz $1.65
19. 30 oz $2.15
20. 29 oz $2.15
21. 24 oz $1.85
22. 26 oz $1.95
23. 32 oz $2.25
24. Find the cost of sending a letter that weighs 9 ounces by first class mail. $1.56
25. Find the cost of sending a letter that weighs $10\frac{1}{4}$ ounces by first class mail. $1.90

16-3 Credit Card Statement

See the Teacher's Manual for the objectives.

Lynn and David Luby use a credit card for some of their purchases. They receive a statement each month that shows the following.

Last date on which purchases are added to bill (points to Billing Date)

Last date for payments (points to Due Date)

ACCOUNT NUMBER	BILLING DATE	DUE DATE	For bill inquiry, call (816) 430-9724
594 89 157	9-6-84	10-3-84	

DATE	STORE	REFERENCE NO.	DESCRIPTION	AMOUNT OF PURCHASE	PAYMENTS, AND CREDITS
8/16	1	280970	HOME FURNISHING	62.44	
8/30	1	223783	PAYMENT, THANK YOU		50.00

PREVIOUS BALANCE	PAYMENTS AND CREDITS	FINANCE CHARGE BALANCE	FINANCE CHARGE	NEW BALANCE	MINIMUM PAYMENT DUE
332.64	50.00	?	?	?	35.00

FINANCE CHARGE IS COMPUTED AT A MONTHLY RATE (PERIODIC RATE) OF 1.5%. Annual percentage rate: 18%

To avoid FINANCE CHARGE next month, payment of New Balance must reach us by Due Date shown above.

Amount subject to finance charge this month. (points to Finance Charge Balance)

EXAMPLE Refer to the monthly statement above to find the following:

a. Finance Charge Balance **b.** Finance Charge **c.** New Balance

Solutions: **a. Finance Charge Balance = Previous Balance − Payments**

$= \$332.64 - \$50.00$

$= \mathbf{\$282.64}$

b. Finance Charge = Finance Charge Balance × Monthly Rate

$= \$282.64 \times 0.015$

$= \mathbf{\$4.24}$ ***Rounded to the nearest cent***

c. New Balance = Finance Charge Balance + Finance Charge + Purchases

$= \$282.64 + \$4.24 + \$62.44$

$= \mathbf{\$349.32}$

REVIEW OF RELATED SKILLS

You may wish to use these exercises before teaching the lesson.

Add or subtract as indicated. (Pages 4–5)

1. \$365.49 + \$5.72 + \$12.17 \$383.38
2. \$424.09 + \$6.14 + \$68.98 \$499.21
3. \$246.75 + \$3.08 + \$165.72 \$415.55
4. \$198.25 + \$2.18 + \$104.75 \$305.18
5. \$342.65 − \$27.50 \$315.15
6. \$416.28 − \$25.00 \$391.28
7. \$292.74 − \$45.50 \$247.24

Write a decimal for each per cent. (Pages 90–91)

8. 1.4% 0.014 **9.** 2.3% 0.023 **10.** 1.6% 0.016 **11.** 3.4% 0.034 **12.** 1.2% 0.012 **13.** 2.6% 0.026

Multiply. Round each answer to the nearest cent. (Pages 8–9, 16–17)

14. \$385.16 × 0.015 \$5.78
15. \$289.76 × 0.015 \$4.35
16. \$424.50 × 0.015 \$6.37

EXERCISES

For Exercises 1–6, find each of the following. The monthly finance charge rate is 1.5%.
a. *Finance charge balance* **b.** *Finance charge* (Example, a and b)

	Previous Balance	Payments	Answer
1.	\$384.20	\$42.00	\$342.20; \$5.13
2.	\$461.95	\$50.00	\$411.95; \$6.18
3.	\$242.76	\$27.00	\$215.76; \$3.24
4.	\$198.99	\$22.00	\$176.99; \$2.65
5.	\$273.65	\$28.00	\$245.65; \$3.68
6.	\$321.78	\$31.00	\$290.78; \$4.36

Complete each form. The finance charge rate is 1.5%.

7. New purchase: \$29.25

PREVIOUS BALANCE	PAYMENTS AND CREDITS	FINANCE CHARGE BALANCE	FINANCE CHARGE	NEW BALANCE	MINIMUM PAYMENT DUE
328.16	35.00	?	?	?	35.00

\$293.16 \$4.40 \$326.81

8. New purchases: \$13.75 and \$47.81

PREVIOUS BALANCE	PAYMENTS AND CREDITS	FINANCE CHARGE BALANCE	FINANCE CHARGE	NEW BALANCE	MINIMUM PAYMENT DUE
265.74	21.00	?	?	?	25.00

\$244.74 \$3.67 \$309.97

9. New purchases: \$102.14, \$12.98, and \$25.00

PREVIOUS BALANCE	PAYMENTS AND CREDITS	FINANCE CHARGE BALANCE	FINANCE CHARGE	NEW BALANCE	MINIMUM PAYMENT DUE
475.60	55.00	?	?	?	50.00

\$420.60 \$6.31 \$567.03

16-4 Credit Cards: Minimum Payments

See the Teacher's Manual for the objectives.

The monthly statement on page 344 showed a minimum payment. The minimum payment is computed by using a table like this one.

New Balance	Minimum Payment	New Balance	Minimum Payment
.01–20.00	Full Balance	350.01–400.00	40.00
20.01–200.00	20.00	400.01–450.00	45.00
200.01–250.00	25.00	450.01–500.00	50.00
250.01–300.00	30.00	500.00 or more	$\frac{1}{5}$ of Balance
300.01–350.00	35.00		

EXAMPLE Refer to this monthly statement to find the following.

a. New balance **b.** Minimum payment.

ACCOUNT NUMBER	BILLING DATE	DUE DATE	For bill inquiry, call (816) 430-9724
594 89 197	10-6-84	11-3-84	

DATE	STORE	REFERENCE NO.	DESCRIPTION	AMOUNT OF PURCHASE	PAYMENTS, AND CREDITS
9/15	1	223783	PAYMENT, THANK YOU		35.00
9/21	4	372489	MEN'S SHOES	$109.72	

PREVIOUS BALANCE	PAYMENTS AND CREDITS	FINANCE CHARGE BALANCE	FINANCE CHARGE	NEW BALANCE	MINIMUM PAYMENT DUE
349.32	35.00	?	?	?	?

FINANCE CHARGE IS COMPUTED AT A MONTHLY RATE (PERIODIC RATE) OF 1.5%. Annual percentage rate: 18%

To avoid FINANCE CHARGE next month, payment of New Balance must reach us by Due Date shown above.

Solutions: **a.** [1] Finance Charge Balance: $349.32 − $35.00 = **$314.32**

[2] Finance Charge: $314.32 × 0.015 = **$4.71**

[3] New Balance: $314.32 + $4.71 + $109.72 = **$428.75**

b. Read the minimum payment from the table above.

The minimum payment due is **$45.00**

REVIEW OF RELATED SKILLS You may wish to use these exercises before teaching the lesson.

Add or subtract. (Pages 4–5)

1. $464.75 − $50.00 $414.75
2. $372.46 − $40.00 $332.46
3. $281.90 − $35.00 $246.90
4. $171.50 + $4.62 + $19.95 $196.07
5. $208.42 + $5.46 + $29.98 $243.86
6. $463.72 + $6.48 + $134.75 $604.95
7. $328.07 + $5.98 + $106.47 $440.52

Multiply. Round each answer to the nearest cent. (Pages 8–9, 16–17)

8. $289.75 × 0.015 $4.35
9. $378.52 × 0.015 $5.68
10. $456.04 × 0.015 $6.84

EXERCISES

For Exercises 1–9, find the minimum payment. Use the table on page 346. (Example, b)

	Balance	Minimum Payment	
1.	$225.46	?	$25.00
2.	$379.18	?	$40.00
3.	$322.47	?	$35.00
4.	$462.75	?	$50.00
5.	$217.42	?	$25.00
6.	$404.98	?	$45.00
7.	$30.40	?	$20.00
8.	$318.59	?	$35.00
9.	$268.58	?	$30.00

For Exercises 10–11, complete the form. The finance charge rate is 1.5%. Use the table on page 346. (Example)

10. New purchases: $14.65 and $27.50

PREVIOUS BALANCE	PAYMENTS AND CREDITS	FINANCE CHARGE BALANCE	FINANCE CHARGE	NEW BALANCE	MINIMUM PAYMENT DUE
324.65	35.00	?	?	?	?
		$289.65	$4.34	$336.14	$35.00

11. New purchases: $19.95, $28.70, and $56.98

PREVIOUS BALANCE	PAYMENTS AND CREDITS	FINANCE CHARGE BALANCE	FINANCE CHARGE	NEW BALANCE	MINIMUM PAYMENT DUE
126.50	20.00	?	?	?	?
		$106.50	$1.60	$213.73	$25.00

For Exercises 12–13, the finance charge rate is 1.5%.

12. Marsha's monthly credit card statement listed a previous balance of $246.59, a payment of $35, and a purchase of $14.95. Find the new balance and the minimum payment. $229.71; $25.00

13. Louis's monthly credit card statement lists a previous balance of $363.49, a payment of $40, and a purchase of $98.75. Find the new balance and the minimum payment. $427.09; $45.00

CREDIT MANAGER

Career lessons are optional. This lesson applies the skill of using a formula.

Glenn Fogg is the **credit manager** for a bank. He uses computer printouts to keep track of all outstanding (unpaid) loans. For example, he noticed that several promissory notes were due to April 4. A **promissory note** is a written agreement to repay a loan at the end of a definite time period.

Sample Promissory Note

$ 800.00 Dallas, Texas February 3 1983

60 days from date I promise to pay to

the Dallas General Trust, Dallas, Texas

Eight Hundred and NO/100 dollars

with interest at 15 per cent a year.

Value received

No. 926 Due April 4 1983 Herman Goody

EXAMPLE 1 Herman Goody signed a promissory note for $800 at 15% simple interest for 60 days. Find the total amount due on the loan. (Banks use a 360-day year to compute the time on a promissory note.)

Solution:

[1] Find the interest.

$i = p \times r \times t$ ◀ $p = \$800;\ r = 0.15;\ t = \frac{60}{360}$, or $\frac{1}{6}$

$i = 800 \times 0.15 \times \frac{1}{6}$

Use paper and pencil or use a calculator to compute the interest.

8 0 0 × . 1 5 ÷ 6 = 20.

[2] Find the total amount due. ——→ $800 + $20 = **$820**

Glenn also keeps track of discount loans. For a discount loan, the interest is computed first. Then it is subtracted from the amount of the loan. This difference is called the **proceeds.** The **proceeds** are the amount the borrower receives.

EXAMPLE 2 Stella Morelli obtained a discount loan of $2000 at 18% simple interest for 117 days. Find the proceeds.

Solution: 1 Find the interest owed.

$i = p \times r \times t$ ◀ $i = \$2000;\ r = 0.18;\ t = \frac{117}{360}$

$i = 2000 \times 0.18 \times \frac{117}{360}$ ◀ *Use paper and pencil or use a calculator.*

2 0 0 0 × . 1 8 × → 360.

1 1 7 ÷ 3 6 0 = → 117.

2 Find the proceeds.

$2000 − $117 = **$1883** ◀ *Amount Borrowed − Interest = Proceeds*

EXERCISES

Note that Exercises 1-12 are non-verbal.

Find the total amount due on each promissory note. (Example 1)

	Amount Borrowed	Interest Rate	Number of Days	
1.	$ 900	15%	30	$911.25
2.	$ 500	12%	60	$510
3.	$1200	18%	90	$1254
4.	$5000	18%	120	$5300
5.	$3000	20%	180	$3300
6.	$ 800	15%	60	$820

Find the proceeds on each discount loan. (Example 2)

	Amount Borrowed	Interest Rate	Number of Days	
7.	$ 300	15%	90	$288.75
8.	$1000	14%	180	$930
9.	$3000	18%	270	$2595
10.	$1500	16%	330	$1280
11.	$1500	18%	90	$1432.50
12.	$1600	15%	120	$1520

13. Hilda Joyce obtained a discount loan of $580 for 60 days. The interest rate was 15%. The loan was due in 60 days. Find the proceeds. $565.50

14. Donald King obtained a discount loan of $980 for 30 days. The interest rate was 18%. What proceeds did Donald receive? $965.30

15. The G.M.D. Corporation signed a promissory note for $90,000 for 60 days. The interest rate was 12%. Find the total amount due. $91,800

16. Newfield Railroad, Inc. signed a promissory note for $80,000 at 15% interest. The note was due in 90 days. Find the amount due. $83,000

16-5 Installment Loans

See the Teacher's Manual for the objectives.

Instead of using a credit card, Alicia Santos uses an installment credit plan to purchase certain items. An **installment loan** is a loan that you repay in several equal payments over a specified amount of time. Each payment includes the **interest**, or **finance charge**, on the loan.

EXAMPLE Alicia used a department store's credit installment plan to purchase a sofa and two chairs for \$1875.00. She needs a down payment of 20% and agreed to pay the rest in equal monthly installments of \$93.57 for 18 months (level–payment loan). What is the finance charge?

Solution:

1 **Down payment = Amount of Purchase × Rate**

$= \$1875 \times 0.20$

$= \mathbf{\$375}$

2 **Amount Borrowed = Original Amount − Down Payment**

$= \$1875 - \$375$

$= \mathbf{\$1500}$ After completing Steps 1 and 2, you may wish to have students do some or all of Exercises 1-8.

3 **Total of Monthly Payments = Monthly Payments × Number of Months**

$= \$93.57 \times 18$

$= \mathbf{\$1684.26}$

4 **Finance Charge = Total of Monthly Payments − Amount Borrowed**

$= \$1684.26 - \$1500.00$

$= \mathbf{\$184.26}$

REVIEW OF RELATED SKILLS

You may wish to use these exercises before teaching the lesson.

Write a decimal for each per cent. (Pages 90–91)

1. 25% 0.25 **2.** 35% 0.35 **3.** 18% 0.18 **4.** 26% 0.26 **5.** 9% 0.09 **6.** 8% 0.08

Multiply. (Pages 8–9)

7. \$1564 × 0.20 \$312.80 **8.** \$1925 × 0.25 \$481.25 **9.** \$2430 × 0.30 \$729 **10.** \$2195 × 0.15 \$329.25

11. \$46.75 × 18 \$841.50 **12.** \$64.88 × 24 \$1557.12 **13.** \$43.36 × 36 \$1560.96 **14.** \$51.71 × 30 \$1551.30

Subtract. (Pages 4–5)

15. \$1950 − \$640 **\$1310** **16.** \$2125 − \$482 **\$1643** **17.** \$1689 − \$346 **\$1343**

18. \$1724.49 − \$1600 **\$124.49** **19.** \$2362.46 − \$2000 **\$362.46** **20.** \$1981.03 − \$1750 **\$231.03**

EXERCISES

For Exercises 1–6, complete the table. (Example, steps 1 and 2)

	Amount of Purchase	Rate of Down Payment	Down Payment	Amount Borrowed
1.	\$1985	20%	? \$397	? \$1588
2.	\$1642	25%	? \$410.50	? \$1231.50
3.	\$2468	30%	? \$740.40	? \$1727.60
4.	\$2137	15%	? \$320.55	? \$1816.45
5.	\$1874	10%	? \$187.40	? \$1686.60
6.	\$1369	20%	? \$273.80	? \$1095.20

7. Debbie bought a kitchen set on the credit installment plan. She put 15% down on the purchase price of \$675. Find the amount borrowed. **\$573.75**

8. Roger purchased a living room set on the credit installment plan. He put 25% down on the purchase price of \$2245. Find the amount borrowed. **\$1683.75**

For Exercises 9–14, complete the table. (Example, steps 3 and 4)

	Amount Borrowed	Monthly Payment	Number of Months	Finance Charge
9.	\$1600	\$105.12	18	? \$292.16
10.	\$1400	\$ 84.32	18	? \$117.76
11.	\$1550	\$ 73.21	24	? \$207.04
12.	\$1785	\$82.56	24	? \$196.44
13.	\$2130	\$78.95	30	? \$238.50
14.	\$2469	\$91.34	30	? \$271.20

15. Simone used the credit installment plan to purchase a tractor lawnmower for \$2400. She made a 20% down payment and agreed to make 30 monthly payments of \$75.31. Find the finance charge. **\$339.30**

16. Robert bought a bedroom set on the credit installment plan for \$1550. He made a 15% down payment and agreed to make 24 monthly payments of \$64.56. Find the finance charge. **\$231.94**

Rounding and Estimation

Consumers use rounding and estimation to solve problems related to buying goods.

EXERCISES See the Teacher's Manual for the objectives.

Skills

Choose the best estimate. Choose a, b, or c.

1. 26% of \$35.98 a — **a.** $\frac{1}{4} \times 36$ **b.** $\frac{1}{3} \times 36$ **c.** $\frac{1}{5} \times 36$
2. 41% of 68.50 b — **a.** 0.40×60 **b.** 0.40×70 **c.** 0.50×70
3. 51.05 − 12.20 c — **a.** $50 - 20$ **b.** $60 - 10$ **c.** $50 - 10$
4. 21.25 + 8.97 + 12.10 b — **a.** $20 + 10 + 20$ **b.** $20 + 10 + 10$ **c.** $30 + 10 + 20$
5. 49.70 + 19.85 + 31.16 c — **a.** $50 + 20 + 40$ **b.** $40 + 10 + 30$ **c.** $50 + 20 + 30$
6. 29.80 × 31 a — **a.** 30×30 **b.** 20×30 **c.** 30×40
7. 42.36 × 19 b — **a.** 40×10 **b.** 40×20 **c.** 50×20

Choose the best estimate. Choose a, b, c, or d.

8. 34% of 89.75 c — **a.** 24 **b.** 36 **c.** 30 **d.** 40
9. 59% of 61.06 b — **a.** 24 **b.** 36 **c.** 30 **d.** 40
10. 62.10 − 23.08 d — **a.** 50 **b.** 60 **c.** 30 **d.** 40
11. 38.95 + 63.20 + 9.95 d — **a.** 90 **b.** 100 **c.** 120 **d.** 110
12. 62.08 + 48.87 + 11.12 c — **a.** 90 **b.** 100 **c.** 120 **d.** 110
13. 37.98 × 43 b — **a.** 1500 **b.** 1600 **c.** 1700 **d.** 1800
14. 51.71 × 38 c — **a.** 1600 **b.** 1800 **c.** 2000 **d.** 2200

Applications

15. Gem Hardware is advertising a 33%-off sale. Estimate the discount on a power drill that regularly sells for \$29.95. c

    a. $\frac{1}{4} \times \$20$

    b. $\frac{1}{4} \times \$30$

    c. $\frac{1}{3} \times \$30$

    d. $\frac{1}{3} \times \$20$

16. Classic Clothing is selling a dress with a discount of \$19.95. The regular price is \$49.98. Estimate the selling price. b

    a. \$40 − \$20

    b. \$50 − \$20

    c. \$50 − \$10

    d. \$40 − \$30

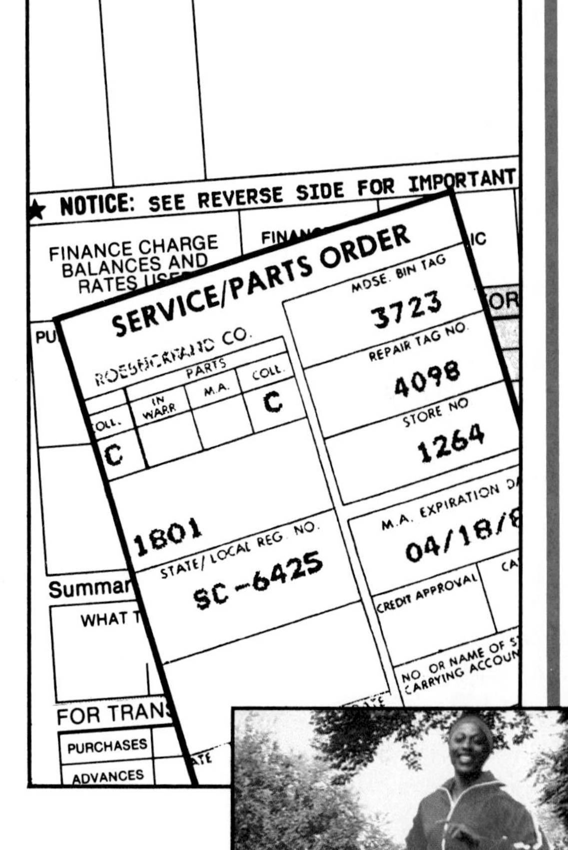

17. The finance charge balance on George Diehl's credit card statement is \$289.65. He made purchases totaling \$61.28. Estimate the new balance. a

    a. \$290 + \$60 **b.** \$300 + \$100
    c. \$280 + \$60 **d.** \$290 + \$70

18. Mr. and Mrs. Joslin purchased a television on an installment credit plan. They agreed to make 21 monthly payments of \$19.75. Estimate the total of the monthly payments. c

    a. 30 × \$20 **b.** 30 × \$10
    c. 20 × \$20 **d.** 20 × \$10

19. Walk-Right Shoes is selling shoes at 24% off. Estimate the discount on a pair of boots that regularly sells for \$78.95. b

    a. \$10 **b.** \$20 **c.** \$30 **d.** \$40

20. Play-More Sports is offering a discount of \$21.40 off all its warm-up suits. The regular price was \$79.95. Estimate the selling price. d

    a. \$40 **b.** \$50
    c. \$80 **d.** \$60

21. Kenneth ordered the following items by mail. Estimate the total cost. a

    1 winter coat at \$99.98
    1 shirt at \$21.40
    1 sweat shirt at \$19.95

    a. \$140
    b. \$120
    c. \$130
    d. \$150

22. The finance charge balance on Diana's credit card statement is \$202.25. She made purchases totaling \$58.60. Estimate the new balance. d

    a. \$270
    b. \$250
    c. \$240
    d. \$260

Chapter Review

These exercises review the vocabulary, skills and applications presented in the chapter as a preparation for the chapter test.

Part 1: VOCABULARY

For Exercises 1–5, choose from the box at the right the word(s) that complete(s) each statement.

postal zone
minimum payment
installment
discount
shipping charge
down payment
credit

1. The ___?___ is the amount of money you save by purchasing an item at the sale price. (Pages 338–339) discount
2. When you order an item from a catalog, you have to pay the cost of the item and the ___?___ to your home. (Pages 340–342) shipping charge
3. You can pay for some purchases without cash by using a ___?___ card. (Pages 344–345) credit
4. Your monthly credit card statement always tells you the ___?___ that you must make. (Pages 346–347) minimum payment
5. A(n) ___?___ loan is a loan that you repay in several equal payments on a specified amount of time. (Pages 350–351) installment

Part 2: SKILLS

Write a decimal for each per cent. (Pages 90–91)

6. 17% 0.17 **7.** 5% 0.05 **8.** 86% 0.86 **9.** 60% 0.60 **10.** 19% 0.19 **11.** 29% 0.29

Find each answer. (Pages 94–95)

12. 50% of \$30 \$15 **13.** 25% of \$90 \$22.50 **14.** 5% of \$190 \$9.50 **15.** 60% of \$120 \$72

16. 20% of \$79.40 \$15.88 **17.** 50% of \$120.26 \$60.13 **18.** 75% of \$185.68 \$139.26 **19.** 30% of \$230.90 \$69.27

Multiply. (Pages 56–57, 8–9)

20. $\frac{1}{2} \times \$280$ \$140 **21.** $\frac{1}{4} \times \$64$ \$16 **22.** $\frac{1}{3} \times \$23.10$ \$7.70 **23.** $\frac{2}{5} \times \$19.45$ \$7.78

24. $5 \times \$8.70$ \$43.50 **25.** $3 \times \$2.05$ \$6.15 **26.** $15 \times \$170.25$ \$2553.75 **27.** $24 \times \$200.00$ \$4800

Subtract. (Pages 2–5)

28. \$506 − \$411 \$95 **29.** \$4044 − \$802 \$3242 **30.** \$1895 − \$604 \$1291

31. \$402.40 − \$60.00 \$342.40 **32.** \$1940.70 − \$1200.00 \$740.70 **33.** \$4002.89 − \$3100.00 \$902.89

Add. (Pages 4–5)

34. \$196.00 + \$9.04 + \$21.00 \$226.04 **35.** \$416.81 + \$4.12 + \$81.21 \$502.14

36. \$33.16 + \$9.75 + \$60.49 + \$18.05 \$121.45 **37.** \$25.60 + \$48.83 + \$7.62 + \$16.41 \$98.46

Multiply. Round each answer to the nearest cent. (Pages 8–9, 16–17)

38. \$420 × 0.010 \$4.20 **39.** \$1600 × 0.30 \$480 **40.** \$3000 × 0.25 \$750

41. \$95.00 × 20 \$1900 **42.** \$270 × 24 \$6480 **43.** \$91.41 × 30 \$2742.30

Part 3: APPLICATIONS

For Exercises 44–47, complete the table. (Pages 338–339)

	Regular Price	Rate of Discount	Amount of Discount
44.	\$82.00	20%	? \$16.40
45.	\$64.20	25%	? \$16.05

	Regular Price	Rate of Discount	Selling Price
46.	\$ 84.00	$\frac{1}{3}$	? \$28
47.	\$274.70	$\frac{1}{10}$	? \$27.47

For Exercises 48–49, find the total shipping charges. Use postal zone 5 and the table on page 340. (Pages 340–342)

48.

Item	Shipping Wt. Each lb	oz
3 pr socks		3
2 pr shoes	2	8

\$2.60

49.

Item	Shipping Wt. Each lb	oz
1 alarm clock	1	14
1 jacket	2	6

\$2.38

For Exercises 50–51, find the total cost of each order. The tax rate is 5%. Use the table on page 340 to find the postage for shipping zone 4. (Pages 340–342)

50.

How Many	Name of Item	Price Each	Shipping Wt. Each lb	oz
14	Ties	\$10.20		3
12 pr	Socks	\$ 1.20		2

\$167.10

51.

How Many	Name of Item	Price Each	Shipping Wt. Each lb	oz
2 pr	Pajamas	\$17.50	1	3
5 pr	Slacks	\$12.50	1	5

\$104.99

In Exercises 52–53, the finance charge rate is 1.5%.

52. Carol's monthly credit card statement showed a new purchase of \$35.70, a previous balance of \$218.76, and a payment of \$80.00. Find her finance charge balance, the finance charge, and her new balance. (Pages 344–345) \$138.76; \$2.08; \$176.54

53. Alex's monthly credit card statement showed a purchase of \$26.80, a previous balance of \$134.55, and a payment of \$50.00. Find the new balance and the minimum payment. Use the table on page 346. (Pages 346–347) \$112.62; \$20.00

54. Ricardo bought a stereo set for \$890 on the installment plan. He made a 21% down payment. Estimate the amount left to pay. (Pages 352–353) a

a. \$720 **b.** \$680 **c.** \$560 **d.** \$640

55. Julia bought a watch at a discount of 26%. The regular price of the watch was \$99.50. Estimate the amount of the discount. (Pages 352–353) c

a. \$40 **b.** \$70 **c.** \$25 **d.** \$60

Chapter Test

The Teacher's Resource Book contains two forms of each chapter test.

Find each answer.

1. 80% of $40 $32 **2.** 20% of $110 $22 **3.** 4% of $98 $3.92 **4.** 70% of $18.23 $12.76

Multiply. Round each answer to the nearest cent.

5. $\frac{1}{3} \times$ $40.20 $13.40 **6.** 6 × $4.15 $24.90 **7.** $390 × 0.020 $7.80 **8.** $412.80 × 0.015 $6.19

Subtract.

9. $803 − $704 $99 **10.** $8120 − $6907 $1213 **11.** $388.40 − $78.00 $310.40 **12.** $1127.50 − $908.00 $219.50

Add.

13. $147.00 + $8.90 + $14.90 $170.80

14. $207.50 + $5.64 + $10.09 $223.23

15. Use the table at the right to find the charge for shipping the following group of items to a local address: 5 shirts (12 ounces each), 1 pair of jeans (2 pounds, 5 ounces), 3 pairs of socks (2 ounces each pair). $1.70

Weight in Pounds	Local Shipping Charges
4 lb 1 oz to 5 lb	$1.47
5 lb 1 oz to 6 lb	$1.64
6 lb 1 oz to 7 lb	$1.70

16. The finance charge balance on Oscar Fleming's credit card statement is $402.85. He made purchases totaling $78.93. Estimate the new balance. c

a. $410 + $80 **b.** $410 + $70

c. $400 + $80 **d.** $400 + $70

17. Mr. Simmons bought an automatic dishwasher on the installment credit plan for $580. He made a 20% down payment and agreed to make 24 monthly payments of $31.80. Find the finance charge. $299.20

18. Andy's latest monthly credit card statement lists a previous balance of $238.72, a payment of $45.00, and a purchase of $28.90. The finance charge rate is 1.5%. Find the new balance. $225.53

19. Pierre bought a shirt on sale at 20% off. The regular price was $33.00. What was the amount of the discount? $6.60

20. Rose bought a skirt on sale at 15% off. The regular price was $38.00. What did Rose pay for the skirt? $32.30

Additional Practice

You may wish to use some or all of these exercises depending on how well students performed on the formal chapter test.

Skills

Find each answer. (Pages 94–95)

1. 60% of $60 $36 **2.** 10% of $95 $9.50 **3.** 7% of $104 $7.28 **4.** 80% of $22.17 $17.74

Multiply. Round each answer to the nearest cent. (Pages 8–9, 16–17, 56–57)

5. $\frac{1}{4} \times \$52$ $13 **6.** 7 × $23.04 $161.28 **7.** $420 × 0.30 $126 **8.** $216.60 × 0.015 $3.25

Subtract. (Pages 2–5)

9. $817 − $790 $27 **10.** $452 − $402 $50 **11.** $1020 − $987 $33 **12.** $904.66 − $60.00 $844.66

Add. (Pages 4–5)

13. $16.17 + $4.91 + $89.20 + $7.08 $117.36 **14.** $80.15 + $53.18 + $17.79 + $19.80 $170.92

Applications

15. Greg bought an umbrella on sale at 15% off. The regular price was $12.00. Find the amount of the discount. (Pages 338–339) $1.80

16. A radio that regularly sells for $89.70 is on sale for $\frac{1}{3}$ off. What is the selling price? (Pages 338–339) $59.80

For Exercises 17–18 find the total cost of each order. The tax rate is 3%. Use the table on page 340 to find the postage for zone 4. (Pages 340–342)

17.

How Many	Name of Item	Price Each	Shipping Wt. Each lb	oz
4	Shirts	$25.20		8
10	Pillow cases	$ 2.00		2
3	Sweaters	$15.70		14

$175.13

18.

How Many	Name of Item	Price Each	Shipping Wt. Each lb	oz
2 pr	Shoes	$38.40	2	10
1	Tablecloth	$ 8.40	1	3
1	Sleeping bag	$45.50	3	7

$137.35

19. The finance charge balance on Raul's credit card statement is $398.40. He made purchases totaling $32.70. Estimate the new balance. (Pages 352–353) b

a. $410 **b.** $430 **c.** $420 **d.** $440

20. Jay bought furniture for his den on the credit installment plan. He made a 25% down payment on a purchase price of $1800 and agreed to make 36 monthly payments of $51.23. Find the finance charge. (Pages 350–351) $494.28

We suggest that some or all of this page be reviewed before proceeding with the chapter.

REVIEW OF RELATED SKILLS FOR CHAPTER 17

Divide. (Pages 12–13)

1. 80,000 ÷ 1000 80 **2.** 65,000 ÷ 1000 65 **3.** 50,000 ÷ 1000 50 **4.** 45,000 ÷ 1000 45

5. 120,000 ÷ 1000 120 **6.** 95,000 ÷ 1000 95 **7.** 140,000 ÷ 1000 140 **8.** 110,000 ÷ 1000 110

Multiply. (Pages 6–9)

9. 30 × $7.40 $222 **10.** 35 × $4.70 $164.50 **11.** 45 × $2.80 $126 **12.** 25 × $3.90 $97.50

13. $140 × 20 $2800 **14.** $185 × 10 $1850 **15.** $175.40 × 30 $5262 **16.** $273.22 × 15 $4098.30

17. 200 × $1.45 $290 **18.** 400 × $6.20 $2480 **19.** 100 × $2.90 $290 **20.** 630 × $4.90 $3087

21. $870 × 4 $3480 **22.** $207 × 4 $828 **23.** $612.50 × 4 $2450 **24.** $218.75 × 4 $875

25. 200 × $41.50 $8300 **26.** 150 × $83.50 $12,525 **27.** 400 × $18.875 $7550

28. $1000 × 1.0507 $1050.70 **29.** $3000 × 1.2611 $3783.30 **30.** $6500 × 1.0829 $7038.85

Divide. Round each answer to the nearest dollar. (Pages 16–17)

31. $83.40 ÷ 12 $7 **32.** $43.68 ÷ 12 $4 **33.** $87.16 ÷ 4 $22 **34.** $23.16 ÷ 12 $2

35. $68.27 ÷ 4 $17 **36.** $94.28 ÷ 12 $8 **37.** $78.13 ÷ 12 $7 **38.** $90.07 ÷ 12 $8

Subtract. (Pages 2–5)

39. $4340.00 − $4000.00 $340 **40.** $2780.00 − 2000.00 $780 **41.** $5750.00 − $5000.00 $750

42. $6240.50 − $6000.00 $240.50 **43.** $8764.20 − $8000.00 $764.20 **44.** $4782.97 − $4000.00 $782.97

45. $8165.00 − $71.00 $8094 **46.** $2650.50 − $85.00 $2565.50 **47.** $8765.54 − $110.75 $8654.79

Write a decimal for each fraction. (Pages 92–93)

48. $\frac{1}{4}$ 0.25 **49.** $\frac{5}{8}$ 0.625 **50.** $\frac{3}{4}$ 0.75 **51.** $\frac{1}{8}$ 0.125 **52.** $\frac{3}{8}$ 0.375 **53.** $\frac{7}{8}$ 0.875

Add. (Pages 2–5)

54. $5500.00 + $76.00 $5576 **55.** $3200.00 + $42.00 $3242 **56.** $4775.00 + $27.00 $4802

57. $6508.45 + $79.00 $6587.45 **58.** $8304.75 + $110.00 $8414.75 **59.** $7650.20 + $95.00 $7745.20

60. $3827.90 + $41.46 $3869.36 **61.** $4820.62 + $57.97 $4878.59 **62.** $9286.50 + $120.87 $9407.37

Divide. Round each answer to the nearest thousandth. (Pages 16–17)

63. $4.70 ÷ $43.50 0.108 **64.** $3.20 ÷ $29.00 0.110 **65.** $1.90 ÷ $28.00 0.068

66. $6.50 ÷ $87.00 0.075 **67.** $7.40 ÷ $82.00 0.090 **68.** $2.40 ÷ $35.00 0.069

69. $2.75 ÷ $31.75 0.087 **70.** $5.65 ÷ $67.25 0.084 **71.** $3.90 ÷ $44.375 0.088

72. $80 ÷ $960 0.083 **73.** $120 ÷ $1320 0.091 **74.** $135 ÷ $1755 0.077

CHAPTER

17 INVESTING MONEY

CONSUMER SKILLS/APPLICATIONS

17-1 Life Insurance: Term/Straight-Life
17-2 Limited Payment Life/Endowment
17-3 Certificates of Deposit
17-4 Buying and Selling Stock
17-5 Dividends/Annual Yield
17-6 Bonds
Rounding and Estimation

CAREER APPLICATIONS

Insurance Clerk
Securities Teller
Investment Counselor

17-1 Life Insurance: Term/Straight-Life

See the Teacher's Manual for the objectives.

One of the deductions from Luis Herrara's pay check is to pay the cost, or **premium,** for **term life insurance.**

TERM INSURANCE

1. Gives financial protection for a specific **term,** such as 5 years, 10 years, or until a certain age.
2. Can be renewed after each term. However, the premium will be higher.
3. The **face value** (amount of insurance) will be paid to the policy holder's beneficiary (wife or husband, etc.) in case of death.

EXAMPLE 1 Suppose that Luis buys a \$30,000 five-year term insurance policy. Luis is 25 years old.

a. Find the yearly premium.

b. Find the total premium for 5 years.

Solutions: **a.** [1] Find the number of 1000's in 30,000.

$$30{,}000 \div 1000 = \mathbf{30}$$

[2] Read the table below to find the yearly premium per \$1000 for a 25–year old man.

5-Year Term Insurance Premium per \$1000 for One Year					
Age	Men	Women	Age	Men	Women
15	\$5.27	\$5.11	30	\$5.32	\$5.16
20	5.29	5.13	35	5.81	5.59
25	5.30	5.14	40	6.75	6.61

[3] **Yearly Premium = Number of \$1000-units × Premium per \$1000**

= 30 × 5.30

= **\$159.00**

b. Total premium for 5 years: \$159.00 × 5 = **\$795.00**

After completing Example 1, you may wish to have students do some or all of Exercises 1-10.

Since Luis is a non-smoker, he will receive a 5% reduction in his yearly premium.

$159.00 × .05 = **$7.95** ◀ ***Yearly savings***

Luis is also considering **straight–life** or **whole life insurance.**

STRAIGHT-LIFE INSURANCE

1. Gives financial protection over entire life of policy holder.
2. The policy holder always pays the same premium.
3. The policy has a cash value and a loan value.

Luis likes the idea of cash value for two reasons.

1. As an investment: Luis can collect the cash value at any time by canceling the policy.
2. As a source of credit: Luis can borrow all or part of the cash value at a low interest rate.

Sample Cash Value

Straight-Life Paid up at 65				
Number of Years	5	10	15	20
Cash Value per $1000	38.06	110.13	192.84	285.51

EXAMPLE 2 Suppose that Luis decides to purchase $10,000 worth of straight-life insurance. Use the table above to find the cash value after 15 years.

Solution: [1] Find the number of 1000's in $10,000.

10,000 ÷ 1,000 = **10**

[2] In the table, find the cash value per $1000 of insurance for 15 years. **192.84**

[3] Multiply: $192.84 × 10 = **$1928.40** ◀ ***Cash value after 15 years***

REVIEW OF RELATED SKILLS

You may wish to use these exercises before teaching the lesson.

Divide. (Pages 12–13)

1. 40,000 ÷ 1000 40 **2.** 70,000 ÷ 1000 70 **3.** 100,000 ÷ 1000 100 **4.** 75,000 ÷ 1000 75

Multiply. (Pages 8–9)

5. 40 × $5.30 $212 **6.** 25 × $5.59 $139.75 **7.** $124 × 10 $1240 **8.** $110.13 × 20 $2202.60 **9.** $285.51 × 25 $7137.75

EXERCISES

For Exercises 1–6, find the yearly premium and the total amount paid for premiums over the term of the insurance policy. Use the table on page 360. (Example 1)

	Male/Female	Age	Face Value	Term	
1.	Female	30	$10,000	10 years	$51.60; $516
2.	Male	25	$20,000	5 years	$106; $530
3.	Female	20	$40,000	5 years	$205.20; $1026

	Male/Female	Age	Face Value	Term	
4.	Female	40	$30,000	5 years	$198.30; $991.50
5.	Male	35	$60,000	10 years	$348.60; $3486
6.	Male	25	$100,000	5 years	$530; $2650

For Exercises 7–10, use the table on page 360.

7. Lu Ann Simmons Buys a $30,000 ten-year term insurance policy. She is 35 years old. Find the yearly premium for Lu Ann's policy. $167.70

8. Derek Hauser buys a $75,000 five-year term insurance policy. He is 30 years old. Find the yearly premium for Derek's policy. $399

9. Sheila Jacobs buys a $30,000 ten-year term insurance policy. She is 30 years old. Find the yearly premium for Sheila's insurance policy. $154.80

10. Mel Cott wants to buy $50,000 worth of term life insurance. He is 20 years old. What is the total amount he will pay in premiums over the 10 years of the policy? $2645

For Exercises 11–20 find the cash value of each straight-life insurance policy for the given number of years. Use the table on page 361. (Example 2)

	Face Value	Term	Cash Value	
11.	$20,000	5 years	?	$761.20
12.	$30,000	10 years	?	$3303.90
13.	$10,000	15 years	?	$1928.40
14.	$35,000	20 years	?	$9992.85
15.	$25,000	15 years	?	$4821

	Face Value	Term	Cash Value	
16.	$50,000	10 years	?	$5506.50
17.	$75,000	20 years	?	$21,413.25
18.	$45,000	15 years	?	$8677.80
19.	$60,000	5 years	?	$2283.60
20.	$100,000	20 years	?	$28,551

For Exercises 21–24, use the table on page 361.

21. Danny wants to buy $20,000 worth of straight-life insurance for protection and as an investment. Find the cash value after 10 years. $2202.60

22. Cindy is planning to buy a $25,000 worth of straight-life insurance. What will the cash value of the policy be after 15 years? $4821

23. Raquel bought a $45,000 straight-life insurance policy. Find its cash value at the end of 15 years. $8677.80

24. Fred wants to invest in a 10-year $10,000 straight-life insurance policy. Find the cash value after 10 years. $1101.30

17-2 Limited-Payment Life/Endowment

See the Teacher's Manual for the objectives.

Diana Georgio liked the advantages of straight-life insurance, but she didn't want to pay premiums for a long period of time. She considered buying **limited-payment life insurance.**

LIMITED-PAYMENT LIFE INSURANCE

1. Gives financial protection for the policy holder's entire life.
2. The same yearly premium is paid for a specific number of years, such as 20 or 30 years.
3. The policy has a cash value and a loan value.

Premiums for limited-payment life insurance are higher than those for straight-life because the premiums are paid for only 20 or 30 years.

Yearly Premium Per $1000 of Life Insurance

Age M	Age F	20-Year Payment	20-Year Endowment
20	25	$25.16	$45.22
25	30	27.63	45.49
30	35	30.60	46.04
35	40	33.97	47.42
40	45	38.69	49.13
45	50	44.49	52.56
50	55	51.38	57.23
55	60	60.15	63.00

EXAMPLE 1 Diana is 25 years old. Suppose that she buys $10,000 worth of life insurance. What is the total amount she will pay in premiums for a 20-year payment policy?

Solution: [1] Find the number of 1000's.

$10{,}000 \div 1000 = \mathbf{10}$

[2] In the table, find the premium per $1000 for a female, aged 25.

[3] Multiply: $\$25.16 \times 10 = \mathbf{\$251.60}$ ◀ *Yearly premium*

[4] Total premium for 20 years: $\$251.60 \times 20 = \mathbf{\$5032.00}$

After completing Example 1, you may wish to have students do some or all of Exercises 1-16.

Diana also considered buying an **endowment policy.** An endowment policy is a combination of life insurance and a savings plan.

ENDOWMENT INSURANCE

1. Gives financial protection for a specified number of years.
2. The same yearly premium is paid for the policy period.
3. The policy has a cash value and a loan value.
4. The policy holder receives the face value at the end of the policy period.

EXAMPLE 2 Suppose that Diana, aged 25, feels that she can afford \$55 per month for a 20-year endowment policy. How much insurance can she purchase?

Solution: Use the table for 20-year endowment insurance on page 363.

[1] Yearly premium for \$1000: **\$45.22**

[2] Monthly cost for \$1000: \$45.22 ÷ 12 = \$3.768 ◀ ***Round to the nearest cent.***
= **\$3.77**

[3] Divide \$55 by \$3.77 to find the number of \$1000-units.

55 ÷ 3.77 = 14.59, or **15** ◀ ***Round to the nearest whole number.***

[4] Amount of insurance Diana can buy: \$1000 × 15 = **\$15,000**

REVIEW OF RELATED SKILLS

You may wish to use these exercises before teaching the lesson.

Multiply. (Pages 8–9)

1. \$30.60 × 20 **\$612** **2.** \$52.56 × 15 **\$788.40** **3.** \$601.50 × 25 **\$15,037.50** **4.** \$460.40 × 15 **\$6906** **5.** \$306.00 × 30 **\$9180**

Divide. Round each answer to the nearest dollar. (Pages 16–17)

6. \$63.00 ÷ 12 **\$5** **7.** \$46.04 ÷ 12 **\$4** **8.** \$72.00 ÷ 4 **\$18** **9.** \$52.56 ÷ 12 **\$4** **10.** \$49.13 ÷ 12 **\$4**

11. \$66 ÷ \$4.09 **\$16** **12.** \$82 ÷ \$3.88 **\$21** **13.** \$61 ÷ \$2.19 **\$28** **14.** \$48 ÷ \$3.23 **\$15** **15.** \$64 ÷ \$2.65 **\$24**

EXERCISES

For Exercises 1–12, find the total premium paid for each 20-year payment insurance policy. Use the table on page 363. (Example 1)

	Male/ Female	Age	Face Value	Total of Premiums
1.	Female	25	\$20,000	? **\$10,064**
2.	Male	30	\$30,000	? **\$18,360**
3.	Female	25	\$30,000	? **\$15,096**
4.	Female	30	\$40,000	? **\$22,104**
5.	Male	20	\$20,000	? **\$10,064**
6.	Male	40	\$50,000	? **\$38,690**
7.	Male	45	\$30,000	? **\$26,694**
8.	Female	50	\$50,000	? **\$44,490**
9.	Female	35	\$40,000	? **\$24,480**
10.	Male	55	\$60,000	? **\$72,180**
11.	Female	45	\$75,000	? **\$58,035**
12.	Male	50	\$55,000	? **\$56,518**

For Exercises 13–16, use the table on page 363.

13. Cesar is 25 years old. He plans to buy a $30,000 20-year payment life insurance policy. Find the total amount he will pay in premiums over 20 years. $16,578

14. Judy wants to buy 20-year payment life insurance. She is 25 years old. What is the total amount in premiums she will pay for a $25,000 policy? $12,580

15. Phil plans to buy a $15,000 20-year payment life insurance policy. He is 20 years old. Find the total cost of the premiums he will pay over 20 years. $7548

16. Natalie is 30 years old. She wants to buy a $20,000 20-year payment life insurance. Find the total amount she will pay in premiums over 20 years. $11,052

For Exercises 17–24, find how much 20-year endowment insurance each person can afford. Use the table on page 363. (Example 2)

	Male/ Female	Age	Maximum Monthly Premium	
17.	Male	20	$75.00	$20,000
18.	Female	35	$40.00	$10,000
19.	Female	25	$95.00	$25,000
20.	Male	35	$60.00	$15,000

	Male/ Female	Age	Maximum Monthly Premium	
21.	Female	40	$100.00	$25,000
22.	Male	40	$80.00	$20,000
23.	Female	30	$115.00	$30,000
24.	Male	50	$120.00	$25,000

For Exercises 25–27, use the table on page 363.

25. Diego Sandoval is 30, and wants to buy a 20-year endowment life insurance policy. He can afford to spend $135 on monthly premiums. How much life insurance can he purchase? $35,000

26. Susan Keller, who is 50, plans to buy 20-year endowment life insurance. She plans to spend $110 per month. How much insurance can she afford? $25,000

27. Gina Padrini is 40. She would like to buy a 20-year endowment insurance policy. How much insurance can she buy for $120 per month? $30,000

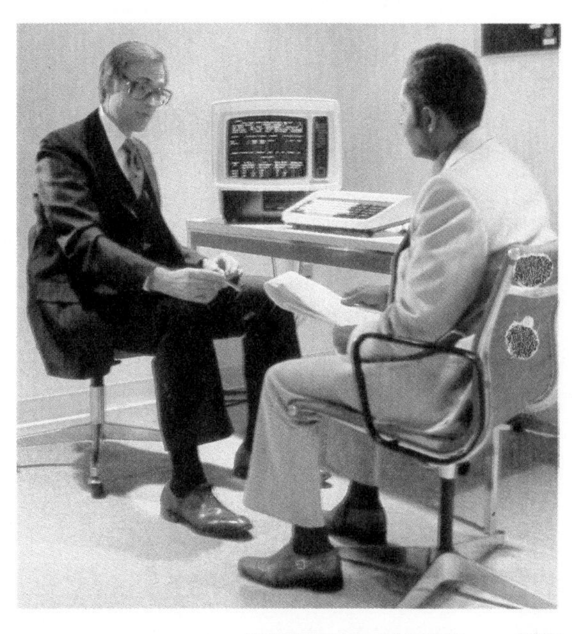

INSURANCE CLERK

Career lessons are optional. This lesson combines the skills of reading a table and using a formula.

Paula Garcia is an **insurance clerk.** Insurance clerks must be able to use tables. One of these tables is a **Mortality Table.**

Mortality tables help insurance companies to predict how much they will have to pay out in claims. This amount tells the insurance companies how much to charge for insurance premiums.

Age M	Age F	Death Rate Per 1,000	Expectation of Life
	0*	6.20	71.17
	1	1.67	70.61
	2	1.41	69.72
	3	1.35	68.82
	4	1.29	67.91
	5	1.24	67.00
	6	1.19	66.08
	7	1.15	65.16
	8	1.12	64.24
	9	1.11	63.31
	10	1.11	62.38
	11	1.12	61.45
	12	1.14	60.51
	13	1.17	59.58
	14	1.21	58.65
0*		7.08	68.30
1		1.76	67.78
2		1.52	66.90
3		1.46	66.00
4		1.40	65.10
5		1.35	64.19
6		1.30	63.27
7		1.26	62.35
8		1.23	61.43
9		1.21	60.51
10		1.21	59.58
11		1.23	58.65
12	15	1.26	57.72
13	16	1.32	56.80
14	17	1.39	55.87
15	18	1.46	54.95
16	19	1.54	54.03
17	20	1.62	53.11
18	21	1.69	52.19
19	22	1.74	51.28
20	23	1.79	50.37
21	24	1.83	49.46
22	25	1.86	48.55
23	26	1.89	47.64
24	27	1.91	46.73
25	28	1.93	45.82
26	29	1.96	44.90
27	30	1.99	43.99
28	31	2.03	43.08
29	32	2.08	42.16
30	33	2.13	41.25
31	34	2.19	40.34
32	35	2.25	39.43
33	36	2.32	38.51
34	37	2.40	37.60
35	38	2.51	36.69
36	39	2.64	35.78
37	40	2.80	34.88
38	41	3.01	33.97
39	42	3.25	33.07
40	43	3.53	32.18
41	44	3.84	31.29

* under 6 months

EXAMPLE 1 Use the portion of the Mortality Table at the right to find the age to which a 15–year–old male can be expected to live. Round the answer to the nearest whole number.

Solution:

1. Find the **Age** column.
   Look down the column under **M** until you reach 15.
2. Look right to the **Expectation of Life** column.
   Read the number. 54.95
3. Add this number to 15.
   15 + 54.95 = 69.95, or about **70.**

The **Death Rate Per 1,000** column can be used to determine how many people can be expected to die at a given age.

EXAMPLE 2 Of 60,000 females who are 40 years old, how many can be expected to die before age 41?

Solution:

1. Find the number of 1000's in 60,000.
   60,000 ÷ 1000 = **60**
2. **Death Rate per 1000** × **Number of 1000's** = **Number of Deaths**
   2.80 × 60 = **168**

EXERCISES

Note that Exercises 1-8 are non-verbal.

Use the Mortality Table to find the age to which each of the following can be expected to live. Round each answer to the nearest whole number.

1. A 14-year-old female 73
2. A 17-year-old female 73
3. A 38-year-old male 72
4. A 20-year-old male 70
5. A 5-year-old male 69
6. A 1-year-old female 72
7. A 40-year-old female 75
8. A 21-year-old male 70
9. Of 80,000 males who are 30 years old, how many can be expected to die before age 31? 170
10. Of 100,000 females who are 43 years old, how many can be expected to die before age 44? 353
11. Of 50,000 males who are 41 years old, how many can be expected to die before age 42? 192
12. Of 90,000 females who are 35 years old, how many can be expected to die before age 36? 203
13. For every 500,000 females who are 39 years old, how many can be expected to die before age 40? 1320
14. For every 500,000 males who are 39 years old, how many can be expected to die before age 40? 1625
15. According to the table, to what age can a female aged 38 expect to live? 75
16. According to the table, to what age can a 33-year-old male expect to live? 72
17. According to the table, to what age can a 28-year-old female expect to live? 74
18. According to the table, to what age can a 25-year-old male expect to live? 71

A mortality table issued in 1941 showed that a 20-year-old male could expect to live for 45.66 more years. Use this information for Exercises 19-20.

19. How does this compare to the life expectancy for 20-year-old males in the Mortality Table on page 366? It is 4.71 years less.
20. Give a reason for the difference in the life expectancies shown in the two tables. Advances in medicine. (Answers will vary.)
21. According to the table on page 366, what is the death rate per 1000 for 20-year-old males? 1.79
22. According to the table on page 366, what is the death rate per 1000 for 20-year-old females? 1.62

17-3 Certificates of Deposit

See the Teacher's Manual for the objectives.

Anna wants to invest $5000 in a **certificate of deposit** offered by her bank. She knows that certificates of deposit earn interest at a higher rate than a regular savings account.

Some certificates must be left on deposit for 6 months. Others must be left for a longer time.

Growth of $1.00 at Interest Compounded Daily

Yearly Rate	Interest Period		
	6 Months	One Year	18 Months
8%	1.0408	1.0832	1.1274
10%	1.0512	1.1051	1.1617
12%	1.0618	1.1274	1.1971
14%	1.0725	1.1502	1.2336
16%	1.0833	1.1734	1.2711

EXAMPLE Anna invested $5000 in a 6-month certificate that pays 14% compounded daily.

a. How much will the certificate pay at the end of 6 months?

b. How much interest will the certificate earn?

Solution: **a.** **1** In the table, find the amount one dollar will pay at 14% interest at the end of 6 months.

Yearly Rate	6 Months
14%	**1.0725**

2 Find the amount $5000 will pay.

$5000 × 1.0725 = **$5362.50** ◀ *Amount paid*

b. Find the interest.

$5362.50 − $5000.00 = **$362.50** ◀ *Interest earned*

Unlike most savings accounts, there is usually a penalty (loss of interest) if all or part of the money is withdrawn before the end of the specified period of deposit.

REVIEW OF RELATED SKILLS

You may wish to use these exercises before teaching the lesson.

Multiply. (Pages 8–9)

1. $1000 × 1.1274 $1127.40
2. $1000 × 1.0833 $1083.30
3. $500 × 1.2711 $635.55
4. $1000 × 1.0408 $1040.80
5. $2000 × 1.1617 $2323.40
6. $3000 × 1.1502 $3450.60
7. $4000 × 1.0725 $4290
8. $5000 × 1.1051 $5525.50

Subtract. (Pages 4–5)

9. $2210.20 − $2000.00 $210.20
10. $3249.90 − $3000.00 $249.90
11. $4646.80 − $4000.00 $646.80
12. $5808.50 − $5000.00 $808.50
13. $8897.70 − $7000.00 $1897.70
14. $7182.60 − $6000.00 $1182.60

EXERCISES

For Exercises 1–12:

a. Find the amount of each certificate at maturity.

b. Find how much interest each certificate earns. Use the table on page 368.

	Face Value	Yearly Rate	Interest Period		Face Value	Yearly Rate	Interest Period
1.	\$2,000	10%	6 months (\$2102.40; \$102.40)	**7.**	\$7,500	12%	18 months (\$8978.25; \$1478.25)
2.	\$1,500	12%	1 year (\$1691.10; \$191.10)	**8.**	\$10,000	16%	1 year (\$11,734; \$1,734)
3.	\$4,000	8%	6 months (\$4163.20; \$163.20)	**9.**	\$10,000	14%	6 months (\$10,725; \$725)
4.	\$3,000	12%	1 year (\$3382.20; \$382.20)	**10.**	\$5,000	16%	1 year (\$5867; \$867)
5.	\$3,500	14%	18 months (\$4317.60; \$817.60)	**11.**	\$6,000	14%	18 months (\$7401.60; \$1401.60)
6.	\$5,000	10%	6 months (\$5256; \$256)	**12.**	\$8,000	16%	18 months (\$10,168.80; \$2168.80)

For Exercises 13–16, use the table on page 368.

13. Donna Reeder invested \$7500 in a one-year certificate of deposit paying 12% compounded daily. Find how much the certificate will pay after one year. \$8455.50

14. Rick Ramsey plans to buy a 6-month certificate that pays 14% interest compounded daily. The face value of the certificate is \$5000. How much interest will Rick receive? \$362.50

15. Ella Mae Schnazz invested \$5000 in a 6-month certificate of deposit. The certificate pays 8% interest compounded daily. How much interest will the certificate pay in six months? \$204

16. Find the difference between the amount of interest Rick received from a 14% certificate (Exercise 14) and the interest Ella Mae received from an 8% certificate (Exercise 15). \$158.50

17-4 Buying and Selling Stock

See the Teacher's Manual for the objectives.

When Michael Jones bought shares of **stock** in Cosgrove Electric Corporation, he became a part owner of the corporation. Stock prices are listed each day in the business section of daily newspapers. Stock prices are usually quoted (listed) in **eighths of a dollar.**

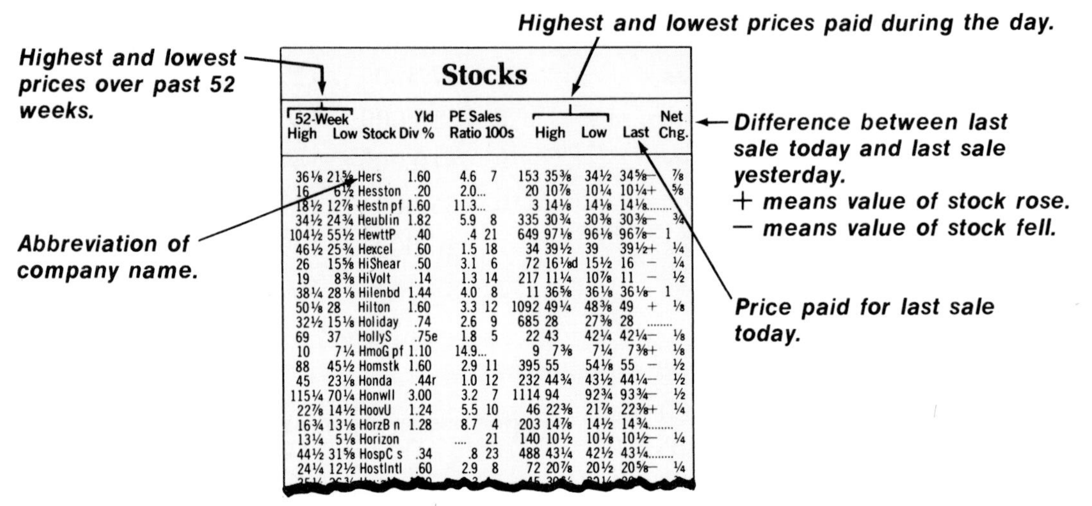

Stocks

52-Week High	52-Week Low	Stock	Div	Yld %	PE Ratio	Sales 100s	High	Low	Last	Net Chg.
36⅛	21⅝	Hers	1.60	4.6	7	153	35⅜	34½	34⅝	− ⅞
16	6½	Hesston	.20	2.0	...	20	10⅞	10¼	10¼	+ ⅝
18½	12⅞	Hestn pf	1.60	11.3	...	3	14⅛	14⅛	14⅛	....
34½	24¾	Heublin	1.82	5.9	8	335	30¾	30⅜	30⅜	− ¾
104½	55½	HewttP	.40	.4	21	649	97⅛	96⅛	96⅞	− 1
46½	25¾	Hexcel	.60	1.5	18	34	39½	39	39½	+ ¼
26	15⅝	HiShear	.50	3.1	6	72	16⅛d	15½	16	− ¼
19	8⅜	HiVolt	.14	1.3	14	217	11¼	10⅞	11	− ½
38¼	28⅛	Hilenbd	1.44	4.0	8	11	36⅝	36⅛	36⅛	− 1
50⅛	28	Hilton	1.60	3.3	12	1092	49¼	48⅜	49	+ ⅛
32½	15⅛	Holiday	.74	2.6	9	685	28	27⅜	28	....
69	37	HollyS	.75e	1.8	5	22	43	42¼	42¼	− ⅛
10	7¼	HmoG pf	1.10	14.9	...	9	7⅜	7¼	7⅜	+ ⅛
88	45½	Homstk	1.60	2.9	11	395	55	54⅛	55	− ½
45	23⅛	Honda	.44r	1.0	12	232	44¾	43½	44¼	− ½
115¼	70¼	Honwll	3.00	3.2	7	1114	94	92¾	93¾	− ½
22⅞	14½	HoovU	1.24	5.5	10	46	22⅜	21⅞	22⅜	+ ¼
16¾	13⅛	HorzB n	1.28	8.7	4	203	14⅞	14½	14¾	....
13¼	5⅛	Horizon		....	21	140	10½	10⅛	10½	− ¼
44½	31⅝	HospC s	.34	.8	23	488	43¼	42½	43¼	....
24¼	12½	HostIntl	.60	2.9	8	72	20⅞	20½	20⅝	− ¼

The total amount you pay for a stock depends on these factors.

1. The cost per share
2. The number of shares purchased
3. The stockbroker's commission

EXAMPLE 1 Michael bought 200 shares of Cosgrove Electric at $\$40\frac{5}{8}$ per share. The stockbroker charged \$90.85 for a commission. Find the total cost.

Solution: [1] $\$40\frac{5}{8} = \$40.625$ ◀ $8\overline{)5.000}$ = 0.625

Cost of Stock = Number of Shares × Cost Per Share

$= 200 \times \$40.625$

$= \mathbf{\$8125.00}$

[2] **Total Cost = Cost of Stock + Commission**

$= \$8125.00 + \$90.85$

$= \mathbf{\$8215.85}$

After completing Example 1, you may wish to have students do some or all of Exercises 1-7.

Michael also had to pay a broker's commission when he sold the stock.

EXAMPLE 2 Michael sold his 200 shares of stock at $\$43\frac{1}{4}$ per share. He paid the broker a commission of $92.80.

a. Find the amount received for the stock.

b. Find the amount of profit or loss.

Solutions: **a.** 1 $\$43\frac{1}{4} = \$43.25$ ◀ $\frac{1}{4} = .25$

Amount of Sale = Number of Shares × Selling Price

= 200 × $43.25

= **$8650.00**

2 **Amount Received = Amount of Sale − Commission**

= $8650.00 − $92.80

= **$8557.20**

b. Since the amount received is greater than the total cost of stock, Michael made a profit.

Profit = Amount Received − Total Cost

= $8557.20 − $8215.85

= **$341.35**

REVIEW OF RELATED SKILLS

You may wish to use these exercises before teaching the lesson.

Write a decimal for each fraction. (Pages 92–93)

1. $\frac{1}{8}$ 0.125 **2.** $\frac{1}{2}$ 0.5 **3.** $\frac{3}{4}$ 0.75 **4.** $\frac{3}{8}$ 0.375 **5.** $\frac{7}{8}$ 0.875 **6.** $\frac{3}{5}$ 0.6

Multiply. (Pages 8–9)

7. 100 × $23.50 $2350 **8.** 250 × $71.25 $17,812.50 **9.** 200 × $19.625 $3925 **10.** 500 × $88.875 $44,437.50

Add or subtract. (Pages 4–5)

11. $4375.00 + $67.50 $4442.50 **12.** $5816.50 + $75.18 $5891.68 **13.** $9404.95 + $110.38 $9515.33

14. $7690.00 − $68.60 $7621.40 **15.** $4775.45 − $80.09 $4695.36 **16.** $9935.48 − $8299.55 $1635.93

EXERCISES

For Exercises 1–2, find the total cost of each stock purchase. (Example 1)

	Stock	Cost Per Share	Number of Shares	Commission	Total Cost
1.	Harvest	$\$15\frac{3}{4}$	50	$32.50	? $820
2.	Central	$\$40\frac{7}{8}$	75	$58.75	? $3124.38

For Exercises 3–5, find the total cost of each stock purchase. (Example 1)

	Stock	Cost Per Share	Number of Shares	Commission	Total Cost
3.	J. Lamb, Inc.	$\$25\frac{1}{2}$	100	$52.83	? $2602.83
4.	Kent Ind.	$33	150	$80.45	? $5030.45
5.	AB Housing	$\$79\frac{1}{8}$	200	$204.21	? $16,029.21

6. Suzanne bought 100 shares of Zebra Oil at $\$62\frac{3}{4}$ per share. The commission charged was $97.46. Find the total cost of the purchase. $6372.46

7. Charlie wants to buy 200 shares of Kaytel Engineering at $\$94\frac{5}{8}$. His broker charges $238.86 as commission. Find the total cost. $19,163.86

For Exercises 8–12, find each of the following
a. The amount received for the sale of the stock
b. The amount of profit or loss (Example 2)

8. $4227.05; $309.27 profit
9. $12,135.20; $2198.34 profit
10. $35,040.64; $1739.65 loss
11. $4978.60; $517.15 profit
12. $6125.52; $761.46 loss

	Stock	Number of Shares	Buying Cost Per Share	Commission	Selling Cost Per Share	Commission
8.	Solar Power	100	$\$38\frac{1}{2}$	$67.78	$43	$72.95
9.	Denton Foods	200	$49	$136.86	$\$61\frac{1}{2}$	$164.80
10.	Quaker Ltd.	500	$\$72\frac{3}{8}$	$592.79	$\$71\frac{1}{4}$	$584.36
11.	Ashton-Hall	300	$\$14\frac{5}{8}$	$73.95	$\$16\frac{7}{8}$	$83.90
12.	Harbor Co.	75	$\$90\frac{3}{4}$	$80.73	$\$82\frac{3}{4}$	$80.73

See above

13. John paid $1500, including commission, for 200 shares of stock. It is now selling for $97 per share. The commission for the sale will be $244.17. Find how much profit or loss John would make by selling the 200 shares. $17,655.83 profit

14. Suzanne decided to sell her 100 shares of Zebra Oil at $71 per share. The broker's commission was $106.68. Find the amount she received for the stock. $6993.32

More Challenging Problems

Use the stock table on page 370.

15. Tammy Chernak plans to buy 100 shares of Hexcel stock at the last price today. The broker's commission is $68.93. Find the total cost. $4018.93

16. Tammy wants to sell the shares at the high price for the last 52 weeks. The commission would be $76.98. How much profit would she make? $554.09

SECURITIES TELLER career

Career lessons are optional. This lesson applies the skills of finding a per cent of a number and using a formula.

One of Cheryl Meek's jobs as a **securities teller** is to explain to customers how to compute the interest on U.S. Savings Bonds. Most of the bonds she sells are Series EE bonds. These replace the Series E bonds which were sold before January 1, 1980.

Series EE bonds can be purchased for 50% of their face value. When held until **maturity** (eleven years), the bonds can be **redeemed** (cashed in) for their face value plus a bonus. The amount of the bonus depends on the face value of the bond. Purchasers of these bonds are supporting the Federal Government by lending it money.

EXAMPLE A Series EE bond with a face value of $1000 is held until maturity and cashed in for $1065.20. Find the interest on the investment.

Solution:

1. Find the purchase price.
   50% of $\$1000 = \frac{1}{2} \times \$1000 = \$500$ ◀ *Cost*
2. Find the interest.
   $1065.20 − $500.00 = **$565.20** ◀ *Maturity Value* − *Purchase Price* = *Interest*

EXERCISES Note that Exercises 1-4 are non-verbal.

Find the interest on each Series EE bond.

	Face Value	*Purchase Price*	*Value at Maturity*
1.	$50	? $25	$53.28 $28.28
2.	$75	? $37.50	$79.92 $42.42
3.	$100	? $50	$106.56 $56.56
4.	$150	? $75	$159.84 $84.84

5. A Series EE bond with a face value of $100 is cashed in after 3 years for $57.88. How much interest did it earn? $7.88

6. A Series EE bond with a face value of $1000 was cashed in after 9 years for $889.20. How much interest did it earn? $389.20

7. Three $50–bonds were redeemed after 6 years for a total of $110.10. How much interest did the bonds earn? $35.10

8. Four $75–bonds were redeemed 9 years after purchase for $266.76. How much interest did the bonds earn? $116.76

17-5 Dividends/Annual Yield

See the Teacher's Manual for the objectives.

When a company makes a profit, it may pay a dividend on each share of its stock. A **dividend** is the portion of the company's earnings that it pays to its stockholders. Dividends are usually paid quarterly (every 3 months).

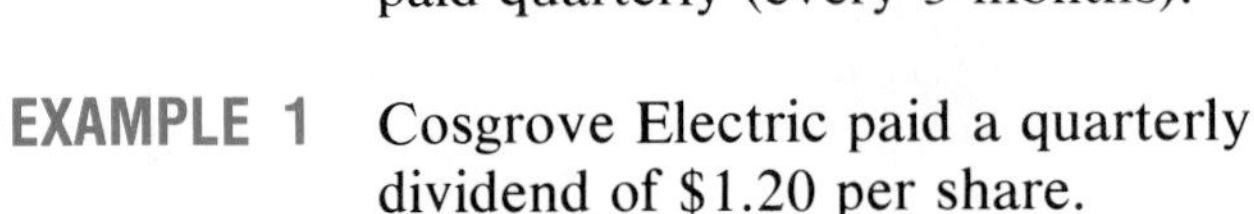

EXAMPLE 1 Cosgrove Electric paid a quarterly dividend of $1.20 per share. Find Michael's yearly dividend for 200 shares.

Solution: [1] Find the total dividends for 1 quarter (3 months).

$200 \times \$1.20 = \mathbf{\$240}$

[2] Find the yearly dividend. There are 4 quarters in 1 year.

$\$240 \times 4 = \mathbf{\$960}$

After completing Example 1, you may wish to have students do some or all of Exercises 1-12.

The per cent of your investment that you receive as income each year is called the **annual yield.** To find the annual yield, divide the annual dividend by the price per share of stock.

EXAMPLE 2 Find the annual yield on Cosgrove Electric common stock when the quarterly dividend is $1.20 per share and the price per share is $\$40\frac{5}{8}$.

Solution: [1] Annual dividend: $\$1.20 \times 4 = \mathbf{\$4.80}$

[2] **Annual Yield = Annual Dividend ÷ Price per Share**

$= \$4.80 \div \$40.625$ ◀ ***$\$40\frac{5}{8} = \$40.625$***

$= 0.1181$ ◀ ***Round to the nearest thousandth.***

$= \mathbf{11.8\%}$

REVIEW OF RELATED SKILLS

You may wish to use these exercises before teaching the lesson.

Multiply. (Pages 6–9)

1. $100 \times \$1.35$ $135 **2.** $300 \times \$2.05$ $615 **3.** $\$270 \times 4$ $1080 **4.** $\$430 \times 4$ $1720 **5.** $\$2.35 \times 4$ $9.40

Divide. Round each answer to the nearest thousandth. (Pages 16–17)

6. $\$5.20 \div \$35.625$ 0.146 **7.** $\$3.50 \div \$27.50$ 0.127 **8.** $\$1.80 \div \$25.75$ 0.070 **9.** $\$4.00 \div \$42.125$ 0.095

EXERCISES

For Exercises 1–10, find the yearly dividend. (Example 1)

	Stock	Number of Shares	Quarterly Dividend Per Share
1.	Samuels Labs	100	\$1.10 \$440
2.	CD Energy	200	\$0.85 \$680
3.	Datel	50	\$1.25 \$250
4.	Cribb Co.	100	\$2.00 \$800
5.	Sands Fuel	75	\$0.90 \$270

	Stock	Number of Shares	Quarterly Dividend Per Share
6.	Skinner	200	\$1.15 \$920
7.	Sorenson Data	150	\$1.40 \$840
8.	Bliss Ind.	100	\$0.75 \$300
9.	Telco	300	\$0.60 \$720
10.	Dimex	500	\$1.20 \$2400

11. Brian owns 300 shares of Computex stock. The company pays a quarterly dividend of \$1.25 per share. Find the yearly dividend. \$1500

12. Claire has 250 shares of Lynn Company stock. Lynn pays a quarterly dividend of \$0.85 per share. Find Claire's yearly dividend. \$850

For Exercises 13–22, find the annual yield on each stock. (Example 2)

	Stock	Price Per Share	Quarterly Dividend Per Share
13.	Barber	$\$34\frac{1}{2}$	\$0.75 8.7%
14.	Connell Intl.	\$43	\$1.10 10.2%
15.	DBC, Inc.	$\$25\frac{7}{8}$	\$0.50 7.7%
16.	Sawyer Co.	$\$50\frac{3}{8}$	\$1.25 9.9%
17.	Finch	$\$35\frac{1}{4}$	\$1.05 11.9%

	Stock	Price Per Share	Quarterly Dividend Per Share
18.	Tanner Data	$\$65\frac{1}{8}$	\$1.15 7.1%
19.	Stretz Aviation	$\$71\frac{1}{4}$	\$1.00 5.6%
20.	Lopez Ind.	$\$45\frac{3}{4}$	\$0.90 7.9%
21.	Pound	\$59	\$1.25 8.5%
22.	Surf, Ltd.	$\$91\frac{7}{8}$	\$1.25 5.4%

23. Tina owns shares of Skyline stock, which she bought at $\$42\frac{1}{8}$ per share. The company pays a quarterly dividend of \$1.30 per share. Find the annual yield on the Skyline stock. 12.3%

24. Sam owns some stock in Hart Industries, which pays a quarterly dividend of \$1.05 per share. Find the annual yield on the stock, which Sam bought at $\$51\frac{3}{4}$ per share. 8.1%

25. Mary has some Tamber Company stock, which she bought at $\$22\frac{5}{8}$ per share. Tamber pays a quarterly dividend of \$0.60 per share. Find the annual yield. 10.6%

17-6 Bonds

See the Teacher's Manual for the objectives.

Many corporations and governments raise money by selling bonds. When you purchase a bond, you are lending money to the corporation or government. The prices of bonds are given as a percent of face value. The **face value** is the amount printed on the bond.

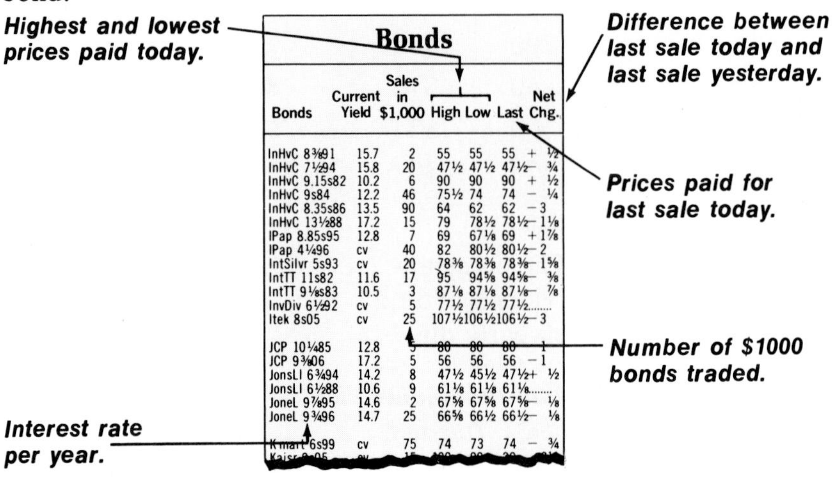

Bonds

Bonds	Current Yield	Sales in $1,000	High	Low	Last	Net Chg.
InHvC 8⅜91	15.7	2	55	55	55	+ ½
InHvC 7½94	15.8	20	47½	47½	47½	− ¾
InHvC 9.15s82	10.2	6	90	90	90	+ ½
InHvC 9s84	12.2	46	75½	74	74	− ¼
InHvC 8.35s86	13.5	90	64	62	62	− 3
InHvC 13½88	17.2	15	79	78½	78½	− 1⅛
IPap 8.85s95	12.8	7	69	67⅛	69	+ 1⅞
IPap 4¼96	cv	40	82	80½	80½	− 2
IntSilvr 5s93	cv	20	78⅜	78⅜	78⅜	− 1⅝
IntTT 11s82	11.6	17	95	94⅝	94⅝	− ⅜
IntTT 9⅛s83	10.5	3	87⅛	87⅛	87⅛	− ⅞
InvDiv 6½92	cv	5	77½	77½	77½	....
Itek 8s05	cv	25	107½	106½	106½	− 3
JCP 10¼85	12.8	5	80	80	80	1
JCP 9⅜06	17.2	5	56	56	56	− 1
JonsLI 6¾94	14.2	8	47½	45½	47½	+ ½
JonsLI 6½88	10.6	9	61⅛	61⅛	61⅛	....
JoneL 9⅞95	14.6	2	67⅝	67⅝	67⅝	− ⅛
JoneL 9¾96	14.7	25	66⅝	66½	66½	− ⅛
Kmart 6s99	cv	75	74	73	74	− ¾

EXAMPLE 1 Find the high price of a $1000 bond in InHvC. The listed high of the day is $47\frac{1}{2}$.

Solution: $47\frac{1}{2}$ means $47\frac{1}{2}\%$.

$\$1000 \times 0.475 = \mathbf{\$475}$

After completing Example 1, you may wish to have students do some or all of Exercises 1-10.

Bondholders receive interest on their bonds. The interest is usually paid twice a year.

To find the **current yield** of a bond, you divide the yearly interest by the market price. The **market price** is the price you would expect to pay for a bond.

EXAMPLE 2 Laura Taylor bought a $1000 bond that pays $30 in interest every six months. The market price is $485. Find the current yield.

Solution: [1] Yearly Interest: $\$30 \times 2 = \mathbf{\$60}$

[2] **Current Yield = Yearly Interest ÷ Market Price**

$= \$60 \div \$485$

$= 0.1237$ ◀ *Round to the nearest thousandth.*

$= \mathbf{12.4\%}$

REVIEW OF RELATED SKILLS You may wish to use these exercises before teaching the lesson.

Multiply. (Pages 8–9)

1. $\$1000 \times 0.615$ $615
2. $\$1000 \times 0.355$ $355
3. $\$5000 \times 0.6625$ $3312.50
4. $\$3000 \times 0.41625$ $1248.75

Divide. Round each answer to the nearest thousandth. (Pages 16–17)

5. $\$40 \div \$620$ 0.065
6. $\$75 \div \$455$ 0.165
7. $\$115 \div \$905$ 0.127
8. $\$92 \div \$725$ 0.127

EXERCISES

For Exercises 1–8, find the day's high price for each $1000 bond. (Example 1)

	Bond	Listed High	High Price
1.	JCP	56	? $560
2.	IPap	82	? $820
3.	K mart	74	? $740
4.	InvDiv	$77\frac{1}{2}$	? $775
5.	JonsLI	$61\frac{1}{8}$	? $611.25
6.	IntSilvr	$78\frac{3}{8}$	? $783.75
7.	IntTT	$87\frac{1}{8}$	? $871.25
8.	Itek	$107\frac{1}{2}$	? $1075

9. Seven Industries issued a bond with a face value of $1000. The newspaper gives $68\frac{3}{4}$ as the last price for today. Find the last price. $687.50

10. A CF Electric bond with a face value of $5000 has a listed low today of $72\frac{7}{8}$. Find the low price of a CF Electric bond. $3643.75

For Exercises 11–18, find the current yield of each bond. Round your answer to the nearest tenth of a per cent. (Example 2)

	6-Month Interest	Market Price	Current Yield
11.	$45	$725	? 12.4%
12.	$25	$610	? 8.2%
13.	$30	$530	? 11.3%
14.	$75	$955	? 15.7%
15.	$60	$765	? 15.7%
16.	$55	$840	? 13.1%
17.	$95	$940	? 20.2%
18.	$80	$985	? 16.2%

19. Bruce Betz bought a $1000 bond that pays $40 in interest every six months. The market price of the bond is $580. Find the current yield. 13.8%

20. Serena Ping has a $5000 bond that pays $260 in interest twice a year. The market price of the bond is $4125. Find the current yield. 12.6%

INVESTMENT COUNSELOR

Career lessons are optional. This lesson combines the skills of reading financial tables and using formulas.

Investment counselors advise people how to invest their money. One common form of investment is a <u>mutual fund</u>. A **mutual fund** combines the investments of many customers to buy various stocks and bonds.

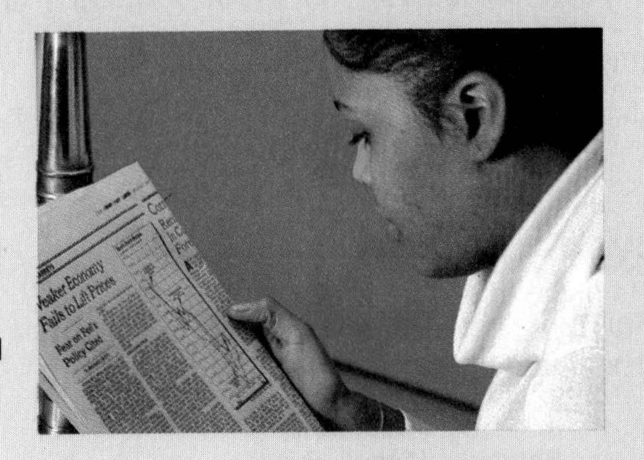

Investors buy shares in a mutual fund and receive dividends. The value of a share changes daily and can be found in the business section of daily newspapers.

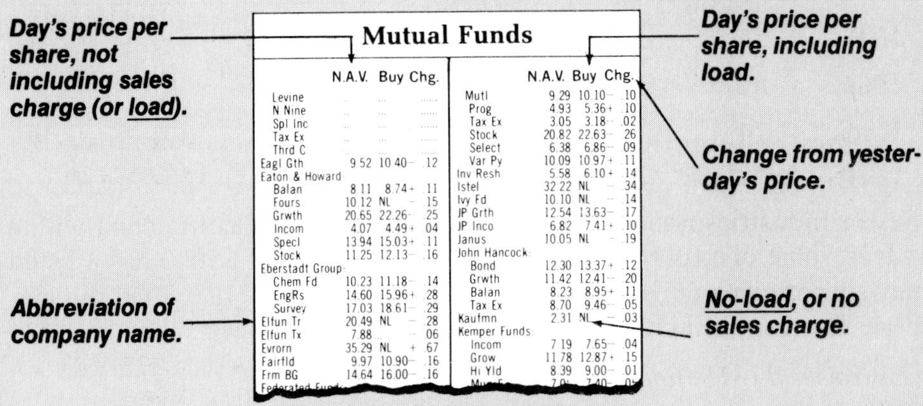

Mutual Funds

	N.A.V.	Buy	Chg.
Levine	...	...	......
N Nine	...	...	......
Spl Inc	...	...	......
Tax Ex	...	...	......
Thrd C	...	...	......
Eagl Gth	9.52	10.40	− .12
Eaton & Howard:			
Balan	8.11	8.74	+ .11
Fours	10.12	NL	− .15
Grwth	20.65	22.26	− .25
Incom	4.07	4.49	+ .04
Specl	13.94	15.03	+ .11
Stock	11.25	12.13	− .16
Eberstadt Group:			
Chem Fd	10.23	11.18	− .14
EngRs	14.60	15.96	+ .28
Survey	17.03	18.61	− .29
Elfun Tr	20.49	NL	− .28
Elfun Tx	7.88	...	− .06
Evrorn	35.29	NL	+ .67
Fairfld	9.97	10.90	− .16
Frm BG	14.64	16.00	− .16

	N.A.V.	Buy	Chg.
Mutl	9.29	10.10	− .10
Prog	4.93	5.36	+ .10
Tax Ex	3.05	3.18	− .02
Stock	20.82	22.63	− .26
Select	6.38	6.86	− .09
Var Py	10.09	10.97	+ .11
Inv Resh	5.58	6.10	+ .14
Istel	32.22	NL	− .34
Ivy Fd	10.10	NL	− .14
JP Grth	12.54	13.63	− .17
JP Inco	6.82	7.41	+ .10
Janus	10.05	NL	− .19
John Hancock:			
Bond	12.30	13.37	+ .12
Grwth	11.42	12.41	− .20
Balan	8.23	8.95	+ .11
Tax Ex	8.70	9.46	− .05
Kaufmn	2.31	NL	− .03
Kemper Funds:			
Incom	7.19	7.65	− .04
Grow	11.78	12.87	+ .15
Hi Yld	8.39	9.00	− .01

Prices as of December 31

EXAMPLE 1 Suzanne Ramos, an investment counselor, advises the Petersons to invest in Eagl Gth mutual funds. Find the number of shares, to the nearest ten thousandth, that the Petersons can buy with a \$1500 investment.

Solution:

$$\textbf{Number of Shares} = \textbf{Amount Invested} \div \textbf{Price Per Share}$$

$$= \$1500 \div \$10.40$$

◀ ***Find the buying price, including sales charge, from the table.***

$$= 144.23077$$

The Petersons can buy **144.2308 shares** of Eagl Gth.

Suzanne advised Jim and Kris Massina to invest in an **Individual Retirement Account (IRA).** Individual investors may pay up to \$2000 into an IRA each year. The amount invested and the interest earned are not taxed until retirement.

EXAMPLE 2 Suzanne suggested that Jim and Kris invest $2000 each in an IRA with Istel mutual funds. The buying price per share was $28.80. The Massinas reinvested their dividends in Istel and bought another 14.0041 shares during the year. Use the table to find the value of their investment at the end of the year.

Solution:

1. Find the amount of shares the Massinas bought.

   $4000 ÷ $28.80 = 138.8889 shares

2. Find the total number of shares they owned by the end of the year.

   138.8889 + 14.0041 = 152.8930 shares

3. Use the table to find the value of the shares at the end of the year.

   Number of Shares × **Price per Share** = **Value of Shares**

   152.8930 × $32.22 = $4926.2125 ◀ ***Round to the nearest cent.***

The value of the Massinas' investment is about **$4926.21.**

EXERCISES

Find the number of shares, to the nearest ten thousandth, that can be bought for $2500. (Example 1)

1. Inv Resh 409.8361
2. Eberstadt Chem Fd 223.6136
3. Kemper Hi Yld 277.7778
4. Eaton & Howard Incom 556.7929
5. John Hancock Grwth 201.4504
6. Fairfld 229.3578

For Exercises 7–12, use the table to find the value of each investment at the end of the year. Round the answer to the nearest cent. (Example 2)

7. 100 shares of Istel $3222
8. 200 shares of JP Grth $2508
9. 125 shares of Elfun Tr $2561.25
10. 1000 shares of Kaufmn $2310
11. 375 shares of Frm BG $5490
12. 2050 shares of Eagl Gth $19,516

13. Jack Darwin advised Juan to invest in JP Grth mutual funds. Juan has $1000 to invest. How many shares, to the nearest ten thousandth, can he buy? 73.3676

14. Henry invested $2000 in an IRA with Inv Resh mutual funds. He reinvested his dividends and bought another 12.5 shares during the year. Use the table to find the value of Henry's investment at the end of the year. $1899.26

Rounding and Estimation

Consumers use rounding and estimation to solve problems related to investing money.

EXERCISES See the Teacher's Manual for the objectives.

Skills

Choose the best estimate. Choose a, b, or c.

1. 22×8.91 b — a. 20×8 b. 20×9 c. 30×9
2. 49×198.16 a — a. 50×200 b. 40×200 c. 50×100
3. $40\frac{1}{8} \times 293$ c — a. 50×200 b. 40×200 c. 40×300
4. $78\frac{7}{8} \times 401$ b — a. 80×500 b. 80×400 c. 70×400
5. $6786.70 - 6395.20$ a — a. $6800 - 6400$ b. $6700 - 6400$ c. $6800 - 6300$
6. $8809.18 - 8193.75$ b — a. $8900 - 8100$ b. $8800 - 8200$ c. $8800 - 8100$
7. $3379.14 + 98.62$ a — a. $3400 + 100$ b. $3400 + 0$ c. $3300 + 100$

Choose the best estimate. Choose a, b, c, or d.

8. 31×9.86 c — a. 240 b. 270 c. 300 d. 330
9. 59×287.98 a — a. 18,000 b. 24,000 c. 10,000 d. 12,000
10. $39\frac{7}{8} \times 405$ b — a. 12,000 b. 16,000 c. 18,000 d. 14,000
11. $81\frac{1}{4} \times 296$ b — a. 20,000 b. 24,000 c. 16,000 d. 22,000
12. $3806.14 - 3189.72$ a — a. 600 b. 500 c. 700 d. 800
13. $6488.08 - 5522.70$ c — a. 1200 b. 800 c. 1000 d. 1100
14. $2103.16 + 104.73$ d — a. 2400 b. 2300 c. 2000 d. 2200

Applications

15. Gabriel Garcia buys a $30,000 term life insurance policy. The premium per $1000 for one year is $6.91. Estimate the total yearly premium. c
    a. $30 \times \$6.00$
    b. $30 \times \$6.50$
    c. $30 \times \$7.00$
    d. $30 \times \$7.50$

16. Marita Bauer purchases $20,000 worth of straight-life insurance. Its cash value per $1000 after 10 years is $103.20. Estimate the total cash value. a
    a. $20 \times \$100$
    b. $10 \times \$100$
    c. $20 \times \$110$
    d. $10 \times \$110$

17. Jim Baker bought 290 shares of stock at $\$39\frac{7}{8}$. Estimate the cost. b

a. $300 \times \$30$ b. $300 \times \$40$

c. $200 \times \$40$ d. $200 \times \$30$

18. The listed high of the day on a $2000 bond in Teltex Inc was $68\frac{7}{8}$. Estimate the high price. c

a. $\$2000 \times 0.60$ b. $\$2000 \times 1.00$

c. $\$2000 \times 0.70$ c. $\$2000 \times 0.50$

19. Hugo Small buys a $20,000 term life insurance policy. The premium per $1000 for one year is $7.05. Estimate the total yearly premium. c

a. $120 b. $130

c. $140 d. $150

20. Beverly Lamberti purchases $40,000 worth of straight-life insurance. Its cash value per $1000 after 15 years is $197.46. Estimate the total cash value. a

a. $8000 b. $6000

c. $9000 d. $7000

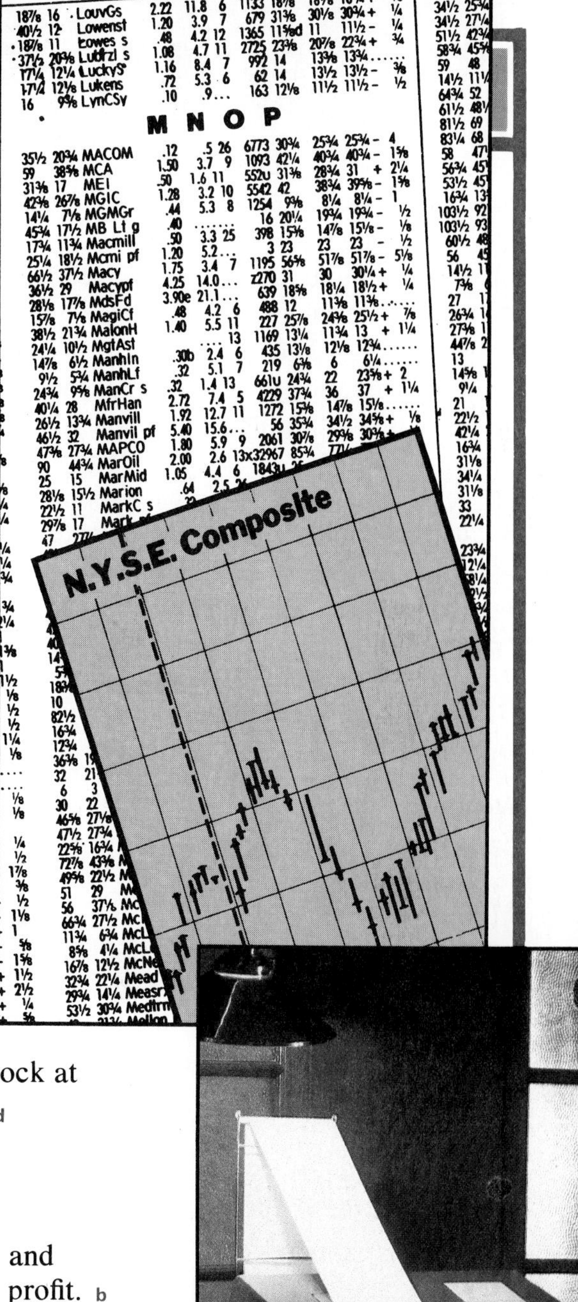

21. Marilyn Sutter bought 310 shares of stock at $\$48\frac{3}{4}$. Estimate the cost of the stock. d

a. $12,000 b. $20,000

c. $10,000 d. $15,000

22. Flora Engel bought stock for $3210.64 and later sold it for $3890.75. Estimate the profit. b

a. $600 b. $700 c. $800 d. $500

23. Amtel Corp. pays a quarterly dividend of $0.52 per share. Estimate the yearly dividend for 100 shares. a

a. $200 b. $100 c. $220 d. $50

Chapter Review

These exercises review the vocabulary, skills and applications presented in the chapter as a preparation for the chapter test.

Part 1: VOCABULARY

For Exercises 1–5, choose from the box at the right the word(s) that complete(s) each statement.

term
annual yield
straight-life
dividend
market price
premium

1. Life insurance that gives financial protection for a specific term, such as 5 years, is called __?__ insurance. (Pages 360–362) term
2. Life insurance that gives financial protection over the entire life of the policy holder is called __?__ insurance. (Pages 360–362) straight-life
3. A portion of a company's earnings that it pays to its stockholders is a __?__. (Pages 374–375) dividend
4. The per cent of your stock investment that you receive as income each year is called __?__. (Pages 374–375) annual yield
5. The price you would expect to pay for a bond is the __?__ of the bond. (Pages 376–377) market price

Part 2: SKILLS

Divide. (Pages 12–13)

6. $74,000 ÷ 1000 $74 **7.** $83,000 ÷ 1000 $83 **8.** $96,000 ÷ 1000 $96 **9.** $122,000 ÷ 1000 $122

Multiply. (Pages 8–9)

10. 36 × $3.19 $114.84 **11.** 45 × $2.10 $94.50 **12.** $642.13 × 5 $3210.65 **13.** $381.20 × 15 $5718

14. 200 × $62.70 $12,540 **15.** 150 × $96.40 $14,460 **16.** $1000 × 1.1507 $1150.70 **17.** $5000 × 1.3241 $6620.50

Divide. Round each answer to the nearest dollar. (Pages 16–17)

18. $64.20 ÷ 12 $5 **19.** $85.14 ÷ 12 $7 **20.** $96.34 ÷ 12 $8 **21.** $44.28 ÷ 12 $4

Add or subtract as indicated. (Pages 2–5)

22. $4300.21 + $74.85 $4375.06 **23.** $6428.36 + $89.78 $6518.14 **24.** $5642 − $5000 $642

25. $4876 − $4000 $876 **26.** $2538.16 − $64.38 $2473.78 **27.** $3148.95 − $112.13 $3036.82

Write a decimal for each fraction. (Pages 92–93)

28. $\frac{1}{2}$ 0.5 **29.** $\frac{3}{8}$ 0.375 **30.** $\frac{4}{5}$ 0.8 **31.** $\frac{2}{3}$ $0.\overline{6}$ **32.** $\frac{3}{4}$ 0.75 **33.** $\frac{2}{5}$ 0.4

Divide. Round each answer to the nearest thousandth. (Pages 16–17)

34. 3.25 ÷ 46.50 0.070 **35.** 6.40 ÷ 57.80 0.111 **36.** 2.35 ÷ 37.25 0.063

37. 45 ÷ 572 0.079 **38.** 30 ÷ 380 0.079 **39.** 65 ÷ 725 0.090

Part 3: APPLICATIONS

For Exercises 40–41, use the table on page 360. (Pages 360–362)

40. Rita Gordon buys a five-year term insurance policy worth $20,000. She is 30 years old. Find the yearly premium. **$103.20**

41. Richard Guerra buys a ten-year term insurance policy worth $65,000. He is 35 years old. Find the yearly premium. **$377.65**

For Exercises 42–45, find the cash value of each straight-life insurance policy for the given number of years. Use the table on page 361. (Pages 360–362)

	Face Value	Terms	Cash Value
42.	$25,000	5 years	? $951.50
43.	$40,000	10 years	? $4405.20
44.	$36,000	10 years	? $3964.68
45.	$65,000	20 years	? $18,558.15

For Exercises 46–47, use the table on page 363. (Pages 363–365)

46. Laureen is 25 years old. She plans to buy a $40,000 20-year payment life insurance policy. Find the total amount she will pay in premiums over 20 years. **$20,128**

47. Jeffrey, who is 30, wants to buy 20-year endowment life insurance. He wants to spend no more than $35 per month. How much insurance can Jefffrey buy? **$9000**

For Exercises 48–49, use the table at the right. (Pages 368–369)

Growth of $1.00 at Interest Compounded Daily

Yearly Rate	Interest Period: 6 Months	One Year	18 Months
12%	1.0618	1.1274	1.1971
14%	1.0725	1.1502	1.2336
16%	1.0833	1.1734	1.2711

48. Sonia invested $8600 in a one-year certificate of deposit paying 14% compounded daily. How much will the certificate pay after one year? **$9891.72**

49. Ray invested $12,000 in a six-month certificate of deposit paying 16% compounded daily. How much interest will Ray receive? **$999.60**

50. Henry bought 200 shares of Comax Ltd. at $\$51\frac{3}{4}$ per share. The commission charged was $85.21. Find the total cost. **$10,435.21** (Pages 370–372)

51. Paula owns Pelco stock, which she bought at $\$31\frac{3}{8}$ per share. Pelco pays a quarterly dividend of $0.75 per share. Find the annual yield. (Pages 374–375) **9.6%**

52. The listed high of the day on a certain $1000 bond was $82\frac{1}{8}$. Estimate the high price. **b** (Pages 380–381)

a. $700 **b.** $800 **c.** $900 **d.** $1000

53. Shares of a certain stock were bought for $4804 and then sold for $5195. Estimate the profit. **c** (Pages 380–381)

a. $300 **b.** $200 **c.** $400 **d.** $500

Chapter Test

The Teacher's Resource Book contains two forms of each chapter test.

Divide. Round each answer as indicated.

1. \$84.45 ÷ 12; nearest dollar \$7

2. \$63.04 ÷ 15; nearest dollar \$4

3. 4.06 ÷ 53.40; nearest thousandth 0.076

4. 55 ÷ 605; nearest thousandth 0.091

Multiply.

5. 36 × \$4.27 \$153.72

6. \$382.03 × 5 \$1910.15

7. 200 × \$48.60 \$9720

8. \$5000 × 1.0512 \$5256

Add or subtract as indicated.

9. \$6425.09 + \$87.42 \$6512.51

10. \$5800 + \$75.46 \$5875.46

11. \$6400 − \$6000 \$400

12. \$4239 − \$4000 \$239

13. \$3695.21 − \$74.86 \$3620.35

14. \$7293.55 − \$128.30 \$7165.25

Write a decimal for each fraction.

15. $\frac{1}{3}$ $0.33\frac{1}{3}$

16. $\frac{1}{5}$ 0.2

17. $\frac{3}{10}$ 0.3

18. $\frac{9}{10}$ 0.9

19. $\frac{4}{5}$ 0.8

20. $\frac{7}{8}$ 0.875

21. Joel plans to buy a 20-year endowment life insurance policy worth \$25,000. The yearly premium per \$1000 is \$47.42. Find the total amount he will pay in premiums over 20 years. \$23,710

22. Ima buys a 5-year term insurance policy worth \$30,000. The yearly premium per \$1000 is \$5.59. Find the total yearly premium. \$167.70

23. Hollis invested \$10,000 in a 6-month certificate of deposit that pays 14% compounded daily. At this rate, \$1 grows to \$1.0725 in 6 months. Find how much the certificate will pay at the end of 6 months. \$10,725

24. Jeanne bought 300 shares of Winlock stock at $\$49\frac{1}{4}$ per share. The commission charged was \$120.16. Find the total cost. \$14,895.16

25. A Consolidated Utilities bond with a face value of \$4000 has a listed price of $90\frac{1}{8}$. d

Estimate the high price of the bond.

a. \$3000 **b.** \$3400

c. \$3200 **d.** \$3600

Additional Practice

You may wish to use some or all of these exercises depending on how well students performed on the formal chapter test.

Skills

Divide. Round each answer as indicated. (Pages 16–17)

1. $65.50 ÷ 12; nearest dollar $5
2. $79.72 ÷ 12; nearest dollar $7
3. 5.40 ÷ 48.90; nearest thousandth 0.110
4. 7.60 ÷ 69.80; nearest thousandth 0.109
5. 60 ÷ 420; nearest thousandth 0.143
6. 120 ÷ 3600; nearest thousandth 0.033

Perform the indicated operation. (Pages 6–9, 2–5)

7. 30 × $6.80 $204
8. 45 × $1.96 $88.20
9. $164.80 × 25 $4120
10. $380.45 × 20 $7609
11. 200 × $1.85 $370
12. 150 × $3.90 $585
13. $1000 × 1.1032 $1103.20
14. $2000 × 1.2314 $2462.80
15. $6400 + $76.50 $6476.50
16. $4832.50 − $4000.00 $832.50
17. $7631.56 − $322.78 $7308.78

Write a decimal for each fraction. (Pages 92–93)

18. $\frac{3}{10}$ 0.3
19. $\frac{4}{5}$ 0.8
20. $\frac{5}{8}$ 0.625
21. $\frac{2}{3}$ $0.\overline{6}$
22. $\frac{2}{7}$ 0.286
23. $\frac{3}{5}$ 0.6

Applications

24. Ava buys a five-year term insurance policy worth $35,000. Her yearly premium per $1000 is $5.16. What is the total amount she will pay for premiums over five years? (Pages 360–362) $903

25. Miguel purchases $15,000 worth of straight-life insurance. After 15 years the cash value per $1000 is $192.84. Find the total cash value. (Pages 360–362) $2892.60

26. Jo is planning to buy 20-year payment life insurance. The yearly premium per $1000 is $27.63. What is the total amount in premiums she will pay for a $35,000 policy? (Pages 363–365) $19,341

27. Yvonne invested $3000 in an 18-month certificate of deposit that pays 12% compounded daily. At that rate, $1 grows to $1.1971 in 18 months. Find the interest earned in 18 months. (Pages 368–369) $591.30

28. Vincent owns shares of Hitech stock, which he bought at 36\frac{1}{4}$ per share. The company pays a quarterly dividend of $1.20 per share. Find the annual yield. (Pages 374–375) 13.2%

29. Eugene bought a $1000 bond issued by Chemco that pays $40 in interest every six months. The market price of the bond is $678. Find the current yield of the bond. (Pages 376–377) 11.8%

30. Louisa bought stock for $4204.60, including commission. She later sold it for $5095.12, after commission. Estimate the profit. c (Pages 380–381)

    a. $700 **b.** $800 **c.** $900 **d.** $1000

31. Antonia bought 205 shares of stock at 39\frac{1}{2}$. Estimate the total cost of the stock. (Pages 380–381) b

    a. $6000 **b.** $8000
    c. $80,000 **d.** $800

We suggest that some or all of this page be reviewed before proceeding with the chapter.

REVIEW OF RELATED SKILLS FOR CHAPTER 18

Find the average (or mean). (Pages 118–119)

1. $14.00; $24.00; $16.00; $28.00 $20.50 **2.** $47.00; $56.00; $29.00; $42.00 $43.50
3. $18.60; $31.20; $39.40; $20.00 $27.30 **4.** $56.80; $99.30; $9.40; $62.70 $57.05
5. $79.97; $18.06; $48.65; $60.24 $51.73 **6.** $31.48; $31.41; $29.58; $34.01 $31.62

Round each number to the nearest dollar. (Pages 16–17)

7. $80.20 $80 **8.** $17.16 $17 **9.** $98.73 $100 **10.** $214.48 $214 **11.** $471.52 $472

Make a circle graph to show the data. (Pages 116–117)

12. **Composition of the Earth's Atmosphere**

Element	Per Cent
Nitrogen	78 281°
Oxygen	20 72°
Argon and Other Gases	2 7°

13. **Age of People in Sayville**

Age (years)	Per Cent
15 and below	17 61°
16–30	21 76°
31–45	22 79°
46–60	16 58°
Over 60	24 86°

Multiply. (Pages 8–9)

14. $800 × 0.15 $120 **15.** $450 × 0.20 $90 **16.** $620 × 0.35 $217 **17.** $740 × 0.05 $37
18. $900 × 0.26 $234 **19.** $1200 × 0.48 $576 **20.** $580 × 0.80 $464 **21.** $1400 × 0.70 $980
22. $620 × 0.75 $465 **23.** $413.50 × 0.80 $330.80 **24.** $98.78 × 0.70 $69.15 **25.** $1682 × 0.75 $1261.50

Write a per cent for each fraction. (Pages 92–93)

26. $\frac{1}{2}$ 50% **27.** $\frac{7}{10}$ 70% **28.** $\frac{1}{3}$ $33\frac{1}{3}$% **29.** $\frac{4}{5}$ 80% **30.** $\frac{3}{4}$ 75% **31.** $\frac{1}{6}$ $16\frac{2}{3}$%

Subtract. (Pages 2–3)

32. $860 − $50 $810 **33.** $912 − $100 $812 **34.** $1420 − $100 $1320 **35.** $87 − $50 $37
36. $607 − $490 $117 **37.** $811 − $344 $467 **38.** $1140 − $948 $192 **39.** $1250 − $904 $346
40. $2300 − $1740 $560 **41.** $1791 − $1548 $243 **42.** $1302 − $884 $418 **43.** $1800 − $1105 $695

Add. (Pages 2–3)

44. $690 + $390 $1080 **45.** $720 + $350 $1070 **46.** $800 + 450 $1250 **47.** $950 + $510 $1460
48. $422 + $204 $626 **49.** $817 + $530 $1347 **50.** $796 + $208 $1004 **51.** $666 + $222 $888
52. $1600 + $901 $2501 **53.** $1407 + $812 $2219 **54.** $1515 + $396 $1911 **55.** $2095 + $889 $2984

CHAPTER

18 BUDGETING MONEY

CONSUMER SKILLS/APPLICATIONS

18-1 Preparing a Budget
18-2 Average Spending
18-3 Health Insurance
18-4 Adjusting a Budget
Rounding and Estimation

CAREER APPLICATIONS

Statistical Clerk
Financial Counselor

18-1 Preparing a Budget

See the Teacher's Manual for the objectives.

A **budget** is a plan for balancing income and expenses. **Fixed expenses,** such as mortgage and car payments, remain the same from month to month. **Variable expenses,** such as electricity and telephone bills, are those that change from one month to the next.

To find how much to budget for a variable expense, you keep a record of the amount spent for that item over several months. Then you find the average for that number of months.

MONTHLY BUDGET	
FIXED EXPENSES	
Mortgage payment:	$285
Property taxes:	$100
Car payments:	$121
Insurance:	$ 75
VARIABLE EXPENSES	
Food:	$425
Clothing:	$ 75
Electricity:	$ 42
Telephone:	$ 20
Recreation:	$ 40
Savings:	$100
Credit card payment:	$ 35

EXAMPLE Over the last five months, the Kendrichs' electricity bills amounted to $82.75, $79.60, $75.30, $76.80, and $80.35. How much should they budget for electricity each month?

Solution:

$$\text{Average} = \frac{\text{Sum of Items}}{\text{Number of Items}}$$

$$= \frac{\$82.75 + \$79.60 + \$75.30 + \$76.80 + \$80.35}{5}$$

$$= \frac{\$394.80}{5}$$

$$= \$78.96$$

Round to the nearest whole dollar.

The Kendrichs should budget **$79** per month for electricity.

REVIEW OF RELATED SKILLS

You may wish to use these exercises before teaching the lesson.

Find the average (or mean). (Pages 118–119)

1. $15.20; $17.95; $24.04; $16.45 $18.41

2. $32.30; $28.50; $29.94; $37.06 $31.95

3. $79.95; $68.13; $70.06; $61.18 $69.83

4. $104.44; $125.65; $98.62; $120.73 $112.36

Round to the nearest dollar. (Pages 16–17)

5. $115.27 $115 **6.** $135.98 $136 **7.** $129.59 $130 **8.** $188.91 $189 **9.** $204.30 $204 **10.** $195.25 $195

EXERCISES

For Exercises 1–6, find how much to budget each month for each variable expense. Round each answer to the nearest dollar.

	Expense	Amount Spent Last 4 Months
1.	Telephone $28	$27.30; $18.06; $35.42; $30.94
2.	Recreation $32	$29.05; $50.25; $14.43; $32.27
3.	Savings $49	$50.00; $70.50; $35.00; $38.50

	Expense	Amount Spent Last 4 Months
4.	Gasoline $88	$72.80; $104.95; $83.36; $90.13
5.	Food $298	$294.36; $330.53; $267.85; $301.14
6.	Dry cleaning $30	$29.45; $37.12; $32.66; $22.09

For Exercises 7–12, round each answer to the nearest dollar.

7. Paul Chou's five most recent telephone bills amounted to $33.78, $90.40, $52.14, $45.67, and $39.91. Find how much Paul should budget for the telephone each month. $52

8. Over the last five months, Cindy Simpson has spent $91.04, $25.60, $72.38, $69.50, and $58.83 on clothing. How much should she budget for clothing? $63

9. The Paulov family spent the following amounts over the last five months for commuter costs: $58.50, $72.15, $60.45, $66.70, and $61.30. Find how much they should budget for commuting each month. $64

10. Fernando Sanchez wants to make a monthly budget for miscellaneous expenses. He has spent $42.55, $21.42, $18.58, $36.69, and $40.31 during the past five months. Find his monthly budget. $32

11. Mrs. Ashford has spent the following amounts during the last five months on food: $240.22, $276.17, $255.47, $285.68, and $246.91. How much should she budget for groceries? $261

12. Tony Dentico kept records of his last five fuel company bills: $117.50, $99.67, $131.12, $125.66, and $116.90. How much should Tony budget for monthly fuel costs? $118

More Challenging Problems

For Exercises 13–15, refer to the sample budget on page 388. Round each answer to the nearest tenth.

13. What per cent of the total budget are the property taxes? 7.6%

14. What per cent of the total budget are the fixed expenses? 44.1%

15. What per cent of the total budget are the variable expenses? 55.9%

18-2 Average Spending

See the Teacher's Manual for the objectives.

It is sometimes helpful to compare a family budget with standard budgets suggested by a government or consumer agency. Remember that standard budgets usually have to be adapted to fit family or personal needs.

Here are two sample standard budgets for families of four persons.

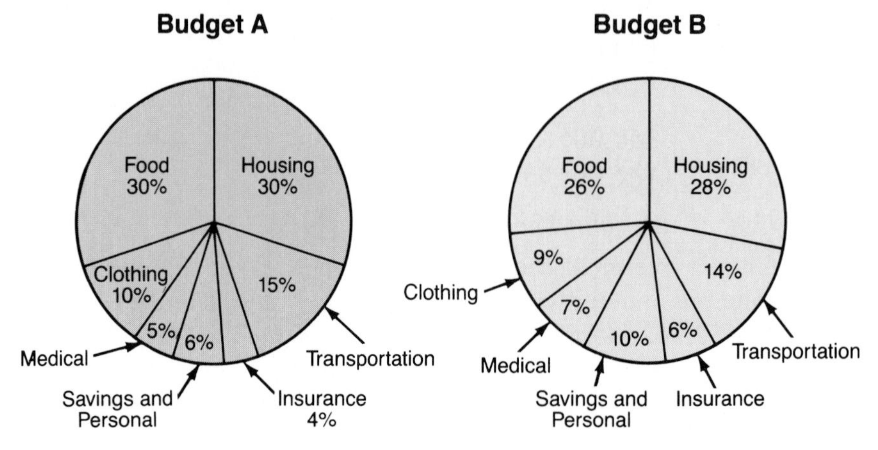

EXAMPLE 1 The Chu family's net pay per month is \$1200. How much will they budget for transportation each month if they follow Budget A?

Solution: On the graph for Budget A, 15% is budgeted for transportation.

$\$1200 \times 0.15 = \mathbf{\$180}$ ◀ ***Monthly budget for transportation***

After completing Example 1, you may wish to have students do some or all of Exercises 1-12.

The Chu family uses estimation to determine whether their spending rate for an item is above or below the rate of standard budgets.

EXAMPLE 2 The Chu family pays \$415 per month for housing. Is this above or below the per cent budgeted for housing in Budget B?

Solution: [1] Chu family rate: $\frac{415}{1200}$ is about $\frac{400}{1200}$.

$\frac{400}{1200} = \frac{1}{3} = \mathbf{33\frac{1}{3}\%}$ ◀ ***Chu family's estimated rate***

Budget B rate: 28% is about **30%**.

[2] Compare the rates: $33\frac{1}{3}\% > 30\%$

The Chu family's rate of spending for housing is **higher** than that of Standard Budget B.

REVIEW OF RELATED SKILLS

You may wish to use these exercises before teaching the lesson.

Make a circle graph to show the data. (Pages 116–117)

1. Number of Children in Sayville Households

Number of Children	Per Cent
None	18 65°
One	22 79°
Two	30 108°
Three	21 76°
Four or more	9 32°

2. U.S. Population by Region

Region	Per Cent
Northeast	22 79°
Southeast	16 58°
North Central	27 97°
South Central	16 58°
Mountain	5 18°
Pacific	14 50°

Multiply. (Pages 8–9)

3. $700 × 0.05 $35 **4.** $350 × 0.10 $35 **5.** $845 × 0.12 $101.40 **6.** $1020 × 0.22 $224.40 **7.** $1435 × 0.32 $459.20

Write a per cent for each fraction. (Pages 92–93)

8. $\frac{1}{5}$ 20% **9.** $\frac{2}{3}$ $66\frac{2}{3}$% **10.** $\frac{3}{4}$ 75% **11.** $\frac{3}{10}$ 30% **12.** $\frac{3}{8}$ $37\frac{1}{2}$% **13.** $\frac{1}{4}$ 25%

EXERCISES

For Exercises 1–12, find the amount to be budgeted for each expense. Use Budget A on page 390 as a guide. (Example 1)

	Expense	Net Pay Per Month	Monthly Budget
1.	Housing	$900	? $270
2.	Insurance	$1300	? $52
3.	Clothing	$850	? $85
4.	Food	$1620	? $486
5.	Medical	$1730	? $86.50
6.	Transportation	$2040	? $306
7.	Savings	$1935	? $116.10
8.	Medical	$1760	? $88
9.	Housing	$2305	? $691.50
10.	Food	$1965	? $589.50

11. Mr. and Mrs. Vozzo have a net monthly pay of $1350. How much should they budget for clothing? $135

12. Paula Kampas has a net monthly pay of $1045. How much will she budget each month for insurance? $41.80

For Exercises 13–14, refer to Budget B on page 390 to find how each family's expenses compare with the budget. (Example 2)

	Family	Net Pay Per Month	Expense	Amount Spent Per Month	Rate of Spending	Above/Below Budget B
13.	Winston	$1000	Food	$295	$\frac{295}{1000} \approx \frac{300}{1000} =$ 30%	? Above
14.	Takada	$800	Housing	$190	$\frac{190}{800} \approx \frac{200}{800} =$? 25 %	? Below

For Exercises 15–18, refer to Budget B on page 390 to find how each family's expenses compare with the budget. (Example 2)

	Family	Net Pay Per Month	Expense	Amount Spent Per Month	Rate of Spending	Above/ Below Budget B
15.	De Vito	\$1100	Clothing	\$108	$\frac{108}{1100} \approx \frac{110}{1100} = \underline{\ ?\ }\%$ 10	Above ?
16.	Luciano	\$1520	Transportation	\$300	$\frac{300}{1520} \approx \frac{300}{1500} = \underline{\ ?\ }\%$ 20	Above ?
17.	Jonsson	\$1180	Insurance	\$55	$\frac{55}{1180} \approx \frac{60}{1200} = \underline{\ ?\ }\%$ 5	Below ?
18.	MacDougal	\$1630	Housing	\$595	$\frac{595}{1630} \approx \frac{600}{1600} = \underline{\ ?\ }\%$ $37\frac{1}{2}$	Above ?

19. The Lopez family has a monthly net pay of \$1065. They paid \$320 last month for medical expenses. Is this above or below the per cent budgeted in Budget B? Above

20. Geoff and Sally Youngblood have a net pay of \$1790 per month. Each month they save \$200. Is this above or below the per cent budgeted in Budget B? Above

21. Gracie Manion spends \$385 on her monthly rent. She has a net pay of \$975 per month. Is this above or below the per cent budgeted for housing in Budget B? Above

22. Pierre Devine's net pay per month is \$1580. He spends \$195 each month on transportation. Is this above or below the per cent budgeted in Budget B? Below

More Challenging Problems

Refer to the budget at the right.

23. The fixed expenses in the budget are: rent, insurance, and car payments. Make a circle graph to show the fixed expenses.

24. Make a circle graph to show the variable expenses.

Monthly Budget

Fixed / Variable

238°	Rent		\$380
	Food	194°	\$410
	Telephone	22°	\$ 45
	Utilities	47°	\$ 95
61°	Insurance		\$100
	Recreation	25°	\$ 55
	Clothing	50°	\$ 105
61°	Car Payments		\$ 95
	Miscellaneous	22°	\$ 45

STATISTICAL CLERK

career

Career lessons are optional. This lesson combines the skills of reading a circle graph and finding a per cent of a number.

Freda Bardone is a **statistical clerk.** She studies the national and regional spending patterns of consumers. Then she compiles the data in the form of tables and graphs to make the data easier to read.

Freda used the circle graph at the right to show how four-member families in one section of the country spend each $100 of take-home pay.

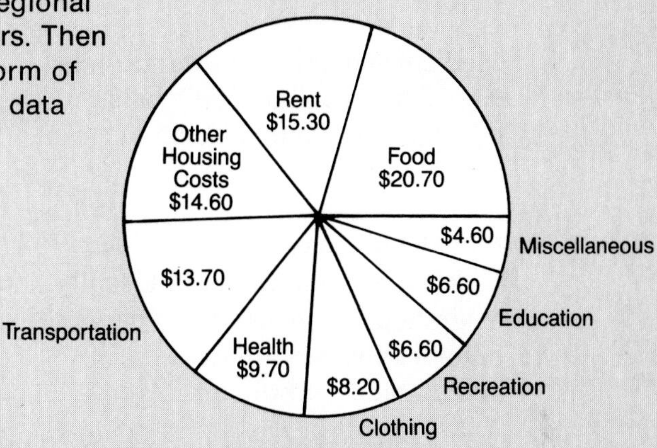

EXERCISES

Use the graph for Exercises 1–8.

1. Out of every $100, how much is spent on transportation? $13.70
2. For which item is the largest portion of each $100 of take-home pay spent? Food
3. Out of every $100, how much is spent on clothing? $8.20
4. For which items is the same portion of each $100 of take-home pay spent? Recreation, Education
5. The graph shows that $15.30 of every $100 is spent on rent. What per cent is this? Round your answer to the nearest whole per cent. 15%
6. Ralph Schneider spends 20% of his take-home pay on rent. Is this more or less than the average amount shown in the graph? More
7. Janet Toner spends 21% of her take-home pay on rent and housing costs. Is this more or less than the average amount shown in the graph? Less
8. Claudia Frye spends 5% of her take-home pay on clothing. Is this more or less than the average amount shown in the graph? Less

18-3 Health Insurance

See the Teacher's Manual for the objectives.

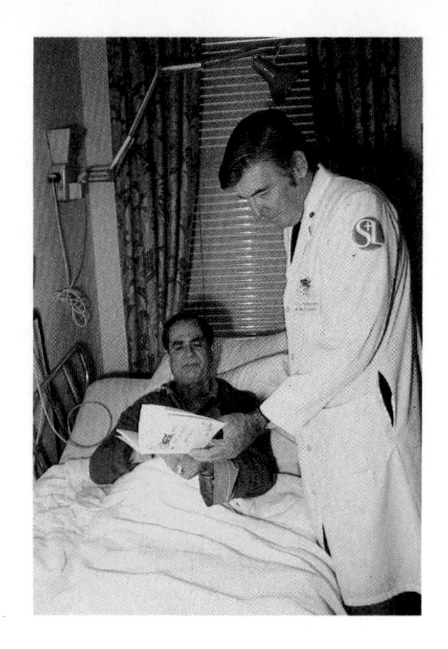

An important item in any budget is the amount budgeted for health care and health insurance.

Medical and dental insurance help pay doctor's and dentist's bills, hospital costs, and the cost of medicine.

Most health insurance policies have a **deductible** amount. Usually, insurance companies pay a per cent of total expenses after the deductible is subtracted.

EXAMPLE William Clyde has medical insurance that has a deductible of \$100. The plan pays 80% of remaining expenses up to a maximum of \$25,000. William recently had medical expenses totaling \$625.

a. How much will the insurance company pay?

b. How much will William pay?

Solution: **a.** [1] Subtract the deductible amount from total expenses.

$\$625 - \$100 = \mathbf{\$525}$

[2] Find 80% of \$525.

$\$525 \times 0.80 = \mathbf{\$420}$ ◀ ***Amount paid by the insurance company***

b. Subtract the amount paid by the insurance company from the total expenses.

$\$625 - \$420 = \mathbf{\$205}$ ◀ ***Amount William pays***

Dental insurance plans are similar to medical insurance plans. After the deductible is subtracted from total expenses, the the insurance company pays a per cent of the remaining expenses.

REVIEW OF RELATED SKILLS

You may wish to use these exercises before teaching the lesson.

Subtract. (Pages 2–3)

1. \$750 − \$100 \$650 **2.** \$920 − \$100 \$820 **3.** \$1125 − \$50 \$1075 **4.** \$730 − \$504 \$226 **5.** \$1270 − \$936 \$334

Multiply. (Pages 8–9)

6. \$600 × 0.80 \$480 **7.** \$450 × 0.75 \$337.50 **8.** \$920 × 0.80 \$736 **9.** \$1465 × 0.70 \$1025.50 **10.** \$1190 × 0.75 \$892.50

EXERCISES

For Exercises 1–12, find each of the following.
a. How much the insurance company will pay
b. How much the policy holder will pay

	Medical Expenses	Insurance Coverage	Deductible	
1.	$250	80%	$100	$120; $130
2.	$700	80%	$100	$480; $220
3.	$950	75%	$100	$637.50; $312.50
4.	$1230	80%	$50	$944; $286
5.	$1065	85%	$100	$820.25; $244.75
6.	$1430	80%	$75	$1084; $346
7.	$95	80%	$50	$36; $59
8.	$1300	75%	$100	$900; $400
9.	$210	80%	$100	$88; $122
10.	$160	80%	$100	$48; $112
11.	$575	80%	$100	$380; $195
12.	$120	85%	$150	$0; $120

13. Betty Brandon recently had a dental bill of $165. Her dental insurance policy has a deductible of $75. The plan pays 80% of the remaining expenses. How much will the company pay? $72

14. Luis Alvarez had medical bills for an operation that amounted to $1670. The insurance company has a deductible of $100, and pays 80% of the remaining expenses. How much will Luis pay? $414

15. Patsy Kyack's insurance policy has a $50 deductible and pays 80% of the remaining expenses. Patsy recently had medical expenses totaling $545. How much will she pay? $149

16. Tom Andico has medical insurance that has a deductible of $100. It pays 75% of the remaining expenses. How much will the company pay on expenses totaling $720? $465

17. Tim Austin has a doctor's bill of $160. The insurance company will pay 75% of the medical expenses. There is *no* deductible. How much will the insurance company pay? $120

18. Kristina Chan has a dental bill of $295. The insurance company will pay 80% of expenses after a $75 deductible. How much will she pay? $119

18-4 Adjusting a Budget

See the Teacher's Manual for the objectives.

When Carl Krebs became ill and was unable to work, the family budget had to be adjusted to meet the family's new needs. Since fixed expenses remained the same and some variable expenses increased, other variable expenses had to be reduced.

Also, other ways of obtaining income had to be found. While he was ill, Carl received $800 per month from his company's disability insurance plan. Julie Krebs took a part-time job for which the new pay was $500 per month.

Regular Monthly Net Income $1745.00

Adjusted Monthly Net Income Insurance: $800; Julie Krebs: $500

Item	*Regular Monthly Budget*	*Adjusted Monthly Budget*
Food	$ 420.00	$ 400.00
Rent	$ 435.00	$ 435.00
Transportation	$ 135.00	$ 120.00
Utilities	$ 75.00	$ 70.00
Clothing	$ 125.00	$ 50.00
Insurance	$ 85.00	$ 85.00
Medical	$ 50.00	$ 250.00
Telephone	$ 30.00	$ 25.00
Debt payments	$ 150.00	$ 150.00
Recreation	$ 40.00	$ 20.00
Savings and Personal	$ 150.00	—
Miscellaneous	$ 50.00	$ 25.00
TOTAL:	$1745.00	$1630.00

The total adjusted monthly budget amounts to $1630. The Krebs family's adjusted monthly net income is $1300. Thus, the family has to find ways to balance their budget.

EXAMPLE Jenny Krebs is 16. She found a part-time job with a net pay of $250 per month. She uses $80 of this for transportation, lunch and personal expenses and contributes the rest to the family budget. How much more will be needed to balance the adjusted budget?

Solution: [1] Amount Jenny contributes: $250 − $80 = **$170**

New family income: $1300 + $170 = **$1470**

[2] Amount needed: $1630 − $1470 = **$160**

REVIEW OF RELATED SKILLS You may wish to use these exercises before teaching the lesson.

Add or subtract. (Pages 2–3)

1. \$650 + \$350 \$1000
2. \$700 + \$450 \$1150
3. \$1070 + \$245 \$1315
4. \$688 + \$794 \$1482
5. \$1165 + \$397 \$1562
6. \$1900 − \$1650 \$250
7. \$1512 − \$1290 \$222
8. \$2341 − \$2089 \$252
9. \$1694 − \$1647 \$47

EXERCISES

For Exercises 1–8, find the difference between the amount budgeted before Carl Krebs' illness and the amount in the adjusted budget. Use the table on page 396.

	Item	Increase (I) or Decrease (D)			Item	Increase (I) or Decrease (D)	
1.	Food	?	D: \$20	5.	Utilities	?	D: \$5
2.	Transportation	?	D: \$15	6.	Savings	?	D: \$150
3.	Medical	?	I: \$200	7.	Clothing	?	D: \$75
4.	Recreation	?	D: \$20	8.	Telephone	?	D: \$5

For Exercises 9–12, use the table on page 396.

9. The Krebs family has certain fixed monthly expenses: rent, insurance and debt payments. Find the total of their fixed monthly expenses. \$670

10. Find the difference between the Krebs' total variable expenses before and after Carl's illness. \$115

11. Jimmy Krebs has a paper route. If he contributes his earnings of \$35.00 per week to the family budget, how much more will be needed to balance the budget? \$20 (1 month = 4 weeks)

12. Julie Krebs can take out a loan on her life insurance policy. The insurance company loans her \$350. For how many months can Julie balance the budget with this loan? 17

The table at the right shows Pilar Centrado's monthly budget.

13. Find the total amount budgeted. \$1490

14. Pilar's fixed expenses are the mortgage, property tax, and insurance payments. Find the total of the fixed expenses each month. \$555

15. Pilar's take-home pay each month is \$1520. How much of her take-home pay is not in the budget? \$30

Monthly Budget	
Mortgage	\$320
Property taxes	\$140
Insurance	\$ 95
Food	\$470
Clothing	\$ 95
Telephone	\$ 35
Electricity/Heat	\$110
Personal	\$ 75
Miscellaneous	\$150

FINANCIAL COUNSELOR

Career lessons are optional. This lesson applies the skill of using formulas.

As a **financial counselor,** Philip Jacobs helps people to develop a balanced budget. In doing this, he is mainly concerned with the variable expenses.

Variable Expenses = Income − Fixed Expenses

He uses the following formula to compute the amount to be budgeted for each variable expense.

$T \times A = R \times V$, or $TA = RV$, where

T = Total Per Cent for Variable Expenses

A = Amount to be Budgeted

R = Per Cent for a Variable Expense

V = Total Amount of Variable Expenses

The Garfield family's take–home pay each month is $1150. They have fixed expenses of $790. Phil advised them to budget 10% for savings, 12% for clothing, and 8% for miscellaneous expenses. How much should be budgeted for savings?

Solution: 1 Find the total amount of the variable expenses.

Variable Expenses = Income − Fixed Expense

Variable Expenses = $1150 − $790

Variable Expenses = **$360** ◀ ***This is V.***

2 Find the total per cent for variable expenses.

10% + 12% + 8% = **30%** ◀ ***This is T.***

3 Use the formula.

$T \times A = R \times V$

$30\% \times A = 10\% \times \$360$

$0.3A = 0.1 \times \$360$ ◀ ***To find A, divide each side by 0.3.***

$A = \dfrac{0.1 \times 360}{0.3}$

Use a paper and pencil or a calculator.

[.] [1] [×] [3] [6] [0] [÷] [.] [3] [=] → 120.

They should budget **$120** each month for savings.

EXERCISES Note that Exercises 1-17 are non-verbal.

Complete the table.

	Monthly Take-Home Pay	Total Fixed Expenses	Total Variable Expenses	Total Variable Expenses (%)	Per Cent for a Variable Expense	Amount For a Variable Expense
1.	$1200	$ 900	? $300	25%	12% for Clothing	? $144
2.	$2000	$ 900	? $1100	55%	10% for Savings	? $200
3.	$1050	$ 735	? $315	30%	8% for Clothing	? $84
4.	$2540	$1651	? $889	35%	15% for Savings	? $381
5.	$2800	$2100	? $700	25%	5% for Cosmetics	? $140

For Exercises 6–17, use the formula $T \times A = R \times V$. 14. $900 15. $300 16. $625 17. $374

	T	R	V			T	R	V			T	R	V
6.	40%	5%	$ 800	$100	10.	20%	12%	$ 600	$360	14.	15%	15%	$ 900
7.	30%	8%	$1200	$320	11.	30%	10%	$1500	$500	15.	40%	12%	$1000
8.	20%	10%	$1000	$500	12.	25%	14%	$ 900	$504	16.	30%	15%	$1250
9.	30%	6%	$ 700	$140	13.	30%	12%	$1100	$440	17.	25%	11%	$ 850

18. Carlos Barbato works for a telephone company. His monthly take–home pay is $1500 per month. Fixed expenses total $900 per month. He budgets 5% for clothing, 10% for savings and 20% for miscellaneous expenses. What amount is budgeted for $342.86 miscellaneous expenses? Round your answer to the nearest cent.

19. Joan Silver's take–home pay as a secretary is $1800 per month. Her fixed expenses amount to $1250 per month. She has been advised to budget 12% for savings, 12% for clothing, and 6% for miscellaneous. What amount is budgeted for savings? $220

Rounding and Estimation

Consumers use rounding and estimation to solve problems related to budgeting money.

EXERCISES See the Teacher's Manual for the objectives.

Choose the best estimate. Choose a, b, or c.

1. 60% of 703 a — **a.** $\frac{3}{5} \times 700$ **b.** $\frac{3}{5} \times 800$ **c.** $\frac{2}{3} \times 700$
2. 80% of 498 b — **a.** $\frac{4}{5} \times 400$ **b.** $\frac{4}{5} \times 500$ **c.** $\frac{7}{8} \times 500$
3. 19% of 1004 c — **a.** $\frac{1}{5} \times 1100$ **b.** $\frac{1}{4} \times 1100$ **c.** $\frac{1}{5} \times 1000$
4. 11% of 697 b — **a.** $\frac{1}{10} \times 600$ **b.** $\frac{1}{10} \times 700$ **c.** $\frac{1}{11} \times 600$
5. 29% of 502 a — **a.** 0.3×500 **b.** 0.3×600 **c.** 0.3×400
6. 649.75 − 487.92 b — **a.** 640 − 490 **b.** 650 − 490 **c.** 650 − 480
7. 1204.18 − 806.25 a — **a.** 1200 − 800 **b.** 1300 − 800 **c.** 1200 − 900

Choose the best estimate. Choose a, b, c, or d.

8. 26% of 798 b — **a.** 100 **b.** 200 **c.** 150 **d.** 250
9. 34% of 603 c — **a.** 100 **b.** 150 **c.** 200 **d.** 250
10. 11% of 699 d — **a.** 30 **b.** 50 **c.** 90 **d.** 70
11. 6% of 397 c — **a.** 10 **b.** 30 **c.** 20 **d.** 40
12. 281.04 − 198.79 b — **a.** 60 **b.** 80 **c.** 100 **d.** 120
13. 898.94 − 702.36 a — **a.** 200 **b.** 150 **c.** 100 **d.** 250
14. 1411.16 − 1288.57 a — **a.** 100 **b.** 200 **c.** 300 **d.** 400

15. Bob Fazio has a net monthly pay of \$986. He is following Standard Budget A on page 390. Estimate the amount he should set aside for savings. a

    a. $\frac{1}{20} \times \$1000$ **b.** $\frac{1}{20} \times \$900$
    c. $\frac{1}{4} \times \$1000$ **d.** $\frac{1}{4} \times \$900$

16. Janet Kusak has a net monthly pay of \$1205. She is following Standard Budget B on page 390. Estimate the amount she should budget for food. c

    a. $\frac{1}{3} \times \$1200$ **b.** $\frac{1}{3} \times \$1300$
    c. $\frac{1}{4} \times \$1200$ **d.** $\frac{1}{5} \times \$1300$

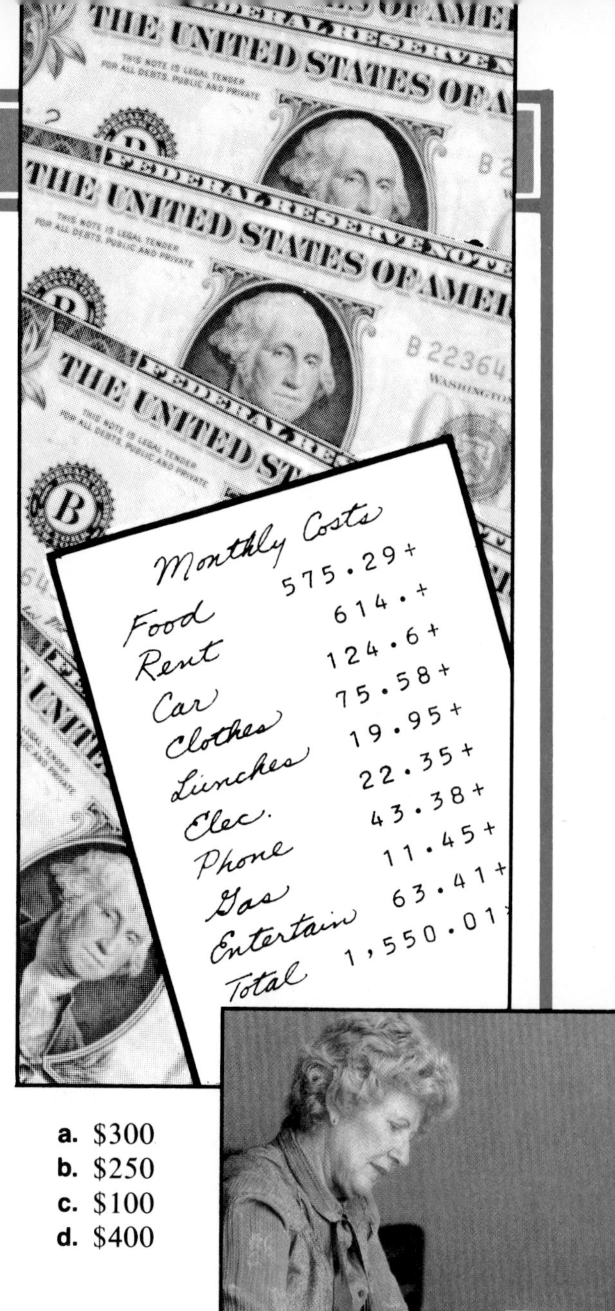

Monthly Costs
Food 575.29+
Rent 614.+
Car 124.6+
Clothes 75.58+
Lunches 19.95+
Elec. 22.35+
Phone 43.38+
Gas 11.45+
Entertain 63.41+
Total 1,550.01

17. Louisa Reynolds has a medical insurance plan that pays 80% of the expenses after the deductible is subtracted. Her expenses after the deductible total \$396.78. Estimate the amount the insurance company will pay. b

a. $\frac{4}{5} \times \$300$ **b.** $\frac{4}{5} \times \$400$
c. $\frac{2}{3} \times \$300$ **d.** $\frac{2}{3} \times \$400$

18. Rick Rodriquez has \$962.48 in medical expenses. His insurance company will pay \$781.14. Estimate the amount that Rick will pay. b

a. \$960 − \$790 **b.** \$960 − \$780
c. \$970 − \$780 **d.** \$950 − \$750

19. Maureen Styles has a net monthly pay of \$905. She budgets 33% of this for housing. Estimate the amount for housing. c

a. \$250 **b.** \$200
c. \$300 **d.** \$350

20. Tony Spivak has a dental plan that pays 80% of the expenses after the deductible is subtracted. His expenses after the deductible total \$503.25. Estimate the amount the insurance company will pay. d

a. \$300
b. \$250
c. \$100
d. \$400

21. Angela Komiski has \$497.52 in medical expenses. Her insurance company will pay \$308.75. Estimate how much Angela will pay. b

a. \$210
b. \$200
c. \$160
d. \$180

Chapter Review

These exercises review the vocabulary, skills and applications presented in the chapter as a preparation for the chapter test.

Part 1: VOCABULARY

For Exercises 1–4, choose from the box at the right the word(s) that complete(s) each statement.

fixed expenses
deductible
budget
variable expenses
average

1. A plan for balancing income and expenses is a __?__. (Pages 388–389) budget
2. Expenses that can change from month to month are __?__. (Pages 388–389) variable expenses
3. Expenses that stay the same every month are __?__. (Pages 388–389) fixed expenses
4. The amount of medical expenses that must be subtracted before an insurance company pays health insurance is the __?__ amount. (Pages 394–395) deductible

Part 2: SKILLS

Find the average (or mean). (Pages 118–119)

5. \$15.65; \$22.41; \$18.97 \$19.01
6. \$23.75; \$46.82; \$55.49 \$42.02
7. \$25.24; \$47.89; \$52.03; \$66.08 \$47.81
8. \$16.89; \$22.47; \$31.25; \$28.03 \$24.66

Round each number to the nearest dollar. (Pages 16–17)

9. \$42.08 \$42
10. \$56.85 \$57
11. \$79.89 \$80
12. \$218.32 \$218
13. \$302.64 \$303

Make a circle graph to show the data. (Pages 116–117)

14. **Vehicles Passing a Toll Booth**

Vehicle	Per Cent
Automobiles	40 144°
Motorcycles	12 43°
Trucks	30 108°
Vans	18 65°

15. **Per Cent of Vote in Election**

Candidate	Per Cent
B. Bryant	30 108°
L. Candito	45 162°
D. Curez	10 36°
M. Montillio	15 54°

Multiply. (Pages 8–9)

16. \$500 × 0.16 \$80
17. \$780 × 0.20 \$156
18. \$518.70 × 0.80 \$414.96
19. \$923.60 × 0.05 \$46.18

Write a per cent for each fraction. (Pages 92–93)

20. $\frac{6}{10}$ 60%
21. $\frac{3}{4}$ 75%
22. $\frac{5}{8}$ $62\frac{1}{2}$%
23. $\frac{4}{5}$ 80%
24. $\frac{1}{3}$ $33\frac{1}{3}$%
25. $\frac{1}{2}$ 50%

Add or subtract as indicated. (Pages 2–3)

26. \$320 + \$30 \$350
27. \$565 + \$100 \$665
28. \$1240 − \$189 \$1051
29. \$921 − \$862 \$59

Part 3: APPLICATIONS

For Exercises 30–33, find how much to budget each month for each variable expense. Round each answer to the nearest dollar. (Pages 388–389)

	Expense	Amount Spent Last 4 Months
30.	Telephone $31	$31.80; $42.60; $28.72; $22.56
31.	Gasoline $69	$65.71; $86.93; $44.86; $79.62
32.	Food $302	$316.14; $298.20; $287.02; $305.16
33.	Savings $32	$27.83; $36.41; $29.44; $35.80

34. Mr. and Mrs. Frichs have a net monthly pay of $2240. They budget 4% of this for insurance. Find the amount budgeted for insurance. (Pages 390–392) $89.60

35. Sam Kajun has a monthly net income of $1200. Last month he spent $130 on clothing. Is this greater or less than 10% of his net income? (Pages 391–392) greater

For Exercises 36–39, find each of the following.
a. How much the insurance company will pay
b. How much the policy holder will pay (Pages 394–395)

	Medical Expenses	Insurance Coverage	Deductible	
36.	$750	80%	$150	$480; $270
37.	$600	70%	$100	$350; $250
38.	$1700	75%	$100	$1200; $500
39.	$1200	80%	$150	$840; $360

40. Louis Garcia budgeted $110 per month for clothing before he broke his leg and stopped working. Now he budgets $25 per month. Find the difference. (Pages 396–397) $85

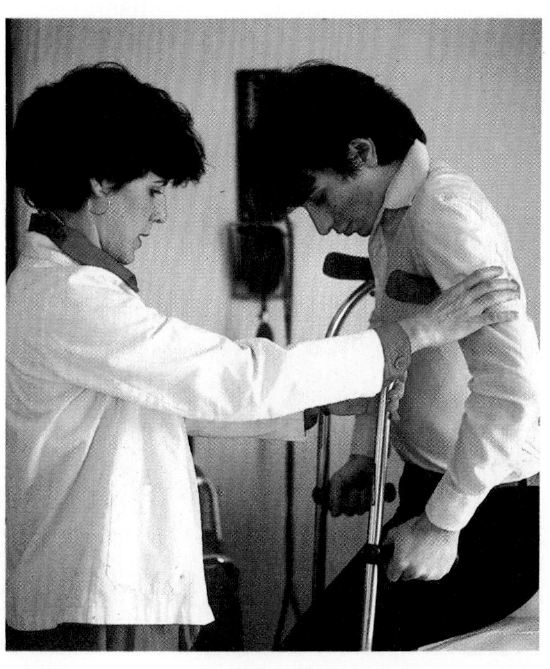

41. Jane Murray has $803.78 in medical expenses. Her insurance company will pay $695.50. Estimate how much Jane will pay. (Pages 400–401) b

a. $900 − $600 **b.** $800 − $700
c. $800 − $600 **d.** $900 − $700

42. Pat Lattis has a net monthly pay of $1006. He budgets 24% of this for food. Estimate the amount for food. (Pages 400–401) a

a. $250 **b.** $300 **c.** $200 **d.** $350

Chapter Test

The Teacher's Resource Book contains two forms of each chapter test.

Find the average (or mean).

1. \$16.84; \$21.38; \$15.98; \$23.44 \$19.41 **2.** \$38.96; \$45.60; \$42.12; \$36.72 \$40.85

Round each number to the nearest dollar.

3. \$28.16 \$28 **4.** \$47.95 \$48 **5.** \$109.80 \$110 **6.** \$123.14 \$123 **7.** \$200.37 \$200

Multiply.

8. $\$300 \times 0.15$ \$45 **9.** $\$800 \times 0.30$ \$240 **10.** $\$1250 \times 0.10$ \$125.00 **11.** $\$950 \times 0.25$ \$237.50

Write a per cent for each fraction.

12. $\frac{1}{3}$ $33\frac{1}{3}\%$ **13.** $\frac{2}{5}$ 40% **14.** $\frac{3}{4}$ 75% **15.** $\frac{1}{2}$ 50% **16.** $\frac{1}{8}$ $12\frac{1}{2}\%$ **17.** $\frac{1}{6}$ $16\frac{2}{3}\%$

Add or subtract as indicated.

18. \$460 + \$390 \$850 **19.** \$500 + \$280 \$780 **20.** \$1280 + \$365 \$1645 **21.** \$942 − \$873 \$69

22. Over the last six months, Tom Harris has spent \$21.98, \$16.50, \$28.40, \$18.20, \$27.56, and \$36.28 on recreation. How much should he budget per month for recreation? \$25

23. Helen Brogan has a monthly net income of \$1300. Last month she spent \$250 on food. Is this greater, or less, than 20% of her monthly net income? less

24. Raquel Ramos recently had a medical bill of \$510. Her health insurance policy has a deductible of \$150. The plan pays 80% of the remaining expenses. How much will the insurance company pay? \$288

25. Russ Preston has a net monthly income of \$989. He budgets 11% of this for transportation. Estimate the amount for transportation. d

a. \$25 **b.** \$50 **c.** \$75 **d.** \$100

Additional Practice

You may wish to use some or all of these exercises depending on how well students performed on the formal chapter test.

Skills

Find the average (or mean). (Pages 118–119)

1. \$22.38; \$25.49; \$31.61; \$27.00 \$26.62
2. \$98.36; \$89.42; \$104.77; \$112.81 \$101.34
3. \$121.46; \$138.75; \$144.34 \$134.85
4. \$246.54; \$239.13; \$253.44 \$246.37

Round each number to the nearest dollar. (Pages 16–17)

5. \$42.69 \$43
6. \$21.20 \$21
7. \$39.76 \$40
8. \$102.93 \$103
9. \$212.14 \$212

Multiply. (Pages 8–9)

10. \$980 × 0.20 \$196
11. \$860 × 0.30 \$258
12. \$1005 × 0.15 \$150.75
13. \$1220 × 0.26 \$317.20

Write a per cent for each fraction. (Pages 92–93)

14. $\frac{3}{5}$ 60%
15. $\frac{7}{8}$ $87\frac{1}{2}$%
16. $\frac{1}{4}$ 25%
17. $\frac{2}{5}$ 40%
18. $\frac{1}{3}$ $33\frac{1}{3}$%
19. $\frac{7}{10}$ 70%

Add or subtract as indicated. (Pages 2–3)

20. \$420 + \$360 \$780
21. \$980 + \$170 \$1150
22. \$385 + \$462 \$847
23. \$873 + \$249 \$1122
24. \$1250 − \$386 \$864
25. \$875 − \$760 \$115
26. \$921 − \$837 \$84
27. \$1000 − \$823 \$177

Applications

28. Audrey Klein's five most recent monthly heating bills amounted to \$163.40, \$156.85, \$178.64, \$132.86, and \$120.70. How much should she budget per month for heating costs? (Pages 388–389) \$150

29. Mr. and Mrs. Radnor have a net monthly pay of \$2250. They budget 24% of this for housing. Find the amount that they budget per month for housing. (Pages 390–392) \$540

For Exercises 30–33, find each of the following.
a. How much the insurance company will pay
b. How much the policy holder will pay (Pages 394–395)

	Medical Expenses	Insurance Coverage	Deductible	
30.	\$900	80%	\$100	\$640; \$260
31.	\$350	70%	\$150	\$140; \$210
32.	\$625	75%	\$150	\$356.25; \$268.75
33.	\$850	85%	\$100	\$637.50; \$212.50

34. Tim Chu has a net monthly income of \$890. He budgets 34% of this for housing. (Pages 400–401) c

    a. \$200 b. \$350
    c. \$300 d. \$250

35. Cissy Stevens budgeted \$278 each month for food. After she left her job, her adjusted food budget was \$232. Estimate the difference. a (Pages 400–401)

    a. \$50 b. \$60 c. \$40 d. \$55

Cumulative Review: Chapters 16–18

Choose the correct answer. Choose a, b, c, or d.

1. Multiply: $\frac{2}{5} \times \$115.95$ d

a. \$23.19 **b.** \$289.88
c. \$115.38 **d.** \$46.38

2. Write a decimal for 7.6%. a

a. 0.076 **b.** 7.60
c. 0.76 **d.** 0.0076

3. Multiply. Round the answer to the nearest cent. a

$\$295.18 \times 0.015$

a. \$4.43 **b.** \$44.28
c. \$4.42 **d.** \$442.77

4. Find 30% of \$25.80. a

a. 7.74 **b.** \$25.50
c. \$26.10 **d.** \$8.60

5. Divide. Round the answer to the nearest tenth of a cent. c

$\$5.60 \div \$51.20$

a. 14.2¢ **b.** 12.3¢
c. 10.9¢ **d.** 11¢

6. Write a per cent for $\frac{2}{5}$. c

a. 20% **b.** 50%
c. 40% **d.** 60%

7. Divide: $75{,}000 \div 1000$ a

a. 75 **b.** 7.5 **c.** 750 **d.** 0.75

8. Find the average (or mean). b

\$21.36; \$42.83; \$35.05

a. \$99.24 **b.** \$33.08
c. \$33.18 **d.** \$11.12

9. Find the sale price. b

a. \$12.60
b. \$23.40
c. \$36.35
d. \$35.36

10. A certain radio regularly sells for \$59.98. It was on sale at 33% off. Estimate the discount. b

a. \$15.00 **b.** \$20.00
c. \$17.50 **d.** \$25.50

11. Find the finance charge. a

Finance Charge Balance	Finance Charge Rate
\$195.80	1.5%

a. \$2.94 **b.** \$198.74
c. \$29.37 **d.** \$225.17

12. Silvia received her monthly credit card statement. It listed a previous balance of \$394.76, a payment of \$40, and a purchase of \$18.24. Find the new balance. d

a. \$453.00 **b.** \$336.52
c. \$354.76 **d.** \$373.00

13. Mikhail bought a living room set for \$2780. He puts 25% down. How much does he owe? a

a. \$2085 **b.** \$2779.75
c. \$695 **d.** \$2780.25

14. Subtract: $90 − $67 b

a. $13 **b.** $23 **c.** $27 **d.** $37

15. Peter is buying a $25,000 five-year term insurance policy. The yearly premium per $1000 of insurance is $5.32. Find the total yearly premium. c

a. $129 **b.** $131.75
c. $133 **d.** $168.75

16. Janice bought a $30,000 straight-life insurance policy ten years ago. The cash value per $1000 is $110.13. Find the total cash value. b

a. $110.13 **b.** $3303.90
c. $285.51 **d.** $330.39

17. Tomaso invested $8000 in a one-year certificate of deposit that pays 14% compounded daily. After one year, $1 is worth $1.1502. How much will the certificate pay after one year? b

a. $8666.40 **b.** $9201.60
c. $9387.20 **d.** $8580

18. Ethel wants to buy 300 shares of Bedouin Oil stock at 27\frac{1}{4}$ per share. The commission charged is $128.57. Find the total cost. c

a. $8046.43 **b.** $8175
c. $8303.57 **d.** $8300

19. Christina owns 200 shares of Shavex Razor stock. The quarterly dividend is $1.75 per share. Find the total yearly dividend. b

a. $7 **b.** $1400
c. $3500 **d.** $175

20. Hugh bought 205 shares of stock at 39\frac{5}{8}$. Estimate the cost. c

a. $6000 **b.** $7000
c. $8000 **d.** $9000

21. A Clark Electronics bond with a face value of $5000 has a listed low today of 82$\frac{1}{2}$. Find the low price. a

a. $4125 **b.** $5082.50
c. $4110 **d.** $5082.20

22. Mike Tirelli's last four telephone bills were $48.25, $41.58, $38.29, and $50.40. How much should he budget per month for the telephone? c

a. $178.52 **b.** $45.63
c. $44.63 **d.** $180.00

23. The Tobins have a net monthly income of $1575. They budget 5% of this income for medical expenses. How much is budgeted for medical expenses? d

a. $31.50 **b.** $315
c. $787.50 **d.** $78.75

24. Pierre has a dental bill of $310. The insurance company will pay 80% of expenses after a $100 deductible. How much will he pay? c

a. $168 **b.** $210
c. $142 **d.** $410

25. Estimate the sale price. b

a. $100
b. $150
c. $80
d. $120

Picture Credits

Key: t top; m middle; b bottom; l left; r right

page 1 (t,r), Culver Pictures; 1 (b,l), Alvis Upitis/The Image Bank; 1 (b,r,), H.E.G. Robinson/Stock Boston; 5, Brian Brake/Photo Researchers; 7, Grant Heilman; 9, Jon Riley/The Stock Shop; 11 (t), Rhoda Sidney/Monkmeyer; 11 (b), courtesy IBM; 15, H.E.G. Robinson/Stock Boston; 17, courtesy IBM; 20, Robert Scurlock/Shostal Associates; 24 (m,r), Alvis Upitis/The Image Bank; 24 (m), Mitchell B. Reiber/Sports Photo File; 24 (b,l), Alvis Upitis/The Image Bank; 25, Robert Motzjin/The Stock Shop; 27 (t,l), Steve Allen/Peter Arnold; 27 (b,l), Kurt Scholz/H. Armstrong Roberts; 27 (b,r,), George Hunter/Shostal Associates; 35, Martin Rotker/Taurus Photos; 36, HBJ Photo; 37, Kurt Scholz/H. Armstrong Roberts; 39 (t,r,), Reininger/Frederic Lewis; 39 (b,r,), David York/The Stock Shop; 42 (t,r,), George Hunter/Shostal Associates; 42 (b,l), Steve Allen/Peter Arnold; 42 (b,r,), HBJ Photo; 45 (t,r,), Cary Wolinsky/Stock Boston; 45 (b,r,), Lawrence Fried/The Image Bank; 45 (b,l), Cary Wolinsky/Stock Boston; 47, Guy Gilllette/Photo Researchers; 49, Lawrence Fried/The Image Bank; 53, Cary Wolinsky/Stock Boston; 55, Earl Roberge/Photo Researchers; 59, Cary Wolinsky/Stock Boston; 62 (t,r,), John Lei/Stock Boston; 62 (b,r,), Henri Dauman/Kay Reese & Associates; 66 (t,r,), Roy Morsch/The Image Bank; 66 (b,l), Freda Leinwand/Monkmeyer; 67 (m,r), HBJ Photo; 67 (b,r,), Richard Choy/Peter Arnold; 71 (t,l), Peter Menschel/Shostal Associates; 71 (b,l), NASA; 71 (b,r,), Michal Heron/Monkmeyer; 73, D. Forer/The Image Bank; 75 Leonard Lee Rue III/Shostal Associates; 77, Runk/Schoenberger/Grant Heilman; 79, Peter Henschel/Shostal Associates; 81, illustration Blaise Zito; 82, Martin Rotker/Taurus Photos; 83, Michal Heron/Monkmeyer; 85, Phil Dotson/DPI; 86 (t,l), Runk/Schoenberger/Grant Heilman; 86 (b,r,), NASA; 87, George Jones III/Photo Researchers; 89 (t,r,), Philip Paoli, Jr.; 89 (m,r), Tom Tracy/The Stock Shop; 89 (b,l), Ira Merritt/Merritt Productions; 91, Tom Tracy/The Stock Shop; 93, Alvis Upitis/Shostal Associates; 97, R. Hobson/Focus on Sports; 98, Illustration, Ruth Gordon; 98 (b,r,), Ira Merritt/Merritt Productions; 101, Jack Weaver, Illustration; 106 (t,r,), Mickey Palmer/Focus on Sports; 106 (m,r), Adrian Atwaters/Shostal Associates; 106 (b,l), Larry Mulvehill/Photo Researchers; 107, Philip Paoli, Jr.; 109 (t,l), Gerald Brimacombe/The Image Bank; 109 (b,l), H. Armstrong Roberts; 109 (b,r,), Sybil Shackman/Monkmeyer; 120, Gerald Brimacombe/The Image Bank; 122, Alvis Upitis/Shostal Associates; 123, illustration Frank Johnson; 125, H. Armstrong Roberts; 127 (t,r,), Sybil Shackman/Monkmeyer; 127 (b,r,), Grant Heilman; 133 (m,r), Jerry Wachter/Focus on Sports; 133 (m,l), HBJ Photo; 137 (t,r,), H. Armstrong Roberts; 137 (b,r,), HBJ Photo; 137 (b,l), Louise Werner/Shostal Associates; 138, Louise Werner/Shostal Associates; 141, Larry Mulvehill/Photo Researchers; 147, H. Armstrong Roberts; 148 R.D. Ullmann/Taurus Photos; 149, M. Roessler/H. Armstrong Roberts; 151, J. Alex Langley/DPI; 154 (b,r,), HBJ Photo; 157 (t,l), Mimi Forsyth/Monkmeyer; 157 (t,r,), Isaac Geib/Grant Heilman; 157 (b,r,), Bill Anderson/Monkmeyer; 158, Isaac Geib/Grant Heilman; 159, A.C. Shelton/H. Armstrong Roberts; 160, Bill Anderson/Monkmeyer; 161, Ewing Galloway; 167, Ewing Galloway; 168, Alvis Upitis/The Image Bank; 171, Mimi Forsyth/Monkmeyer; 175, Jonathan Taylor/The Stock Shop; 176, Chris Sorenson/DPI; 177, Marcia Weinstein; 179 (t,l), Hugh Rogers/Monkmeyer; 179 (m,r), Mimi Forsyth/Monkmeyer; 179 (b), Hugh Rogers/Monkmeyer; 180, H. Armstrong Roberts; 182, Mimi Forsyth/Monkmeyer; 184, HBJ Photo; 185, Hugh Rogers/Monkmeyer; 186, Mimi Forsyth/Monkmeyer; 187, Mimi Forsyth/Monkmeyer; 191, Lawrence Fried/The Image Bank; 197 (m,r), Andy Rakoczy; 197 (b,r,), Tom Morton/Shostal Associates; 199, HBJ Photo; 201, Chris Reeberg/DPI; 207 (t,l), HBJ Photo; 207 (b,l), Arthur Grace/Stock Boston; 207 (b,r,), H. Armstrong Roberts; 209, HBJ Photo; 210, HBJ Photo; 211, Dick Hanley/Photo Researchers; 212, HBJ Photo; 215, Gabe Palmer/The Image Bank; 216, HBJ Photo; 218, HBJ Photo; 220, Marcia Weinstein; 221, David Forbert/Shostal Associates; 223, Alvis Upitis/The Image Bank; 254, Freda Leinwand/Monkmeyer; 255, Ace Williams/Shostal Associates; 225, H. Armstrong Roberts; 226, Arthur Grace/Stock Boston; 227, H. Armstrong Roberts; 229 (t,r,), Marcia Weinstein; 229 (b,l), Milton Feinberg/Alpha; 229 (b,r,), HBJ Photo; 231, Milton Feinberg/Alpha; 233, HBJ Photo; 235, J. McNee/Alpha; 236, Andrew Rakoczy; 237, Marcia Weinstein; 238, Wil Blanche/DPI; 240, H. Armstrong Roberts; 241, William Kelley/Shostal Associates; 243, George Dodge,/DPI; 246, Ellis Herwig/Stock Boston; 249 (t,l), H. Armstrong Roberts; 249 (b,l), Eastern Airlines; 249 (b,r,), Freda Leinwand/Monkmeyer; 250 (t,r,), courtesy of American Telephone & Telegraph; 250 (m,r), Marcia Weinstein; 251, H. Armstrong Roberts; 254, Freda Leinwand/Monkmeyer; 255, Ace Williams/Shostal Associates; 257, Karl Kummels/Shostal Associates; 258, (t), Brent Jones; 258 (m), Blaise Zito; 259, Eastern Airlines; 261, Eric Carle/Shostal Associates; 263, Gridley/The Image Bank; 264, Chris Reeberg/DPI; 269 (t,r,), HBJ Photo; 269 (b,r,), Grant Heilman; 269 (b,l), Michal Heron/Monkmeyer; 271, Andrew Rakoczy; 273, Bill Gallery/Stock Boston; 275, HBJ Photo; 279, Michal Heron/Monkmeyer; 280, J. Forte/Alpha; 281, Bernard Wolf/DPI; 283, Andrew Rakoczy; 286, Jon Riley/The Stock Shop; 289 (t,l), Alvis Upitis/The Image Bank; 289 (b,l), HBJ Photo; 289 (b,r,), Kent Oppenheimer/Shostal Associates; 291, A. Teufen/H. Armstrong Roberts; 293 (t,r,), H. Lambert/Frederick Lewis; 293 (b,r,), Kent Oppenheimer/Shostal Associates; 294, Hal Yeager/Alpha; 297, Mimi Forsyth/Monkmeyer; 298, Ron Keneske/Shostal Associates; 301 (t,r,), Ira Merritt/Merritt Productions; 301 (b,r,), Donald Dietz/Stock Boston; 302, C.B. Jones/Taurus Photos; 303, Eric Carle/Shostal Associates; 304, Jon Riley/The Stock Shop; 305, HBJ Photo; 307, Ralph Krubner/H. Armstrong Roberts; 309, Robert F. Elliott/H. Armstrong Roberts; 310, Richard Woods/Taurus Photos; 313 (t,r,), Richard Laird/The Stock Shop; 313 (b,r,), Mark Warner; 313 (b,l), Sybil Shelton/Peter Arnold; 315, Barry Runk/Grant Heilman; 316, Conklin/Monkmeyer; 317 (b,l), John Lei/Stock Boston; 317 (b,r,), Geoff Gove/Photo Researchers; 318, Tim Beiber/The Image Bank; 323, Richard Laird/The Stock Shop; 324, G. Palmer/The Image Bank; 325, Ewing Galloway; 329, Mark Warner; 331 (m,r), Sybil Shelton/Peter Arnold; 331 (b,r,), Andrew Rakoczy; 337 (t,l), Sybil Shelton/Peter Arnold; 337 (b,l), Andrew Rakoczy; 337 (b,r,), Mimi Forsyth/Monkmeyer; 338 (t,l), Victoria Arlak/Merritt Productions; 338 (t,l), Marcia Weinstein; 338 (t,r,), H. Lambert/Frederick Lewis; 338 (t,r,), Andrew Rakoczy; 338 (t,r,), J. Fesler/Shostal Associates; 339, Sybil Shelton/Peter Arnold; 343, Mimi Forsyth/Monkmeyer; 348, J. Alex Langley/DPI; 350, David York/The Stock Shop; 351, Fredrik Bodin/Stock Boston; 353, M. Martin/The Image Bank; 356, HBJ Photo; 359 (t,r), Marcia Weinstein; 359 (b,r), Tom Tracy/The Stock Shop; 359 (b,l), Alvis Upitis/The Image Bank; 365, Susan McCartney/Photo Researchers; 367, Ed Pieratt/Stock Boston; 369, Marcia Weinstein; 372, HBJ Photo; 373, Alvis Upitis/The Image Bank; 374, Alvis Upitis/Shostal Associates; 375 (m,r), HBJ Photo; 375 (b,r), The Stock Shop; 378, HBJ Photo; 379, Tom Tracy/The Stock Shop; 381, HBJ Photo; 384, Greg Mancuso/Stock Boston; 387 (t,l), H. Armstrong Roberts; 387 (m,r), Hugh Rogers/Monkmeyer; 387 (b), Ewing Galloway; 389, Wil Blanche/DPI; 392, Henri Dauman/Kay Reese & Associates; 393, Hugh Rogers/Monkmeyer; 394, Marion Bernstein; 395, H. Armstrong Roberts; 398, Ewing Galloway; 399 (m,r), courtesy American Telephone & Telegraph Company; 399 (b,r), H. Armstrong Roberts; 401, HBJ Photo; 403, John Lei/Stock Boston; 404, Andrew Rakoczy; 415, Ralph Krubner/H. Armstrong Roberts; 417, ZEFA/H. Armstrong Roberts; 419, Mickey Palmer/Focus on Sports; 424, General Dynamics; 426 top to bottom: Mattel Electronics/INTELLIVISION®; News Bureau/University of Pennsylvania; Radio Shack/A Tandy Company; courtesy of American Telephone & Telegraph Company; 427 (t), Apple Computer; 427 (m), HBJ Photo; 427 (b), Marcia Weinstein; 432 (t), HBJ Photo; 432 (b), Focus on Sports; 434, Fred Lyons/Photo Researchers.

APPENDIX A

INTRODUCTION TO
ALGEBRA

A-1 Squares and Square Roots

See the Teacher's Manual for the objectives.

When you multiply a number by itself, the product is called the **square** of the number. For example:

Read: "8 squared." $8^2 = 8 \times 8 = 64$ *In 8^2, the "2" is an exponent.*

PROCEDURE To square a number, multiply the number by itself.

EXAMPLE 1 Complete: **a.** $9^2 = \underline{\ ?\ }$ **b.** $12^2 = \underline{\ ?\ }$

Solutions: **a.** $9^2 = 9 \times 9$
$9^2 = \mathbf{81}$ *81 is the square of 9.*

b. $12^2 = 12 \times 12$
$12^2 = \mathbf{144}$ *144 is the square of 12.*

After completing Example 1, you may wish to have students do some or all of Exercises 1-24.

In each problem in Example 1, two equal numbers were multiplied to give a product. Either of these equal numbers is the **square root** of the product.

Since $4 \times 4 = 16$, $\sqrt{16} = 4$. *Read: "The square root of 16 equals 4."*

PROCEDURE To find the square root of a number, find one of the two equal factors of the number.

EXAMPLE 2 Complete: **a.** $\sqrt{36} = \underline{\ ?\ }$ **b.** $\sqrt{121} = \underline{\ ?\ }$

Solutions: **a. Think:** $36 = 6 \times 6$, So $\sqrt{36} = \mathbf{6}$.

b. Think: $121 = 11 \times 11$. So, $\sqrt{121} = \mathbf{11}$.

EXERCISES

Find each answer. (Example 1)

1. 3^2 9 **2.** 5^2 25 **3.** 10^2 100 **4.** 7^2 49 **5.** 15^2 225 **6.** 1^2 1

7. 20^2 400 **8.** 30^2 900 **9.** 40^2 1600 **10.** 13^2 169 **11.** 14^2 196 **12.** 100^2 10,000

13. 2^2 4 **14.** 4^2 16 **15.** 16^2 256 **16.** 21^2 441 **17.** 50^2 2500 **18.** 25^2 625

19. 19^2 361 **20.** 70^2 4900 **21.** 80^2 6400 **22.** 18^2 324 **23.** 200^2 40,000 **24.** 300^2 90,000

(Example 2)

25. $\sqrt{4}$ 2 **26.** $\sqrt{1}$ 1 **27.** $\sqrt{49}$ 7 **28.** $\sqrt{100}$ 10 **29.** $\sqrt{900}$ 30 **30.** $\sqrt{2500}$ 50

31. $\sqrt{1600}$ 40 **32.** $\sqrt{8100}$ 90 **33.** $\sqrt{4900}$ 70 **34.** $\sqrt{6400}$ 80 **35.** $\sqrt{400}$ 20 **36.** $\sqrt{3600}$ 60

37. $\sqrt{81}$ 9 **38.** $\sqrt{169}$ 13 **39.** $\sqrt{9}$ 3 **40.** $\sqrt{25}$ 5 **41.** $\sqrt{256}$ 16 **42.** $\sqrt{289}$ 17

43. $\sqrt{625}$ 25 **44.** $\sqrt{441}$ 21 **45.** $\sqrt{196}$ 14 **46.** $\sqrt{484}$ 22 **47.** $\sqrt{225}$ 15 **48.** $\sqrt{144}$ 12

A-2 Using a Table of Squares and Square Roots

See the Teacher's Manual for the objectives.

You can use the table on page 413 to find the squares and square roots of some numbers.

PROCEDURE To use a square and square root table:

1. Find the number in the "Number" column.
2. Look directly to the right.
   - **a.** Read the square of the number in the "Square" column.
   - **b.** Read the square root of the number in the "Square Root" column.

EXAMPLE 1 Complete:

a. $45^2 = \underline{\ ?\ }$ **b.** $\sqrt{95} = \underline{\ ?\ }$

Solutions: **a.** Find 45 in the "Number" column.

$45^2 = \mathbf{2025}$

Number	Square
45 →	2025

b. Find 95 in the "Number" column.

$\sqrt{95} = \mathbf{9.747}$

Number	Square	Square Root
95 →	9025 →	9.747

After completing Example 1, you may wish to have students do some or all of Exercises 1-24.

NOTE: Most numbers in the "Square Root" column in the table are approximations correct to thousandths. Thus, when you find the square root of a number in the table, you may be asked to round your answer to the nearest tenth or to the nearest hundredth.

PROCEDURE To use the table to find the square roots of numbers greater than 150, first find the number in the "Square" column. Then read the square root in the "Number" column.

EXAMPLE 2 Complete: $\sqrt{22{,}201} = \underline{\ ?\ }$

Solution: Find 22,201 in the "Square" column. Look directly to the left.

$\sqrt{22{,}201} = \mathbf{149}$

Number	Square
149 ←	22,201

EXERCISES

13. 11.576 14. 11.358 15. 10.488 16. 6.557 17. 9.747 18. 10.863 19. 10.149 20. 11.180 21. 9.327 22. 8.718 23. 11.533 24. 10.677

Use the table on page 413 to find each answer. (Example 1)

1. 19^2 361
2. 34^2 1156
3. 62^2 3844
4. 87^2 7569
5. 102^2 10,404
6. 136^2 18,496
7. 67^2 4489
8. 29^2 841
9. 89^2 7921
10. 75^2 5625
11. 133^2 17,689
12. 117^2 13,689

See above

13. $\sqrt{134}$
14. $\sqrt{129}$
15. $\sqrt{110}$
16. $\sqrt{43}$
17. $\sqrt{95}$
18. $\sqrt{118}$
19. $\sqrt{103}$
20. $\sqrt{125}$
21. $\sqrt{87}$
22. $\sqrt{76}$
23. $\sqrt{133}$
24. $\sqrt{114}$

(Example 2) 25. 101 26. 120

25. $\sqrt{10,201}$
26. $\sqrt{14,400}$
27. $\sqrt{13,689}$ 117
28. $\sqrt{19,321}$ 139
29. $\sqrt{4624}$ 68
30. $\sqrt{2916}$ 54
31. $\sqrt{1156}$ 34
32. $\sqrt{7921}$ 89
33. $\sqrt{12,769}$ 113
34. $\sqrt{16,641}$ 129
35. $\sqrt{17,956}$ 134
36. $\sqrt{15,876}$ 126

APPLICATIONS: Using Square Roots

A car that brakes quickly in an emergency will skid a certain distance before stopping completely. You can use the following formula to estimate the speed of the car before braking.

$s = \sqrt{252df}$

***s* = speed in kilometers per hour**
***d* = distance of skid in meters**
***f* = coefficient of friction**

The coefficient of friction is a number that varies according to the driving conditions.

Type of Surface	Coefficient of Friction	
	Dry Road	Wet Road
Asphalt	0.85	0.65
Concrete	0.90	0.60
Gravel	0.65	0.65

You can use a calculator to find s.

EXAMPLE: A car skidded 16 meters on dry concrete. Find its speed per hour before braking to the nearest kilometer.

Solution: Replace the known values in the formula:

$s = \sqrt{252df} \longrightarrow s = \sqrt{252 \times 16 \times 0.9}$ ***f* = 0.9 from the table.**

2 5 2 × 1 6 × . 9 = √ 60.239521

The car was traveling at about **60 kilometers per hour.**

Use the formula and the coefficients of friction shown above to find s in Exercises 37–42. Round each answer to the nearest whole kilometer.

37. A car skidded 18 meters on dry concrete. 64 km/hr
38. A car skidded 24 meters on wet asphalt 63 km/hr
39. A car skidded 33 meters on wet gravel 74 km/hr
40. A car skidded 36 meters on dry gravel 77 km/hr
41. A car skidded 30 meters on wet concrete 67 km/hr
42. A car skidded 32 meters on dry asphalt 83 km/hr

Table of Squares and Square Roots

Number	Square	Square Root	Number	Square	Square Root	Number	Square	Square Root
1	1	1.000	**51**	2601	7.141	**101**	10,201	10.050
2	4	1.414	**52**	2704	7.211	**102**	10,404	10.100
3	9	1.732	**53**	2809	7.280	**103**	10,609	10.149
4	16	2.000	**54**	2916	7.348	**104**	10,816	10.198
5	25	2.236	**55**	3025	7.416	**105**	11,025	10.247
6	36	2.449	**56**	3136	7.483	**106**	11,236	10.296
7	49	2.646	**57**	3249	7.550	**107**	11,449	10.344
8	64	2.828	**58**	3364	7.616	**108**	11,664	10.392
9	81	3.000	**59**	3481	7.681	**109**	11,881	10.440
10	100	3.162	**60**	3600	7.746	**110**	12,100	10.488
11	121	3.317	**61**	3721	7.810	**111**	12,321	10.536
12	144	3.464	**62**	3844	7.874	**112**	12,544	10.583
13	169	3.606	**63**	3969	7.937	**113**	12,769	10.630
14	196	3.742	**64**	4096	8.000	**114**	12,996	10.677
15	225	3.873	**65**	4225	8.062	**115**	13,225	10.724
16	256	4.000	**66**	4356	8.124	**116**	13,456	10.770
17	289	4.123	**67**	4489	8.185	**117**	13,689	10.817
18	324	4.243	**68**	4624	8.246	**118**	13,924	10.863
19	361	4.359	**69**	4761	8.307	**119**	14,161	10.909
20	400	4.472	**70**	4900	8.367	**120**	14,400	10.954
21	441	4.583	**71**	5041	8.426	**121**	14,641	11.000
22	484	4.690	**72**	5184	8.485	**122**	14,884	11.045
23	529	4.796	**73**	5329	8.544	**123**	15,129	11.091
24	576	4.899	**74**	5476	8.602	**124**	15,376	11.136
25	625	5.000	**75**	5625	8.660	**125**	15,625	11.180
26	676	5.099	**76**	5776	8.718	**126**	15,876	11.225
27	729	5.196	**77**	5929	8.775	**127**	16,129	11.269
28	784	5.292	**78**	6084	8.832	**128**	16,384	11.314
29	841	5.385	**79**	6241	8.888	**129**	16,641	11.358
30	900	5.477	**80**	6400	8.944	**130**	16,900	11.402
31	961	5.568	**81**	6561	9.000	**131**	17,161	11.446
32	1024	5.657	**82**	6724	9.055	**132**	17,424	11.489
33	1089	5.745	**83**	6889	9.110	**133**	17,689	11.533
34	1156	5.831	**84**	7056	9.165	**134**	17,956	11.576
35	1225	5.916	**85**	7225	9.220	**135**	18,225	11.619
36	1296	6.000	**86**	7396	9.274	**136**	18,496	11.662
37	1369	6.083	**87**	7569	9.327	**137**	18,769	11.705
38	1444	6.164	**88**	7744	9.381	**138**	19,044	11.747
39	1521	6.245	**89**	7921	9.434	**139**	19,321	11.790
40	1600	6.325	**90**	8100	9.487	**140**	19,600	11.832
41	1681	6.403	**91**	8281	9.539	**141**	19,881	11.874
42	1764	6.481	**92**	8464	9.592	**142**	20,164	11.916
43	1849	6.557	**93**	8649	9.644	**143**	20,449	11.958
44	1936	6.633	**94**	8836	9.695	**144**	20,736	12.000
45	2025	6.708	**95**	9025	9.747	**145**	21,025	12.042
46	2116	6.782	**96**	9216	9.798	**146**	21,316	12.083
47	2209	6.856	**97**	9409	9.849	**147**	21,609	12.124
48	2304	6.928	**98**	9604	9.899	**148**	21,904	12.166
49	2401	7.000	**99**	9801	9.950	**149**	22,201	12.207
50	2500	7.071	**100**	10,000	10.000	**150**	22,500	12.247

A-3 Adding Positive and Negative Numbers

See the Teacher's Manual for the objectives.

Temperatures above and below zero can be represented by positive and negative numbers.

10° or +10° means 10 degrees above zero.

−5° means 5 degrees below zero.

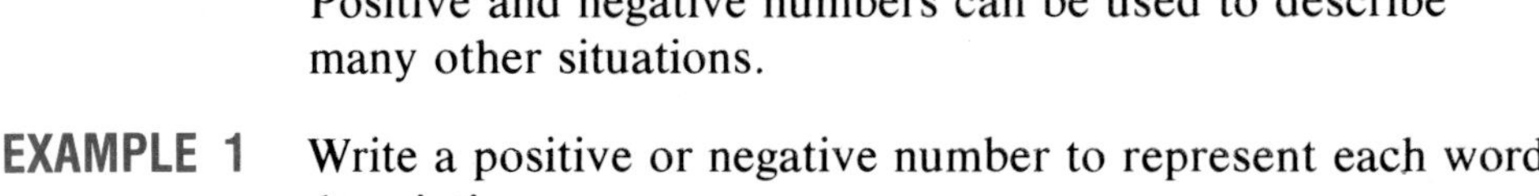

Positive and negative numbers can be used to describe many other situations.

EXAMPLE 1 Write a positive or negative number to represent each word description.

Word Description	Number Description
a. A profit of $150	**150**
b. A 7-yard loss in football	**−7**
c. 3 minutes before rocket lift-off	**−3**

After completing Example 1, you may wish to have students do some or all of Exercises 1-8.

You can use a number line to add positive and negative numbers.

PROCEDURE To use a number line to add two numbers:

[1] Graph the first number.

[2] Draw an arrow to represent the second number.

a. Draw the arrow to the right when the second number is positive.

b. Draw the arrow to the left when the second number is negative.

[3] Read the answer at the tip of the arrow.

EXAMPLE 2 Use a number line to find each sum.

a. $-3 + 7$ **b.** $6 + (-8)$

Solutions:

a. [1] Graph −3.

[2] Draw an arrow for 7.

[3] Read the answer: **4**

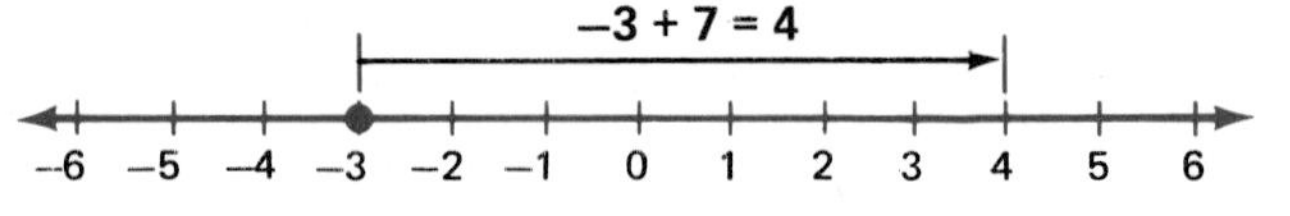

b. [1] Graph 6.

[2] Draw an arrow for −8.

[3] Read the answer: **−2**

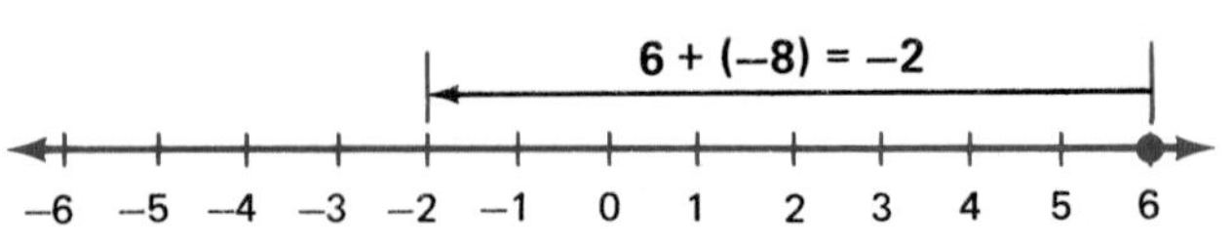

EXERCISES

Write a positive or negative number to represent each word description. (Example 1)

1. A rise of 15° in temperature +15

2. 600 meters below sea level −600

3. A 5-yard loss in football −5

4. A profit of $200 +200

5. A loss in weight of 2 kilograms −2

6. Two seconds after rocket lift-off +2

7. A bank deposit of $125 +125

8. A bank withdrawal of $160 −160

Use a number line to find each sum. (Example 2)

9. $1+7$ 8	**10.** $4+3$ 7	**11.** $-2+6$ 4	**12.** $-1+8$ 7
13. $6+(-4)$ 2	**14.** $9+(-5)$ 4	**15.** $3+(-7)$ −4	**16.** $2+(-7)$ −5
17. $-3+(-1)$ −4	**18.** $-2+(-5)$ −7	**19.** $-3+(-4)$ −7	**20.** $-5+(-6)$ −11
21. $3+2$ 5	**22.** $10+7$ 17	**23.** $8+(-8)$ 0	**24.** $13+(-13)$ 0
25. $-2+(-2)$ −4	**26.** $-5+(-5)$ −10	**27.** $-9+9$ 0	**28.** $-7+7$ 0
29. $0+(-4)$ −4	**30.** $(-6)+0$ −6	**31.** $12+(-8)$ 4	**32.** $-6+(-9)$ −15
33. $-2+5$ 3	**34.** $-8+5$ −3	**35.** $-5+(-8)$ −13	**36.** $-4+(-1)$ −5
37. $4+4$ 8	**38.** $7+1$ 8	**39.** $-10+2$ −8	**40.** $-8+4$ −4
41. $8+(-3)$ 5	**42.** $11+(-6)$ 5	**43.** $-1+(-6)$ −7	**44.** $-3+(-1)$ −4

APPLICATIONS: Using Addition of Positive and Negative Numbers

45. A football team was on their own 15–yard line. From there, they gained 8 yards and then lost 12 yards. On what yard line are they now? 11

46. Tomas deposited $185 in his checking account. He then wrote checks for $12.50, $25.00, and $31.95. How much was left in the account? $115.55

47. A balloon was 600 meters above the ground. It dropped 150 meters and then rose 75 meters. How many meters above the ground was it then? 525

48. A submarine dove 50 meters below sea level. Then it dove another 125 meters. How many meters does it have to rise to reach the surface of the water? 175

49. The temperature at 8:00 A.M. on January 26 last year was 5°C. It rose 11°C by 2:00 P.M. Then it dropped 6°C by 5:30 P.M. What was the temperature at 5:30 P.M.? 10°C

A-4 Subtracting Positive and Negative Numbers

See the Teacher's Manual for the objectives.

The numbers 4 and -4 are each 4 units from 0.

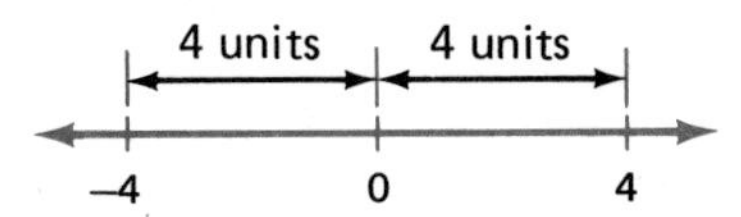

The numbers 4 and -4 are on *opposite sides of 0* on the number line. 4 and -4 are **opposites.** The number 0 is its own opposite.

Subtracting a number is the same as adding its opposite.

TABLE Subtraction	Think	Related Addition
$7-5$	The opposite of 5 is -5.	$7+(-5)$
$-1-4$	The opposite of 4 is -4.	$-1+(-4)$
$8-(-6)$	The opposite of (-6) is 6.	$8+6$
$-3-(-2)$	The opposite of (-2) is 2.	$-3+2$

You may wish to have students do some or all of Exercises 1-12 before proceeding with the lesson.

PROCEDURE To subtract two integers:

[1] Write an addition problem for the subtraction problem.

[2] Add.

EXAMPLE Use a number line to subtract.

a. $4-6$ **b.** $-4-(-5)$

Solutions: Write an addition problem for each subtraction problem.

[1] **a.** $4-6=4+(-6)$ **b.** $-4-(-5)=-4+5$

[2]

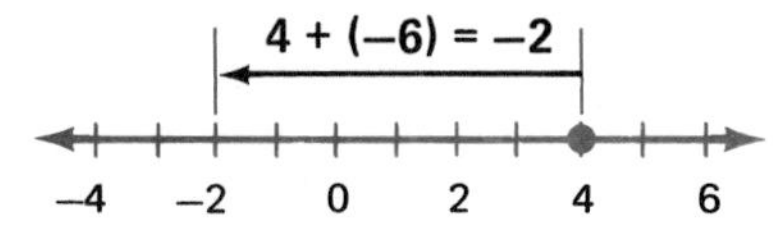

The tip of the arrow is at -2.
So, $4-6=\mathbf{-2}$.

$-4+5=1$

The tip of the arrow is at 1.
So, $-4+5=\mathbf{1}$.

EXERCISES

Write an addition problem for each subtraction problem. (Table)

1. $6-2$ $6+(-2)$
2. $4-1$ $4+(-1)$
3. $-8-3$ $-8+(-3)$
4. $-10-3$ $-10+(-3)$
5. $-12-(-9)$ $-12+9$
6. $-15-(-5)$ $-15+5$
7. $-8-(-11)$ $-8+11$
8. $-4-(-1)$ $-4+1$
9. $13-(-30)$ $13+30$
10. $12-(-25)$ $12+25$
11. $22-(-11)$ $22+11$
12. $32-(-4)$ $32+4$

Use a number line to subtract. (Example)

13. $-5-1$ −6	**14.** $-4-2$ −6	**15.** $7-5$ 2	**16.** $8-3$ 5
17. $9-10$ −1	**18.** $8-12$ −4	**19.** $6-(-2)$ 8	**20.** $9-(-8)$ 17
21. $-1-(-10)$ 9	**22.** $-8-(-2)$ −6	**23.** $-7-(-2)$ −5	**24.** $-3-(-8)$ 5
25. $0-(-6)$ 6	**26.** $0-(-3)$ 3	**27.** $-7-(-6)$ −1	**28.** $4-(-1)$ 5
29. $-9-4$ −13	**30.** $-8-4$ −12	**31.** $-3-(-1)$ −2	**32.** $-4-(-5)$ 1
33. $12-7$ 5	**34.** $-5-7$ −12	**35.** $-8-4$ −12	**36.** $4-8$ −4
37. $-2-(-7)$ 5	**38.** $-6-(-3)$ −3	**39.** $0-(-8)$ 8	**40.** $0-(-7)$ 7
41. $11-4$ 7	**42.** $6-8$ −2	**43.** $-111-(-9)$ −102	**49.** $-7-(-3)$ −4
45. $-9-2$ −11	**46.** $-13-(-1)$ −12	**47.** $2-(-6)$ 8	**48.** $-2-5$ −7
49. $-8-(-1)$ −7	**50.** $-6-(-5)$ −1	**51.** $-15-5$ −20	**52.** $-16-10$ −26
53. $9-(-11)$ 20	**54.** $6-(-9)$ 15	**55.** $-4-(-9)$ 5	**56.** $-4-(-7)$ 3

APPLICATIONS: Using Subtraction of Positive and Negative Numbers

Find each temperature change.

57. From 18°C to 24°C 6°	**58.** From 5°C to 18°C 13°	**59.** From −3°C to 8°C 11°
60. From −2°C to 0°C 2°	**61.** From 8°C to −1°C −9°	**62.** From 4°C to −2°C −6°
63. From −3°C to 10°C 13°	**64.** From −1°C to 12°C 13°	**65.** From 16°C to 7°C −9°

A combination of cold temperatures and high winds can make a person feel colder than the actual temperature. This is called **wind chill.**

Find the difference between the actual temperature and the wind chill temperature.

	Actual Temperature	Wind Chill Temperature
66.	0°	−22° 22°
67.	20°	−10° 30°
68.	25°	−13° 38°
69.	10°	−24° 34°

70. The actual temperature on a windy January day was 15°F. The wind chill temperature was −9°F. How many degrees colder was that? 24°

71. The wind chill temperature last December 18 was −11°F. The actual temperature was 6°F. What was the difference in temperature? 17°

A-5 Multiplying Positive and Negative Numbers

See the Teacher's Manual for the objectives.

Each pair of numbers below has **unlike signs.**

-8×9 $\quad 15 \times -6$ $\quad -4 \times 9$ $\quad 1 \times -15.$

The product of two numbers having unlike signs is negative.

The product of any number and zero equals zero.

PROCEDURE To find the product of two numbers having unlike signs:

1. Multiply the numbers.
2. Insert a negative sign before the product.

EXAMPLE 1 Multiply.

a. 9×-6 **b.** -3×12 **c.** 0×-4

Solutions: **a.** $9 \times -6 = \mathbf{-54}$ **b.** $-3 \times 12 = \mathbf{-36}$ **c.** $0 \times -4 = \mathbf{0}$

After completing Example 1, you may wish to have students do some or all of Exercises 1-20.

Each pair of numbers below has **like signs.**

2×10 $\quad -4 \times -5$ $\quad -1 \times -8$ $\quad 3 \times 20$

The product of two numbers having like signs is positive.

PROCEDURE To find the product of two numbers having like signs:

1. Multiply.
2. Insert a positive sign (or no symbol at all) before the product.

EXAMPLE 2 Multiply.

a. 13×9 **b.** $-4 \times (-7)$ **c.** $-31 \times (-1)$

Solutions: **a.** $13 \times 9 = \mathbf{117}$ **b.** $-4 \times (-7) = \mathbf{28}$ **c.** $-31 \times (-1) = \mathbf{31}$

EXERCISES

Multiply. (Example 1)

1. -4×5 −20 **2.** -6×3 −18 **3.** -11×2 −22 **4.** -16×3 −48

5. $8 \times (-4)$ −32 **6.** $9 \times (-9)$ −81 **7.** $12 \times (-8)$ −96 **8.** $7 \times (-11)$ −77

9. -3×17 −51 **10.** -5×45 −225 **11.** $27 \times (-2)$ −54 **12.** $32 \times (-3)$ −96

13. $200 \times (-1)$ −200 **14.** -1×62 −62 **15.** -6×16 −96 **16.** $22 \times (-4)$ −88

17. -93×2 −186 18. -46×5 −230 19. $8 \times (-12)$ −96 20. $21 \times (-7)$ −147

(Example 2)

21. $-17 \times (-3)$ 51 22. $-13 \times (-10)$ 130 23. $-7 \times (-7)$ 49 24. $-8 \times (-8)$ 64

25. $-1 \times (-1)$ 1 26. $-15 \times (-100)$ 1500 27. $-35 \times (-3)$ 105 28. $0 \times (-1)$ 0

29. 18×3 54 30. 54×2 108 31. 40×19 760 32. 60×5 300

33. $-60 \times (-5)$ 300 34. $-10 \times (-10)$ 100 35. $-15 \times (-8)$ 120 36. -7×-9 63

Mixed Practice

37. -2×24 −48 38. 21×-7 −147 39. $-12 \times (-10)$ 120 40. 17×8 136

41. $12 \times (-11)$ −132 42. -12×11 −132 43. $-12 \times (-12)$ 144 44. $-11 \times (-11)$ 121

45. $64 \times (-8)$ −512 46. -64×8 −512 47. -6×18 −108 48. $6 \times (-18)$ −108

49. 6×18 108 50. $0 \times (-120)$ 0 51. $-18 \times (-18)$ 324 52. $-16 \times (-11)$ 176

APPLICATIONS: Using Multiplication

55. $3 \times (-4) = -12$ 56. $2 \times 1.5 = 3$

Use positive and negative numbers to represent each situation as a multiplication problem. Then find the product.

53. Five penalties of 4 yards each. $5 \times (-4) = -20$
54. Two bonuses of \$750 each. $2 \times 750 = 1500$
55. Three times a temperature drop of 4°
56. Twice a temperature gain of 1.5° See above.
57. Eight times a depth of 46 meters below sea level $8 \times (-46) = -368$
58. Three times a loss of 6 yards in rushing $3 \times (-6) = -18$
59. Three withdrawals of \$50 each from a savings account $3 \times (-50) = -150$

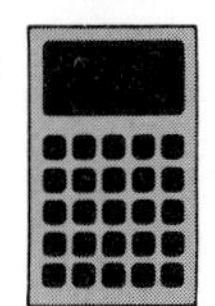

CHECKING MULTIPLICATION

Use a calculator to check each answer. Be sure to check whether the product is a positive or a negative number. Correct any wrong answers.

1. $286 \times (-12) = -3432$ Checks
2. $421 \times (-18) = -7576$ −7578
3. $-342 \times (-318) = -108{,}756$ 108, 756
4. $-628 \times (-287) = 180{,}236$ Checks
5. $84.7 \times 29.2 = 247.324$ 2473.24
6. $-65.8 \times 73.7 = 4849.46$ −4849.46
7. $-38 \times 723 = 27{,}474$ −27,474
8. $486 \times (-39) = -18{,}954$ Checks
9. $6.40 \times (-3.75) = 24$ −24
10. $-8.14 \times 5.21 = 42.4094$ −42.4094

A-6 Dividing Positive and Negative Numbers

See the Teacher's Manual for the objectives.

The quotient of two numbers having unlike signs is negative.

The quotient of two numbers having like signs is positive.

PROCEDURE To find the quotient of two numbers:

1. Divide.
2. a. Insert a negative sign before the quotient when the numbers have unlike signs.

   b. Insert a positive sign before the quotient when the numbers have like signs.

EXAMPLE Find each quotient.

a. $54 \div (-9)$ **b.** $-63 \div 7$ **c.** $-132 \div (-11)$

Solutions:

a. $54 \div (-9) = -6$ ← *Procedure 2a*

b. $-63 \div 7 = -9$ ← *Procedure 2a*

c. $-132 \div (-11) = 12$ ← *Procedure 2b*

EXERCISES

Divide.

1. $35 \div 7$ 5 **2.** $-35 \div 7$ −5 **3.** $35 \div (-7)$ −5 **4.** $-35 \div (-7)$ 5

5. $100 \div (-25)$ −4 **6.** $-100 \div 25$ −4 **7.** $-100 \div (-25)$ 4 **8.** $-25 \div 1$ −25

9. $-25 \div (-1)$ 25 **10.** $-20 \div (-4)$ 5 **11.** $-18 \div (-2)$ 9 **12.** $18 \div 2$ 9

13. $18 \div (-2)$ −9 **14.** $-48 \div 4$ −12 **15.** $20 \div (-1)$ −20 **16.** $-20 \div 1$ −20

17. $-20 \div (-1)$ 20 **18.** $-36 \div (-9)$ 4 **19.** $-40 \div (-5)$ 8 **20.** $60 \div (-12)$ −5

21. $65 \div (-13)$ −5 **22.** $-33 \div 11$ −3 **23.** $-63 \div (-7)$ 9 **24.** $-54 \div 9$ −6

25. $-15 \div (-5)$ 3 **26.** $28 \div (-7)$ −4 **27.** $-76 \div (-19)$ 4 **28.** $-68 \div 17$ −4

29. $24 \div 4$ 6 **30.** $-144 \div 16$ −9 **31.** $156 \div (-12)$ −13 **32.** $-112 \div (-8)$ 14

More Challenging Problems

Find the missing number.

33. $50 \div \underline{\ ?\ } = 5$ 10 **34.** $\underline{\ ?\ } \div (-3) = 12$ −36 **35.** $-72 \div \underline{\ ?\ } = 6$ −12

36. $-90 \div \underline{\ ?\ } = -10$ 9 **37.** $\underline{\ ?\ } \div 7 = -7$ −49 **38.** $\underline{\ ?\ } \div 18 = -5$ −90

39. $-44 \div \underline{\ ?\ } = -11$ 4 **40.** $\underline{\ ?\ } \div (-20) = 5$ −100 **41.** $\underline{\ ?\ } \div 1 = -9$ −9

42. $\underline{\ ?\ } \div (-7) = 0$ 0 **43.** $-156 \div \underline{\ ?\ } = 39$ −4 **44.** $-65 \div \underline{\ ?\ } = -13$ 5

A-7 Graphing Equations

See the Teacher's Manual for the objectives.

You can use an **ordered pair** of numbers to locate points in a **coordinate plane.** First, draw a horizontal number line. This is called the **x axis.** Through the point 0 on this axis, draw a vertical number line. This is called the **y axis.** The point 0 is the **origin.** In the figure at the right, the ordered pair (4, 3) gives the location of point A.

A(4, 3)

***x* coordinate** → 4; 3 ← ***y* coordinate**

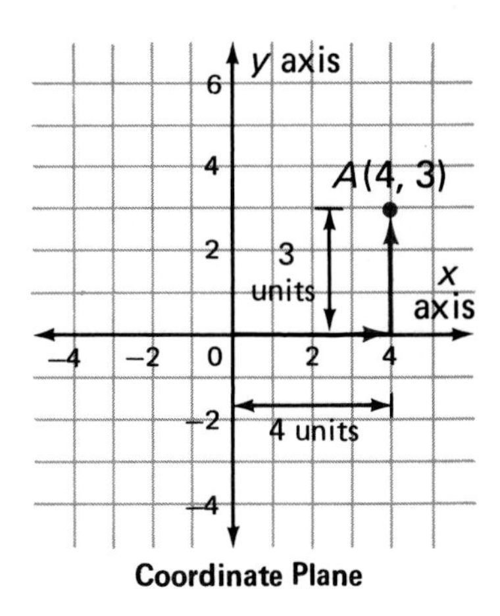

Coordinate Plane

PROCEDURE To locate (or to graph) a point on the coordinate plane:

1. Start at the origin. Count the number of units to the right (positive number) or to the left (negative number). This is the x coordinate.
2. Count the number of units up (positive number) or down (negative number). This is the y coordinate.
3. Write (or graph) the point, $P(x, y)$.

EXAMPLE 1 Use the graph at the right to

a. give the coordinates of point P.

b. graph $Q(-2, 3)$.

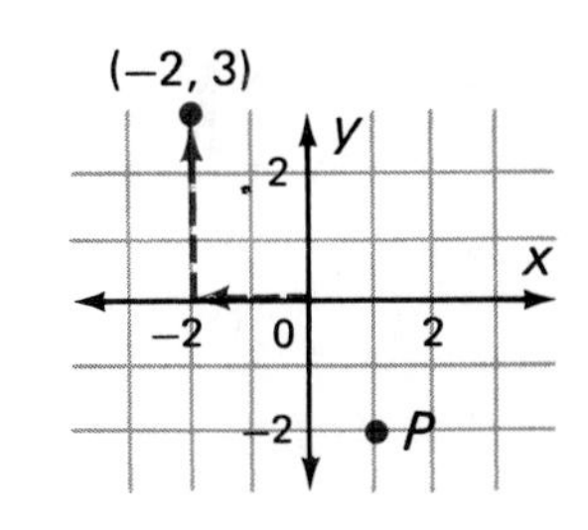

Solutions: **a.** Start at the origin. Point P is 1 unit to the *right* and 2 units *down.* Ordered pair: **(1, −2)**

b. Start at the origin. Nove 2 units to the *left.* Then move 3 units *up*. Label the point Q.

After completing Example 1, you may wish to have students do some or all of Exercises 1-17.

You use a table of ordered pairs to graph an equation.

PROCEDURE To graph an equation:

1. Make a table of ordered pairs.
2. Graph the ordered pairs. Draw a straight line connecting them.

EXAMPLE 2 The equation $I = 0.12P$ gives the yearly interest on P dollars invested at 12%. Graph this equation.

Solution: [1] Make a table. Choose at least 3 values for P.

P	$0.12P = I$	P	I
100	$(0.12)(100) = 12$	100	12
200	$(0.12)(200) = 24$	200	24
300	$(0.12)(300) = 36$	300	36

[2] Graph the ordered pairs.

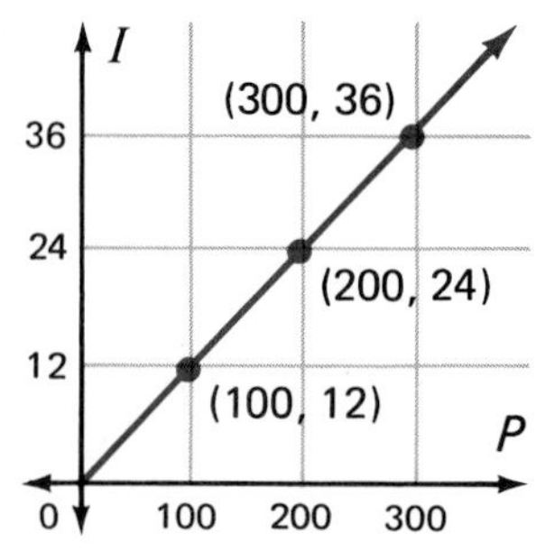

EXERCISES

For Exercises 1–12, give the coordinates (ordered pair) for each point graphed at the right. (Example 1)

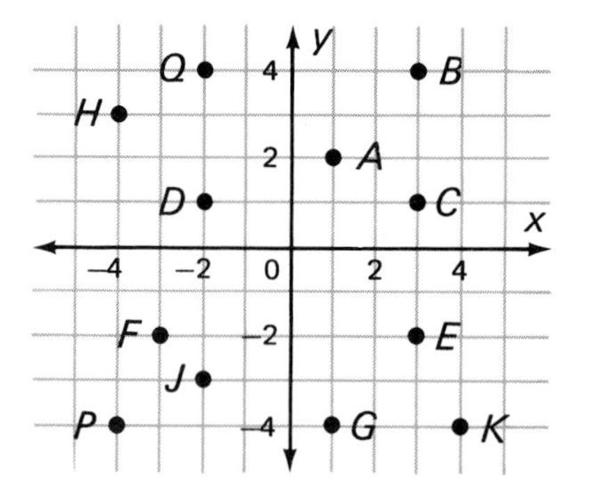

1. A **(1, 2)**
2. B **(3, 4)**
3. C **(3, 1)**
4. D **(−2, 1)**
5. E **(3, −2)**
6. F **(−3, −2)**
7. G **(1, −4)**
8. H **(−4, 3)**
9. J **(−2, −3)**
10. K **(4, −4)**
11. P **(−4, −4)**
12. Q **(−2, 4)**

For Exercises 13–17, draw and label a pair of axes. Then graph the point for each ordered pair. Label each point.

13. P(3, 1) **13. 3 units to the right; 1 unit up**
14. Q(−1, 1) **14. 1 unit to the left; 1 unit up**
15. R(−3, −4) **15. 3 units to the left; 4 units down**
16. T(4, −6) **16. 4 units to the right; 6 units down**
17. V(−3, −5) **17. 3 units to the left; 5 units down**

For each equation in Exercises 18–19, complete the table and then graph the equation. (Example 2)

18. The equation $I = 0.14P$ gives the yearly interest on P dollars invested at 14%. **The graph is the line joining the points.**

P	100	200	300
I	? **14**	? **28**	? **42**

19. The equation $m = 10c$ gives the number of millimeters, m, in c centimeters. **The graph is the line joining the points.**

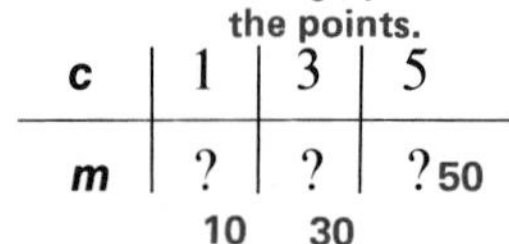

c	1	3	5
m	? **10**	? **30**	? **50**

Appendix Review

The exercises review the vocabulary, skills, and applications presented in the appendix.

Part 1: VOCABULARY

For Exercises 1–5, choose from the box at the right the word(s) that completes each statement.

origin
square root
x axis
square
y axis
negative

1. When you multiply a number by itself, the product is called the __?__ of the number. (Page 410) square
2. One of the two equal factors of a number is the __?__ of the number. (Page 410) square root
3. The product of two numbers with unlike signs is __?__. (Pages 418–419) negative
4. In a coordinate plane, the horizontal number line is called the __?__. (Pages 421–422) x axis
5. The x axis and the y axis meet a point called the __?__. (Pages 421–422) origin

Part 2: SKILLS

Find each answer. (Page 410)

6. 8^2 64
7. 2^2 4
8. 12^2 144
9. 11^2 121
10. 21^2 441
11. 32^2 1024
12. $\sqrt{9}$ 3
13. $\sqrt{4}$ 2
14. $\sqrt{25}$ 5
15. $\sqrt{81}$ 9
16. $\sqrt{121}$ 11
17. $\sqrt{169}$ 13

Use the table on page 413 to find each answer. (Pages 411–413)

18. 83^2 6889
19. 97^2 9409
20. 65^2 4225
21. 74^2 5476
22. 121^2 14,641
23. 142^2 20,164
24. $\sqrt{22}$ 4.690
25. $\sqrt{37}$ 6.083
26. $\sqrt{78}$ 8.832
27. $\sqrt{8836}$ 94
28. $\sqrt{19{,}044}$ 138
29. $\sqrt{12{,}996}$ 114

Use a number line to find each sum. (Pages 414–415)

30. $6 + 8$ 14
31. $4 + 5$ 9
32. $-3 + 9$ 6
33. $-7 + 4$ −3
34. $3 + (-6)$ −3
35. $9 + (-4)$ 5
36. $-8 + (-7)$ −15
37. $-2 + (-5)$ −7

Use a number line to subtract. (Pages 416–417)

38. $-4 - 2$ −6
39. $-3 - 8$ −11
40. $6 - 5$ 1
41. $3 - 7$ −4
42. $-5 - (-2)$ −3
43. $-9 - (-12)$ 3
44. $0 - 7$ −7
45. $0 - (-6)$ 6

Multiply. (Pages 418–419)

46. -3×5 −15
47. -7×6 −42
48. $3 \times (-9)$ −27
49. $4 \times (-12)$ −48
50. $-9 \times (-8)$ 72
51. $-6 \times (-5)$ 30
52. $-12 \times (-13)$ 156
53. $-11 \times (-10)$ 110

Divide. (Page 420)

54. $16 \div (-4)$ −4
55. $28 \div (-7)$ −4
56. $-48 \div 6$ −8
57. $-56 \div 8$ −7
58. $-14 \div (-2)$ 7
59. $-21 \div (-7)$ 3
60. $-100 \div (-10)$ 10
61. $-50 \div (-25)$ 2

For Exercises 62–73, give the coordinates (ordered pair) for each point graphed at the right. (Pages 421–422)

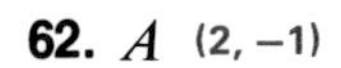

62. A (2, −1) **63.** B (3, 2) **64.** C (−2, 4)

65. D (−3, 1) **66.** E (−2, −3) **67.** F (−1, 1)

68. G (2, 4) **69.** H (3, −3) **70.** J (5, −2)

71. K (−4, −1) **72.** L (−3, −2) **73.** M (1, 2)

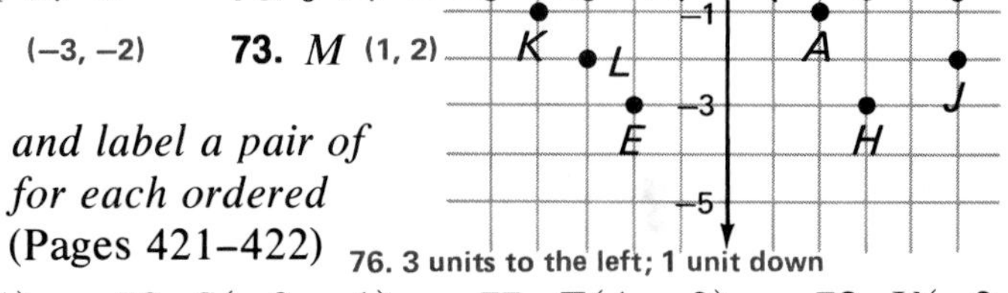

For Exercises 74–78, draw and label a pair of axes. Then graph the point for each ordered pair. Label each point. (Pages 421–422)

74. $P(3, 2)$ **75.** $Q(-2, 1)$ **76.** $S(-3, -1)$ **77.** $T(4, -2)$ **78.** $V(-2, -4)$

74. 3 units to the right; 2 units up 75. 2 units to the left; 1 unit up. 76. 3 units to the left; 1 unit down 77. 4 units to the right; 2 units down 78. 2 units to the left; 4 units down

For each equation in Exercises 79–80, complete the table and then graph the equation. (Pages 421–422)

79. There are 12 inches in 1 foot. The equation $I = 12F$ describes this relation. The graph is the line joining the points.

F	1	2	3
I	?	?	?
	12	24	36

80. The equation $I = 0.17P$ gives the yearly simple interest on P dollars invested at 17%. The graph is the line joining the points.

P	100	200	300
I	?	?	?
	17	34	51

Part 3: APPLICATIONS

For Exercises 81–82, use a calculator. Round each answer to the nearest whole kilometer. (Pages 411–412)

81. Use the formula $s = \sqrt{252df}$ to find s when $d = 20$ meters and $f = 0.60$. 55 km/hr

82. Use the formula $s = \sqrt{252df}$ to find s when $d = 30$ meters and $f = 0.85$. 80 km/hr

83. A submarine dove 40 meters below sea level. Then it dove another 38 meters. How many meters does it have to rise to reach the surface of the water? (Pages 414–415) 78

84. Find the temperature change from 9°C to −2°C. (Pages 416–417) −11°

85. The actual temperature on a windy February day was 11°F. The wind chill temperature was −4°F. How many degrees colder was that? (Pages 416–417) 15°

APPENDIX B

INTRODUCTION TO COMPUTERS

B-1 The Language of Computers

See the Teacher's Manual for the objectives.

In today's world everyone comes in contact with computers. You probably have played video games. Your report card may be printed by a computer. No matter what your career will be, you must learn to deal with computers.

The first electronic computer was completed in 1945 at the University of Pennsylvania. Named **ENIAC** ("**E**lectrical **N**umerical **I**ntegrator **a**nd **C**omputer"), it weighed almost 30 tons and filled the entire basement of a building. It could do 5000 additions in one second.

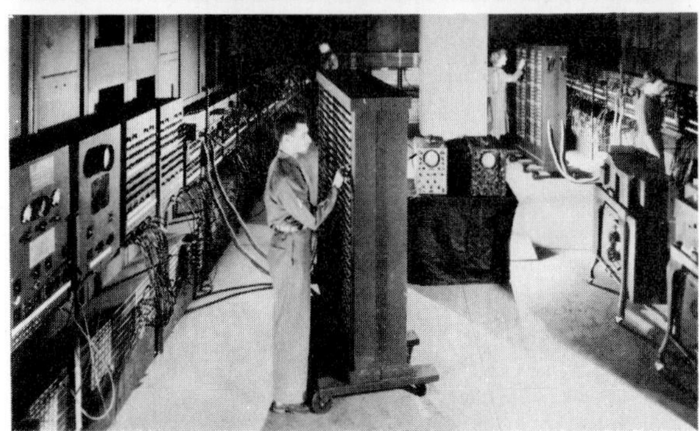

Since ENIAC, computers have steadily gotten smaller, faster, and more reliable. Today schools, businesses, and homes have **microcomputers** which sit on desktops. The "brain" of one of these machines is a **microprocessor,** a tiny "chip" that can fit on your thumb and do millions of calculations in one second.

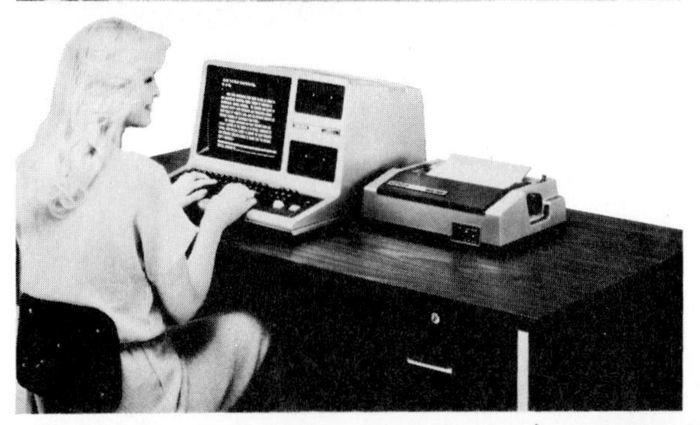

Like a calculator, a computer cannot do anything on its own. It must be given instructions in a step-by-step form called a **computer program.** A program must be written in a language that the computer understands. The most common language for microcomputers is called BASIC (**B**eginners' **A**ll-purpose **S**ymbolic **I**nstruction **C**ode), which was created at Dartmouth College in 1965. (Later in this appendix you will learn how to write simple programs in BASIC.)

A tiny chip on an enlarged stamp.

Any computer program has four phases.

1. INPUT: A program and data are entered into the machine from a keyboard, a tape, or a diskette. Some computers also accept input from punched cards.

2. STORAGE: Anything entered into a computer goes into **memory.** Memory can hold thousands of numbers and words. Larger systems have additional storage in the form of diskettes or tapes.

3. PROCESSING: When told to RUN ("execute") a program, a computer does what the program tells it to do. It computes values and can make decisions based on those values.

4. OUTPUT: The results of a program are usually typed on a **printer** or shown on a television screen ("cathode ray tube" or "CRT"). Computers can also put answers on tapes or diskettes.

EXERCISES

Classify each component of a computer system as (A) input, (B) storage, (C) processing, or (D) output. Some items may be classified in more than one way.

1. keyboard (A)
2. tape (A), (B), (D)
3. memory (B)
4. cathode ray tube (C)
5. microprocessor (C)
6. punched card (A)
7. diskette (A), (B), (D)
8. printer (D)
9. television screen (D)

Complete each statement.

10. The first electronic computer was completed in the year _?_. 1945
11. The name of the first electronic computer was _?_. ENIAC
12. The most common language for microcomputers is _?_. BASIC
13. Any data entered into a computer goes into _?_. memory
14. When told to _?_ a program, a computer does what the program tells it to do. run
15. Since a computer can do nothing on its own, it must have a(n) _?_ to direct it. computer program

B-2 Formulas

See the Teacher's Manual for the objectives.

Computers can work with expressions or formulas. A formula involves numbers and operations. In most microcomputers, the following symbols are used.

SYMBOL	OPERATION
+	Addition
−	Subtraction
*	Multiplication
/	Division
↑	Raising to a **power** (such as 3^2)

EXAMPLE 1 Write $20 + 3 \times 8 \div 6$ as a computer formula.

Solution:

```
20 + 3 * 8 / 6
```

After completing Example 1, you may wish to have students do some or all of Exercises 1-12.

The multiplication sign (*) must always be shown. Thus, $3(8 + 4)$ is entered into a computer as

```
3 * (8 + 4).
```

In working out a formula, a computer follows the usual "order of operations."

Order of Operations

1. Raising to a power is done first.
2. Multiplication and division are done from left to right.
3. Additions and subtractions are done, from left to right.
4. Parentheses are used to change the order.

EXAMPLE 2 Evaluate: **a.** `20 + 3 * 8/6` **b.** `5 ↑ 2 * (4 + 2)`

Solutions:

a.
```
20 + 3 * 8/6 = 20 + 24/6
             = 20 + 4
             = 24
```

b.
```
5 ↑ 2 * (4 + 2) = 5 ↑ 2 * 6
                = 25 * 6
                = 150
```

A formula may contain a variable. A **variable** is a letter that the computer can replace with a number.

EXAMPLE 3 If X = 3, what value would a computer get for each of the following?

a. 5 * X − 4 **b.** 15 / (X + 2)

Solutions: Replace X with 3 and follow the order of operations.

a. 5 * X − 4 = 5 * (3) − 4
= 15 − 4
= **11**

b. 15 / (X + 2) = 15 / (3 + 2)
= 15 / 5
= **3**

EXERCISES

Write each arithmetic formula as a computer formula. (Example 1)

1. $45 - 6 \times 7$ 45 − 6 * 7
2. $18 \div 3 + 5$ 18 / 3 + 5
3. $10 \times 20 \div 5$ 10 * 20 / 5
4. $3^2 + 4^2$ 3 ↑ 2 + 4 ↑ 2
5. $8 \times 9 + 4 \times 5$ 8 * 9 + 4 * 5
6. $6 \div 3 - 9 \div 9$ 6 / 3 − 9 / 9
7. $14 \div 7 \times 3 + 4$ 14 / 7 * 3 + 4
8. $17 - 9 + 6 \times 4$ 17 − 9 + 6 * 4
9. $(4 + 5) \times 4$ (4 + 5) * 4
10. $40 - (8 \times 5)$ 40 − (8 * 5)
11. $12 \div (3 + 3)$ 12 / (3 + 3)
12. $(5 + 6) \times (12 - 2)$ (5 + 6) * (12 − 2)

13. Evaluate each computer formula in Exercises 1–12. (Example 2)
1:3; 2:11; 3:40; 4:25; 5:92; 6:1; 7:10; 8:32; 9:36; 10:0; 11:2; 12:110

What value would a computer get for these formulas if X = 2 ? (Example 3)

14. X + 5 7
15. 2 * X + 5 9
16. 3 * (X - 1) 3
17. 30 − 5 * X 20
18. 5 * X / 2 5
19. 40 / X 20
20. (X + 7) / 3 3
21. 16 / (X − 1) 16
22. 50 / (5 * X) 5
23. X ↑ 2 4
24. (X - 1) ↑ 2 1
25. 100 - X ↑ 2 96

MORE CHALLENGING PROBLEMS

What value would a computer get for these formulas if X = 4 *and* Y = 3*?*

26. 2 * X + Y 11
27. 3 * Y − X 5
28. (X + Y) / 2 $\frac{7}{2}$
29. X * Y / 6 2
30. 6 * Y / X $\frac{9}{2}$
31. 31 / (X − Y) 31
32. (X + Y) * 2 14
33. X * 4 - 3 * Y 7

There is no square root sign ($\sqrt{\ }$) on computer keyboards. The abbreviation SQR *means square root. Evaluate these computer formulas if* X = 16.

34. SQR (X) 4
35. SQR (X + 9) 5
36. 15 / SQR (X − 7) 5
37. SQR (X − 7) / 15 $\frac{1}{5}$

B-3 Program Statements

See the Teacher's Manual for the objectives.

Picture part of the computer's memory as 26 "boxes". Each box is named by a letter. Each box can hold a number. To store a number in a computer, you must assign the number to a memory location (box). For example, in the BASIC language,

A	B	C	. . .	X	Y	Z

```
LET X = 10
```

puts a 10 in location X.

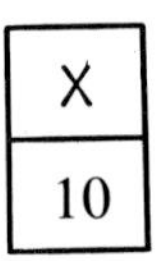

Once numbers are in memory, they can be added, subtracted, multiplied, and so on. The statement

```
LET Y = X + 7
```

makes the computer take the number in location X, add 7 to it, and then put the result in Y. Thus,

if X = 10, then Y = 10 + 7 = **17.**

EXAMPLE 1 What is the value in location Y after the computer does these steps?

a.
```
LET X = 9
LET Y = 5 * X
```

b.
```
LET A = 7
LET B = 4
LET Y = A - B
```

Solutions:

a. Y = 5 * X   ◀ *X* = 9
= 5 * 9 = **45**

b. Y = A − B   ◀ *A* = 7, *B* = 4
= 7 − 4 = **3**

After completing Example 1, you may wish to have students do Exercises 1-3.

To see the number stored in a location, use the PRINT command. For example,

```
PRINT Y
```

causes the number in location Y to be printed or shown on a CRT screen.

EXAMPLE 2 What number is printed after the computer does the steps shown at the right?

```
LET R = 12
LET Y = R / 3
PRINT Y
```

Solution: Y = R / 3   ◀ *R* = 12
= 12 / 3 = **4**

After completing Example 2, you may wish to have students do Exercises 4-7.

Another way to put a number in memory is the INPUT command. For example,

```
INPUT X
```

takes a number typed on the keyboard and stores it in location X.

EXAMPLE 3 What number will the computer print for Y if 20 is entered for X?

```
INPUT X
LET Y = 2 * X - 5
PRINT Y
```

Solution:

```
Y = 2 * X - 5    ◀ X = 20
Y = 2 * 20 - 5
Y = 40 - 5 = 35
```

The statements in Example 3 almost form a BASIC program that you can enter into a computer. You must number each line and add an END statement as shown at the right.

```
1Ø INPUT X
2Ø LET Y = 2 * X - 5
3Ø PRINT Y
4Ø END
```

The symbol Ø is used to distinguish zero from the letter "O". The numbers 1Ø, 2Ø, 3Ø, and 4Ø are **line numbers.**

When you type RUN, the machine will show a question mark (?). You then enter a number for X. The computer will print the value for Y.

EXERCISES

Give the value in Y after the computer does these steps. (Example 1) 11. 8:90; 9:900; 10:3 12. 8:180; 4:3600; 10:$\frac{3}{2}$

1.
```
LET R = 9
LET S = 8
LET Y = R + S
```
17

2.
```
LET M = 2Ø
LET P = 4
LET Y = M / P
```
5

3.
```
LET N = 12
LET T = 4
LET Y = T * N
```
48

What number is printed after the computer does these steps? (Example 2)

4.
```
LET J = 6
LET Y = 2 * J - 3
PRINT Y
```
9

5.
```
LET P = 3Ø
LET Y = (P + 2) / 8
PRINT Y
```
4

6.
```
LET Q = 15
LET Y = 6Ø / (2 * Q)
PRINT Y
```
2

7.
```
LET T = 9
LET V = 4Ø * (T / 3)
PRINT V
```
120

What number will the computer print if 10 is entered for X? (Example 3)

8.
```
INPUT X
LET Y = X * 3
PRINT Y
```
30

9.
```
INPUT X
LET Y = X ↑ 2
PRINT Y
```
100

10.
```
INPUT X
LET Y = 9Ø / X
PRINT Y
```
9

11. In Exercises 8–10, what number will the computer print if 30 is entered for X? See above

12. In Exercises 8–10, what number will the computer print if 60 is entered for X?

B-4 Basic Programs in BASIC

See the Teacher's Manual for the objectives.

The types of statements discussed in the last lesson can be used to write BASIC programs to solve problems.

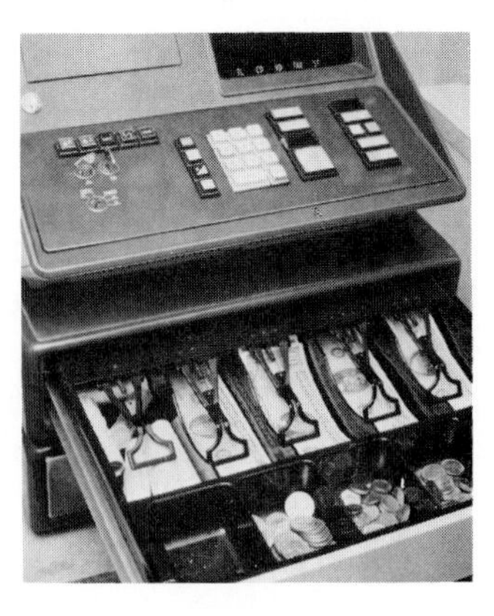

EXAMPLE 1 Write a program which, when given the amount of a purchase (under $1.00), will print the change due from a $1.00 bill.

Solution: Let A = the amount of the purchase.
Let C = the amount of change.

```
10 INPUT A
20 LET C = 1.00 - A
30 PRINT C
40 END
```

Do not put a "$" in statement 20.

Statement 30 of the program in Example 1 can be changed to add a message to the output.

```
30 PRINT "CHANGE = "; C
```

Also, another PRINT statement can be inserted at the beginning of the program to "prompt" the user. Since the first line number is 10, you can insert a new first step without having to renumber the program. Thus, we can number the new first step "5."

```
5 PRINT "WHAT IS THE AMOUNT";
```

The number in front of a statement can be any positive integer. However, at first you should use multiples of 10 to allow for adding statements later.

EXAMPLE 2 Write a program which accepts a baseball player's times–at–bat and number of hits, and prints the batting average.

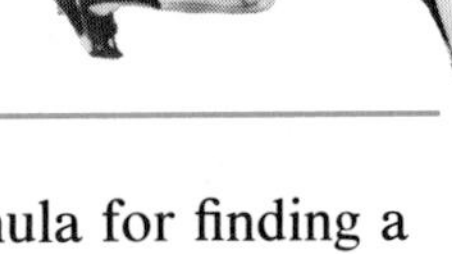

Solution:

```
10 PRINT "HOW MANY TIMES AT BAT";
20 INPUT B
30 PRINT "HOW MANY HITS";
40 INPUT H
50 LET A = H / B
60 PRINT "BATTING AVERAGE = "; A
70 END
```

Statement 50 "LET A = H / B" is the formula for finding a batting average.

Batting Average = Number of Hits ÷ Times at Bat

Example 3 uses the formula for perimeter of a rectangle, $P = 2l + 2w$. This is statement 30 in the program.

EXAMPLE 3 Given the length and the width of a rectangle, print the perimeter.

Solution:

```
1Ø PRINT "WHAT ARE THE LENGTH AND WIDTH";
2Ø INPUT L, W
3Ø LET P = 2 * L + 2 * W
4Ø PRINT "PERIMETER = "; P
5Ø END
```

Notice in statement 2Ø of Example 3 that more than one value can be INPUT in the same step. Also, statement 3Ø could read as follows:

```
3Ø LET P = 2 * (L + W)
```

◀ $P = 2(l + w)$

EXERCISES

Supply the missing statement in each program. (Examples 1, 2, 3)

1.
```
1Ø INPUT X
2Ø LET Y = 2 * X
3Ø  ?     PRINT Y
4Ø END
```

2.
```
1Ø  ?     INPUT A
2Ø LET Z = A + 1Ø
3Ø PRINT Z
4Ø END
```

3.
```
1Ø PRINT "ENTER A
    NUMBER."
2Ø INPUT Y
3Ø LET X = Y / 4
4Ø PRINT "ANSWER = "; X
5Ø  ?     END
```

4.
```
1Ø PRINT "GIVE YOUR
    AGE."
2Ø  ?     INPUT A
3Ø LET D = 365 * A
4Ø PRINT "DAYS = "; D
5Ø END
```

Correct any errors in these programs.

5.
```
1Ø INPUT R
2Ø LET T = 4R          LET T = 4 * R
3Ø PRINT "T = ; T      PRINT "T = "; T
4Ø END
```

6.
```
1Ø INPUT X, Y
2Ø LET X + Y = Z       LET Z = X + Y
3Ø PRINT "SUM = "; Z
4Ø END
```

7.
```
1Ø PRINT GIVE A        PRINT "GIVE
    NUMBER.            A NUMBER."
2Ø INPUT N
3Ø LET X = N SQUARED
4Ø PRINT X             LET X = N ↑ 2
5Ø END
```

8.
```
1Ø PRINT "NUMBER,
    PLEASE."
2Ø INPUT X             INPUT Z
3Ø LET Y = 5 * Z
4Ø PRINT Z
5Ø END
```

The answers for Exercises 9-16 are on page 462.

For Exercises 9–16, write a BASIC *program for each problem. (The references refer to text pages where this material was taught.)*

9. Given the number of wins and losses of a team, compute the winning percentage.

$$\textbf{Winning Percentage} = \textbf{Number of Wins} \div \textbf{Games Played} \times 100$$

10. Enter the number of miles a car has traveled and the number of gallons of gasoline used. Print the average miles–per–gallon of the car. (Pages 236–237)

11. Compute a worker's weekly pay, given the number of hours worked and the rate per hour. (Pages 138–139)

12. Given the length of one side of a square, print the perimeter of the square. (Pages 30–31)

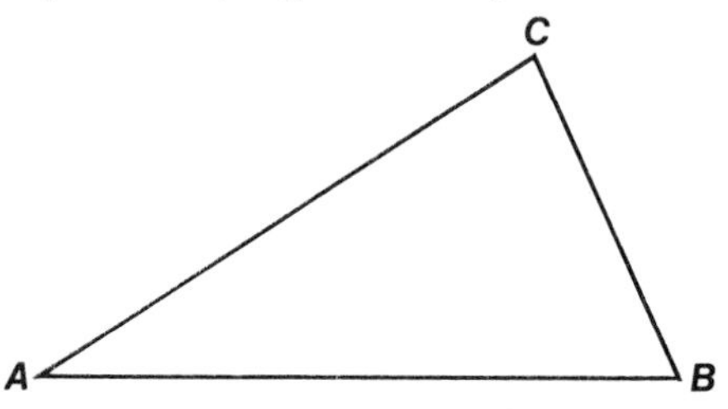

13. *The sum of the measures of the angles of any triangle is 180 degrees.* Given the measures of two angles of a triangle, calculate the measure of the third angle.

14. Given the number of earned runs and innings pitched, compute a baseball pitcher's "earned–run average" ("ERA"). Assume that a whole number of innings has been pitched.

$$\textbf{ERA} = \textbf{Number of Earned Runs} \times 9 \div \textbf{Innings Pitched}$$

More Challenging Problems

15. The "slugging percentage" of a baseball batter is the number of total bases divided by the at–bats. Enter a batter's number of singles, doubles, triples, home runs, and and at-bats. Print the batter's slugging percentage.

Total Bases = 1 × Number of Singles +
2 × Number of Doubles +
3 × Number of Triples +
4 × Number of Home Runs

16. A coin is flipped a number of times. Given the number of heads and the number of tails that occur, compute the per cent of the total flips that are heads.

Per Cent of Heads = 100 × Number of Heads ÷ Total Number of Flips

Appendix Review

The exercises review the vocabulary, skills, and applications presented in the appendix.

Part 1: VOCABULARY

For Exercises 1–4, choose from the box at the right the word(s) that completes each statement.

output
computer program
memory
input
processing

1. The step-by-step form in which instructions are given to a computer is called a __?__. (Pages 426–427) 1. computer program
2. Information entered into a computer is called __?__. input (Pages 426–427)
3. The results of a computer program that are printed or shown on a screen are called __?__. (Pages 426–427) 3. output
4. Anything entered into a computer goes into __?__. memory (Pages 426–427)

Part 2: SKILLS

5. Write a computer formula for: **a.** $24 \div 3 \times 9$ 24 / 3 * 9 **b.** $4^2 - 3^2$ 4 ↑ 2 − 3 ↑ 2 (Pages 428–429)

What value would a computer get for these formulas if X = 3? (Pages 428–429)

6. X + 7 10
7. 2 * X − 4 2
8. 7 * (X + 2) 35
9. (X + 2) ↑ 2 25

What number will the computer print if 12 is entered for X? (Pages 430–431)

10.
```
INPUT X
LET Y = X * 4
PRINT Y
```
48

11.
```
INPUT X
LET Y = X ↑ 2
PRINT Y
```
144

12.
```
INPUT X
LET Y = 48/X
PRINT Y
```
4

Supply the missing statement in each program. (Pages 432–434)

13.
```
1Ø INPUT B
2Ø LET D = B + 7
3Ø PRINT D
4Ø  ?
```
END

14.
```
1Ø  ?
2Ø LET G = F * 6
3Ø PRINT G
4Ø END
```
INPUT F

Correct any errors in these programs. (Pages 432–434)

15.
```
1Ø INPUT X
2Ø LET Y = X²
3Ø PRINT Y
4Ø END
```
20 LET Y = X ↑ 2

16.
```
1Ø INPUT A
2Ø LET C = 4 * B
3Ø PRINT "PRODUCT ="; C
4Ø END
```
10 INPUT B

17.
```
10 INPUT S, R
20 LET E = S * R
30 PRINT E
40 END
```

18.
```
10 INPUT G, D
20 LET N = G − D
30 PRINT N
40 END
```

Part 3: APPLICATIONS

Write a BASIC program for each Exercise. (Pages 432–434)

17. Find a salesperson's earnings, given the amount of sales and the rate of commission. (Pages 142–143)
18. Compute a worker's net pay, given the gross pay and the total deductions. (Pages 144–145)

TABLES OF MEASUREMENT

METRIC SYSTEM OF MEASURES

Length

10 millimeters (mm) = 1 centimeter (cm)
10 centimeters = 1 decimeter (dm)
100 millimeters = 1 decimeter (dm)
10 decimeters = 1 meter (m)
100 centimeters = 1 meter (m)
1000 meters = 1 kilometer (km)

Area

100 sq millimeters (mm^2) = 1 sq centimeter (cm^2)
10,000 sq centimeters = 1 sq meter (m^2)
100 sq meters = 1 are (a)
10,000 sq meters = 1 hectare (ha)

Volume

1000 cu millimeters (mm^3) = 1 cu centimeter (cm^3)
1000 cu centimeters = 1 cu decimeter (dm^3)
1,000,000 cu centimeters = 1 cu meter (m^3)

Mass

1000 milligram (mg) = 1 gram (g)
1000 grams = 1 kilogram (kg)
1000 kilograms = 1 metric ton (t)

Capacity

1000 milliliters (mL) = 1 liter (L)
1000 liters = 1 kiloliter (kL)

Temperature

Water freezes at 0° Celsius (°C).
Water boils at 100° Celsius.
Normal body temperature is 37° Celsius.

CUSTOMARY SYSTEM OF MEASURES

Length

12 inches (in) = 1 foot (ft)
3 feet = 1 yard (yd)
36 inches = 1 yard (yd)
1760 yards = 1 mile (mi)
5280 feet = 1 mile (mi)
6076 feet = 1 nautical mile

Area

144 sq inches (sq in) = 1 sq foot (sq ft)
9 sq feet = 1 sq yard (sq yd)
4840 sq yards = 1 acre (A)

Volume

1728 cu inches (cu in) = 1 cu foot (cu ft)
27 cu feet = 1 cu yard (cu yd)

Weight

16 ounces (oz) = 1 pound (lb)
2000 pounds = 1 ton (T)

Capacity

8 fluid ounces (fl oz) = 1 cup (c)
2 cups = 1 pint (pt)
2 pints = 1 quart (qt)
4 quarts = 1 gallon (gal)

Temperature

Water freezes at 32° Fahrenheit (°F).
Water boils at 212° Fahrenheit.
Normal body temperature is 98.6° Fahrenheit.

ANSWERS TO REVIEW OF RELATED SKILLS

CHAPTER 1 **Whole Numbers and Decimals**

Page X 1. 13 2. 13 3. 15 4. 11 5. 11 6. 10 7. 15 8. 17 9. 17 10. 16 11. 18 12. 16 13. 19 14. 15 15. 17 16. 25 17. 19 18. 39 19. 29 20. 49 21. 49 22. 19 23. 28 24. 39 25. 48 26. 3 27. 3 28. 5 29. 5 30. 4 31. 1 32. 15 33. 25 34. 45 35. 33 36. 21 37. 12 38. 211 39. 421 40. 1061 41. 2142 42. 1154 43. 2121 44. 6312 45. 1114 46. 1121 47. 2111 48. 72 49. 20 50. 42 51. 24 52. 40 53. 54 54. 42 55. 215 56. 392 57. 336 58. 87 59. 180 60. 4417 61. 1375 62. 1221 63. 5628 64. 1380 65. 1710 66. 1190 67. 3456 68. 1435 69. 3504 70. 7 71. 10 72. 7 73. 9 74. 6 75. 12 76. 8 77. 16 78. 13 79. 16 80. 15 81. 48 82. 16 83. 27 84. 17 85. 95 86. 31 87. 171 88. 231 89. 89

CHAPTER 2 **Applying Metric Measures**

Page 26 1. 460 2. 280 3. 5600 4. 72,000 5. 4630 6. 72,900 7. 244,000 8. 6200 9. 54,000 10. 64,000 11. 5700 12. 4800 13. 32 14. 480 15. 6700 16. 8 17. 70 18. 400 19. 212 20. 43,800 21. 62.4 22. 38.2 23. 4.81 24. 3.89 25. 2.546 26. 1.381 27. 1.462 28. 36.48 29. 562.3 30. 372.9 31. 6.2 32. 7.5 33. 0.081 34. 0.097 35. 0.0036 36. 0.0086 37. 0.07 38. 0.006 39. 0.0003 40. 0.04 41. 24 42. 51 43. 125 44. 62 45. 94 46. 158 47. 16.3 48. 17 49. 24.6 50. 48.5 51. 45.5 52. 5.3 53. 202.2 54. 247.5 55. 195.3 56. 98 57. 135 58. 864 59. 684 60. 672 61. 1944 62. 1148 63. 900 64. 273 65. 1554 66. 342 67. 700 68. 108 69. 336 70. 120 71. 168 72. 5244 73. 8109 74. 11,520 75. 15,912 76. 9.52 77. 63.99 78. 5.44 79. 315.24 80. 293.22 81. 914.76 82. 1835.52 83. 225.262 84. 35.712 85. 320.775 86. 153.468 87. 2.592 88. 1553.256 89. 2786.994 90. 2721.642

CHAPTER 3 **Fractions**

Page 44 1. 3 2. 6 3. 15 4. 4 5. 1 6. 17 7. 17 8. 14 9. 25 10. 3 11. 5 12. 14 13. 10 14. 16 15. 16 16. 3 17. 3 18. 3 19. 4 20. 8 21. 9 22. 12 23. 5 24. 4 25. 3 26. 4 27. 3 28. 4 29. 6 30. 5 31. 7 r 3 32. 6 r 3 33. 3 r 3 34. 9 r 5 35. 9 r 1 36. 24 37. 33 38. 35 39. 78 40. 32 41. 44 42. 38 43. 83 44. 100 45. 61 46. 57 47. 43 48. 37 49. 40 50. 44 51. 60 52. 74 53. 71 54. 69 55. 65 56. 39 57. 41 58. 55 59. 88 60. 39 61. 54 62. 103 63. 91 64. 104 65. 29 66. 2 67. 12 68. 45 69. 48 70. 16 71. 11 72. 52 73. 58 74. 17 75. 3 76. 9 77. 6 78. 6 79. 9 80. 9 81. 9 82. 6 83. 3 84. 18 85. 22 86. 26 87. 8 88. 8 89. 27 90. 9 91. 28 92. 25 93. 11 94. 6 95. 7 96. 40 97. 54 98. 48 99. 77 100. 63 101. 48 102. 55 103. 147 104. 243 105. 112 106. 162 107. 78 108. 120 109. 72 110. 114 111. 306 112. 130 113. 154 114. 276 115. 252 116. 221 117. 336 118. 285 119. 462 120. 312 121. 576 122. 450 123. 672 124. 682 125. 285 126. 486 127. 630 128. 589 129. 240 130. 204

CHAPTER 4 **Equations/Ratio/Proportion**

Page 70 1. 6 2. 10 3. 9 4. 19 5. 7 6. 8 7. 44 8. 13 9. 57 10. 139 11. 266

12. 215 13. 67 14. 276 15. 317 16. 3.1 17. 1.6 18. 4.8 19. 42.7 20. 7.5
21. 4.6 22. 5.6 23. 5.7 24. 4.6 25. 7.9 26. 18.0 27. 8.4 28. 28 29. 53
30. 47 31. 55 32. 124 33. 138 34. 153 35. 161 36. 198 37. 283 38. 170
39. 112 40. 173 41. 454 42. 455 43. 11.0 44. 16.2 45. 20.9 46. 15.7
47. 21.0 48. 22.4 49. 42.6 50. 23.7 51. 26.2 52. 19.6 53. 59.5 54. 45.2
55. 2 56. 3 57. 24 58. 27 59. 7 60. 6 61. 3 62. 15 63. 24 64. 6
65. 3 66. 3 67. 10 68. 6 69. 2 70. 5 71. 20 72. 10 73. 40 74. 4
75. 2 76. 0.4 77. 9 78. 128 79. 200 80. 1152 81. 2814 82. 7000 83. 189
84. 156 85. 672 86. 960 87. 2016 88. 182 89. 350 90. 1472 91. 1728
92. 936 93. 13.0 94. 12.6 95. 72.0 96. 7.77 97. 10.58 98. 23.46 99. 92.82
100. 56.58 101. $\frac{1}{2}$ 102. $\frac{1}{4}$ 103. $\frac{8}{15}$ 104. $\frac{9}{10}$ 105. $\frac{4}{7}$ 106. $\frac{2}{5}$ 107. $\frac{2}{5}$ 108. $\frac{2}{5}$

CHAPTER 5 Per Cent

Page 88 1. $\frac{3}{50}$ 2. $\frac{21}{50}$ 3. $\frac{3}{20}$ 4. $\frac{9}{50}$ 5. $\frac{13}{20}$ 6. $\frac{29}{50}$ 7. $\frac{1}{400}$ 8. $\frac{3}{500}$ 9. $\frac{7}{800}$ 10. $\frac{1}{3}$
11. $\frac{7}{8}$ 12. 80 13. 125 14. 32 15. 24 16. 8 17. $\frac{1}{150}$ 18. $\frac{1}{140}$ 19. $\frac{1}{450}$
20. $\frac{1}{300}$ 21. $\frac{1}{350}$ 22. $\frac{1}{225}$ 23. $\frac{3}{500}$ 24. $\frac{1}{120}$ 25. $\frac{1}{160}$ 26. $\frac{1}{125}$ 27. $\frac{10}{3}$
28. $\frac{5}{2}$ 29. $\frac{15}{8}$ 30. $\frac{75}{2}$ 31. $\frac{200}{3}$ 32. $\frac{100}{9}$ 33. 0.60 34. $0.87\frac{1}{2}$ 35. $0.44\frac{4}{9}$
36. 0.70 37. $0.85\frac{5}{7}$ 38. 5.88 39. 9.28 40. 12.32 41. 58.5 42. 1 43. 3.2
44. 103.4 45. 205.4 46. 6 47. 8 48. 8 49. 16 50. 120 51. 20 52. 160
53. 200 54. 384 55. 306 56. 375 57. 96 58. 336 59. 135 60. 196 61. 152
62. 50 63. 500 64. 400 65. 320 66. 312.5 67. 470 68. 5000 69. 400
70. 10,000 71. 55 72. 0.57 73. 48.7 74. 0.838

CHAPTER 6 Statistics

Page 108 1. 60 2. 60 3. 40 4. 50 5. 680 6. 800 7. 500 8. 300 9. 900 10. 600
11. 2000 12. 1400 13. 7000 14. 4000 15. 5000 16. 8000 17. 11,000
18. 12,000 19. 9 20. 26 21. 6 22. 8 23. 33 24. 16 25. 85 26. 169
27. 179 28. 138 29. 136 30. 175 31. 89 32. 49 33. 123 34. 135 35. 0.43
36. 0.54 37. 0.05 38. 0.06 39. 0.172 40. 0.478 41. $\frac{3}{20}$ 42. $\frac{3}{10}$ 43. $\frac{3}{4}$
44. $\frac{12}{25}$ 45. $\frac{5}{8}$ 46. $\frac{2}{3}$ 47. 162 48. 223.2 49. 54 50. 270 51. 291.6 52. 86.4
53. 64.8 54. 115.2 55. 21 56. 35 57. 79 58. 64 59. 123 60. 142 61. 2702
62. 3164 63. 1169 64. 2237 65. 3184 66. 2413 67. 24 68. 63 69. 98
70. 56 71. 64 72. 57 73. 63 74. 51 75. 58 76. 19

CHAPTER 7 Income

Page 136 1. $183.75 2. $126.00 3. $154.00 4. $201.60 5. $24.45 6. $18.60 7. $11.25
8. $16.50 9. $37.50 10. $56.25 11. $84.50 12. $147.00 13. $9.00 14. $12.00
15. $15.30 16. $11.40 17. $1233.75 18. $1774.63 19. $1631.52 20. $2007.87
21. $1571.15 22. $2714.25 23. 0.06 24. 0.08 25. 0.1 26. 0.12 27. 0.075
28. 0.035 29. 0.035 30. 0.091 31. 0.478 32. 0.023 33. 0.0401 34. 0.1233
35. 0.0704 36. 0.019 37. 0.218 38. 0.112 39. 0.0674 40. 0.1843 41. $\frac{1}{2}$
42. $\frac{3}{4}$ 43. $\frac{1}{10}$ 44. $\frac{2}{3}$ 45. $\frac{1}{8}$ 46. $\frac{4}{5}$ 47. $\frac{3}{20}$ 48. $\frac{1}{4}$ 49. $\frac{3}{10}$ 50. $\frac{11}{20}$ 51. $\frac{7}{10}$
52. $\frac{12}{25}$ 53. $\frac{1}{200}$ 54. $\frac{1}{400}$ 55. $\frac{3}{8}$ 56. $\frac{1}{3}$ 57. $\frac{5}{8}$ 58. $\frac{1}{7}$ 59. $136 60. $525

61. $798 62. $360 63. $405 64. $544 65. $1200 66. $2400 67. $5400 68. $220 69. $1050 70. $60,250 71. 38.50 72. 48.65 73. 105.00 74. 45.56 75. 37.94 76. 37.44 77. 83.71 78. 90.29 79. 45.02 80. 62.13 81. 90.69 82. 62.27 83. $74.85 84. $302.34 85. $381.10 86. $52.47 87. $511.73 88. $215.00 89. $97.05 90. $150.86 91. $276.16 92. $403.51 93. $279.00 94. $374.83

Page 139 1. $97.50 2. $184.00 3. $220.40 4. $215.25 5. $192.50 6. $244.00 7. $29.75 8. $78.00 9. $21.75 10. $10.50 11. $12.30 12. $10.05 13. $9.00 14. $6.00 15. $18.00 16. $12.00

Page 142 1. 0.05 2. 0.07 3. 0.14 4. 0.2 5. 0.045 6. 0.105 7. $\frac{1}{10}$ 8. $\frac{1}{4}$ 9. $\frac{1}{20}$ 10. $\frac{3}{20}$ 11. $\frac{1}{3}$ 12. $\frac{1}{8}$ 13. $45 14. $750 15. $360 16. $14

Page 144 1. $41.35 2. $50.72 3. $84.17 4. $65.57 5. $28.46 6. $33.86 7. $99.78 8. $49.27 9. $45.17 10. $545.02 11. $754.94 12. $312.44 13. $222.85 14. $201.14 15. $190.21 16. $226.35 17. $323.83 18. $291.05

Page 146 1. 0.067 2. 0.072 3. 0.0935 4. 0.093 5. 0.0665 6. 0.0705 7. $958.10 8. $1514.34 9. $1089.93 10. $689.43 11. $1590.48 12. $2244.50 13. $975.52 14. $1593.26 15. $2939.85

CHAPTER 8 Income Tax

Page 156 1. $81.00 2. $715.40 3. $68.75 4. $198.00 5. $70.00 6. $210.00 7. $81.00 8. $133.00 9. $179.20 10. $89.60 11. $186.20 12. $268.80 13. $140.00 14. $189.00 15. $209.10 16. $201.65 17. $150.35 18. $137.20 19. $202.50 20. $260.40 21. $13,023.35 22. $14,254.10 23. $29,505.75 24. $8792.51 25. $15,127.86 26. $29,182.72 27. $17,887.69 28. $25,773.13 29. $844.00 30. $70.00 31. $89.13 32. $2313.41 33. $890.07 34. $193.40 35. $3582.59 36. $618.73 37. $95.85 38. $738.04 39. $313.25 40. $113.52 41. $1544 42. $1555 43. $1808 44. $2750 45. $24,917 46. $17,148 47. $18,333 48. $20,438 49. $34,154 50. $27,542 51. 0.15 52. 0.21 53. 0.13 54. 0.14 55. 0.03 56. 0.05 57. 0.08 58. 0.09 59. 0.034 60. 0.029 61. 0.042 62. 0.047 63. 0.021 64. 0.055 65. 0.065 66. 0.073 67. 0.024 68. 0.032 69. 5.76 70. 7.5 71. 13.44 72. 2.88 73. 5.2 74. 6 75. 35.28 76. 38.304 77. 40.8

Page 159 1. $152.00 2. $205.20 3. $81.25 4. $153.00 5. $150.00 6. $240.00 7. $140.00 8. $144.20 9. $204.00 10. $84.00

Page 161 1. $11,871.46 2. $14,529.08 3. $17,408.06 4. $10,882.85 5. $20,769.59 6. $10,066.36

Page 163 1. 8024.74 2. 9197.69 3. 17,963.17 4. 30.85 5. 172.46 6. 212.34

Page 167 1. $1888 2. $2176 3. $2233 4. $1608 5. $40,582 6. $25,342 7. $18,521

Pages 170-171 1. $1381 2. $1946 3. $479 4. $1146.10 5. $1623.40 6. $1008.20 7. 0.12 8. 0.14 9. 0.07 10. 0.09 11. 0.023 12. 0.041 13. $57.78 14. $158.73 15. $161.04

CHAPTER 9 Banking

Page 178 1. 874.19 2. 1115.17 3. 639.79 4. 1124.83 5. 968.72 6. 531.59 7. 2643.90 8. 1770.59 9. 1798.91 10. 692.26 11. 600.00 12. 300.00 13. 200.00 14. 900.00 15. 224.50 16. 154.40 17. 238.25 18. 216.92 19. 249.35 20. 374.20 21. 270.16 22. 495.52 23. 1224.11 24. 349.45 25. 1253.25 26. 2570.46 27. 0.17 28. 0.15 29. 0.13 30. 0.12 31. 0.2 32. 0.16 33. 0.025 34. 0.043 35. 0.068 36. 0.055 37. 0.035 38. 0.029 39. 0.0525 40. 0.045 41. 0.0675 42. 0.055 43. 0.035 44. 0.0275 45. 225.00 46. 272.00 47. 468.00 48. 306.00 49. 88.00 50. 97.50 51. 48.90 52. 72.80 53. 63.00 54. 56.00 55. 62.50 56. 71.50 57. 72.25 58. 103.50 59. 150.00 60. 232.00 61. 6700.50 62. 8029.20 63. 8605.10 64. 13,014.90 65. 13.55 66. 32.10 67. 42.41 68. 8.11 69. 12.06 70. 5.08 71. 8.02 72. 7.20 73. 37.71 74. 12.41 75. 7.20 76. 6.16 77. 21.05 78. 36.36 79. 72.98 80. 56.08 81. 43.56 82. 55.78 83. 47.32 84. 59.08 85. 86.94 86. 94.09 87. 195.64 88. 203.45 89. 731.09 90. 328.65 91. 406.35 92. 2.5 93. 4.5 94. 4.25 95. 3 96. 4.75 97. 2.25 98. 3.75 99. 5.25 100. 2.75 101. 4

Page 181 1. 469.57 2. 581.56 3. 373.40 4. 492.75 5. 613.55 6. 1330.13 7. 300.00 8. 456.00 9. 436.60 10. 238.20

Page 183 1. 0.04 2. 0.06 3. 0.055 4. 0.0475 5. 0.0525 6. 0.045 7. $77.00 8. $54.00 9. $78.75 10. $162.00 11. $9.10 12. $14.75 13. $11.27 14. $8.11 15. 14.68 16. 25.42 17. 346.48 18. 288.04 19. 597.96 20. 1614.85 21. 49.30 22. 589.43 23. 1421.36

Page 185 1. 4 2. 3.5 3. 3.75 4. 1.25 5. 1.75 6. 5307 7. 9380.7 8. 12,840 9. 7788 10. 16,401 11. 16,473.6 12. 18,441.8 13. 9414 14. 564.25 15. 427 16. 1548.22 17. 350

Page 189 1. 370.22 2. 470.92 3. 544.31 4. 451.01 5. 365.61 6. 669.04 7. 275.31 8. 134.75 9. 371.02 10. 236.56

Page 194 1. 385.26 2. 163.50 3. 801.75 4. 638.22 5. 854.85 6. 463.62 7. 117.72 8. 116.64 9. 90.68 10. 235.36 11. 70.59 12. 543.91 13. 47.82 14. 378.35

CHAPTER 10 Buying a Car

Page 206 1. 2210 2. 781 3. 9652 4. 7180.96 5. 9699.30 6. $1120.50 7. $9456.85 8. $6773.55 9. $5379.40 10. $7612.43 11. $8707.46 12. $6519.60 13. $8620.54 14. $6978.19 15. 0.01 16. 0.06 17. 0.1 18. 0.045 19. 0.087 20. 0.035 21. 0.17 22. 0.23 23. 0.67 24. 0.94 25. 1.02 26. 1.3 27. 2.25 28. 3.14 29. 0.062 30. 0.057 31. 0.75 32. 0.82 33. 342.5 34. 300.4 35. 528 36. 498 37. 6280 38. 6027 39. 4650 40. 4620 41. 400 42. 1210 43. 900 44. 1000 45. 2352 46. 4050 47. 2747 48. 1188 49. 1118 50. 12,903 51. 1092.0 52. 1429.7 53. 640.56 54. 1758.28 55. 650.16 56. 4711.20 57. 1936 58. 602 59. 2944 60. 5504 61. 1222.0 62. 1192.4 63. 171.35 64. 757.12 65. 369.6 66. 1383.8 67. 119.34 68. 239.94 69. 71 70. 11 71. 35 72. 48 73. 112 74. 314 75. 3.1 76. 6.7 77. 41.3 78. 67.62 79. 6.49 80. 1.73 81. 325 82. 370 83. 8346 84. $610.40 85. $411.23 86. $5193.50 87. $335.75 88. $498.87 89. $2490.25

Page 209 1. $9292 2. $8079 3. $5911 4. $9654.61 5. $7082.40 6. $7995.57 7. 0.08 8. 0.04 9. 0.09 10. 0.53 11. 0.065 12. 0.048 13. 600 14. 340 15. 282 16. 327.84

Page 210 1. $10,126.10 2. $8309.90 3. 0.95 4. 0.6 5. 0.85 6. 0.76 7. 0.84 8. 0.773 9. $5772.00 10. $6536.25 11. $7700.00 12. $10,557.00

Page 213 1. $5280 2. $6912 3. $10,224 4. $5040 5. $6144 6. $10,000 7. $8290 8. $10,031 9. $9899 10. $3740 11. $1225 12. $2343 13. $1609

Page 217 1. $585.20 2. $793.60 3. $361.60 4. $307.20 5. $121.90 6. $224.57 7. $76.80

Page 219 1. $316.83 2. $279.50 3. $709.10 4. $48.12 5. $229 6. $185 7. $195 8. $310

CHAPTER 11 Owning A Car

Page 228 1. $125.88 2. $137.62 3. $184.54 4. $209.40 5. $3375.55 6. $3087.28 7. 0.02 8. 0.04 9. 0.07 10. 0.11 11. 0.14 12. 0.17 13. $0.02 14. $0.02 15. $0.01 16. $0.03 17. $63.20 18. $14.55 19. $4.96 20. $3.95 21. $2296 22. $5160 23. $986 24. $2397 25. 67 26. 55 27. 56 28. 68,000 29. 208,000 30. 32,000 31. 95,400 32. 0.03 33. 0.06 34. 0.08 35. 0.08 36. 0.06 37. $0.05 38. $0.09 39. $0.05 40. $0.08 41. $0.06 42. $0.07 43. 43 44. 16 45. 82 46. 46 47. 48 48. 65 49. 2485 50. 2184 51. 1836 52. $0.468 53. $0.147 54. $0.421 55. $0.374 56. $0.312 57. $0.303 58. $0.388 59. $0.409 60. $0.322

Pages 230-231 1. $104.33 2. $120.90 3. $50.97 4. $60.32 5. 0.04 6. 0.06 7. 0.05 8. 0.08 9. 0.1 10. 0.15 11. $0.02 12. $0.06 13. $0.02 14. $0.02 15. $25.60 16. $15.25 17. $1.79 18. $3.01

Pages 232-233 1. 69 2. 49 3. 50 4. $2240 5. $768 6. $1333 7. $1890 8. 54,000 9. 105,000 10. 76,000 11. 47,600 12. 0.05 13. 0.03 14. 0.06 15. 0.04 16. 0.07 17. $0.09 18. $0.06 19. $0.08

Pages 236-237 1. 21 2. 19 3. 26 4. 19 5. 26 6. 32 7. 19 8. 20 9. 41 10. 24 11. 0.04 12. 0.06 13. 0.06 14. 0.08 15. 0.05 16. 0.05 17. $0.05 18. $0.08 19. $0.05 20. $0.05

Page 239 1. $3965.75 2. $2549.95 3. 2016 4. 1656 5. 1800 6. 1932 7. $0.296 8. $0.144 9. $0.241

CHAPTER 12 Other Ways to Travel

Page 248 1. $108.00 2. $205.60 3. $306.60 4. $437.00 5. $348.00 6. $444.00 7. $68.49 8. $431.10 9. $39.90 10. $180.00 11. $204.90 12. $374.40 13. $277.20 14. $352.50 15. $367.50 16. $322.00 17. $123.20 18. $96.00 19. $120.40 20. $126.96 21. $330.05 22. $383.29 23. $348.92 24. $211.94 25. $290.59 26. $500.37 27. $410.54 28. $332.05 29. 30¢ 30. 35¢ 31. 80¢ 32. 80¢ 33. 90¢ 34. 75¢ 35. 95¢ 36. 95¢ 37. 70¢ 38. $18.00 39. $22.10 40. $56.00 41. $7.50 42. $13.00 43. $29.75 44. $27.00 45. $16.50 46. $13.50 47. $23.75 48. $19.80 49. $30.00 50. $7.00 51. $27.00 52. $32.20 53. $57.00 54. $20.00 55. $12.00 56. $40.80 57. $18.00 58. $40.00 59. $58.00 60. $48.00 61. $62.40 62. $58.00 63. $760 64. $630 65. $1320 66. $2460 67. $480 68. $597 69. $864 70. $680 71. $353.00 72. $733.60 73. $914.10 74. $1025.20 75. $894.46 76. $1017.54 77. $2431.92 78. $2034.24 79. $24.00 80. $20.00 81. $14.00 82. $30.00 83. $22.50 84. $16.80 85. $27.00 86. $11.10 87. $8.11 88. $20.43 89. $20.82 90. $32.81 91. $22.77 92. $14.57

Page 250 1. $85.00 2. $70.50 3. $305.60 4. $184.40 5. $32.30 6. $162.50 7. $210.25 8. $245.28 9. $73.00 10. $44.80 11. $119.52 12. $130.20 13. $290.60 14. $368.95 15. $366.16 16. $314.05 17. $283.16 18. $283.89 19. $347.97 20. $361.05

Page 254 1. $0.90 2. $1.20 3. $0.95 4. $87.50 5. $97.90 6. $152.00 7. $32.00 8. $22.80 9. $17.00 10. $26.40 11. $34.50 12. $72.80 13. $40.00 14. $41.80

Page 256 1. $495 2. $860 3. $240 4. $350.00 5. $26.00 6. $22.65 7. $10.80 8. $12.96 9. $609 10. $764.40 11. $624.35 12. $563.05 13. $674 14. $556.50 15. $753.61 16. $679.70

CHAPTER 13 Food Costs

Page 268 1. 4.9 2. 3.0 3. 9.5 4. 5.0 5. 49.1 6. 83.2 7. 13.1 8. 47.4 9. 66.1 10. 18.0 11. 138.2 12. 166.7 13. 52.3 14. 23.5 15. 3.8 16. 3.8 17. 4.9 18. 7.3 19. 3.4 20. 9.2 21. 0.3 22. 1.4 23. $7.32 24. $3.27 25. $2.09 26. $2.75 27. $10.51 28. $5.68 29. $5.83 30. $7.95 31. $7.35 32. $2.46 33. $4.05 34. $1.21 35. $1.21 36. $0.27 37. $2.16 38. $3.10 39. $1.59 40. $2.26 41. $0.88 42. $1.39 43. $0.09 44. $0.50 45. $0.80 46. $1.70 47. $1.94 48. $1.48 49. $2.16 50. $2.30 51. $2.48 52. $4.02 53. $3.62 54. $0.51 55. $0.81 56. $0.42 57. $0.22 58. $0.84 59. $1.81 60. $2.08 61. $5.56 62. $7.19 63. $4.01 64. $\frac{9}{2}$ 65. $\frac{7}{2}$ 66. $\frac{25}{4}$ 67. $\frac{26}{5}$ 68. $\frac{55}{6}$ 69. $\frac{22}{3}$ 70. $\frac{9}{4}$ 71. $\frac{26}{3}$ 72. $\frac{36}{5}$ 73. $\frac{45}{4}$ 74. $\frac{43}{7}$ 75. $\frac{19}{9}$ 76. $3.12 77. $3.34 78. $1.50 79. $1.47 80. $1.77 81. $5.85 82. $7.08 83. $3.81 84. $0.94 85. $0.97 86. $1.51 87. $2.83 88. $0.99 89. $0.94 90. $2.04 91. $1.26

Page 270 1. 3.5 2. 4.5 3. 7.0 4. 5.0 5. 23.6 6. 42.8 7. 46.9 8. 32.1 9. 57.3 10. 19.0 11. 156.4 12. 237.6 13. 74.5 14. 19.7 15. 2.7 16. 4.9 17. 3.1 18. 3.0 19. 3.6 20. 8.6 21. 0.2 22. 0.6

Page 272 1. $3.18 2. $2.79 3. $2.15 4. $2.61 5. $3.98 6. $4.98 7. $0.86 8. $2.23 9. $0.69 10. $3.35 11. $0.79 12. $1.16 13. $3.52 14. $0.08

Page 276 1. $2.30 2. $2.32 3. $2.48 4. $2.32 5. $2.62 6. $4.63 7. $0.70 8. $1.26 9. $2.08 10. $1.96 11. $2.34 12. $0.77 13. $0.93 14. $2.41 15. $4.25

Page 279 1. $\frac{3}{2}$ 2. $\frac{10}{3}$ 3. $\frac{5}{3}$ 4. $\frac{21}{5}$ 5. $\frac{9}{4}$ 6. $\frac{25}{8}$ 7. $7\frac{1}{5}$ 8. $3\frac{1}{5}$ 9. $2\frac{6}{7}$ 10. $5\frac{1}{4}$ 11. $2\frac{2}{3}$ 12. $1.59 13. $1.27 14. $1.32 15. $0.95

CHAPTER 14 Housing

Page 288 1. $433 2. $490 3. $895 4. $306 5. $480 6. $516 7. $1266 8. $1010 9. $1134 10. $1426.50 11. 0.5 12. 0.4 13. 0.35 14. 0.2 15. 0.05 16. 0.45 17. 0.38 18. 0.07 19. 0.33 20. 0.16 21. 0.49 22. 0.87 23. $18,000 24. $24,000 25. $7500 26. $34,300 27. $49,500 28. $31,850 29. $168,960 30. $180,000 31. $144,000 32. $185,220 33. $322,056 34. $219,897.60 35. $50,000 36. $40,000 37. $58,000 38. $136,050 39. $179,500 40. $133,249 41. $528.00 42. $435.00 43. $61.40 44. $76.00 45. $86.00 46. $108.50 47. $943.20 48. $921.90 49. $1220.60 50. $741.02 51. $3393.00 52. $2538.00 53. $3493.20 54. $3158.61 55. $\frac{4}{5}$ 56. $\frac{3}{10}$ 57. $\frac{3}{20}$ 58. $\frac{7}{20}$ 59. $\frac{7}{10}$ 60. $\frac{9}{10}$ 61. $\frac{2}{5}$ 62. $\frac{3}{5}$ 63. $\frac{13}{20}$ 64. $\frac{11}{20}$ 65. $\frac{33}{100}$ 66. $\frac{6}{25}$ 67. $32.00 68. $47.00

69. $44.00 70. $51.00 71. $13.00 72. $16.17 73. $33.50 74. $17.17 75. $41.92 76. $51.42 77. $55.83 78. $35.67

Page 290 1. $309.00 2. $964.00 3. $292.00 4. $510.00 5. $202.50 6. $1196.00 7. $1608.00 8. $740.00 9. $567.00 10. $732.00

Page 292 1. 0.25 2. 0.3 3. 0.4 4. 0.23 5. 0.18 6. 0.17 7. $19,500 8. $28,800 9. $20,160 10. $18,900 11. $259,500 12. $342,216 13. $257,928 14. $188,450 15. $131,260 16. $157,978

Page 296 1. 80 2. 90 3. 75 4. 104 5. $719.00 6. $877.50 7. $1088.85 8. $1028.25

Page 300 1. $\frac{1}{10}$ 2. $\frac{1}{2}$ 3. $\frac{1}{5}$ 4. $\frac{1}{4}$ 5. $\frac{2}{5}$ 6. $\frac{3}{4}$ 7. 0.15 8. 0.17 9. 0.24 10. 0.23 11. 0.28 12. 0.31 13. $16,000 14. $35,000 15. $5000 16. $9000 17. $24.00 18. $25.17 19. $38.25 20. $15.67 21. $35.42

Pages 304-305 1. 0.34 2. 0.41 3. 0.5 4. 0.62 5. 0.45 6. 0.31 7. $34,400 8. $31,500 9. $22,500 10. $39,600 11. 486 12. 524 13. 375 14. 543 15. $3326.40 16. $2291.00 17. $3995.20 18. $4109.90

CHAPTER 15 Housing Costs

Page 312 1. 17 2. 25 3. 1 4. 12 5. 21 6. 0.16 7. 0.41 8. 0.07 9. 0.79 10. 0.35 11. 0.19 12. 0.32 13. 0.94 14. 0.02 15. 0.21 16. 18% 17. 15% 18. 30% 19. 24% 20. $135.80 21. $287.56 22. $134.80 23. $41.30 24. 1400 25. 500 26. 5900 27. 1800 28. $2.40 29. $4.80 30. $2 31. $1.86 32. $5.20 33. $10.40 34. $77.40 35. $36.52 36. $2.45 37. $0.95 38. $1.92 39. $6.45 40. $1.25 41. $109.50 42. $6.48 43. 109 44. 78 45. 233 46. 1304 47. 311 48. 12.5 49. 9.5 50. 6.5 51. 8.5 52. 4.5 53. 15.8 54. 12.6 55. 19 56. 19.6 57. 14 58. 12 59. 9 60. 7 61. 15 62. 38.3 63. 31.4 64. 43.0 65. 41.8 66. 34.2 67. 28.4 68. 13.1 69. 44.1 70. 79.7 71. 169.6 72. 8 73. 9 74. 8 75. 6 76. 10 77. 8 78. 9 79. 10 80. 13 81. 16

Pages 314-315 1. 9° 2. 3° 3. 6° 4. 7° 5. 8° 6. 0.18 7. 0.39 8. 0.08 9. 0.21 10. 0.63 11. 0.14 12. 12% 13. 21% 14. 9% 15. 6% 16. $54 17. $120 18. $76.50 19. $129.60 20. $214.50 21. $232.96

Page 316 1. $1.60 2. $4.30 3. $0.50 4. $0.60 5. $1.28 6. $0.49 7. $0.63 8. $9 10. $0.90 11. $0.70

Page 321 1. 160 2. 475 3. 1017 4. 14 5. 68 6. 1600 7. 700 8. 3300 9. 1900 10. 2100

Page 323 1. 6.5 2. 6.5 3. 6.5 4. 7.5 5. 7.5 6. 13 7. 16 8. 10 9. 5 10. 12

Page 326 1. 14 2. 15.6 3. 20 4. 9 5. 15.2 6. 10 7. 51.5 8. 50.5 9. 14.0 10. 16.0 11. 12.8 12. 6 13. 8 14. 7 15. 8 16. 7

CHAPTER 16 Buying Goods

Page 336 1. 0.13 2. 0.07 3. 0.34 4. 0.40 5. 0.17 6. 0.27 7. 0.019 8. 0.024 9. 0.037 10. 0.027 11. 0.032 12. 0.018 13. $15 14. $15 15. $20 16. $17 17. $9.60 18. $9.60 19. $19.20 20. $36 21. $8.75 22. $33 23. $38.21 24. $48.72 25. $33 26. $80 27. $12 28. $174 29. $30.87 30. $26.53 31. $15.34

32. $95.68 33. $175 34. $35 35. $57 36. $2241 37. $1272 38. $1280 39. $1270 40. $938 41. $12.16 42. $3.63 43. $821.23 44. $424.80 45. $479.06 46. $1114.72 47. $41.10 48. $15.96 49. $15.76 50. $5.85 51. $152.40 52. $174.93 53. $509.50 54. $199.98 55. $1285.92 56. $3614.25 57. $2400 58. $3497.60 59. $206.22 60. $455.04 61. $298.99 62. $592.79 63. $81.62 64. $96.55 65. $0.39 66. $0.60 67. $7.08 68. $500 69. $299.20 70. $922.20 71. $760.80 72. $1920 73. $2160 74. $648 75. $2474.28 76. $6426

Page 339 1. 0.14 2. 0.15 3. 0.20 4. 0.30 5. 0.05 6. 0.08 7. $11.40 8. $5.61 9. $7.56 10. $25.08 11. $12.99 12. $12.60 13. $45.50 14. $61.92 15. $5 16. $9 17. $6.01 18. $2.52

Page 341 1. $17.85 2. $9.98 3. $8.94 4. $39.90 5. $54.95 6. $170 7. $343.77 8. $245.78 9. $75.79 10. $59.40 11. $80.33 12. $105.12

Page 345 1. $383.38 2. $499.21 3. $415.55 4. $305.18 5. $315.15 6. $391.28 7. $247.24 8. 0.014 9. 0.023 10. 0.016 11. 0.034 12. 0.012 13. 0.026 14. $5.78 15. $4.35 16. $6.37

Page 347 1. $414.75 2. $332.46 3. $246.90 4. $196.07 5. $243.86 6. $604.95 7. $440.52 8. $4.35 9. $5.68 10. $6.84

Pages 350-351 1. 0.25 2. 0.35 3. 0.18 4. 0.26 5. 0.09 6. 0.08 7. $312.80 8. $481.25 9. $729 10. $329.25 11. $841.50 12. $1557.12 13. $1560.96 14. $1551.30 15. $1310 16. $1643 17. $1343 18. $124.49 19. $362.46 20. $231.03

CHAPTER 17 Investing Money

Page 358 1. 80 2. 65 3. 50 4. 45 5. 120 6. 95 7. 140 8. 110 9. $222 10. $164.50 11. $126 12. $97.50 13. $2800 14. $1850 15. $5262 16. $4098.30 17. $290 18. $2480 19. $290 20. $3087 21. $3480 22. $828 23. $2450 24. $875 25. $8300 26. $12,525 27. $7550 28. $1050.70 29. $3783.30 30. $7038.85 31. $7 32. $4 33. $22 34. $2 35. $17 36. $8 37. $7 38. $8 39. $340 40. $780 41. $750 42. $240.50 43. $764.20 44. $782.97 45. $8094 46. $2565.50 47. $8654.79 48. 0.25 49. 0.625 50. 0.75 51. 0.125 52. 0.375 53. 0.875 54. $5576 55. $3242 56. $4802 57. $6587.45 58. $8414.75 59. $7745.20 60. $3869.36 61. $4878.59 62. $9407.37 63. 0.108 64. 0.110 65. 0.068 66. 0.075 67. 0.090 68. 0.069 69. 0.087 70. 0.084 71. 0.088 72. 0.083 73. 0.091 74. 0.077

Page 361 1. 40 2. 70 3. 100 4. 75 5. $212 6. $139.75 7. $1240 8. $2202.60 9. $7137.75

Page 364 1. $612 2. $788.40 3. $15,037.50 4. $6906 5. $9180 6. $5 7. $4 8. $18 9. $4 10. $4 11. $16 12. $21 13. $28 14. $15 15. $24

Page 368 1. $1127.40 2. $1083.30 3. $635.55 4. $1040.80 5. $2323.40 6. $3450.60 7. $4290 8. $5525.50 9. $210.20 10. $249.90 11. $646.80 12. $808.50 13. $1897.70 14. $1182.60

Page 371 1. 0.125 2. 0.5 3. 0.75 4. 0.375 5. 0.875 6. 0.6 7. $2350 8. $17,812.50 9. $3925 10. $44,437.50 11. $4442.50 12. $5891.68 13. $9515.33 14. $7621.40 15. $4695.36 16. $1635.93

Page 374 1. $135 2. $615 3. $1080 4. $1720 5. $9.40 6. 0.146 7. 0.127 8. 0.070 9. 0.095

Page 377 1. $615 2. $355 3. $3312.50 4. $1248.75 5. 0.065 6. 0.165 7. 0.127 8. 0.127

CHAPTER 18 **Budgeting Money**

Page 386 1. $20.50 2. $43.50 3. $27.30 4. $57.05 5. $51.73 6. $31.62 7. $80 8. $17 9. $100 10. $214 11. $472 12. 281°; 72°; 7° 13. 61°; 76°; 79°; 58°; 86° 14. $120 15. $90 16. $217 17. $37 18. $234 19. $576 20. $464 21. $980 22. $465 23. $330.80 24. $69.15 25. $1261.50 26. 50% 27. 70% 28. $33\frac{1}{3}\%$ 29. 80% 30. 75% 31. $16\frac{2}{3}\%$ 32. $810 33. $812 34. $1320 35. $37 36. $117 37. $467 38. $192 39. $346 40. $560 41. $243 42. $418 43. $695 44. $1080 45. $1070 46. $1250 47. $1460 48. $626 49. $1347 50. $1004 51. $888 52. $2501 53. $2219 54. $1911 55. $2984

Page 388 1. $18.41 2. $31.95 3. $69.83 4. $112.36 5. $115 6. $136 7. $130 8. $189 9. $204 10. $195

Page 391 1. 65°; 79°; 108°; 76°; 32° 2. 79°; 58°; 97°; 58°; 18°; 50° 3. $35 4. $35 5. $101.40 6. $224.40 7. $459.20 8. 20% 9. $66\frac{2}{3}\%$ 10. 75% 11. 30% 12. $37\frac{1}{2}\%$ 13. 25%

Page 394 1. $650 2. $820 3. $1075 4. $226 5. $334 6. $480 7. $337.50 8. $736 9. $1025.50 10. $892.50

Page 397 1. $1000 2. $1150 3. $1315 4. $1482 5. $1562 6. $250 7. $222 8. $252 9. $47

ANSWERS TO THE ODD-NUMBERED EXERCISES

CHAPTER 1 **Whole Numbers and Decimals**

Page 3 Exercises 1. 904 3. 1234 5. 2010 7. 10,729 9. 3808 11. 7165 13. 3146 15. 10,040 17. 4749 19. 1191 21. 261 23. 2458 25. 49 27. 6695 29. 2089 31. 2182 33. 7634 35. 824 37. 7787 39. 3937 41. 397 43. 20,054,000 45. 1,349,000

Page 5 Exercises 1. 53.40 3. 285.555 5. 910.675 7. 197.082 9. 237.367 11. 137.961 13. 59.281 15. 227.721 17. 403.29 19. 13.51 21. 3.884 23. 5.89 25. 2.503 27. 2.89 29. 8.387 31. 34.179 33. 18.73 35. 20.99 37. 77.954 39. 47.467 41. 2.05 inches 43. 11.65 inches

Page 7 Exercises 1. 3772 3. 15,762 5. 1827 7. 98,098 9. 25,259 11. 1863 13. 18,879 15. 4473 17. 211,839 19. 1659 21. 12,501 23. 54,288 25. 149,688 27. 448 29. 2520 31. 182,781 33. 189,744 35. 124,836 37. 20,880 39. 15,782 41. 14,587 43. 54,270 45. 166,221 47. 21,627 49. 146,718 51. 14,889 53. 235,936 55. 16,362 57. 105 59. 165 61. 636

Pages 8-9 Exercises 1. 12.8 3. 12.8 5. 1.280 7. 58.4 9. 84.1 11. 0.64 13. 13.79 15. 518.82 17. 49.1656 19. 1.1648 21. 6.253 23. 65.333 25. 2203.952 27. 0.00133 29. 0.000133 31. 0.0054 33. 0.064 35. 0.00648 37. 0.0008 39. 0.0049 41. 0.001798 43. 0.020703 45. 0.0195 47. 0.013662 49. 0.015668 51. $9.12 53. $1.08 55. 6.3 pounds

Page 10 Mid-Chapter Review 1. 807 3. 2381 5. 10,106 7. 2152 9. 639 11. 210 13. 154.20 15. 291.771 17. 469.362 19. 18.133 21. 89.65 23. 45.61 25. 15,216 27. 293,370 29. 65,661 31. 125,028 33. 49.3 35. 0.033985 37. 464 39. 68,600

Page 10 Calculator Exercises 1. 462,658 3. 14,333 5. 1,936,424

Page 11 Career 1. ┌⊔ 0 ┘ 3. ⊔┌┐⊏ 5. ┐⊐└⊔ 7. $857

Page 13 Exercises 1. 40 3. 260 5. 440 7. 770 9. 2610 11. 1920 13. 800 15. 4900 17. 7400 19. 400 21. 16,100 23. 8100 25. 9000 27. 11,000 29. 15,000 31. 38,000 33. 9000 35. 87 37. 76 39. 703 41. 13 43. 11 r 25 45. 72 r 6 47. 109 r 20 49. 25 r 8 51. 65 53. 37 r 200 55. 6 r 212 57. 19 59. 30 r 444 61. 3161 yards 63. 70 units; 50 yards left over

Page 15 Exercises 1. 4.68 3. 1.267 5. 0.138 7. 0.094 9. 6.09 11. 0.204 13. 3.26 15. 2.561 17. 0.56 19. 0.021 21. 3.56 23. 0.317 25. 0.034 27. 0.106 29. 6.2 31. 93 33. 23 35. 576 37. 65 39. 785 41. 2.6 43. 1.05 45. 1.2 47. 3.8 49. 85 51. 25 53. 5.5 55. 2.7 57. 60 59. 130 61. 32 miles 63. 41 miles

Pages 16-17 Exercises 1. 30 3. 26 5. 10 7. 17 9. 11 11. 6 13. 31.3 15. 17.8 17. 76.1 19. 62.3 21. 11.4 23. 124.6 25. 37.29 27. 59.14 29. 77.11 31. 47.30 33. 88.23 35. 62.19 37. 8.294 39. 0.292 41. 2.646 43. 1.330 45. 2.112 47. 1.194 49. 18.7 51. 1.5 53. 3.1 55. 3.0 57. 4.9 59. 9.7 61. 1.5 63. 1.2 65. 1.36 67. 1.75 69. 7.71 71. 3.00 73. 0.62 75. 40.07 77. 1.02 79. 1.68 81. 0.279 83. 0.314 85. 0.298 87. 0.266

Pages 18-19 Exercises 1. b 3. c 5. c 7. b 9. c 11. d 13. b 15. d 17. c 19. b

Page 19 Calculator Exercises Estimated answers will vary, depending on the places to which the given numbers are rounded. Therefore, only exact answers are given. 1. 281 3. 3619 5. 12,749 7. 68.6

Pages 20-21 Career 1. Millbury 3. Chicopee, Springfield 5. Palmer 7. D-2 9. E-2 11. Wallingford 13. Hartford 15. Meriden 17. D-4 19. D-1 21. C-2, C-3, C-4, B-4

Pages 22-24 Chapter Review 1. decimal points 3. product 5. approximately equal to 7. 137 9. 3688 11. 12,672 13. 4317 15. 592 17. 2886 19. 1057 21. 7303 23. 143 25. 49 27. 56.01 29. 162.38 31. 24.077 33. 6.443 35. 17.95 37. 2.12 39. 6.288 41. 2523 43. 635,712 45. 9250 47. 72.492 49. 0.001558 51. 70 53. 60 55. 250 57. 700 59. 4300 61. 9100 63. 8000 65. 88,000 67. 49,000 69. 65 71. 21 r 5 73. 43 r 29 75. 35 r 435 77. 6.4 79. 0.83 81. 0.029 83. 0.342 85. 26.68 87. 97 89. 10 91. 86 93. 36.6 95. 7.5 97. 5.2 99. 6.0 101. 2.50 103. 6.51 105. 11.48 107. 0.50 109. d 111. b 113. 3.03 inches 115. 6.22 inches 117. 36 miles 119. b 121. 2630 yards

Page 25 Chapter Test 1. 3570 3. 504 5. 10.53 7. 0.0512 9. 18 11. 0.074 13. 20.86 15. 88.5 17. b 19. a 21. 172,900 23. 12 25. 6

CHAPTER 2 Applying Metric Measures

Page 29 Exercises 1. b 3. c 5. b 7. 1000 9. 1000 11. a 13. b 15. c 17. 0.346 19. 0.122 21. 500 23. 0.064 25. 28,000 27. 31,000 29. 32 cm 31. 2.41 m

Page 31 Exercises 1. 8.8 cm 3. 95 mm 5. 4.0 m 7. 22 cm 9. 2.2 m 11. 84 cm 13. 318 m 15. 9.2 m 17. 17.2 m

Pages 32-33 Exercises 1. b 3. a 5. a 7. a 9. a 11. a 13. 25,000 15. 4200 17. 4.325 19. 0.0038 21. 25,000 23. 21,800 25. 6.421 27. 0.00481 29. 0.025 31. 0.0675 33. 35,000 35. 160 37. 17,612 kg 39. 118,476 kg

Pages 34-35 Exercises 1. a 3. b 5. b 7. a 9. b 11. b 13. b 15. c 17. a 19. 37,000 21. 321,000 23. 3400 25. 22,300 27. 2.478 29. 0.386 31. 0.022 33. 0.005 35. 0.0068 37. 800 39. 40 41. 0.021 43. 70 45. 4

Page 37 Exercises 1. 10,500 mm^2 3. 17.64 m^2 5. 4.5 m^2 7. 1.44 m^2 9. 0.63 m^3 11. 240 m^3 13. 27.216 m^3 15. 12,500 cm^2 17. 3931.29 m^2 19. 960 cm^3

Page 38 Exercises 1. c 3. a 5. b 7. b 9. b 11. No 13. the heat

Page 39 Career 1. 4000 watts 3. 300 watts 5. 6700 watts 7. 6500 watts 9. 4600 watts

Pages 40-42 Chapter Review 1. length 3. mass 5. capacity 7. volume 9. b 11. c 13. 0.43 15. 5000 17. 0.423 19. 12 m 21. a 23. c 25. 5.212 27. 0.043 29. 14,000 31. a 33. 0.120 35. 15,000 37. 0.0192 39. 0.19 m^2 41. 910 cm^2 43. 80 cm^2 45. 648 mm^2 47. 454.92 cm^2 49. 30 cm^3 51. 72 m^3 53. 2520 cm^3 55. 7500 cm^3 57. 4.4 m 59. 2700 cm^2 61. 1.1 m 63. with 65. 216 m^2

Page 43 Chapter Test 1. b 3. b 5. c 7. 0.23 9. 0.0438 11. 1.481 13. 350 m 15. 5.32 m^2 17. 600 cm^3 19. 2660 kg

CHAPTER 3 Fractions

Page 47 Exercises 1. $1\frac{4}{5}$ 3. $2\frac{1}{3}$ 5. $2\frac{2}{5}$ 7. $2\frac{5}{8}$ 9. $3\frac{1}{4}$ 11. $1\frac{9}{11}$ 13. $1\frac{8}{11}$ 15. $3\frac{1}{12}$ 17. $4\frac{13}{21}$ 19. $2\frac{12}{13}$ 21. $4\frac{7}{9}$ 23. $1\frac{5}{6}$ 25. $1\frac{3}{5}$ 27. $1\frac{5}{8}$ 29. $4\frac{4}{15}$ 31. $7\frac{4}{11}$ 33. $5\frac{2}{3}$ 35. $5\frac{1}{4}$ 37. $4\frac{12}{13}$ 39. $5\frac{13}{15}$ 41. $2\frac{7}{11}$ 43. $3\frac{5}{23}$ 45. $6\frac{1}{11}$ 47. $3\frac{11}{17}$ 49. $3\frac{6}{19}$ 51. $4\frac{1}{14}$ 53. $2\frac{21}{31}$ 55. $3\frac{13}{27}$ 57. $2\frac{2}{7}$ 59. $3\frac{7}{9}$ 61. $6\frac{11}{14}$ 63. $5\frac{3}{13}$ 65. $\frac{1}{3}$ 67. $\frac{1}{9}$ 69. $\frac{1}{4}$ 71. $\frac{4}{15}$ 73. $\frac{2}{3}$ 75. $4\frac{1}{6}$ 77. $\frac{1}{2}$ 79. $\frac{1}{6}$ 81. $\frac{2}{3}$ 83. $2\frac{1}{5}$ 85. $\frac{1}{3}$ 87. $1\frac{3}{4}$ 89. $3\frac{1}{3}$ 91. $2\frac{1}{9}$ 93. $\frac{7}{8}$ 95. $1\frac{1}{3}$ 97. 5 99. $2\frac{1}{2}$ 101. $\frac{1}{3}$ 103. $\frac{49}{72}$ 105. $\frac{1}{6}$ 107. $\frac{1}{2}$ 109. $2\frac{1}{3}$ 111. 2 113. $\frac{1}{3}$ 115. $\frac{1}{19}$ 117. $2\frac{4}{5}$ 119. $1\frac{7}{12}$ 121. $1\frac{1}{15}$ 123. $1\frac{1}{10}$ 125. $\frac{3}{5}$ 127. $\frac{8}{99}$ 129. $1\frac{4}{5}$ 131. $2\frac{1}{3}$

Page 49 Exercises 1. $\frac{3}{4}$ 3. $\frac{4}{7}$ 5. $\frac{7}{13}$ 7. 1 9. $\frac{1}{5}$ 11. $\frac{1}{7}$ 13. $\frac{1}{2}$ 15. $\frac{1}{2}$ 17. $\frac{3}{5}$ 19. $\frac{1}{5}$ 21. $\frac{1}{2}$ 23. $\frac{3}{4}$ 25. $\frac{5}{7}$ 27. $\frac{2}{5}$ 29. 6 31. 8 33. 12 35. 12 37. 8 39. 28 41. 14 43. 36 45. 14 47. 42 49. $\frac{3}{6}, \frac{4}{6}$ 51. $\frac{9}{12}, \frac{8}{12}$ 53. $\frac{21}{48}, \frac{12}{48}$ 55. $\frac{5}{12}, \frac{9}{12}$ 57. $\frac{14}{21}, \frac{12}{21}$ 59. $\frac{8}{20}, \frac{15}{20}$ 61. $\frac{32}{36}, \frac{15}{36}$ 63. $\frac{34}{50}, \frac{15}{50}$ 65. $\frac{1}{2}$ mile 67. $1\frac{2}{5}$ miles

Page 51 Exercises 1. $\frac{7}{8}$ 3. $1\frac{2}{5}$ 5. $\frac{7}{18}$ 7. $\frac{23}{24}$ 9. $\frac{19}{24}$ 11. $\frac{23}{30}$ 13. $1\frac{1}{20}$ 15. $1\frac{8}{21}$ 17. $\frac{5}{6}$ 19. $1\frac{1}{6}$ 21. $\frac{19}{45}$ 23. $5\frac{3}{4}$ 25. $6\frac{11}{24}$ 27. $5\frac{17}{21}$ 29. $8\frac{1}{6}$ 31. $6\frac{1}{24}$ 33. $6\frac{13}{20}$ 35. $2\frac{11}{24}$ 37. $22\frac{1}{10}$ 39. $53\frac{23}{40}$ 41. $3\frac{19}{22}$ 43. $1\frac{9}{16}''$ 45. $8\frac{27}{32}''$

Page 53 Exercises 1. $\frac{4}{15}$ 3. $\frac{7}{45}$ 5. $\frac{7}{39}$ 7. $\frac{1}{2}$ 9. $\frac{16}{35}$ 11. $\frac{3}{14}$ 13. $2\frac{13}{72}$ 15. $4\frac{5}{21}$ 17. $4\frac{5}{12}$ 19. $3\frac{1}{6}$ 21. $4\frac{2}{15}$ 23. $7\frac{7}{18}$ 25. $1\frac{17}{36}$ 27. $\frac{13}{36}$ 29. $2\frac{17}{20}$ 31. $3\frac{10}{21}$ 33. $2\frac{5}{6}$ 35. $2\frac{11}{12}$ 37. $12\frac{11}{20}$ 39. $4\frac{1}{3}$ 41. $3\frac{7}{9}$ 43. $7\frac{7}{8}$ 45. $1\frac{35}{36}$ 47. $13\frac{47}{60}$ 49. $3\frac{3}{4}$ 51. $2\frac{59}{72}$ 53. $4\frac{5}{8}$ inches 55. $2\frac{7}{8}$ inches

Page 54 Mid-Chapter Review 1. $2\frac{2}{3}$ 3. $1\frac{1}{4}$ 5. $1\frac{6}{7}$ 7. $1\frac{1}{11}$ 9. $2\frac{1}{8}$ 11. $3\frac{3}{4}$ 13. $4\frac{7}{10}$ 15. $3\frac{5}{6}$ 17. $\frac{1}{3}$ 19. $\frac{1}{5}$ 21. $\frac{3}{4}$ 23. $\frac{1}{4}$ 25. $3\frac{1}{2}$ 27. $1\frac{1}{2}$ 29. $1\frac{1}{2}$ 31. $1\frac{1}{2}$ 33. $\frac{4}{5}$ 35. $\frac{1}{2}$ 37. $\frac{1}{3}$ 39. $\frac{6}{15}, \frac{5}{15}$ 41. $\frac{2}{12}, \frac{9}{12}$ 43. $\frac{25}{40}, \frac{24}{40}$ 45. $1\frac{1}{3}$ 47. $5\frac{13}{15}$ 49. $10\frac{9}{16}$ 51. $\frac{14}{45}$ 53. $1\frac{1}{6}$ 55. $2\frac{7}{24}$ 57. $3\frac{7}{9}$ 59. $7\frac{1}{4}$ 61. $2\frac{19}{24}$ 63. $1\frac{3}{8}$ inches 65. $3\frac{3}{4}$ feet

Page 55 Career 1. 1590 miles 3. 2550 miles 5. 30 miles

Page 57 Exercises 1. $\frac{1}{15}$ 3. $\frac{10}{21}$ 5. $\frac{7}{30}$ 7. $\frac{1}{16}$ 9. $\frac{18}{65}$ 11. $\frac{33}{160}$ 13. $\frac{3}{14}$ 15. $\frac{1}{16}$ 17. $\frac{5}{56}$ 19. $\frac{2}{13}$ 21. $\frac{16}{45}$ 23. $\frac{1}{14}$ 25. $\frac{39}{8}$ 27. $\frac{41}{8}$ 29. $\frac{47}{7}$ 31. $\frac{9}{4}$ 33. $\frac{29}{7}$ 35. $\frac{21}{8}$ 37. $\frac{19}{4}$ 39. $17\frac{1}{2}$ 41. $22\frac{1}{5}$ 43. $13\frac{7}{8}$ 45. 6 47. $1\frac{1}{3}$ 49. 88 51. $3\frac{1}{7}$ 53. $5\frac{11}{16}$ 55. $1\frac{1}{8}$

Page 59 Exercises 1. $\frac{3}{2}$ 3. $\frac{7}{9}$ 5. $\frac{1}{4}$ 7. $\frac{7}{6}$ 9. $\frac{1}{15}$ 11. $\frac{2}{3}$ 13. $\frac{13}{8}$ 15. $\frac{13}{6}$ 17. $\frac{3}{4}$ 19. $2\frac{2}{7}$ 21. $\frac{1}{20}$ 23. 24 25. $1\frac{1}{4}$ 27. 14 29. $1\frac{1}{2}$ 31. $\frac{7}{10}$ 33. 12 35. $\frac{1}{44}$ 37. 2 39. 81 41. $\frac{4}{5}$ 43. 54 45. 1 47. $\frac{1}{2}$ 49. 2 51. $\frac{2}{5}$ 53. $2\frac{1}{2}$ 55. 3 57. $16\frac{2}{5}$ 59. 8 61. $1\frac{6}{13}$ 63. 9 65. $1\frac{5}{6}$ 67. 10 69. $\frac{2}{3}$ 71. $\frac{2}{3}$ 73. 6 75. $\frac{4}{7}$ 77. 32 79. 170

Pages 60-61 Exercises 1. 3 3. 2 5. 16 7. 12 9. 4 11. 6 13. 5 15. 4 17. 6 19. 4 21. 3 23. c 25. c 27. d 29. b 31. d 33. d 35. c 37. c

Page 61 Calculator Exercises 1. 5 3. 0.75 5. 0.5 7. 1.5

Pages 62-63 Career 1. 6000 Btu's 3. 6000 Btu's 5. 28,800 Btu's 7. 10,368 Btu's 9. 11,016 Btu's 11. 14,400 Btu's 13. 18,000 Btu's

Pages 64-66 Chapter Review 1. mixed number 3. like fractions 5. fractions 7. $1\frac{5}{13}$ 9. $1\frac{7}{9}$ 11. $2\frac{8}{11}$ 13. $1\frac{15}{23}$ 15. $\frac{2}{3}$ 17. $2\frac{1}{2}$ 19. $\frac{1}{4}$ 21. $1\frac{2}{5}$ 23. $\frac{5}{7}$ 25. $\frac{3}{5}$ 27. $\frac{2}{3}$ 29. $\frac{8}{20}, \frac{5}{20}$ 31. $\frac{16}{24}, \frac{3}{24}$ 33. $\frac{10}{24}, \frac{9}{24}$ 35. $1\frac{1}{2}$ 37. $4\frac{7}{22}$ 39. $4\frac{1}{3}$ 41. $\frac{3}{14}$ 43. $1\frac{5}{24}$ 45. $\frac{13}{22}$ 47. $5\frac{7}{18}$ 49. $6\frac{11}{12}$ 51. $8\frac{13}{20}$ 53. $\frac{1}{12}$ 55. $\frac{18}{35}$ 57. $1\frac{1}{2}$ 59. $1\frac{1}{7}$ 61. $10\frac{1}{2}$ 63. $\frac{14}{3}$ 65. $\frac{27}{5}$ 67. $\frac{17}{4}$ 69. $24\frac{1}{2}$ 71. 2 73. 118 75. $15\frac{5}{7}$ 77. $3\frac{1}{2}$ 79. $\frac{8}{3}$ 81. $\frac{1}{5}$ 83. $\frac{2}{3}$ 85. $\frac{1}{4}$ 87. $\frac{5}{6}$ 89. 8 91. 2 93. $2\frac{1}{3}$ 95. $6\frac{4}{5}$ 97. 5 99. 1 101. 17 103. b 105. c 107. c 109. a 111. $3\frac{11}{24}$ feet 113. b 115. 3 teaspoons 117. 4 cubic feet 119. $1\frac{1}{2}$ inches

Page 67 Chapter Test 1. $\frac{3}{2}$ 3. 6 5. $\frac{4}{5}$ 7. $\frac{1}{2}$ 9. $16\frac{19}{30}$ 11. $4\frac{4}{15}$ 13. $\frac{3}{35}$ 15. $2\frac{1}{2}$ 17. $1\frac{1}{2}$ 19. $2\frac{3}{8}$ 21. 10 teaspoons 23. $10\frac{1}{12}$ miles 25. c

Pages 68-69 Cumulative Review: Chapters 1-3 1. d 3. c 5. b 7. b 9. a 11. c 13. a 15. c 17. a 19. c 21. b 23. b 25. a 27. b 29. c

CHAPTER 4 Equations/Ratio/Proportion

Pages 72-73 Exercises 1. 5 3. 9 5. 19 7. 7 9. 12 11. 5 13. 13 15. 38 17. 6 19. 17 21. 24 23. 66 25. 2.2 27. 3.8 29. 17 31. 11 33. 37 35. 39 37. 88 39. 28 41. 55 43. 91 45. 87 47. 102 49. 109 51. 90 53. 9.3 55. 9.6 57. 15 59. 24 61. 41 63. 9 65. 84 67. 56 69. 154 71. 15 73. 62 75. 73 77. 152 79. 108 81. 3.6 83. 14.3 85. $6.48 87. $19.99

Pages 74-75 Exercises 1. 6 3. 8 5. 5 7. 164 9. 14 11. 2 13. 4 15. 5 17. 23 19. 4 21. 20 23. 5 25. 6 27. 8 29. 7 31. 12 33. 9 35. 12 37. 54 39. 33 41. 64 43. 8 45. 54 47. 162 49. 48 51. 84 53. 91 55. 175 57. 88 59. 234 61. 288 63. 420 65. 190 67. 56.1 69. 94 71. 200 73. 132 75. 217 77. 9 79. 2 81. 2 83. 20 85. 4 87. 544 89. 121 91. 15 seconds 93. 12 seconds

Pages 76-77 Exercises 1. Subtract 4 from each side. 3. Add 9 to each side. 5. Add 8 to each side. 7. Add 50 to each side. 9. Subtract 65 from each side. 11. 5 13. 8 15. 11 17. 10 19. 5 21. 3 23. 1.3 25. 1.6 27. 3.1 29. 21 31. 30 33. 42 35. 24 37. 40 39. 169 41. 2 43. 5 45. 5 47. 11 49. 31 51. 14 53. 187 55. 72 57. 441 59. 10 61. 5 63. 5 65. 25 67. 5 69. 30 71. 77 73. 119 75. 182

Pages 78-79 Exercises 1. $\frac{5}{9}$ 3. $\frac{2}{5}$ 5. $\frac{2}{5}$ 7. $\frac{4}{3}$ 9. $\frac{2}{7}$ 11. $\frac{1}{3}$ 13. $\frac{6}{19}$ 15. $\frac{4}{3}$ 17. $\frac{1}{9}$ 19. $\frac{1}{11}$ 21. $\frac{1}{9}$ 23. $\frac{1}{8}$ 25. $\frac{1}{5}$ 27. $\frac{1}{1}$ 29. $\frac{1}{14}$ 31. $\frac{4}{1}$ 33. Yes 35. Yes 37. No 39. Yes 41. No 43. No 45. Yes 47. Yes 49. Yes 51. Yes 53. No 55. Yes 57. Yes 59. No 61. Yes 63. Yes 65. No 67. No 69. Yes 71. Yes 73. No 75. No 77. Yes 79. Yes 81. Yes 83. No 85. $\frac{4}{15}$ 87. $\frac{2}{59}$

Pages 80-81 Exercises 1. 1 3. 1 5. 3 7. 6 9. 12 11. 15 13. 1 15. 3 17. 1 19. 13 21. 3 23. 18 25. 8 27. 60 29. 56 31. 40 33. 39 35. 50 37. 100 39. 60 41. 50 43. 126 45. 192 47. 32 49. 120 51. 120 53. 42 55. 80 57. 2 59. 15 61. 9 63. 126 65. 7 67. 150 69. 7 71. 3 73. 60 75. 12 77. 16 79. 68 81. 7 83. 100 85. 600 87. 400 kilometers 89. 12.5 centimeters

Pages 82-83 Career 1. 10 mL 3. 10 mL 5. 2.5 mL 7. 4.5 mL 9. 6 mL 11. 2.2 mL 13. 6 mL 15. 8 mL

Pages 84-86 Chapter Review 1. equation 3. add 4 to 5. equivalent 7. 14 9. 20 11. 13 13. 9 15. 9 17. 53 19. 137 21. 32 23. 26.0 25. 4.4 27. 17.0 29. 40.6 31. 4 33. 8 35. 13 37. 4 39. 5.5 41. 2 43. 48 45. 46 47. 99.6 49. 55.2 51. 7 53. 9 55. 5 57. 1.5 59. 90 61. 2 63. 5 65. 24 67. 8.2 69. $\frac{1}{2}$ 71. $\frac{1}{4}$ 73. $\frac{2}{3}$ 75. $\frac{1}{10}$ 77. $\frac{2}{5}$ 79. $\frac{1}{7}$ 81. $\frac{6}{1}$ 83. $\frac{7}{20}$ 85. No 87. Yes 89. No 91. Yes 93. No 95. No 97. No 99. No 101. 4 103. 75 105. 8 107. 3 109. 78 111. 3 113. 5 115. 27 117. 6 119. 13 121. $15.52 123. $79.99 125. 147 127. 7.5 kilometers 129. $8.50

Page 87 Chapter Test 1. 9 3. 12 5. 12.1 7. 6 9. $\frac{9}{10}$ 11. $\frac{9}{10}$ 13. No 15. No 17. 5 19. 21 21. $29.99 23. 12 centimeters 25. 25° C

CHAPTER 5 Per Cent

Page 91 Exercises 1. 0.36 3. 0.85 5. 0.34 7. 0.25 9. 0.46 11. 0.83 13. 0.44 15. 0.98 17. 0.51 19. 0.56 21. 0.73 23. 0.53 25. 0.06 27. 0.04 29. 0.03 31. 1.21 33. 3.73 35. 1.29 37. $0.33\frac{1}{3}$ 39. $0.16\frac{2}{3}$ 41. $0.11\frac{1}{9}$ 43. $\frac{19}{100}$ 45. $\frac{37}{100}$ 47. $\frac{1}{2}$ 49. $\frac{3}{10}$ 51. $\frac{1}{4}$

53. $\frac{3}{4}$ 55. $\frac{21}{50}$ 57. $\frac{14}{25}$ 59. $\frac{12}{25}$ 61. $\frac{13}{20}$ 63. $\frac{39}{50}$ 65. $\frac{7}{50}$ 67. $\frac{1}{300}$ 69. $\frac{1}{800}$ 71. $\frac{1}{1000}$
73. $\frac{1}{150}$ 75. $\frac{2}{3}$ 77. $\frac{5}{8}$ 79. 0.16 81. $\frac{1}{4}$ 83. $\frac{1}{25}$

Pages 92-93 Exercises 1. 37% 3. 32% 5. 41% 7. 28% 9. 91% 11. 33% 13. 4% 15. 3% 17. 15% 19. 132% 21. 1102% 23. 715% 25. 22.4% 27. 57.5% 29. 44.3% 31. 134.6% 33. 719.9% 35. 326.4% 37. 0.2% 39. 0.5% 41. 200.8% 43. $37\frac{1}{2}$% 45. $62\frac{1}{2}$% 47. $66\frac{2}{3}$% 49. $28\frac{1}{4}$% 51. $44\frac{5}{8}$% 53. $27\frac{1}{4}$% 55. 30% 57. 8% 59. 36% 61. 60% 63. 25% 65. 25% 67. 90% 69. 55% 71. 20% 73. 65% 75. 66% 77. 30% 79. $66\frac{2}{3}$% 81. $58\frac{1}{3}$% 83. $2\frac{1}{2}$% 85. $8\frac{1}{3}$% 87. $14\frac{2}{7}$% 89. $22\frac{2}{9}$% 91. $33\frac{1}{3}$% 93. $18\frac{3}{4}$% 95. $43\frac{3}{4}$% 97. 390% 99. 815% 101. 580% 103. $283\frac{1}{3}$% 105. $562\frac{1}{2}$% 107. $1212\frac{1}{2}$% 109. 420% 111. 570% 113. 380% 115. 75% 117. 20% 119. 25%

Pages 94-95 Exercises 1. 44.1 3. 4 5. 16.8 7. 5.5 9. 19 11. 3.32 13. 50.4 15. 8.4 17. 1 19. 3 21. 4.32 23. 8.82 25. 42.5 27. 140 29. 1.616 31. 11.7 33. 87 35. 105 37. 27 39. 21 41. 11 43. 24 45. 80 47. 19 49. 30 51. 56 53. 10 55. 60 57. 24 59. 20 61. 9 63. 9 65. 21 67. 3 69. 22 71. 9 73. 10 75. 2.8 77. 53.6 79. 6 81. 3.9 83. 3.77 85. 24 87. 32 89. 1900 91. 434

Pages 96-97 Exercises 1. $n \times 20 = 14$ 3. $n \times 70 = 35$ 5. $20 = n \times 80$ 7. $17 = n \times 68$ 9. $n \times 8 = 32$ 11. $n \times 200 = 150$ 13. 25% 15. 60% 17. $42\frac{6}{7}$% 19. 25% 21. 20% 23. 75% 25. 40% 27. $12\frac{1}{2}$% 29. $66\frac{2}{3}$% 31. 20% 33. 25% 35. $12\frac{1}{2}$% 37. $12\frac{1}{2}$% 39. 20% 41. 40% 43. 20% 45. $62\frac{1}{2}$% 47. $33\frac{1}{3}$% 49. 30% 51. $33\frac{1}{3}$% 53. 75% 55. $33\frac{1}{3}$% 57. 50% 59. 55% 61. $66\frac{2}{3}$% 63. 80% 65. 15%

Pages 98-99 Career 1. 4 cm 3. 8 cm 5. 25 cm 7. 6.0 cm 9. 150% 11. $33\frac{1}{3}$% 13. 75% 15. 85% 17. 8 cm 19. 120%

Pages 100-101 Exercises 1. $60 = 0.25 \times n$ 3. $15 = \frac{1}{3} \times n$ 5. $7 = \frac{1}{6} \times n$ 7. $32 = 0.40 \times n$ 9. $9 = \frac{1}{8} \times n$ 11. 45 13. 15 15. 20 17. 300 19. 550 21. 56 23. 250 25. 450 27. 120 29. 18 31. 730 33. 64 35. 102 37. 72 39. 32 41. 400,000 43. 3,000,000

Pages 102-103 Exercises 1. c 3. c 5. b 7. b 9. b 11. c 13. b 15. c 17. b 19. c 21. c 23. b

Page 103 Calculator Exercises 1. 1.12 3. 3 5. 51.2 7. 24

Pages 104-106 Chapter Review 1. hundredths 3. 100 5. right 7. 0.58 9. 0.21 11. 0.95 13. 0.08 15. 0.07 17. 2.36 19. $\frac{3}{4}$ 21. $\frac{6}{25}$ 23. $\frac{29}{100}$ 25. $\frac{12}{25}$ 27. $\frac{3}{400}$ 29. $\frac{5}{9}$ 31. 59% 33. 48% 35. 628% 37. 58.2% 39. 726.8% 41. $12\frac{1}{2}$% 43. 16% 45. 35% 47. $37\frac{1}{2}$% 49. $11\frac{1}{9}$% 51. 650% 53. $166\frac{2}{3}$% 55. 4.59 57. 89.1 59. 55.005 61. 1.44 63. 9 65. 11 67. 66 69. 13 71. $n \times 90 = 75$ 73. $27 = n \times 135$ 75. $16\frac{2}{3}$% 77. $33\frac{1}{3}$% 79. 16% 81. 30% 83. $17 = 0.15 \times n$ 85. $56 = \frac{1}{8} \times n$ 87. 84 89. 590 91. 400 93. 130 95. a 97. a 99. 80% 101. 525 103. 0.03 105. 75%

Page 107 **Chapter Test** 1. 93% 3. 60% 5. $133\frac{1}{3}\%$ 7. 243 9. 25% 11. $16\frac{2}{3}\%$ 13. 20 15. a 17. 960 19. 5,000,000

CHAPTER 6 Statistics

Pages 110-111 **Exercises** 1. Florida 3. Texas 5. Florida 7. California, Florida 9. wrestling 11. soccer, wrestling 13. Shown at the right.

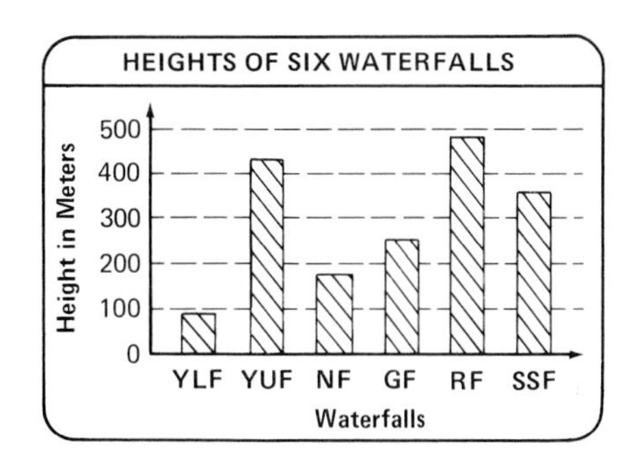

Pages 112-113 **Exercises** 1. July, September 3. January 5. January, February 7. 50 9. 1960-1980 11. 1970 13. Shown at the right.

Page 114 **Exercises** 1. 28° 3. 90° 5. 137° 7. acute 9. right 11. obtuse 13. acute

Page 115 **Mid-Chapter Review** 1. skiing 3. walking 5. Shown at the right. 7. February-March 9. February 11. obtuse 13. right 15. acute

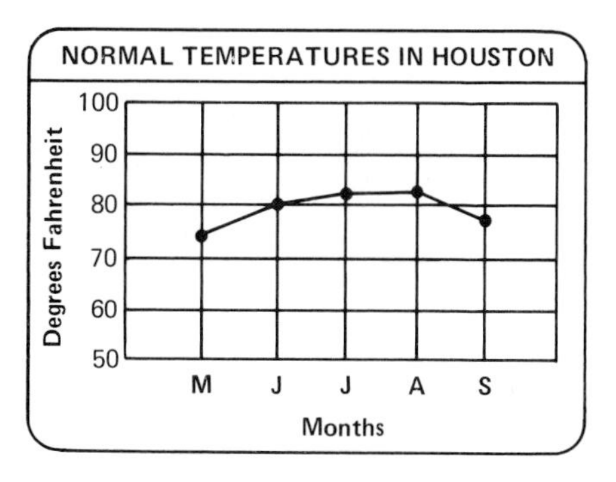

Page 117 **Exercises** 1. Pacific - 155°, Atlantic - 140°, Indian - 18°, Others - 47° 3. Food and Shelter - 162°, Clothing - 18°, Medical - 36°, Gasoline - 36°, Misc. - 108° 5. Music - 180°, Commercials - 47°, Sports - 36°, Chatter - 25°, News and Weather - 72° 7. muscle 9. about 9 kg

Pages 118-119 **Exercises** 1. 43 3. 413 5. $7\frac{1}{2}$ 7. 23.4 9. 85-89 11. 4-6 P.M.

Page 121 **Exercises** 1. 56 3. 60 5. 163,114 7. 8.601

Pages 122-123 **Career** 1. 56 3. 35 5. the mode 7. 3.4 9. 6 11. He has the most customers at those times.

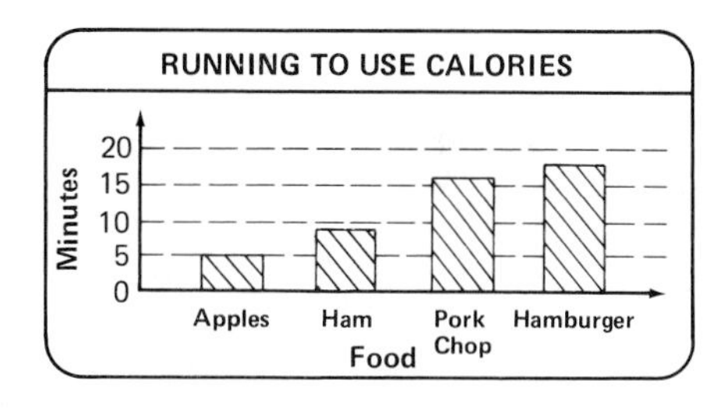

Pages 124-126 **Chapter Review** 1. number 3. 360 5. mode 7. crabs 9. scallops 11. See below. 13. 1978-79 15. $2.50 17. See below. 19. $236.25 21. 12-2 P.M.

Pages 126-127 **Chapter Test** 1. Blue 3. Fin 5. July 7. 2 inches 9. 6 11. Grape Ivy

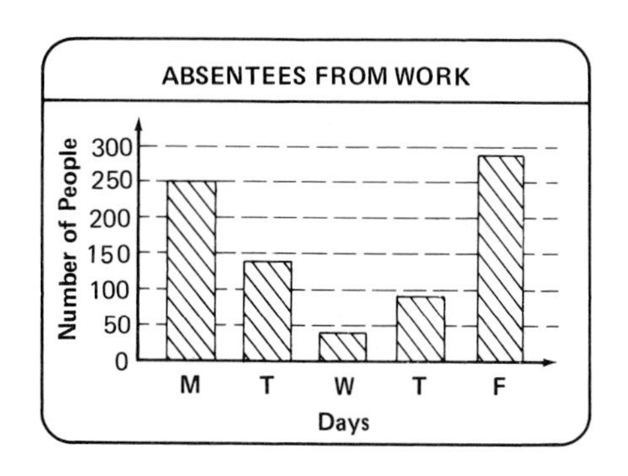

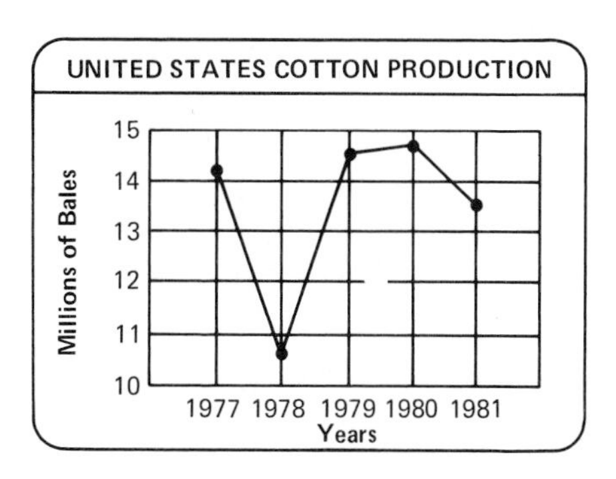

Pages 128-129 Cumulative Review: Chapters 4-6 1. a 3. b 5. c 7. c 9. c 11. c 13. a 15. a 17. a 19. b 21. b 23. b 25. d 27. b 29. b

Pages 130-135 Sample Competency Test: Chapters 1-6 1. c 3. b 5. a 7. c 9. a 11. a 13. a 15. c 17. c 19. b 21. c 23. b 25. b 27. b 29. a 31. c 33. b 35. c 37. b 39. b 41. a 43. c 45. a 47. b 49. c 51. c 53. b 55. c 57. b 59. b

CHAPTER 7 Income

Page 139 Exercises 1. $160.00 3. $210.00 5. $297.50 7. $301.00 9. $233.75 11. $175.00 13. $160.00

Pages 140-141 Career 1. One-way distance: 949 miles; Round trip distance: 1898 miles; Total earnings: $474.50 3. One-way distance: 648 miles; Round trip distance: 1296 miles; Total earnings: $272.16 5. One-way distance: 527 miles; Round trip distance: 1054 miles; Total earnings: $252.96 7. $650.88 9. $420.90 11. $243.20

Page 143 Exercises 1. $360 3. $520 5. $6300.00 7. $50.40 9. $1100 11. $1083 13. $1400 15. $135.00 17. $302.50 19. $1042.80

Page 145 Exercises 1. $84.46; $165.54 3. $45.12; $137.88 5. $280.93; $319.07 7. $432.90 9. $1069.59 11. $4.50 13. $36.47 15. $180.00

Page 147 Exercises 1. $963.53 3. $907.58 5. $738.49 7. $1069.99 9. $2271.30 11. $2039.08 13. $1129.55 15. $2271.30 17. $1703.94 19. $904.50 21. $3066.75 23. $1908.83 25. $2316.60

Pages 148-149 Career 1. $325.60 3. $319.00 5. $213.40 7. $1272 9. $302.10; $188.80; $490.90 11. $628.84 13. $928.20

Pages 150-151 Exercises 1. a 3. b 5. c 7. b 9. c 11. a 13. a 15. b 17. a 19. b 21. d 23. a 25. b

Pages 152-153 Chapter Review 1. overtime pay 3. graduated 5. net pay 7. $131.25 9. $24.50 11. $1162.50 13. $1075.02 15. 0.05 17. 0.075 19. $0.16\frac{2}{3}$ 21. $\frac{1}{3}$ 23. $\frac{1}{2}$ 25. $\frac{1}{10}$ 27. $125 29. $830 31. 22.93 33. 102.29 35. 265.25 37. $160 39. $147 41. $233.75 43. $650.00 45. $42.16 47. $152.65 49. $1443.85 51. $1299.67 53. a

Page 154 Chapter Test 1. $243.25 3. $643.20 5. 28.58 7. 155.44 9. 0.225 11. $\frac{3}{8}$ 13. $491.00 15. $263.50 17. $432.60 19. $2190.90

Page 155 Additional Practice 1. $180.73 3. $384.30 5. 39.80 7. 74.23 9. 133.26 11. $109.20 13. $187.56 15. $98.00 17. $172.90 19. $340.58 21. c 23. $235.56 25. $2190.90

CHAPTER 8 Income Tax

Page 159 Exercises 1. $22.60 3. $22.80 5. $12.70 7. $12.60 9. $24.70 11. a. $120.00; b. $16.10 13. a. $185.00; b. $29.10 15. $17.90 17. $29.10

Page 161 Exercises 1. $9724.55 3. $14,310.61 5. $13,132.75 7. $21,989.55 9. $12,556.86 11. Do not itemize 13. Itemize 15. Itemize 17. Do not itemize 19. Yes 21. Yes

Page 162 Career 1. $0.78 3. $0.64 5. $0.95 7. $10.76 9. $0.94 11. $7.82 13. $17.27

Page 164 Exercises 1. 478-12-4836 3. No 5. Single 7. 0 9. $16,482.00 11. $16,536.00 13. $2689.00 15. $24 17. $87 due 19. $220 due 21. $407 refund 23. $212 due 25. $351 refund

Page 167 Exercises 1. $14,341 3. $10,449 5. $23,582 7. $3,291 9. $2,563 11. $2,634

Pages 168-169 Career 1. Day 1: $7\frac{1}{2}$; Day 2: 7; Day 3: $7\frac{1}{4}$; Day 4: $6\frac{1}{4}$; Day 5: $4\frac{1}{2}$; Hours: $32\frac{1}{2}$; Earnings: $203.13 3. Day 1: 8; Day 2: $7\frac{1}{2}$; Day 3: 9; Day 4: $8\frac{1}{2}$; Day 5: $8\frac{1}{2}$; Hours: $41\frac{1}{2}$; Earnings: $311.25 5. Regular: $240.00; Overtime Rate: $9.00; Overtime Earnings: $45.00; Total: $285.00 7. $222.50

Page 171 Exercises 1. $1214.00 3. $1696.80 5. $2144.00 7. $1444.88 9. $1220.60 11. $449.00 13. $471.05 15. $650.20 17. $460.90 19. $575.62

Pages 172-173 Exercises 1. b 3. a 5. b 7. b 9. b 11. d 13. c 15. a 17. b 19. d 21. b 23. c

Pages 174-175 Chapter Review 1. exemptions 3. deduction 5. taxable income 7. $835.20 9. $403.20 11. $1394 13. $27,309.23 15. $30,298 17. $2986.00 19. $382.01 21. 0.23 23. 0.02 25. 0.056 27. 12.06 29. 72.68 31. $22.80 33. $15.00 35. $24,500.80 37. $25,552.40 39. Itemize 41. $17,378 43. Refund: $125; Balance due: 0 45. $2683 47. c

Page 176 Chapter Test 1. $240.70 3. $240.00 5. $3973 7. $20,392 9. $321.81 11. 0.17 13. 0.023 15. 0.057 17. 19.2 19. 4.472 21. $20.70 23. $640 25. $266

Page 177 Additional Practice 1. $229.40 3. $90.00 5. $5785 7. $14,898 9. $175.76 11. 46.2 13. 1.56 15. $12.70 17. Itemize 19. $734.77 21. $615

CHAPTER 9 Banking

Page 181 Exercises 1. TOTAL: 406.00 NET DEPOSIT: 406.00 3. TOTAL: 532.44 NET DEPOSIT: 507.44 5. TOTAL: 337.95 NET DEPOSIT: 287.45 7. $229.79 9. $84.50

Page 183 Exercises 1. $25.00 3. $72.00 5. $228.00 7. $24.00 9. $42.00 11. $37.50; $3037.50 13. $38.44; $3113.91 15. $48.00; $3248.00 17. $49.45; $3346.17

Page 185 Exercises 1. 1.5%; 2; $618.12 3. 3.5%; 4; $1721.25 5. 4%; 10; $6512.88 7. $1655.70 9. $984.06 11. $1231.80

Pages 186-187 Career 1. 9 3. 81 5. 144 7. 343 9. 27 11. 16 13. 625 15. 10,000 17. 1024 19. 1 21. 1.1025 23. 1.1664 25. 1.155625 27. $1041.29 29. $1197.90 31. $5724.50 33. $3025.00 35. $10,870.07 37. $933.12 39. $13,604.89 41. $1322.50

Pages 189-190 Exercises 1. Total: $176.94; Bal. For'd.: $157.65 3. Bal. For'd.: $133.27 5. Bal. For'd.: $270.21; Total: $270.21; Bal. For'd.: $233.73 7. Bal. For'd. is $153.00. 9. Bal. For'd. is $231.36. 11. $437.04 13. $424.40; $124.40; $101.22; $329.35

Page 192 Exercises 1. three and $\frac{47}{100}$ 3. thirty-four and $\frac{21}{100}$ 5. seventy-five and $\frac{00}{100}$ 7. one hundred twenty-one and $\frac{14}{100}$ 9. two hundred one and $\frac{18}{100}$ 11. six hundred fifty-five and $\frac{00}{100}$ 13. one thousand two hundred fourteen and $\frac{75}{100}$ 15. one thousand five hundred and $\frac{00}{100}$ 17. No. fifteen and $\frac{67}{100}$ 19. The amount, written as a decimal 21. Payment for a new chair 23. Buckley's Flowers 25. a

Pages 194-195 Exercises 1. $356.14; $204.21; Yes 3. $436.39; $329.58; Yes 5. $187.42; $119.27; Yes 7. $83.07 9. $238.15 11. $429.93 13. A: $124.60; B: $0.00; C: $124.60; D: $65.70; E: $58.90 15. A: $213.79; B: $59.50; C: $273.29; D: $117.08; E: $156.21

Pages 196-197 Career 1. a 3. a 5. Ex. 5 is done in the text. 7. $10-bills: 1; $5-bills: 0; $1-bills: 4; Quarters: 1; Dimes: 0; Nickels: 0; Pennies: 1 9. Change Due: $5.45; $10-bills: 0; $5-bills: 1; $1-bills: 0; Quarters: 1; Dimes: 2; Nickels: 0; Pennies: 0 11. Change Due: $15.37; $10-bills: 1; $5-bills: 1; $1-bills: 0; Quarters: 1; Dimes: 1; Nickels: 0; Pennies: 2 13. a. $4.31; b. 4 $1-bills, 1 quarter; 1 nickel, 1 penny 15. a. $8.60; b. 1 $5-bill, 3 $1-bills; 2 quarters, 1 dime 17. a. $0.18; b. 1 dime, 1 nickel, 3 pennies 19. a. $29.78; b. 1 $20-bill, 1 $5-bill, 4 $1-bills, 3 quarters, 3 pennies

Pages 198-199 Exercises 1. b 3. a 5. b 7. c 9. c 11. a 13. b 15. b 17. c 19. c 21. b

Pages 200-201 Chapter Review 1. deposit slip 3. outstanding 5. 2008.42 7. 3050.71 9. 400.00 11. 386.46 13. 0.18 15. 0.08 17. 0.045 19. 154 21. 97.5 23. 16.20 25. 7.55 27. 63.46 29. 122.37 31. 148.13 33. b 35. Balance Forward: $213.66 37. 156 39. Purchase of stationery 41. A: $203.56; B: $56.00; C: $259.56; D: $98.82; E: $160.74 43. $16 45. $1928.16

Page 202 Chapter Test 1. 335.81 3. 210 5. 0.16 7. 72.06 9. TOTAL: $59.80; NET DEPOSIT: $44.80 11. the signature 13. Purchase of bookcase 15. 72 17. $50 19. $92.28

Page 203 Additional Practice 1. 193.29 3. 301.25 5. 0.25 7. 0.08 9. 0.095 11. 1873.76 13. 20.92 15. 5.79 17. 25.96 19. NET DEPOSIT: $287.95 21. A: $125.63; B: $63.00; C: $188.63; D: $5.89; E: $182.74 23. c

Pages 204-205 Cumulative Review: Chapters 7-9 1. a 3. b 5. c 7. d 9. b 11. d 13. b 15. c 17. c 19. d 21. b 23. a 25. c

CHAPTER 10 Buying A Car

Page 209 Exercises 1. $10,235.80 3. $7848.75 5. $9640.00 7. $9452.00 9. $700.00; $10,700.00 11. $375; $7875 13. $744; $13,144 15. a. $10,775.85; b. $11,314.64

Page 211 Exercises 1. $7296.80 3. $10,435 5. $7207.60 7. $10,008.00 9. $7880 11. $9060

Page 213 Exercises 1. $10,260 3. $9888 5. $8546 7. $9920 9. $2008 11. $2996 13. $2588

Pages 214-215 Career 1. $3806.25 3. $4857.80 5. $2635.20 7. $4793.25 9. $5226.12 11. $6079.50 13. $6195.30 15. $4307.84 17. standard 19. compact 21. $1050.00

Page 217 Exercises 1. $632.80 3. $307.20 5. $250.80 7. $67.80 9. $62.70

Page 219 Exercises 1. $420 3. $33.94 5. $186.63 7. $130; $27 9. $45; $20 11. $79

Pages 220-221 Career 1. 5 3. 9 5. 7.2 7. 7.8 9. 9.8 11. 12.6 13. 7 15. 275°F 17. 265°F 19. 5 21. 280°F 23. 212°F

Pages 222-223 Exercises 1. b 3. a 5. b 7. b 9. a 11. c 13. a 15. b 17. b 19. a 21. a

Pages 224-225 Chapter Review 1. down payment 3. bodily injury 5. collision 7. $178 9. $310 11. $9422 13. $9444.85 15. $641.10 17. $42.14 19. $841.01 21. $9600 23. $10,656 25. $522.50 27. $293.80 29. 0.05 31. 0.06 33. 0.023 35. 0.4 37. 0.86 39. 0.412

41. 581 43. 630.63 45. 3570 47. 6960 49. $1450 51. $768; $10,368 53. $518; $7918 55. $10,800 57. $358.40 59. b

Page 226 Chapter Test 1. $8105 3. $436 5. $35.24 7. $2916 9. $336.40 11. 92 13. 7091.25 15. $8417 17. $7852.75 19. d

Page 227 Additional Practice 1. 1224 3. 612 5. 3654 7. 903.12 9. 0.02 11. 0.11 13. 0.9 15. $9027 17. $11,940 19. b

CHAPTER 11 Owning A Car

Page 231 Exercises 1. $5.93; $124.51 3. $4.84; $101.54 5. $83.65 7. 2¢ 9. 4¢ 11. 3¢ 13. 4¢ per kilometer 15. 3¢ per mile

Page 233 Exercises 1. $2400 3. $1360 5. $4544 7. $4128 9. $2208 11. $4662 13. $3698 15. $3712 17. 5¢ (per kilometer) 19. 9¢ (per kilometer) 21. 4¢ (per mile) 23. 9¢ (per mile) 25. $2924; 5¢ per kilometer

Pages 234-235 Career 1. 1951 3. 1870 5. 258 7. 301 9. 2237 cubic centimeters 11. 173 cubic inches 13. 179 cubic inches 15. 306 cubic inches

Page 237 Exercises 1. 27 (mpg) 3. 28 (mpg) 5. 20 (mpg) 7. 10 (kilometers per liter) 9. 13 (kilometers per liter) 11. First car 13. Second car 15. 4¢ (cost per kilometer) 17. 6¢ (cost per kilometer) 19. 6¢ (cost per kilometer) 21. 7¢ (cost per mile) 23. 7¢ (cost per mile) 25. 8¢ (cost per mile) 27. 7¢ per mile

Page 239 Exercises 1. $5691; 28.5¢ 3. $6168.25; 29.4¢ 5. a. $3410; b. $1800, $2229.70; c. $5989.70; d. 24.0¢ 7. a. $3850; b. $1290, $1598.75; c. $5648.75; d. 37.7¢

Pages 240-241 Career 1. 38.5 feet 3. 60.5 feet 5. 28.6 feet 7. 224 9. 63 11. 35 13. 68 15. 82 17. 33 feet 19. 50 feet 21. 16 feet 23. 30 feet

Pages 242-243 Exercises 1. c 3. c 5. c 7. a 9. c 11. b 13. d 15. b 17. c 19. d 21. b 23. b

Pages 244-245 Chapter Review 1. maintenance costs 3. fuel economy 5. variable costs 7. 49 9. $45.73 11. $165.33 13. $2334.45 15. 0.05 17. 0.09 19. 0.11 21. $56.70 23. $80.00 25. $40.69 27. $640.80 29. 108,000 31. 120,000 33. 2470 35. 2088 37. 0.06 39. 0.04 41. 0.02 43. 0.08 45. 0.17 47. 0.16 49. 0.09 51. 31 53. 49 55. 20 57. $8.83; $155.93 59. $8.04; $141.99 61. $6512 63. 5¢ (per kilometer) 65. 5¢ (per kilometer) 67. 16¢ (per mile) 69. 10¢ (per mile) 71. Second car 73. a

Page 246 Chapter Test 1. 70 3. $194.98 5. 0.03 7. 0.18 9. 0.47 11. 3239 13. $0.04 15. 0.28 17. $2944 19. 12 kilometers per liter

Page 247 Additional Practice 1. 57 3. $172.50 5. 163,500 7. 2346 9. $1.28 11. $3876.00 13. 0.05 15. $72.24 17. c 19. First car 21. $6300; 26.3¢ 23. $5100; 42.5¢

CHAPTER 12 Other Ways to Travel

Page 251 Exercises 1. $286.15 3. $647.20 5. $237.63 7. $974.26 9. $505.93 11. $245.16 13. $8.70 15. $586.04

Pages 252-253 Career 1. $3173.10 3. $1772.50 5. $2649.60 7. $12,184 9. $13,860 11. $768 13. $2904 15. $18,624

Page 255 Exercises 1. $41.40 3. $40.80 5. $41.80 7. $52.50 9. $52.80 11. $125.70 13. $113.85 15. $126.85 17. $134.05 19. $125.80

Page 257 Exercises 1. $748.80 3. $686.40 5. $686.40 7. $1565.20 9. $1466.00 11. $1292.75 13. 52.4 hours 15. 356 miles 17. $82.50

Pages 258-259 Career 1. Eastern Time, Central Time, Mountain Time 3. Central Time, Eastern Time 5. 7:00 A.M. 7. 11:00 P.M. 9. 11:00 P.M. 11. 2 hours 13. 2 hours 15 minutes 15. 3 hours 30 minutes 17. 3 hours 30 minutes 19. Melissa's; 1 hour 21. 10:15 P.M.

Pages 260-261 Exercises 1. c 3. b 5. a 7. c 9. a 11. a 13. c 15. a 17. b 19. b 21. a

Pages 262-263 Chapter Review 1. 25 3. commuting 5. $176.00 7. $104.40 9. $39.90 11. $189.00 13. $259.80 15. $126.13 17. $244.13 19. 65¢ 21. $30.00 23. $37.50 25. $960 27. $30 29. $262.78 31. $1064.96 33. $543.70 35. $332.60 37. $30.40 39. c 41. $903 43. $1008 45. $1119.50

Page 264 Chapter Test 1. $189 3. $281.20 5. $2220 7. $36.00 9. $298.10 11. 65¢ 13. $1.05 15. $220.60 17. $827.20 19. $102.00

Page 265 Additional Practice 1. $170 3. $310.75 5. $3100 7. $36 9. $636.50 11. 90¢ 13. $1.15 15. $774.60 17. $109.40 19. $224.64 21. $858.00 23. c

Pages 266-267 Cumulative Review: Chapters 10-12 1. a 3. d 5. a 7. b 9. c 11. c 13. a 15. c 17. d 19. c 21. a 23. c 25. d

CHAPTER 13 Food Costs

Page 271 Exercises 1. 3¢/g 3. 3.1¢/g 5. 8.3¢/oz 7. 2.5¢/oz 9. 2.1¢/mL 11. 25¢ each 13. 0.2¢ per gram 15. 2.9¢ per ounce 17. Larger 19. Larger 21. Larger 23. Larger 25. Larger 27. Larger 29. The 720-milliliter bottle

Pages 272-273 Exercises 1. $0.64 3. $0.55 5. $0.79 7. $0.26 9. $0.68 11. $0.69 13. $0.45 15. $0.93 17. $0.67 19. $0.89

Pages 274-275 Career 1. $12,561.80 3. $14,604.95 5. $15,646.30 7. $11,411.35 9. $11,696.75 11. $12,393.50 13. $13,529.35 15. $7987.05

Page 277 Exercises 1. $0.45 3. $0.69 5. $0.39 7. $0.70 9. $1.50 11. $0.95 13. $2.65 15. $0.55 17. $1.24 19. $3.41

Page 279 Exercises 1. 3 3. 2 5. 4 7. 4 pounds 9. $1.08 11. $0.76 13. $0.50 15. Chicken breasts

Pages 280-281 Career 1. $11.88 3. $3.90 5. $5.30 7. $2.60 9. $4.39 11. $5024.25

Page 282-283 Exercises 1. b 3. a 5. c 7. c 9. a 11. c 13. d 15. b 17. a 19. a 21. c 23. c 25. a

Pages 284-285 Chapter Review 1. unit price 3. no-name 5. Servings per pound 7. 5.8 9. 2.6

11. \$7.04 13. \$4.23 15. \$12.61 17. \$2.25 19. \$5.42 21. \$0.11 23. \$0.19 25. \$0.70 27. \$1.60 29. \$2.30 31. \$0.33 33. \$0.50 35. \$1.04 37. \$9.11 39. \$3.21 41. \$4.08 43. \$6.85 45. \$3.69 47. \$0.91 49. 8.5¢/lb 51. 4¢/oz 53. 0.3¢/mL 55. The 5-pound bag. 57. \$1.79 59. $\frac{4}{5}$ 61. $1\frac{1}{3}$ 63. $\frac{3}{4}$ 65. a

Page 286 Chapter Test 1. \$10.32 3. \$6.47 5. \$0.99 7. \$1.50 9. \$2.50 11. \$4.14 13. \$2.93 15. 7.9¢ per ounce 17. \$0.37 19. \$0.40 21. \$2.79 23. 3 pounds 25. 20¢

Page 287 Additional Practice 1. \$11.81 3. \$7.07 5. \$0.95 7. \$1.60 9. \$2.92 11. \$3.50 13. \$4.81 15. b 17. \$0.30 19. \$0.49 21. \$1.80 23. 2 25. \$0.52

CHAPTER 14 Housing

Pages 290-291 Exercises 1. \$395.00; \$526.67; Yes 3. \$437.50; \$583.33; No 5. \$493.75; \$658.33; No 7. No 9. Yes 11. Yes 13. Yes

Page 293 Exercises 1. \$13,000; \$52,000 3. \$12,375; \$70,125 5. \$19,950; \$59,850 7. \$14,850; \$84,150 9. \$10,000; \$40,000 11. \$13,350; \$31,150 13. \$341,460 15. \$284,472 17. \$238,896 19. \$216,996 21. \$326,570 23. \$136,440

Pages 294-295 Career 1. 26 3. 25 5. 37 7. 17 km 9. 45 m

Page 297 Exercises 1. \$979.55 3. \$1143.80 5. \$862.80 7. \$1061.76 9. \$747.45 11. \$1026.90 13. \$1026.72 15. \$1008.75 17. Yes

Page 298 Career 1. \$37,500 3. \$12,500 5. \$32,500 7. \$17,500 9. \$147,500 11. \$47,500

Pages 300-301 Exercises 1. \$30,000; \$6000; \$30,000; \$12,000 3. \$45,000; \$9000; \$45,000; \$18,000 5. \$35,000; \$7000; \$35,000; \$14,000 7. \$75,000; \$15,000; \$75,000; \$30,000 9. \$8000; \$40,000 11. \$90,000; \$9000; \$18,000 13. \$20.92 15. \$17.33 17. \$48.42 19. \$48.42 21. \$26.42

Pages 302-303 Career 1. \$102,200 3. \$118,300 5. \$69,900 7. \$79,000 9. \$73,000 11. \$131,600 13. \$100,000

Page 305 Exercises 1. \$34,400 3. \$22,500 5. \$78,000 7. \$38,250 9. \$2918.40 11. \$6994.60 13. \$7369.50 15. \$3762.00 17. \$3919.20 19. \$4447.70

Pages 306-307 Exercises 1. a 3. b 5. b 7. c 9. d 11. c 13. c 15. c 17. c 19. c 21. b 23. c

Pages 308-309 Chapter Review 1. down payment 3. homeowner's insurance 5. market value 7. \$284 9. \$818 11. \$225,000 13. \$191,577.60 15. \$1280.70 17. 0.6 19. 0.04 21. 0.47 23. \$24,000 25. \$54,880 27. \$21,000 29. \$15 31. \$28.92 33. \$52.42 35. \$348; \$464; Yes 37. \$450.00; \$600.00; No 39. \$20,400; \$47,600 41. \$834.35 43. \$1251.90 45. \$953.55 47. \$1170.15 49. \$50,000; \$10,000 51. b

Page 310 Chapter Test 1. \$1374 3. \$836.78 5. 0.8 7. 0.12 9. 0.79 11. \$46,500 13. \$34 15. \$48.33 17. \$160,251.20 19. c

Page 311 Additional Practice 1. \$36.67 3. \$898.28 5. \$20,300 7. \$16,000 9. \$675 11. \$868 13. $\frac{3}{4}$ 15. $\frac{2}{5}$ 17. $\frac{19}{20}$ 19. a 21. \$647.10 23. \$50,000 25. \$4015

CHAPTER 15 Housing Costs

Page 315 Exercises 1. \$96 3. \$43.20 5. \$153 7. \$156.60 9. \$194.40 11. \$292.50 13. \$406.35 15. \$157.50 17. \$144 19. \$193.20

Page 317 Exercises 1. 50¢ 3. 96¢ 5. 60¢ 7. 63¢ 9. 39¢ 11. \$10.75 13. 56¢ 15. 13¢ 17. 56¢ 19. \$6.83

Pages 318-319 Career 1. 817 3. 559 5. 629 7. \$54.62 9. \$57.67 11. \$68.76 13. \$96.23 15. 9341 17. \$90.41

Page 321 Exercises 1. 7103 3. 6386 5. 367 7. 1319 9. 393 11. 13,700 13. 5500

Page 323 Exercises 1. 9 3. 12 5. 15 7. 15 9. 14 11. 10

Pages 324-325 Career 1 3 cm 3. 10 cm 5. 5 cm 7. 4.5 cm 9. 6 cm by 5 cm 11. 5 cm by 4 cm 13. $3\frac{1}{8}$ in by $2\frac{1}{4}$ in 15. 2 in by $2\frac{1}{4}$ in

Page 327 Exercises 1. 56.6 m^2; 82 m^2; 10 3. 76.2 m^2; 120 m^2; 14 5. 5 7. 8 9. 12 11. \$21.60

Pages 328-329 Exercises 1. c 3. b 5. c 7. a 9. d 11. a 13. c 15. d 17. c 19. c 21. c 23. b

Pages 330-331 Chapter Review 1. kilowatt hours 3. cubic feet 5. area 7. 5 9. 165 11. 303 13. 8.5 15. 15.8 17. 6300 19. \$40.80 21. \$2.10 23. \$5.10 25. \$1.96 27. 10.5 29. 165.6 31. 7 33. 9 35. 17 37. \$50.40 39. \$108 41. \$535.50 43. \$109.20 45. 8425 47. 13 49. a

Page 332 Chapter Test 1. 14 3. 6 5. 351 7. 10.5 9. 10.5 11. 3200 13. \$37.50 15. \$0.88 17. 20.77 19. 9 21. \$165 23. 12,300 25. 15

Page 333 Additional Practice 1. 3 3. 6 5. 306 7. 7.5 9. 7.5 11. 0.07 13. 0.43 15. 0.98 17. \$6.60 19. \$2.20 21. 15 23. 9 25. 13 27. 51.0 29. 14.6 31. \$148.50 33. d 35. 60.3 m^2; 92 m^2; 11

Pages 334-335 Cumulative Review: Chapters 13-15 1. c 3. a 5. d 7. c 9. a 11. c 13. d 15. d 17. a 19. a 21. c 23. b 25. c

CHAPTER 16 Buying Goods

Page 339 Exercises 1. \$9.60 3. \$26.25 5. \$5.96 7. \$20.52 9. \$44.48 11. \$51.54 13. \$84.12 15. \$123.60

Page 342 Exercises 1. \$2.04 3. \$2.16 5. \$71.07 7. \$119.94

Page 343 Career 1. 37¢ 3. \$1.39 5. \$1.05 7. 20¢ 9. \$2.07 11. \$1.05 13. \$1.05 15. 55¢ 17. \$1.45; \$1.55 19. \$2.15 21. \$1.85 23. \$2.25 25. \$1.90

Page 345 Exercises 1. \$342.20; \$5.13 3. \$215.76; \$3.24 5. \$245.65; \$3.68 7. \$293.16; \$4.40; \$326.81 9. \$420.60; \$6.31; \$567.03

Page 347 Exercises 1. \$25.00 3. \$35.00 5. \$25.00 7. \$20.00 9. \$30.00 11. \$106.50; \$1.60; \$213.73; \$25.00 13. \$427.09; \$45

Pages 348-349 Career 1. $911.25 3. $1254 5. $3300 7. $288.75 9. $2595 11. $1432.50 13. $565.50 15. $91,800

Page 351 Exercises 1. $397; $1588 3. $740.40; $1727.60 5. $187.40; $1686.60 7. $573.75 9. $292.16 11. $207.04 13. $238.50 15. $339.30

Pages 352-353 Exercises 1. a 3. c 5. c 7. b 9. b 11. d 13. b 15. c 17. a 19. b 21. a

Pages 354-355 Chapter Review 1. discount 3. credit 5. installment 7. 0.05 9. 0.60 11. 0.29 13. $22.50 15. $72 17. $60.13 19. $69.27 21. $16 23. $7.78 25. $6.15 27. $4800 29. $3242 31. $342.40 33. $902.89 35. $502.14 37. $98.46 39. $480 41. $1900 43. $2742.30 45. $16.05 47. $27.47 49. $2.38 51. $104.99 53. $112.62; $20 55. c

Page 356 Chapter Test 1. $32 3. $3.92 5. $13.40 7. $7.80 9. $99 11. $310.40 13. $170.80 15. $1.70 17. $229.20 19. $6.60

Page 357 Additional Practice 1. $36 3. $7.28 5. $13 7. $126 9. $27 11. $33 13. $117.36 15. $1.80 17. $175.13 19. b

CHAPTER 17 Investing Money

Page 362 Exercises 1. $51.60; $516 3. $205.20; $1026 5. $348.60; $3486 7. $167.70 9. $154.80 11. $761.20 13. $1928.40 15. $4821 17. $21,413.25 19. $2283.60 21. $2202.60 23. $8677.80

Pages 364-365 Exercises 1. $10,064 3. $15,096 5. $10,064 7. $26,694 9. $24,480 11. $58,035 13. $16,578 15. $7548 17. $20,000 19. $25,000 21. $25,000 23. $30,000 25. $35,000 27. $30,000

Pages 366-367 Career 1. 73 3. 72 5. 69 7. 75 9. 170 11. 192 13. 1320 15. 75 17. 74 19. It is 4.71 years less. 21. 1.79

Page 369 Exercises 1. $2102.40; $102.40 3. $4163.20; $163.20 5. $4317.60; $817.60 7. $8978.25; $1478.25 9. $10,725; $725 11. $7401.60; $1401.60 13. $8455.50 15. $204

Pages 371-372 Exercises 1. $820 3. $2602.83 5. $16,029.21 7. $19,163.86 9. $12,135.20; $2198.34 p 11. $4978.60; $517.15 p 13. $17,655.83 profit 15. $4018.93

Page 373 Career 1. Purchase price: $25; Interest: $28.28 3. Purchase price: $50; Interest: $56.56 5. $7.88 7. $35.10

Page 375 Exercises 1. $440 3. $250 5. $270 7. $840 9. $720 11. $1500 13. 8.7% 15. 7.7% 17. 11.9% 19. 5.6% 21. 8.5% 23. 12.3% 25. 10.6%

Page 377 Exercises 1. $560 3. $740 5. $611.25 7. $871.25 9. $687.50 11. 12.4% 13. 11.3% 15. 15.7% 17. 20.2% 19. 13.8%

Pages 378-379 Career 1. 409.8361 3. 277.7778 5. 201.4504 7. $3222 9. $2561.25 11. $5490 13. 73.3676

Pages 380-381 Exercises 1. b 3. c 5. a 7. a 9. a 11. b 13. c 15. c 17. b 19. c 21. d 23. a

Pages 382-383 Chapter Review 1. term 3. dividend 5. market price 7. $83 9. $122 11. $94.50 13. $5718 15. $14,460 17. $6620.50 19. $7 21. $4 23. $6518.14 25. $876 27. $3036.82 29. 0.375 31. $0.\overline{6}$ 33. 0.4 35. 0.111 37. 0.079 39. 0.090 41. $377.65 43. $3964.68 45. $18,558.15 47. $9000 49. $999.60 51. 9.6% 53. c

Page 384 Chapter Test 1. $7 3. 0.076 5. $153.72 7. $9720 9. $6512.51 11. $400 13. $3620.35 15. $0.\overline{3}$ 17. 0.3 19. 0.8 21. $23,710 23. $10,725 25. d

Page 385 Additional Practice 1. $5 3. 0.110 5. 0.143 7. $204 9. $4120 11. $370 13. $1103.20 15. $6476.50 17. $7308.78 19. 0.8 21. $0.\overline{6}$ 23. 0.6 25. $2892.60 27. $591.30 29. 11.8% 31. b

CHAPTER 18 Budgeting Money

Page 389 Exercises 1. $28 3. $49 5. $298 7. $52 9. $64 11. $261 13. 7.6% 15. 55.9%

Pages 391-392 Exercises 1. $270 3. $85 5. $86.50 7. $116.10 9. $691.50 11. $135 13. Above 15. 10%; Above 17. 5%; Below 19. Above 21. Above 23. Fixed: rent, 238°; insurance, 61°; car payment, 61°; Variable: Food, 194°; Telephone, 22°; Utilities, 47°; Recreation, 25°; Clothing, 50°; Miscellaneous, 22°

Page 393 Career 1. $13.70 3. $8.20 5. 15% 7. Less

Page 395 Exercises 1. $120; $130 3. $637.50; $312.50 5. $820.25; $244.75 7. $36; $59 9. $88; $122 11. $380; $195 13. $72 15. $149 17. $120

Page 397 Exercises 1. D: $20 3. I: $200 5. D: $5 7. D: $75 9. $670 11. $20 13. $1490 15. $30

Pages 398-399 Career 1. Total Variable Expenses: $300; Amount for Clothing: $144 3. Total Variable Expenses: $315; Amount for Clothing: $84 5. Total Variable Expenses: $700; Amount for Cosmetics: $140 7. $320 9. $140 11. $500 13. $440 15. $300 17. $374 19. $220

Pages 400-401 Exercises 1. a 3. c 5. a 7. a 9. c 11. c 13. a 15. a 17. b 19. c 21. b

Pages 402-403 Chapter Review 1. budget 3. fixed expenses 5. $19.01 7. $47.81 9. $42 11. $80 13. $303 15. Bryant, 108°; Candito, 162°; Curez, 36°; Montillio, 54° 17. $156 19. $46.18 21. 75% 23. 80% 25. 50% 27. $665 29. $59 31. $69 33. $32 35. Greater 37. $350; $250 39. $840; $360 41. b

Page 404 Chapter Test 1. $19.41 3. $28 5. $110 7. $200 9. $240 11. $237.50 13. 40% 15. 50% 17. $16\frac{2}{3}$% 19. $780 21. $69 23. Less 25. d

Page 405 Additional Practice 1. $26.62 3. $134.85 5. $43 7. $40 9. $212 11. $258 13. $317.20 15. $87\frac{1}{2}$% 17. 40% 19. 70% 21. $1150 23. $1122 25. $115 27. $177 29. $540 31. $140; $210 33. $637.50; $212.50 35. a

Pages 406-407 Cumulative Review: Chapters 16-18 1. d 3. a 5. c 7. a 9. b 11. a 13. a 15. c 17. b 19. b 21. a 23. d 25. b

APPENDIX A INTRODUCTION TO ALGEBRA

Page 410 Exercises 1. 9 3. 100 5. 225 7. 400 9. 1600 11. 196 13. 4 15. 256 17. 2500 19. 361 21. 6400 23. 40,000 25. 2 27. 7 29. 30 31. 40 33. 70 35. 20 37. 9 39. 3 41. 16 43. 25 45. 14 47. 15

Page 412 Exercises 1. 361 3. 3844 5. 10,404 7. 4489 9. 7921 11. 17,689 13. 11.576 15. 10.488 17. 9.747 19. 10.149 21. 9.327 23. 11.533 25. 101 27. 117 29. 68 31. 34 33. 113 35. 134 37. 64 39. 74 41. 67

Page 415 Exercises 1. +15 3. −5 5. −2 7. +125 For Ex. 9-43, the graph of the first addend and direction for the second addend are given, followed by the sum. 9. Graph 1; 7 right; 8 11. Graph −2; 6 right; 4 13. Graph 6; 4 left; 2 15. Graph 3; 7 left; −4 17. Graph −3; 1 left; −4 19. Graph −3; 4 left; −7 21. Graph 3; 2 right; 5 23. Graph 8; 8 left; 0 25. Graph −2; 2 left; −4 27. Graph −9; 9 right; 0 29. Graph 0; 4 left; −4 31. Graph 12; 8 left; 4 33. Graph −2; 5 right; 3 35. Graph −5; 8 left; −13 37. Graph 4; 4 right; 8 39. Graph −10; 2 right; −8 41. Graph 8; 3 left; 5 43. Graph −1; 6 left; −7 45. 11 47. 525 49. 10°C

Pages 416-417 Exercises 1. 6 + (−2) 3. −8 + (−3) 5. −12 + 9 7. −8 + 11 9. 13 + 30 11. 22 + 11 For Exercises 13-55, the related addition is given, followed by the answer. 13. −5 + (−1); −6 15. 7 + (−5); 2 17. 9 + (−10); −1 19. 6 + 2; 8 21. −1 + 10; 9 23. −7 + 2; −5 25. 0 + 6; 6 27. −7 + 6; −1 29. −9 + (−4); −13 31. −3 + 1; −2 33. 12 + (−7); 5 35. −8 + (−4); −12 37. −2 + 7; 5 39. 0 + 8; 8 41. 11 + (−4); 7 43. −111 + 9; −102 45. −9 + (−2); −11 47. 2 + 6; 8 49. −8 + 1; −7 51. −15 + (−5); −20 53. 9 + 11; 20 55. −4 + 9; 5 57. 6° 59. 11° 61. −9° 63. 13° 65. −9° 67. 30° 69. 34° 71. 17°

Pages 418-419 Exercises 1. −20 3. −22 5. −32 7. −96 9. −51 11. −54 13. −200 15. −96 17. −186 19. −96 21. 51 23. 49 25. 1 27. 105 29. 54 31. 760 33. 300 35. 120 37. −48 39. 120 41. −132 43. 144 45. −512 47. −108 49. 108 51. 324 53. 5 × (−4); −20 55. 3 × (−4); −12 57. 8 × (−46); −368 59. 3 × (−50); −150

Page 419 Calculator Exercises 1. checks 3. 108,756 5. 2473.24 7. −27,474 9. −24

Page 420 Exercises 1. 5 3. −5 5. −4 7. 4 9. 25 11. 9 13. −9 15. −20 17. 20 19. 8 21. −5 23. 9 25. 3 27. 4 29. 6 31. −13 33. 10 35. −12 37. −49 39. 4 41. −9 43. −4

Page 422 Exercises 1. (1, 2) 3. (3, 1) 5. (3, −2) 7. (1, −4) 9. (−2, −3) 11. (−4, −4) 13. 3 units to the right; 1 unit up 15. 3 units to the left; 4 units down 17. 3 units to the left; 5 units down

19.

c	1	3	5
m	10	30	50

; the graph is the line joining the points.

Pages 423-424 Appendix Review 1. square 3. negative 5. origin 7. 4 9. 121 11. 1024 13. 2 15. 9 17. 13 19. 9409 21. 5476 23. 20,164 25. 6.083 27. 94 29. 114 31. Graph 4; 5 right; 9 33. Graph −7; 4 right; −3 35. Graph 9; 4 left; 5 37. Graph −2; 5 left; −7 39. −3 + (−8); −11 41. 3 + (−7); −4 43. −9 + 12; 3 45. 0 + 6; 6 47. −42 49. −48 51. 30 53. 110 55. −4 57. −7 59. 3 61. 2 63. (3, 2) 65. (−3, 1) 67. (−1, 1) 69. (3, −3) 71. (−4, −1) 73. (1, 2) 75. 2 units to the left; 1 unit up 77. 4 units to the right; 2 units down 79.

F	1	2	3
I	12	24	36

; the graph is the line joining the points. 81. 55 83. 78 85. 15°

APPENDIX B INTRODUCTION TO COMPUTERS

Page 427 Exercises 1. (A) input 3. (B) storage 5. (C) processing 7. (A) input; (B) storage; (D) output 9. (D) output 11. ENIAC 13. memory 15. computer program

Page 429 Exercises 1. 45 – 6 * 7 3. 10 * 20/5 5. 8 * 9 + 4 * 5 7. 14/7 * 3 + 4 9. (4+5) * 4 11. 12/(3+3) 13. 1: 3; 2: 11; 3: 40; 4: 25; 5: 92; 6: 1; 7: 10; 8: 32; 9: 36; 10: 0; 11: 2; 12: 110 15. 9 17. 20 19. 20 21. 16 23. 4 25. 96 27. 5 29. 2 31. 31 33. 7 35. 5 37. $\frac{1}{5}$

Page 431 Exercises 1. 17 3. 48 5. 4 7. 120 9. 100 11. 8: 90; 9: 900; 10: 3

Pages 433-434 Exercises 1. PRINT Y 3. END 5. 2Ø LET T = 4 * R; 3Ø PRINT "T ="; T 7. 1Ø PRINT "GIVE A NUMBER."; 3Ø LET X = N↑2

9.
```
1Ø INPUT W, L
2Ø LET T = W+L
3Ø LET P = (W/T) * 1ØØ
4Ø PRINT P
5Ø END
```

11.
```
1Ø INPUT H, R
2Ø LET P = H * R
3Ø PRINT P
4Ø END
```

13.
```
1Ø INPUT A, B
2Ø LET C = 18Ø – (A+B)
3Ø PRINT C
4Ø END
```

15.
```
1Ø INPUT S, D, T, H, A
2Ø LET B = 1 * S + 2 * D + 3 * T + 4 * H
3Ø LET P = (B/A) * 1ØØ
4Ø PRINT P
5Ø END
```

Page 435 Appendix Review 1. computer program 3. output 5. a: 24/3 * 9; b: 4↑2 – 3↑2 7. 2 9. 25 11. 144 13. END 15. 2Ø LET Y = X↑2

17.
```
1Ø INPUT S, R
2Ø LET E = S * R
3Ø PRINT E
4Ø END
```

Page 434 Answers to the even-numbered exercises.

10.
```
1Ø INPUT M, G
2Ø LET A = M / G
3Ø PRINT A
4Ø END
```

12.
```
1Ø INPUT S
2Ø LET P = 4 * S
3Ø PRINT P
4Ø END
```

14.
```
1Ø INPUT R, I
2Ø LET E = R * 9 / I
3Ø PRINT E
4Ø END
```

16.
```
1Ø INPUT H, T
2Ø LET F = H + T
3Ø LET P = 1ØØ * H / F
4Ø PRINT P
5Ø END
```

GLOSSARY

The following definitions and statements reflect the usage of terms in this textbook.

Acute angle An angle whose measure is less than 90°. (Page 114)

Adjusted gross income The sum of all kinds of income a person may have, which must be reported for figuring income tax. (Page 160)

Area The measure in square units of the amount of surface inside a closed, plane figure. (Page 36)

Average, or **mean**

$$average = \frac{\text{sum of measures}}{\text{number of measures}} \quad \text{(Page 118)}$$

Axis (Plural: axes) A horizontal or vertical number line used to locate points. (Page 110)

Bar graph A *bar graph* uses horizontal or vertical bars to show data. (Page 110)

Bonds Sold by many governments and corporations to raise money. People who buy them are lending money to the corporation or government. In turn, bondholders receive interest (usually twice a year) on their bonds. (Page 376)

Budget A plan for balancing income and expenses. (Page 388)

Canceled checks Checks that the bank has paid. (Page 193)

Celsius scale A scale used to measure temperature. On this scale, the freezing point of water is 0°C and the boiling point is 100°C. (Page 38)

Centimeter A unit of length in the metric system. *100 centimeters* equal 1 meter. (Page 28)

Certificate of deposit A way of investing money at a bank that allows the owner to earn interest at a higher rate than a regular savings account. Certificates must be left on deposit for 6 months or longer and interest is lost if all or some of the money is withdrawn early. (Page 368)

Circle graph A graph in the shape of a circle used to show data. The graph uses per cents to show parts of a whole. (Page 116)

Collision insurance A type of car insurance that helps pay for repairs on a car if it is damaged in an accident. (Page 218)

Commission An amount, usually a per cent of goods sold, given to a salesperson, real estate agent, and so on, for services. (Page 142)

Compound interest Interest that is computed on the principal plus the interest previously earned. (Page 184)

Comprehensive car insurance Insurance that protects the owner from losses due to theft, fire, vandalism, and so on. (Page 218)

Cubic centimeter The capacity of this container is 1 *cubic centimeter* (abbreviated: 1 cm^3). (Page 36)

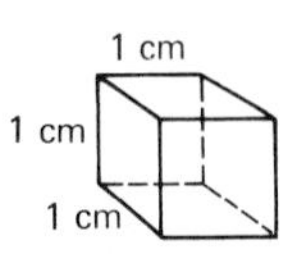

Deductible Any amount that the owner pays to cover damages before the insurance company pays the rest. (Page 218)

Deductions **For wages:** amounts subtracted from gross income for taxes and personal items such as insurance and pension. **For income tax:** amounts subtracted from adjusted gross income to determine taxable income. (Pages 144, 166)

Degree A measure used to describe the size of an angle such as 30°, 90°, and so on. (Page 114)

Depreciation The decrease in value of a car because of its age and condition. (Page 232)

Discount An amount subtracted from the regular (list) price to obtain the sale price or a per cent of the regular price. (Page 338)

Down payment The amount of money paid before financing the purchase of a home or car. (Page 212)

Endowment life insurance A type of policy that gives financial protection for a specified number of years and has a cash value and loan value. The policy holder pays the same premium for the policy period, then receives the face value at the end of the period. (Page 363)

Equation A mathematical statement that uses "=", such as $x + 6 = 9$. (Page 72)

Equivalent ratios Equal ratios: $\frac{2}{3}$ and $\frac{4}{6}$. (Page 78)

Estimation The process of calculating with rounded numbers. (Page 18)

Exemptions The number of people a worker claims to support. The number includes the worker. (Page 158)

Exponent A number that tells how many times a number is used as a factor. (Page 186)

Factors The numbers that are multiplied, such as 8 and 5 in $8 \times 5 = 40$. (Page 6)

Finance charge The amount of interest paid for borrowing money or for buying on credit. (Page 212)

Formula A rule stated in words or in symbols that can be used in solving problems. (Page 30)

Gram A commonly used unit of mass in the metric system. *One gram* equals 0.001 kilogram. (Page 32)

Generic products Items that have no brand names and which are usually less expensive than brand-name products. (Page 272)

Gross pay The total income, before deductions are subtracted. (Page 144)

Installment loan A loan that is repaid in several equal payments, with interest, over a specified amount of time. (Page 350)

Interest An amount paid for the use of money. *Interest* is usually a per cent of the amount invested, or lent, or borrowed. (Page 182)

Kilogram The base unit of mass in the metric system. (Page 32)

Kilometer A unit of distance in the metric system. *One kilometer* equals 1000 meters. (Page 28)

Kilowatt-hour A measure of electricity used. *One kilowatt-hour* is 1000 watts of electricity used for 1 hour. (Page 316)

Liability insurance A type of car insurance, required by many states, that protects the owner from financial loss if others are injured by the car or if the car damaged someone's property. (Page 216)

Limited-payment life insurance A type of policy that gives financial protection for the policy holder's entire life and has a cash value and a loan value. The same yearly premium is paid for a specific number of years. (Page 363)

Line graph A graph that shows the amount of change over a period of time. (Page 112)

Liter The base unit of capacity in the metric system. (Page 34)

Lowest terms A fraction is in *lowest terms* when its numerator and denominator have no common factors other than 1. (Page 46)

Markup An amount added to the dealer's cost to cover profit and expenses. (Page 73)

Mass The amount of matter an object contains. (Page 32)

Mean Another name for *average*. The *mean* of 2, 5, 6, and 7 is $2 + 5 + 6 + 7 \div 4$, or 5. (Page 118)

Median When a series of measures are listed in order, the middle number is the *median*. The *median* of 1.6, 2.9, 3.4, 7.8, and 12.2 is 3.4. (Page 120)

Meter The base unit of length in the metric system. (Page 28)

Milligram A unit of mass in the metric system. *One milligram* equals 0.001 gram. (Page 32)

Milliliter A unit of capacity in the metric system. *One milliliter* equals 0.001 liter. (Page 34)

Millimeter A unit of length in the metric system. *One millimeter* equals 0.001 meter. (Page 28)

Mode In a series, the one that occurs most often. (Page 118)

Mortgage loan A loan obtained from a bank or other lending institution used to pay for a home. (Page 292)

Mutual fund A form of investment that combines the investments of many customers to buy various stocks and bonds. (Page 378)

Net pay Take-home pay, found by substracting deductions from gross pay. (Page 144)

Numerator In the fraction $\frac{9}{10}$, 9 is the *numerator*. (Page 46)

Obtuse angle An angle whose measure is greater than 90°. (Page 114)

Octagon A polygon with eight sides. (Page 30)

Ordered pair Two numbers used in a certain order, such as (3, 2). (Page 421)

Origin The point (0, 0) in the coordinate plane at which the *x axis* and the *y axis* intersect. (Page 421)

Outstanding checks Checks that have been written but not paid by the bank. (Page 193)

Overtime Hours worked beyond the number of hours agreed upon for a regular week's pay. (Page 138)

Perimeter The sum of the lengths of the sides of a polygon, such as a rectangle. (Page 30)

Premium The amount paid each year or every six months for insurance. (Page 216)

Principal An amount of money deposited in a savings account to earn interest. (Page 182)

Proceeds The amount a borrower receives after the interest is subtracted from the amount of a discount loan. (Page 348)

Promissory note A written agreement to repay a loan at the end of a definite time period. (Page 348)

Proportion An equation which states that two ratios are equal. (Page 80)

Ratio A comparison of two numbers expressed as 2 to 5 or $\frac{2}{5}$, or 2 : 5. (Page 78)

Reciprocal Two numbers whose product is 1 are *reciprocals* of each other. Thus, $\frac{3}{4}$ and $\frac{4}{3}$ are *reciprocals*, because $\frac{3}{4} \times \frac{4}{3} = 1$. (Page 58)

Rectangular prism A space figure having two equal rectangles as bases. The bases are parallel. (Page 36)

Rectangle A four-sided polygon whose opposite sides are equal and whose angles are right angles. (Page 30)

Right angle An angle whose measure is 90°. (Page 114)

Social security tax An amount deducted from the gross pay to provide benefits for retired and disabled workers. Also called F.I.C.A., or Federal Insurance Contribution Act. (Page 146)

Square of a number The product of a number and itself. (Page 410)

Square root One of two equal factors of a number. The symbol for square root is $\sqrt{\ }$. Since $3 \times 3 = 9$, $\sqrt{9} = 3$. (Page 410)

Sticker price The price of a new car that includes the base price, the cost of optional equipment, and the delivery charges. (Page 208)

Stock Shares of a corporation that people buy to become part owners of a corporation and to share in its profits. (Page 370)

Stock dividend The portion of a company's earnings that it pays (usually every 3 months) to its stockholders. (Page 374)

Straight-life insurance A type of policy that gives financial protection over the entire life of the policy holder. It has both a cash value and a loan value. The premium is always the same. (Page 361)

Taxable income For purposes of income tax, the difference between adjusted gross income and the total of exemptions and deductions. (Page 166)

Term life insurance A type of policy that gives financial protection for a specific period of time or until a certain age. It can be renewed after each term, but at a higher premium. The amount of the insurance will be paid to the policy holder's beneficiary in case of death. (Page 360)

Triangle A polygon with three sides. (Page 30)

Unit price The cost per gram, per pound, per liter, and so on. The *unit price* of a 16-ounce container of cottage cheese that sells for $0.96 is 6¢ per ounce. (Page 270)

Volume The measure of the amount of space inside a space figure. (Page 36)

X coordinate The first number in an ordered pair. (Page 421)

Y coordinate The second number in an ordered pair. (Page 421)

INDEX

Boldface numerals indicate the pages that contain formal or informal definitions.

CAREER SKILLS AND APPLICATIONS